Elements of
MODERN PHYSICS

A Course in Those Aspects

of Modern Physics That Underlie

Important Engineering Developments

PAUL L. COPELAND
ILLINOIS INSTITUTE OF TECHNOLOGY

WILLIAM E. BENNETT
UNIVERSITY OF BUFFALO

  New York

OXFORD UNIVERSITY PRESS · 1961

Elements of Modern Physics

Preface

Conventional engineering curricula have, in past decades, included a two-semester course in physics, which presented introductory material in mechanics, electricity, heat, sound, and light, most of which developed prior to 1900. The increasing tempo with which the results of modern physics are being incorporated into engineering practice makes it imperative that engineering students be introduced to the more recent developments in physics.

Some contemporary texts in general physics have been modernized by introducing here and there references to modern developments and problems that involve modern nomenclature. This solution is inadequate, because it is impossible to eliminate enough of the conventional subject matter to provide room for as complete a treatment of modern physics as would be desirable.

A current trend is to introduce an extra semester of physics into engineering curricula for the purpose of providing an introduction to the basic ideas of modern physics. The purpose of this book is to provide a text for this extra semester of general physics. There is no lack of excellent introductory texts on modern physics. However, the aim here is to make a selection of topics and treatments which will most adequately meet the needs of the engineering students, within the limits of a one-semester course.

This book is a survey of basic ideas. A "survey" is usually stigmatized as being qualitative in approach. Here for the most part the approach is quantitative, and equations are used freely. It is assumed that students using the text have completed two semesters of calculus as well as the usual two-semester course in classical physics. Some differential equations are used, but it is hoped that their use will

v

be clear to a student who has not yet had a special course in that field. In some cases where the details of an analytical treatment might unduly encumber the presentation, the more exact and quantitative treatments have been deferred to appendices. Problems, which involve the use of algebra and calculus, are provided at the ends of most of the chapters.

The introductory sections are historical in the sense that they review the situations in physics which required the introduction of new ideas. The historical approach also justifies the development of ideas, such as the Bohr theory of the atom, that provide a partial understanding of modern developments. Some of the more recent and exact theories require a degree of mathematical sophistication beyond the scope of this text.

We should be disappointed if what has been included in these pages were sufficient to satisfy the curiosity of all readers. Each chapter is followed by references, which, in addition to providing an independent treatment for the assistance of the reader when difficulties arise, stimulate and encourage a more extensive reading on points of particular interest. Notes and comments on these references have been included to make them more useful.

This book is divided into three parts. Part I, "The Rise of Atomic Physics," develops the particular aspects of the structure of those media which seem continuous on casual inspection. Gases are found to consist of molecules, electricity of electrons, light of photons, and so on. Classical mechanics can be used to some extent to predict the behavior of the particles, and to this extent the behavior can be readily pictured by analogy with familiar events, such as the collisions between billiard balls. The study of the particles is pursued until the limitations of these concepts become apparent. The chapter on relativity is not part of this pattern but appears in Part I in order that this important topic should not be unduly deferred.

Part II introduces some of the ideas of wave or quantum mechanics. To make extensive applications would involve methods of solving partial differential equations and would presuppose familiarity with special mathematical functions. Nevertheless, the Schroedinger equation is applied to a few simplified problems for the purpose of developing some of the qualitative ideas which are peculiar to quantum mechanics. These ideas are necessary for an understanding of the periodic table, the behavior of electrons in metals, and the band structure of semiconductors. It is to be expected that the student will feel dissatisfied with the formulation of mechanics in the wave-mechanical form. To some extent, this may arise because the background of the student's knowledge of wave phenomena is not yet sufficiently extensive. Some effort, therefore, has been devoted to presenting background material in this connection. However, the few applications of wave mechanics presented here do not illustrate enough of its many successes to be entirely convincing to the student.

Part III is an introduction to nuclear physics. The first problem here is to present enough of the methods and results of experimentation to give the nomenclature observational significance. Examples of typical nuclear occurrences have been described, the relations among different observations have been discussed whenever they are straightforward, and applications to technology have been indicated.

Physics is a quantitative science. There are relatively few basic principles. These are ordinarily formulated in equations. A great part of our knowledge of scientific facts, and certainly the integration of our knowledge into an understandable structure, depends upon the mathematical deduction of consequences from the basic principles. Sometimes many steps are required and the equations become quite numerous. In order to help the reader, the equations are numbered for identification. The part of the number appearing before the dash is the number of the chapter in which the equation first appears. After the dash, equations important enough to be identified for reference are numbered consecutively within the chapter. Sometimes an entire set is used so frequently together that it is identified as a set. When this is done, Roman numerals are used for the purpose.

The number of equations is large, and intensive study of each is not required. The equations expressing basic principles and important results are emphasized for special attention. When an equation is first introduced for the formulation of a basic principle, it is enclosed in a double box for the purpose of calling attention to its importance. It should be given careful study, so that its significance is understood and so that the principle will be remembered. A single box denotes an equation of intermediate importance, such as an important conclusion of a mathematical development.

P. L. C.
W. E. B.

November 1960

Acknowledgments

Many people have contributed in numerous ways to the production of this text. Their number is too large to list in detail. The entire staff of the Department of Physics at Illinois Institute of Technology has taken a very active interest in this work, and their constructive criticisms have aided us greatly. It is a pleasure to thank especially Dr. F. F. Cleveland, whose detailed review of the manuscript represented an output of energy and time very rarely equaled. Definite contributions were also made by Dr. I. Hauser, Mr. A. Attard, and Mr. John Ritter.

Our debt is obviously great to those whose researches in physics have contributed important ideas or clarified our understanding of phenomena. Many names are cited in the text and lists of references at appropriate places. We thank Dr. William Shockley and Dr. Esther Conwell for permission to use material from their published papers.

Mrs. Bruce Murray (née Coleen Byrne), through drawings which were very accurately and beautifully done as well as through other detailed work on the manuscript, contributed much to the usefulness of the lithoprinted edition out of which the present volume has been developed. Miss Gertrude Kornfeld took intense interest in this work and went over a large portion of the galleys with a thoroughness rarely made available to authors.

Contents

Part I **THE RISE OF ATOMIC PHYSICS**

1	Elements of the Kinetic Theory of Gases	3
2	Laws for the Motion of Charged Particles and the Identification of Atomic Constituents	34
3	The Special Theory of Relativity	54
4	The Origin of the Quantum Theory	74
5	First Theories of Atomic Structure	92
6	The Arrangement of Atoms in Solids and the Analysis of Crystals	111
7	Evidence for Corpuscular Properties Associated with Electromagnetic Radiation	141
8	Coupled Oscillators and the Propagation of Waves Through Periodic Structures	153

Part II **CONFIGURATIONS OF ELECTRONS**

9	Basic Ideas of Wave Mechanics	173
10	Standing Wave Patterns and Quantum Numbers	198
11	Basic Aspects of Atomic Behavior	211
12	Electrons in Metals	229
13	Electrons in a Periodically Varying Potential Distribution	245
14	Imperfections and Their Influence on the Properties of Crystals	260

15   Experimental Studies Concerning Behavior of
      Carriers   278
16   Early Applications of Semiconductors   293

Part III NUCLEAR PHYSICS

17   The Nuclear Atom   309
18   Absorption of Alpha, Beta, and Gamma Rays   321
19   Detection of Radiation   336
20   Spontaneous Transformations   349
21   Nuclear Reactions   365
22   Neutrons   378
23   Nuclear Structure   391
24   Atomic Energy   407

APPENDICES

  I   Analytic Representation of Vectors Illustrated
        by Electric and Magnetic Fields   427
 II   Methods for Representing Vibrations   441
III   Standing Waves in Bounded Media   446
 IV   Group Velocity and the Variation of Phase
        Velocity   450
  V   Harmonic Analysis of Wave Forms   453
 VI   Bound Particle in a Potential Well with Finite
        Boundaries   458
VII   The Wave Equation in Spherical Coordinates   461
VIII   Surface Charge Distributions and Forces   467
 IX   Periodic Potential Variations and Allowed
        Energies   473
  X   A Step in the Derivation of Rutherford
        Scattering   481
 XI   The Schroedinger Equation   482

Tables   485

Index   493

PART I | The Rise of Atomic Physics

1 | Elements of the Kinetic Theory of Gases

Introduction

All gases are similar in certain fundamental respects. For example, the density of gases is quite low as compared with the liquid and solid states in which matter may be found. Furthermore, in sharp contrast with solids and liquids, gases have no fixed volume, but expand to occupy the entire available volume within a containing vessel. On the walls of the container, a uniform pressure normal (perpendicular) to the surface is observable. The density of the gas, which is observed as an average value over the appreciable time required for making an observation, is nearly constant over the entire volume within the containing vessel. As long as the volume is fixed, the density does not change with temperature, but the pressure in this case increases linearly with the temperature. If, on the other hand, the pressure is maintained constant, the volume V increases linearly with the temperature T. A very remarkable thing is that the coefficient of expansion is almost the same for all gases, and extrapolation of the line obtained by plotting V against T to zero volume provides a means of estimating the zero point of temperature on the Kelvin or "absolute scale."

The phenomena exhibited by gases are quite general. All substances vaporize if the temperature is high enough, and the vapors at sufficiently high temperatures behave like gases. Considering the gases contained in the atmosphere of the earth, the density, although practically constant at a given level, decreases quite slowly with height. The density of the atmosphere approaches zero as the height above sea level increases without limit.

The generality of these properties indicates that they are fundamental, and scientists have studied them intensively. It has proved possible to develop a model which accounts for the observed laws in a satisfactory

TABLE 1-1. SYMBOLS USED IN CHAPTER 1

Symbol	Name	Quantity Designated
V		volume
u		x-component of velocity
v, w		y-, z-components of velocity respectively
c		speed of particle ($c = \sqrt{u^2 + v^2 + w^2}$)
N		number of particles
N_0		initial number of particles
N_1		number of particles per unit volume
m		mass
P		pressure
p_i		relative frequency of occurrence n_i/N
P_i		probability corresponding to class i
r		radius
u_e		effective (rms) speed
Φ	phi	function which represents the distribution of particles in speed
ρ	rho	density
α	alpha	most probable speed in Maxwellian distribution
U'		relatively large velocity of particles in a beam
U		potential energy
W		work (energy)
θ	theta	angle with respect to a selected direction
n		number of moles
L		mean-free-path
k		Boltzmann's constant 1.38×10^{-23} joules/°K
e		base of natural logarithms
$\exp(x) = e^x$		exponential function
T		temperature
t		time
F		force
R		gas constant referred to as a mole
Δ	delta	operation of taking finite increments
d		operation of differentiation
∂		where function depends on several variables, differentiation with respect to one while the others are kept constant
f		frequency function
A		area
s		distance
D		diameter of sphere
Σ	sigma	summation
$\int$		integration

manner. Thus, the gaseous phase was the first state of matter for which a satisfactory theory was developed. This was the kinetic theory of gases, which was worked out in the nineteenth century.

In the kinetic theory of gases, the gaseous material is pictured as consisting of small particles called atoms or molecules which occupy a very small fraction of the gaseous volume, and which move about independently of each other. These particles collide with the walls and with each other. Between collisions, they move in straight lines with constant speed. The collisions are elastic, which means that the total kinetic energy remains constant despite the collisions. As long as the gas is isolated from its surroundings, it is pictured as executing a sort of perpetual motion.

This kinetic picture is justified only if it leads to calculated results which are in agreement with experimental observation. For example, it has been found possible to account for the pressure exerted by a gas in terms of the momentum transferred to a boundary wall by the molecules striking it. Another noteworthy achievement of the theory has been a satisfactory explanation of the observed heat capacities of gases.

Transfer of Momentum to a Target from a Molecular Beam

As an approach to the kinetic theory of gases, let us analyze a situation which is frequently encountered in modern experimental arrangements. Consider a beam of identical particles each of mass m and velocity $\mathbf{u}$,* constituting a beam which is striking a target surface. For simplicity, we first assume that the particles stick to the surface. Newton's second law may be used to determine the force which the molecules exert on the surface. According to this law, the time rate of change of the momentum $m\mathbf{u}$ gives the force $\mathbf{F}$ exerted on the surface. Thus, we may write

$$\frac{d}{dt}(m\mathbf{u}) = \mathbf{F}. \tag{1-1}$$

If, as in the case we are considering, the force averaged over an appreciable time is constant, the integration of Eq. (1) over the time Δt gives

$$\Delta(m\mathbf{u}) = \mathbf{F}\,\Delta t. \tag{1-2}$$

From information about the beam, we may determine an expression for the change of momentum. Let N_1' represent the number of particles per unit volume which have a mass m and a velocity $\mathbf{u}$ in a direction parallel to the x-axis. A small target in the form of a square of area A, having the perpendicular to its surface in the x-direction, is brought into

* To indicate that $\mathbf{u}$ is a vector quantity, it is set in boldface type. See Appendix I.

the beam. We assume that the action of the beam is constant over the entire area A of the target. Now since Eq. (2) expresses the force in terms of the change of momentum, it is easy to determine the force which the beam exerts on this target. Each molecule gives its momentum $(m\mathbf{u})$ to the target and sticks to it. To determine the number of molecules arriving in the time Δt on the area A, we erect a rectangular prism the length of which is equal to $u\,\Delta t$, as shown in Fig. 1-1. Since the velocity of the particles is $\mathbf{u}$, all the particles in this prism will strike the area A in the time Δt. The volume of this prism is $Au\,\Delta t$, and since the number of molecules per unit volume is N_1', the total number of particles which strike the target in the time Δt is $N_1'\,Au\,\Delta t$. Since each particle gives its momentum $m\mathbf{u}$ to the target, the total impulse $\mathbf{F}\,\Delta t$ given to the target in time Δt is

$$\mathbf{F}\,\Delta t = (m\mathbf{u})(N_1'\,Au\,\Delta t), \tag{1-3}$$

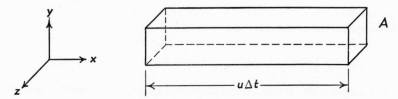

Fig. 1-1. Volume of a beam striking the surface A in a time of Δt.

and to determine the force we divide by Δt. Hence

$$\mathbf{F} = (m\mathbf{u})(N_1'Au). \tag{1-4}$$

Ordinarily the quantity in which we are interested is the pressure P, which by definition is the force per unit area. We obtain this by dividing Eq. (4) by A. Thus,

$$P = \frac{F}{A} = (mu)(N_1'u). \tag{1-5}$$

A fact of considerable interest is that the pressure is proportional to the translational kinetic energy $(\tfrac{1}{2}mu^2)$ of the particles in the beam. This proportionality arises from the fact that the momentum itself is proportional to the velocity and that the length of the box giving the volume of the beam striking the surface in a given time interval Δt is also proportional to the velocity. The product of the two gives the proportionality to the kinetic energy. Since N_1' represents the number of particles per unit volume, $N_1'(\tfrac{1}{2}mu^2)$ represents the kinetic energy per unit volume of the beam and the pressure given in Eq. (5) may be interpreted as twice the translational kinetic energy of the particles contained in one unit volume of the beam.

If the molecules, instead of sticking to the target, are elastically reflected with the velocity $-\mathbf{u}$, the momentum transferred to the surface by each particle is doubled. In this case, however, the total number of particles per unit volume is doubled, because there is an incident beam having N_1' particles per unit volume and a reflected beam also having N_1' particles per unit volume. Thus, the pressure is still expressible as twice the kinetic energy of all the particles contained in a unit volume of the space traversed by both beams.

Force Resulting from a Beam Having Molecules of a Number of Different Speeds

Suppose that the molecular beam, instead of having particles of a single velocity, contains several groups of identical particles with all those in a given group having the same velocity, while those in different groups have different velocities. To represent this situation, we take a beam in which the particles all move parallel to the x-axis. The beam contains N_1' particles per unit volume having the velocity u_1, N_2' particles per unit volume having the velocity u_2, and N_3' particles per unit volume having the velocity u_3. The argument of the preceding section may now be repeated for each of the three beams to give the force per unit area which arises from each of the three beams and the total force is obtained by adding these three results. Thus, for the pressure P, we obtain

$$P = N_1'mu_1{}^2 + N_2'mu_2{}^2 + N_3'mu_3{}^2 = N_T'mu_e{}^2, \qquad (1\text{-}6)$$

where N_T' is the total number of the particles per unit volume and u_e is an effective velocity which would give the same pressure if each molecule had this velocity. From Eq. (6), we get

$$u_e = \left[\frac{N_1'u_1{}^2 + N_2'u_2{}^2 + N_3'u_3{}^2}{N_T'}\right]^{1/2}. \qquad (1\text{-}7)$$

The result expressed by Eq. (7) is sufficiently important to be given a name. Because of the way the individual numbers and velocities are used in Eq. (7), u_e is called the root-mean-square (rms) velocity. If a beam is not homogeneous, the pressure may still be obtained by multiplying the mean-square velocity by the mass of the molecule and by the total number of particles per unit volume in the beam. The result is still exactly twice the total kinetic energy of all the particles per unit volume in the beam. There is, of course, no need to restrict the argument just given to any limited number of groups of particles. It is possible to increase the number of groups of particles without limit and to arrive at the general conclusion that, when the particles in a beam have velocities restricted to a given direction, the pressure produced by these particles falling normally on a surface is twice the kinetic energy of all the particles in a unit volume of the beam.

Velocities Not Restricted to a Single Direction

We have used the beam of particles for showing the manner in which a momentum transfer gives rise to pressure. Such beams are frequently encountered in physical experiments, and they do result in just the pressure which we have discussed. Our primary concern at this time, however, is to understand the nature of a gas. It is quite true that in a gas, such as the air in which we live, the molecules have their velocity vectors in all the directions of space. We, therefore, eliminate the restriction on direction, and for our model of a gas in which there are no convection currents, we assume that the velocity vectors all start at a common

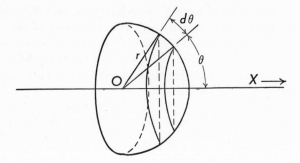

Fig. 1-2. Molecules having a common component of velocity along the normal to a surface.

origin in velocity space and have their terminal points distributed uniformly over the surface of a sphere. (For the moment, to simplify the argument, we retain the assumption that all molecules have the same speed u.) The model with which we deal in the present section is a region of space containing N_1' molecules per unit volume all having the same speed u, but with velocities uniformly distributed in all directions. To determine the proportion of the molecules having the same component of velocity along the normal to a surface, consider Fig. 1-2. Here the x-axis represents the normal to the surface on which the molecules fall, and the angle θ is measured relative to this line. The solid angle subtended at O, corresponding to all possible directions between θ and $\theta + d\theta$, is

$$(2\pi r \sin \theta)(r \, d\theta)/r^2 = 2\pi \sin \theta \, d\theta.$$

Thus the number of molecules having velocity vectors lying in this ring is

$$dN_1' = \frac{2\pi \sin \theta \, d\theta \, N_1'}{4\pi} = \frac{N_1' \sin \theta}{2} d\theta. \tag{1-8}$$

In this case, because of random directions, we find that particles cross all boundaries of a box, like that shown in Fig. 1-1, which we erect on the area A placed in the gas, but, because of the random distribution of velocities throughout the volume of the gas, for every molecule lost from the box another molecule enters; so the conclusion concerning momentum transfer, which is based on using the box as a model, is still valid. The x-component of the velocity of a molecule moving along r at the angle θ is $u \cos \theta$, and in an "elastic" reflection this velocity component is changed to $-u \cos \theta$. If the other components of velocity are unchanged, the reflection is called "regular," and the entire momentum transfer is given by $2 \, mu \cos \theta$. The number of all such molecules striking the surface of area A in time Δt is

$$A \, dN_1' u \cos \theta \, \Delta t$$

and the momentum transfer is

$$A \, d\theta \, N_1' \frac{\sin \theta}{2} (2mu \cos \theta)(u \cos \theta \, \Delta t).$$

The total impulse given to the surface by all molecules striking it in time Δt is

$$F \, \Delta t = A \, \Delta t \int_0^{\pi/2} N_1' mu^2 \cos^2 \theta \sin \theta \, d\theta$$

$$= A \, \Delta t \, N_1' mu^2 \left[-\frac{\cos^3 \theta}{3} \right]_0^{\pi/2}$$

$$= A \, \Delta t \, N_1' mu^2 \tfrac{1}{3}. \tag{1-9}$$

The pressure is obtained through division by $A \, \Delta t$. Thus,

$$\boxed{P = N_1' mu^2/3.} \tag{1-10}$$

The kinetic energy of each molecule is $\tfrac{1}{2}mu^2$, and N_1' is the number of molecules per unit volume. The pressure is to be interpreted as equal to two-thirds of the kinetic energy of all the molecules contained in unit volume.

Having arrived at this simple expression for the pressure arising from molecules of a single speed, it is possible to add the pressures due to molecules of different speeds. The single speed u_e, which must be used in Eq. (10) together with the total number of molecules per unit volume N_1' to give the pressure, is the root-mean-square speed. This also is the speed which gives the average kinetic energy of a molecule. Thus, the total kinetic energy per unit volume is given by $N_1'(\frac{1}{2}mu_e^2)$ joules. Hence, regardless of the nature of the distribution of speeds, if the velocity distribution of every particular speed is random with respect to direction, the pressure exerted by a gas is equal to two-thirds of the kinetic energy of all the particles contained in unit volume, or

$$P = (N_1 mu_e^2)/3. \tag{1-11}$$

The Theory Compared with Results for a Real Gas

We have now arrived at results of sufficient generality to make the comparison with the behavior of a real gas significant. First, we notice that at a given temperature the behavior of permanent gases is satisfactorily represented by Boyle's law,

$$PV = \text{constant.}$$

If we now take our expression, Eq. (11), and multiply it by a volume V, we obtain

$$PV = (N_1 V mu_e^2)/3. \tag{1-12}$$

The right-hand side of Eq. (12) when applied to a given number of molecules of a gas $N_1 V$, is in fact constant so long as m and u_e are constants, as assumed in the derivation of Eq. (11). Kinetic theory, therefore, not only accounts for Boyle's law, but it also gives an assignable value to the PV product.

The general gas law is

$$PV = nRT, \tag{1-13}$$

where n is the number of moles, T is the absolute temperature, and R is the universal gas constant. This law was formulated to represent the experimentally observed behavior of actual gases, and only very small deviations from it are observed for gases of low density. This equation should be derivable from the kinetic theory of gases if the theory is correct. The expression $(N_1 V mu_e^2)/3$ is the theoretical value of PV, and nRT is the experimental value. Aside from the constants, the theoretical value is proportional to the average kinetic energy of a molecule, whereas the experimental value is proportional to the temperature. There is no real discrepancy if the average kinetic energy of a molecule is proportional to temperature. The concept of temperature is based upon thermometry, but a further development of the concept is possible if one thinks of the reading of a thermometer placed in a gas as being governed by the bombardment of the bulb of the thermometer by molecules of a certain average energy. Because of this kinetic concept of temperature, the motions of the molecules are referred to as thermal motions, and the process of heating a gas is thought of as feeding energy into the gas so that the kinetic energies of the thermal motions are increased.

The exact relationship between the temperature and the average molecular kinetic energy can be found by equating the theoretical and experimental values of PV. Thus,

$$(N_1 V m u_e^2)/3 = nRT, \tag{1-14}$$

and the average kinetic energy of a molecule is

$$\boxed{W = \tfrac{1}{2}m u_e^2 = 3nRT/2N_1 V = 3kT/2,} \tag{1-15}$$

where k is a new universal constant, called Boltzmann's constant, which can be evaluated from the quantities it replaces. The quantity $N_1 V/n$ is the number of molecules per mole, or Avogadro's number. Thus, the Boltzmann's constant is the universal gas constant divided by Avogadro's number. Its value is

$$k = 1.38 \times 10^{-23} \text{ joules/}^\circ\text{K}. \tag{1-16}$$

It may be noticed that our derivation has taken no account of the fact that the molecules themselves occupy a finite part of the space V. If the finite diameter of the molecules is taken into account, the previously computed number of impacts on the boundary is increased. Furthermore, if the molecules do not really act like hard elastic spheres, but exert appreciable long-range forces on one another on account of their basically electrical nature, the observed pressure might be changed. Such effects have been used in deriving equations of state for actual gases. One of the simplest of these is van der Waals' equation.

In Eq. (11), $N_1 m = \rho$, the density of the gas, and this is a constant which may be measured for a given gas at a definite temperature and pressure. The pressure P is also a definitely measurable quantity. Thus Eq. (11), in the form

$$\boxed{P = (\rho u_e^2)/3,} \tag{1-17}$$

provides us with a means of determining the mean-square speed u_e^2 or its square root u_e, the rms speed. The calculated speeds turn out to be quite high, a result which when first encountered may be somewhat surprising. For example, for hydrogen, under a pressure of a standard atmosphere (101,300 newtons/m^2), $\rho = 0.0899$ kg/m^3,

$$u_e = \left[\frac{3P}{\rho}\right]^{1/2} = \left[\frac{3 \times 101,300 \text{ newtons/m}^2}{0.0899 \text{ kg/m}^3}\right]^{1/2} = 1.84 \times 10^3 \text{ m/sec.}$$

(1-17')

This is a speed slightly greater than a mile a second. The density of a gas is proportional to the molecular mass; and, as shown in Eq. (17'), the rms speed is inversely proportional to the square root of the density. For oxygen, therefore, the speed that accounts for the average translational kinetic energy of the molecules is 462 m/sec.

Heat Capacity of Gases and Equipartition

The heat capacity of a gas at constant volume represents, according to kinetic theory, the amount of energy required to increase the kinetic energy of the molecules by an amount corresponding to a rise in temperature of 1° C. According to the above relationship (restricted to translational energy), this is $\frac{3}{2}k$ per molecule. For a mole of the gas, the heat capacity is greater by a factor equal to the number of molecules in a mole, or Avogadro's number. Therefore, the molal heat capacity at constant volume should be given by $\frac{3}{2}R$. The accepted experimental value of the universal gas constant is 8.317×10^7 ergs deg^{-1} mole^{-1}, or in mks (meter, kilogram, second) units 8.317×10^3 joules deg^{-1} kg-mole^{-1}. The heat capacity thus should be 12.474×10^3 joules deg^{-1} kg-mole^{-1}, and should be the same for all gases.

For monatomic gases, the experimental heat capacities at constant volume are in good agreement with this value. For example, 12.5×10^3 joules deg^{-1} kg-mole^{-1} is obtained from experiments on argon. For diatomic gases near room temperature, the values are about $\frac{5}{3}$ of this (20.2 and 20.6×10^3 in the same units for hydrogen and nitrogen, respectively). These results for the diatomic gases can be accounted for by supposing that the contributions of atomic vibrations are negligible, and that each molecule has rotational energy about two mutually perpendicular axes which are perpendicular to the axis of the molecule. This is an interesting example of a theorem called the principle of equipartition of energy. As applied to translational motions, there are three components of the velocity along the three coordinate axes and an average energy of $\frac{1}{2}kT$ would be associated with each of the three components of motion. The principle implies that molecules are set in rotation by the collisions between molecules and that the average energy associated with each type of rotation is also $\frac{1}{2}kT$. The proof of this theorem is not obvious.

Size of Molecules

Very small particles, which are visible through a microscope, are observed to be in random motion when they are situated in a gaseous or liquid medium. This is called Brownian motion, after its discoverer.

In 1905 Einstein quantitatively developed the idea that Brownian motion was due to the irregular bombardment of the microscopic particle by molecules in rapid motion. Essentially what Einstein conceived was that the law of equipartition of energy should extend to the microscopic particle, which on the average, would have the same kinetic energy as the molecules bombarding it. The motion of the microscopic particle can be observed, and this rather obviously provides a means of determining the average translational kinetic energy of the molecules. Since according to Eq. (17) the root-mean-square speed is readily deduced from the pressure exerted by a gas, the combination of the two observations (W from an experimental observation and u_e from Eq. (17)) when used in Eq. (15) would yield the mass of the individual molecule.

The achievement of Einstein in this connection was that he carried the theory to a point where the migration of a particle in a given direction (by random processes analogous to molecular diffusion) could be used for determining the number of molecules in a mole. Jean Perrin then took this as an experimental problem and made a study of the displacement of particles in the Brownian motion. One result was that Einstein's explanation of the Brownian motion quickly became well established. By 1908 the experimental results of Perrin established the order of magnitude of the molecular mass. The results of Perrin's work may be summarized by stating that there are about 6.0×10^{26} molecules in one kg-mole of a substance. This in the mks system of units is the expression for Avogadro's number.

Once the number of molecules in a mole was determined, various estimates of the size of different atoms became possible. For example, one might say that a metal crystal consisted of spherical atoms closely packed, and could determine from the density of the metal and Avogadro's number the radius of the sphere. Representative results of such calculations were one or two Ångström units (1 Å $= 10^{-10}$ m). Subsequent study of the distances that molecules of various substances, such as monatomic mercury, move between collisions, has established the fact that there is a fairly definite sphere of influence giving a radius which confirms the view that an atomic system has a radius in the order of 1 or 2×10^{-10} m.

Statistical Methods and Probability

In the preceding sections, we have shown that the pressure exerted by a gas is proportional to its translational kinetic energy per unit volume. Subject to the condition that the velocity vectors are random as to direction, this means that any distribution of speeds having the same total energy would give rise to the same pressure. This has enabled us to give a simple account of the behavior of a gas without taking into account the frequencies with which the different speeds would be observed if measurements were made on all molecules of the gas. In many problems, however, the classification of the molecules according to velocity becomes important.

This problem is statistical in nature. There are, of course, a very great number of molecules in a laboratory sample of a gas. Even if it were possible to select and observe a given molecule of the gas, it would be impossible to say in advance what its velocity at a given instant would be, for collisions with other molecules keep changing its velocity. If, therefore, we were able to follow the history of a molecule over a long time, it would take on a great number of velocities, but velocities in some ranges would be a great deal more likely than those in other equal velocity ranges. Similarly, if we were able to obtain complete information about the velocity of every molecule in the gas at a selected instant of time, we would find a great many different velocities represented, and more molecules would have velocities in some ranges than in other equal ranges.

Assuming that it is physically meaningful to speak of the exact velocity of each molecule in a gas, a statistical analysis of the data is required to give information, in a usable form, about the velocities. To specify the exact velocity of each molecule in a sample containing as few as one billion molecules would be virtually impossible. The complexity of the resulting data would make their use prohibitive. What can be done is to place in one class all of the molecules having a certain small range of velocities about a selected velocity called the "class mark," and to place in another class all the molecules having the same small range of velocities about another class mark. The intervals are usually chosen to divide the molecules into perhaps 100 classes and the class marks are so chosen that each velocity is found in only one class.

As an illustration of the statistical procedure, the molecules may be classified according to the values of the x-components u of their velocities, without reference to other data. Using a suitably chosen class interval, we would set the class boundaries at $\ldots$, $-2\,\Delta u$, $-\Delta u$, 0, Δu, $2\,\Delta u$, etc. The distribution would then be specified in terms of the number of molecules appearing in each class. When this is done, the resulting statistical data are sufficiently simple to be usable.

Suppose that the molecules are divided into m classifications by the class boundaries and that of the N molecules thus classified, n_1 are in the first class, n_2 in the second class, n_i in the i-th class, and finally n_m are in the last class m. Since each molecule is in one, and only one, class, we may write

$$\sum_{i=1}^{m} n_i = N,$$

(1-18)

or

$$\frac{1}{N} \sum_{i=1}^{m} n_i = 1.$$

(1-18')

The terms, $n_i/N = p_i$, serve as an empirical evaluation of the "probability" of finding a given molecule in the i-th class. If N is chosen so that the various n_i values are not sufficiently large, there would be a considerable accidental variation in the results when various samples, each containing N molecules, are classified. However, if many samples each of size N are analyzed, the averages of the various n_i values will be established with only small uncertainties. The same result may be achieved by increasing N until the smallest value of n_i for any class i is itself a large number. The ratio of the large number n_i to the still larger number N is thus established with only a small uncertainty, and this ratio gives a measure of the probability of finding a given molecule in the physical state identified by the subscript i. The probability P_i that a molecule will appear in the state i is sometimes said to be represented by the limit of $p_i = n_i/N$ as N increases without limit. Thus,

$$P_i = \underset{N \to \infty}{\text{Limit}} (n_i/N).$$

(1-19)

The classes are chosen in such a way that a molecule is certain to fall into one (and only one) of them, and the result expressed by Eq. (18') means that the sum of the probabilities for all the classes is unity, and, thus, in this representation of probability, unity stands for certainty. Conversely, a probability of zero corresponds to an impossible event. Small finite values of P_i refer to improbable events.

The Maxwell-Boltzmann Distribution

The number of molecules in a laboratory sample is sufficiently great to make the use of the differential notation appropriate. Since the choice of the positive x-axis is an arbitrary one, the distribution is symmetrical about $u = 0$. There is in mathematical statistics a symmetrical distribution, called the normal or Gaussian distribution, which occurs very frequently in problems concerning the random distribution of events. An argument based on natural physical assumptions will show that the Gaussian function is the one required to give the distribution of molecules in one component of velocity. In the first place, it is reasonable to suppose that the distributions are identical in the three dimensions of ordinary space. The probability $P(u,du)$ of finding a molecule in the range du at u is proportional to du and to some function of u represented by $f(u)$, which we will call the frequency function. Thus,

$$P(u,du) = f(u)\ du. \qquad\qquad (1\text{-}20)$$

Similarly,

$$P(v,dv) = f(v)\ dv$$

and

$$P(w,dw) = f(w)\ dw$$

for the y- and z-components of the velocity. The probability of finding a molecule simultaneously in du at u, in dv at v *and* in dw at w is the product of these separate probabilities. Thus,

$$P(u,du,v,dv,w,dw) = P(u,du)P(v,dv)P(w,dw)$$

$$= f(u)f(v)f(w)\ du\ dv\ dw. \qquad (1\text{-}21)$$

Division by $du\ dv\ dw$ gives

$$\frac{P(u,du,v,dv,w,dw)}{du\ dv\ dw} = f(u)f(v)f(w). \qquad (1\text{-}22)$$

The components of the velocity can be added to give the magnitude c of the velocity of a molecule, since $c^2 = u^2 + v^2 + w^2$. Fig. 1-3 shows the velocity vectors c for a few of the molecules in the sample. The vectors start at the origin and terminate at various points in velocity space. The expression $P(u,du,v,dv,w,dw)$ signifies the fraction of the velocity vectors that terminate in the region $du\ dv\ dw$. Division by $du\ dv\ dw$ gives the density of the molecules in the velocity space, expressed as a fraction of the total number of molecules in the sample. It is obvious from the symmetry of the problem that this density should depend only upon the magnitude of c and be independent of the relative magnitudes of the components.

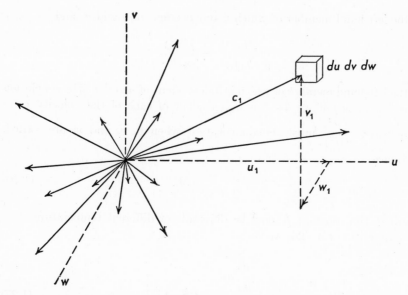

Fig. 1-3. Velocity vectors of the molecules. Here *du dv dw* is an element of volume in velocity space.

The left-hand side of Eq. (22) can be expressed as a function of c, or for convenience as $\Phi(c^2)$. Therefore,

$$f(u)f(v)f(w) = \Phi(c^2) = \Phi(\xi). \qquad (1\text{-}23)$$

Differentiation of this equation with respect to u gives

$$f'(u)f(v)f(w) = \frac{d\Phi(\xi)}{d\xi}\frac{\partial\xi}{\partial u} = \Phi'(\xi)2u = \Phi'(c^2)2u, \qquad (1\text{-}24)$$

where $f'(u) = df(u)/du$ and $\Phi'(\xi) = d\Phi(\xi)/d\xi$.
Division of Eq. (24) by Eq. (23) gives

$$\frac{f'(u)}{2uf(u)} = \frac{\Phi'(c^2)}{\Phi(c^2)}, \qquad (1\text{-}25)$$

in which the left-hand member is independent of v and w. Similarly, we obtain

$$\frac{f'(v)}{2vf(v)} = \frac{\Phi'(c^2)}{\Phi(c^2)},$$

the left-hand member of which is independent of u and w, and

$$\frac{f'(w)}{2wf(w)} = \frac{\Phi'(c^2)}{\Phi(c^2)},$$

the left-hand member of which is independent of u and w. The conclusion is that, since $\Phi'(c^2)/\Phi(c^2)$ is independent of each of the velocity components, $\dfrac{\Phi'(c^2)}{\Phi(c^2)}$ must remain constant when u, v, and w are varied. Hence,

$$\frac{f'(u)}{2uf(u)} = K, \tag{1-26}$$

where the constant K may be different for different temperatures.

Rewriting Eq. (26) we get

$$\boxed{\frac{\dfrac{df}{du}\,du}{f(u)} = K2u\,du,} \tag{1-27}$$

which upon integration gives

$$\ln f(u) = Ku^2 + K' \tag{1-28}$$

or

$$f(u) = e^{K'}e^{Ku^2}, \tag{1-29}$$

where K' is a constant. To satisfy the boundary condition that $f(u) \to 0$ as $u^2 \to \infty$, K must be a negative constant, and may be set equal to $-1/\alpha^2$. The constant $e^{K'}$ serves for the "normalization" of the probability, by which we mean that a summation or an integration of the probability over all the classes, yields unity.

The value of the normalization factor $e^{K'}$ is given by

$$\int_{-\infty}^{\infty} f(u)\,du = e^{K'}\int_{-\infty}^{\infty} (e^{-u^2/\alpha^2})\,du = 1.$$

From tables of definite integrals,

$$\int_{-\infty}^{\infty} e^{-u^2/\alpha^2}\,du = \alpha\sqrt{\pi} \text{ or } \alpha\pi^{\frac{1}{2}}.$$

Thus, the normalization constant is

$$e^{K'} = \frac{1}{\alpha\sqrt{\pi}}. \tag{1-30}$$

Hence, the normalized function $f(u)$ is

$$f(u) = \frac{1}{\alpha\sqrt{\pi}} e^{-u^2/\alpha^2}. \tag{1-31}$$

Substituting this value in Eq. (20) gives

$$P(u,du) = \frac{1}{\alpha\sqrt{\pi}} e^{-u^2/\alpha^2} du. \tag{1-32}$$

If we multiply the probability $P(u,du)$ of finding one molecule in du at u by the total number N_T of molecules, the result will be the number of molecules dN that are expected to be found in du at u. Hence, we may write

$$\frac{dN}{du} = N_T \frac{1}{\alpha\sqrt{\pi}} e^{-u^2/\alpha^2}, \tag{1-33}$$

where N_T represents the total number of molecules in the distribution, u is the x-component of velocity, and α is a parameter of the distribution, which is to be identified later. Since the choice of the axes is arbitrary, it will be recognized that there are similar expressions in v, the y-component of velocity, and in w the z-component of velocity. We, therefore, can set down the additional relationships

and

$$\frac{dN}{dv} = N_T \frac{1}{\alpha\sqrt{\pi}} e^{-v^2/\alpha}$$

$$\frac{dN}{dw} = N_T \frac{1}{\alpha\sqrt{\pi}} e^{-w^2/\alpha^2}.$$

These might equally well have been established through integrations similar to that shown for u.

The derivation of the velocity distribution depends upon the assumption that the probabilities of occurrence of the components of velocity can be multiplied together, and this is justifiable only if the three probabilities are independent of each other. We shall proceed on the basis of this assumption to evaluate the density of molecules in the velocity space as given by Eq. (22).

The relative density of molecules in the velocity space is

$$f(u)f(v)f(w) = \left(\frac{1}{\alpha\sqrt{\pi}} e^{-u^2/\alpha^2}\right)\left(\frac{1}{\alpha\sqrt{\pi}} e^{-v^2/\alpha^2}\right)\left(\frac{1}{\alpha\sqrt{\pi}} e^{-w^2/\alpha^2}\right)$$

$$= \frac{1}{(\alpha\sqrt{\pi})^3} e^{-(u^2+v^2+w^2)/\alpha^2}$$

$$= \frac{1}{(\alpha\sqrt{\pi})^3} e^{-c^2/\alpha^2}, \tag{1-34}$$

where $c^2 = u^2 + v^2 + w^2$. The volume of velocity space which lies between c and $c + dc$ is $4\pi c^2 \, dc$. Therefore, the number of molecules dN which have the velocity c within the interval dc is

$$dN = N_T \frac{1}{(\alpha\sqrt{\pi})^3} e^{-c^2/\alpha^2}(4\pi c^2 \, dc). \qquad (1\text{-}35)$$

The total number of molecules N_T appears because the density of molecules in the velocity space was calculated as a fraction of the total number of molecules. The final result is

$$\boxed{dN = N_T \frac{4}{\alpha^3\sqrt{\pi}} c^2 e^{-c^2/\alpha^2} \, dc.} \qquad (1\text{-}36)$$

This is the well-known Maxwellian distribution of molecular speeds in a gas. The shape of the distribution is shown in Fig. 1-4, where $dP/dc \equiv dN/(N_T \, dc)$ is plotted as ordinate against c as abscissa.

The curve starts out in the form of a parabola because when $c = 0$, $e^{-c^2/\alpha^2} = 1$, and the factor c^2 multiplying the exponential determines the shape of the curve. In the other extreme, when $c \to \infty$, the shape of the curve is dominated by the exponential factor. It is well to locate the position of the maximum of the curve analytically. This is done by taking the derivative of the ordinate and setting the result equal to zero. Thus,

$$\frac{d^2P}{dc^2} = \frac{4}{\alpha^3\pi^{1/2}} e^{-c^2/\alpha^2} \left[2c - \frac{2c^3}{\alpha^2} \right] = 0,$$

from which $c_{\max} = \alpha$. We are thus able to interpret the parameter α, which enters the distribution functions, as the value of the speed at which the distribution as a function of speed attains its maximum value, or, in brief, α represents the most probable speed in the distribution.

Besides the most probable speed α, the average speed $\bar{c}$ in a Maxwellian distribution is of some interest. This can be evaluated from the expression for an average value which is

$$\bar{c} = \frac{1}{N} \int_0^{N_T} c \, dN. \qquad (1\text{-}37)$$

The Maxwellian expression for dN should be used and the value of the definite integral can be obtained from a table of definite integrals. The evaluation of the average speed is left to the student.

A more important quantity is the average value $\overline{c^2}$ of c^2, because this would be needed to evaluate the average energy of a molecule. The average value of $\overline{c^2}$ is given by

$$\overline{c^2} = \frac{1}{N} \int_0^{N_T} c^2 \, dN$$

$$= \frac{1}{N} \int_0^{\infty} c^2 N \, \frac{4}{\alpha^3 \pi^{\frac{1}{2}}} \, c^2 e^{-c^2/\alpha^2} \, dc$$

$$= \frac{4}{\alpha^3 \sqrt{\pi}} \int_0^{\infty} c^4 e^{-c^2/\alpha^2} \, dc. \tag{1-38}$$

The definite integral has the value $\frac{3}{8}\sqrt{\pi}\,\alpha^5$. Hence,

$$\boxed{\overline{c^2} = \tfrac{3}{2}\alpha^2.} \tag{1-39}$$

The average kinetic energy of a molecule is $mc^2/2 = 3m\alpha^2/4$. But the average kinetic energy of a molecule has already been evaluated in terms of the temperature, as $3kT/2$. Equating the two values of average kinetic energy, we have

$$\boxed{\tfrac{3}{2}kT = \tfrac{3}{4}m\alpha^2}$$

or

$$\alpha^2 = \frac{2kT}{m} = \frac{2RT}{M}, \tag{1-40}$$

where R is the universal gas constant and M is the mass of the gas per mole. The quantity α, which appeared first in the theory as a constant (when u, v, and w were the variables), and which was later found to represent the most probable speed in a Maxwellian distribution, is now shown to depend upon the temperature. The Maxwellian distribution of speeds can now be written, to show its dependence upon the

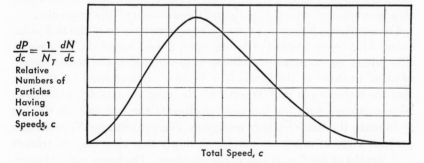

$$\frac{dP}{dc} = \frac{1}{N_T}\frac{dN}{dc}$$

Relative
Numbers of
Particles
Having
Various
Speeds, c

Total Speed, c

Fig. 1-4. Distribution of molecules in speed according to Maxwell.

temperature, as

$$dN = N_T 4\pi \left(\frac{M}{2\pi RT}\right)^{3/2} c^2 e^{-mc^2/2kT} \, dc. \qquad (1\text{-}41)$$

The Distribution of Free Molecular Paths for Molecules of a Beam and the Mean-Free-Path

Thus far we have been treating the molecules as massive points. Even in the early days of the kinetic theory it was understood that the molecules had appreciable linear dimensions. Visualizing the molecules as spheres, it was natural to specify the size in terms of the diameter. One of the earliest bits of evidence pointing toward the finite size of the molecules was an apparent paradox. It was known that the molecular velocities were large, about a kilometer per second, for example. Despite this, it was observed that when molecules of ammonia were released in the atmosphere, as for example by opening a bottle, it took appreciable time for these molecules to be detected at the other end of a room, say ten meters away. To reconcile these two facts, Clausius postulated that because the molecule had finite size, it would undergo frequent collisions in which its velocity would change abruptly in both magnitude and direction. In these circumstances, a given molecule would bounce around in random directions and its displacement in a given direction would be governed by the laws of chance, a process which is called diffusion. The progress of a molecule in a selected direction, therefore, is understandably slow.

It is obvious that the average distance a molecule will travel between a collision with one molecule and the collision with the next molecule is one of the important constants of the kinetic theory. This distance is called the "mean-free-path." We can derive the distribution of free paths from a very simple model which will give, in addition, the relationship between the mean-free-path and the diameter of the molecules.

For simplicity, however, we return to a consideration of the molecular beam. This beam, instead of falling upon a solid target, in the present case enters an enclosure containing a gas in which the *molecules* are *identical* to those in the beam. The beam is characterized by the fact that the molecules in it all travel with the same velocity U', which is so large compared with the thermal velocities of the molecules in the gas as to make the latter entirely negligible. The gas contains N_1 molecules per unit volume, which are moving so slowly that they may be treated as if located at fixed positions in the enclosure. The beam consists originally of a total of N_0 molecules per unit volume as it enters the enclosure where $|dN|$ is the number of molecules having paths which terminate between x and $x + dx$.

From Eqs. (42) and (43),

$$|dN| = N_1 N \pi D^2 \, dx$$
$$= N_1 N_0 e^{-N_1 \pi D^2 x} D^2 \pi \, dx.$$

Hence,

$$L = \int_0^\infty \pi x N_1 e^{-N_1 \pi D^2 x} D^2 \, dx. \tag{1-44}$$

Letting

$$y = N_1 \pi D^2 x,$$

we obtain

$$L = \frac{1}{N_1 \pi D^2} \int_0^\infty y \, dy \, e^{-y}$$

$$= \frac{1}{N_1 \pi D^2} [(-y - 1)e^{-y}]_0^\infty$$

$$= \frac{1}{N_1 \pi D^2}. \tag{1-45}$$

Thus, Eq. (43) may be written as

$$N = N_0 e^{-x/L}, \tag{1-46}$$

which is the law for the distribution in free paths that gives rise to the mean-free-path L. Since this is a negative exponential function, decreasing monotonically from its value at $x = 0$, it is to be noticed that the distribution of free paths does not come to a maximum at the value L. In this sense the distribution, although its average is L, is not concentrated in the neighborhood of L, nor, as we might say, is it clustered about the value L.

The model used above in the dermination of free paths is a very definite one. The gas consisted of small, hard, and perfectly elastic spheres. Those identified as target molecules had relatively small velocities and they were considered to be at rest. The bombarding molecules were represented as similar small, hard spheres. The velocity U' of all the molecules in the beam was taken to be the same, but the mean-free-path was found to be independent of this velocity. The mean-free-time would of course be velocity dependent and would be equal to L/U'.

The major concept that resulted from the model was a cross section that determined the likelihood of a collision and hence the mean-free-path of the molecules in the beam. The concept of cross section, whether

at $x = 0$ with the velocity U' in the direction x. As soon as a m
of the beam collides with a gas molecule, it is scattered from the

It is our purpose to determine, as a function of position, the n
N of molecules per unit volume of the beam which have not yet s
collision. If the diameter of the molecules is D, it is clear that th
molecules will collide if their centers come within the distance D o
other. The number of collisions would be the same if the beam mole
had a radius D and the target molecules had zero radius, or conve
The molecules of the beam are aimed at the volume containing the t
molecules, but they cannot be aimed at individual molecules, and
number of collisions is governed by probability. Each molecule of
beam sweeps out a volume $\pi D^2 \, dx$ as it moves through the layer, a
collision occurs if the center of a target atom lies within this volu
The total volume swept out by the N molecules in the beam is $N\pi D^2$
and since there are N_1 molecules per unit volume in the target, the nu
ber of collisions is $N_1 N \pi D^2 \, dx$. Each collision reduces N by unity,
the change in N is

$$\boxed{-dN = N_1 N \pi D^2 \, dx.}$$ (1-4

This is an equation giving the number of molecules in the beam as
function of distance; the constants N_1 and D are also involved.

The differential equation

$$\frac{dN}{N} = -N_1 \pi D^2 \, dx$$

can be solved by integrating both sides, giving

$$\ln N = -N_1 \pi D^2 x + K.$$

The constant of integration K can be evaluated by putting $N = N_0$
when $x = 0$. After putting $K = \ln N_0$ and taking antilogarithms, the
final equation is

$$\boxed{N = N_0 \exp(-\pi N_1 D^2 x).}$$ (1-43)

This shows that the number of molecules in the collimated beam decreases exponentially with the distance. This is a typical absorption
equation of which we will see many examples.

The average distance traveled by a molecule is the average value of x,
and this is called the mean-free-path L. To evaluate the mean-free-path,
we follow the usual procedure for averaging. Thus,

$$L = \bar{x} = \frac{1}{N_0} \int_0^{N_0} x \, |dN|,$$

or not it can be expressed as πD^2, is a useful one although there are cases where the cross section is found to vary quite rapidly with energy. The idea of cross section is also useful when it is analyzed to give the fraction for various types of events which on the average are observed. There are models that are capable of giving theoretically the variation of partial cross sections with energy in some cases.

It is obvious that one cannot see whether or not molecules are spherical. For a few gases, such as helium, the molecules are supposed to consist of single atoms which have spherically symmetric charge distributions. Other atoms, on the basis of chemical evidence are thought to have the asymmetrical charge distributions responsible for directed chemical valences. However, most of the common gases are composed of diatomic or triatomic molecules. Some examples of diatomic molecules are N_2, O_2, and H_2, and some examples of triatomic molecules are H_2O and CO_2.

Mean-Free-Path of Molecules in an Atmosphere

In the interior of an actual gas, the concept of mean-free-path is applicable. It is the average distance traveled by the molecules of the gas between two successive collisions. If, following a collision, the distance s is measured along the path of a molecule no matter what its direction, the formula

$$N = N_0 e^{-s/L}$$

applies, where N_0 is the number of free paths under consideration, and N is the number of times that the distance s is exceeded before a second collision occurs. The mean-free-path depends upon the sizes of the molecules, much as it does for the molecular beam previously considered. However, some refinement is necessary because of the motion of the molecules which are struck by the molecule under consideration.

For simplicity, we assume that all molecules have exactly the same speed, designated by the symbol u, and that the angle between the two velocities is θ. It is the relative velocity c which determines the mean-free-time between collisions. The relative velocity c is the vector difference between the velocities of the

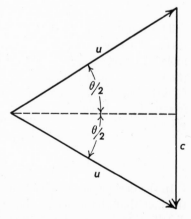

Fig. 1-5. Relative velocity of two molecules with the same speed.

two molecules, as shown in Fig. 1-5. Now $c = 2u \sin \frac{1}{2}\theta$, and, to obtain the effective value, c must be averaged for a sample of molecules which surround the molecule in question. Thus,

$$\bar{c} = \frac{1}{N} \int_0^N c \, dN,$$

where N is the number of surrounding molecules and dN is the number of those for which the relative velocity is c. The limits of integration should be such as to include all possible values of c. The number of molecules which make angles between θ and $\theta + d\theta$ is given by $N \dfrac{2\pi \sin \theta \, d\theta}{4\pi}$, the second factor being a ratio of two solid angles, namely, the solid angle which lies between θ and $\theta + d\theta$ divided by the total solid angle, 4π. Thus,

$$\bar{c} = \frac{1}{N} \int_0^\pi \left(2u \sin \frac{\theta}{2} \right) N \frac{2\pi \sin \theta \, d\theta}{4\pi}$$

$$= u \int_0^\pi \sin \frac{\theta}{2} \left(2 \sin \frac{\theta}{2} \cos \frac{\theta}{2} \right) d\theta$$

$$= 4u \int_0^\pi \sin^2 \frac{\theta}{2} \cos \frac{\theta}{2} \frac{d\theta}{2}$$

$$= \frac{4u}{3}. \tag{1-47}$$

The result shows that the average velocity of a molecule relative to surrounding molecules is $\frac{4}{3}$ of what it would have been if the surrounding molecules had been at rest. Collisions will be more frequent in time by the factor $\frac{4}{3}$, and the mean distance traveled between collisions will be $\frac{3}{4}$ as great. If this correction is included in the expression for the mean-free-path, we have

$$\boxed{L = \frac{3}{4N_1 \pi D^2}.} \tag{1-48}$$

In the derivation of this result, we have still failed to take into account the fact that the molecules have a distribution in speeds as well as the distribution in directions for their velocities. As we frequently find in such cases, however, the correction of the result just derived is not large. Maxwell carried through the calculation for the mean-free-path, on the basis of his distribution of velocities, and obtained the result

$$L = 1/\sqrt{2}\,\pi N_1 D^2. \tag{1-49}$$

Particles Crossing a Barrier Surface

In some physical problems, particles with a Maxwellian distribution of velocities cross into a region where the particles have a different potential energy. The change in potential energy is accomplished at the ex-

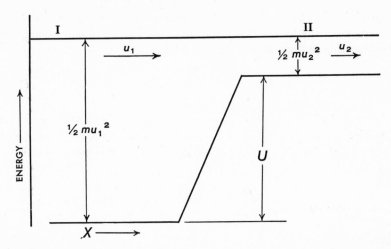

Fig. 1-6. Change in kinetic energy of individual particles when they pass into a region of different potential energy.

pense of an opposite change in kinetic energy. It is desirable to see how the change in velocity affects the Maxwellian distribution.

Fig. 1-6 shows two regions, in the first of which it is *assumed* that particles of a gas have a Maxwellian velocity distribution. The particles in general have three components of velocity (u, v, and w). Between regions I and II, the potential energy of a particle increases as it moves in the positive x-direction, and the total change of potential energy is identified as the magnitude of the potential barrier U. The force arising from this barrier has only an x-component; so the y- and z-components of velocity remain unchanged. A particle that passes through the potential barrier from region I to region II does this at the expense of the energy associated with its x-component of velocity, and the relationship is

$$\tfrac{1}{2}mu_1^2 = \tfrac{1}{2}mu_2^2 + U, \tag{1-50}$$

where u_1 is the initial x-component of velocity and u_2 is the x-component of velocity as the particle enters region II after crossing the barrier. Only those particles for which $\frac{1}{2}mu_1^2 > U$ can reach region II. Particles for which $\frac{1}{2}mu_1^2 < U$ are reflected into region I.

Since the barrier has no influence on v and w, we can analyze the situation through an explicit consideration of u alone. In region I, the number of particles between u_1 and $u_1 + du_1$ is given by

$$dN(u_1) = \frac{N_1}{\alpha\sqrt{\pi}} e^{-u_1^2/\alpha^2} du_1.$$

Multiplying by u_1 to obtain the number of particles of this velocity arriving from the left at the unit area of the barrier in one second, and denoting this particle flux by dI, we have

$$dI(u_1) = \frac{N_1}{\alpha\sqrt{\pi}} e^{-u_1^2/\alpha^2} u_1 \, du_1. \tag{1-51}$$

If $\frac{1}{2}mu_1^2 < U$, the particles are reflected and there is an identical return flux. If, however, $\frac{1}{2}mu_1^2 > U$, a particle incident on the barrier with x-component of velocity u_1, enters region II with this component equal to u_2 as given by Eq. (50). Hence,

$$dI(u_2) = dI(u_1).$$

But from Eq. (50),

$$u_1 \, du_1 = u_2 \, du_2,$$

whence

$$dI(u_2) = \frac{N_1}{\alpha\sqrt{\pi}} e^{-\left(u_2^2 + \frac{2U}{m}\right)/\alpha^2} u_2 \, du_2$$

$$= \frac{(N_1 e^{-2U/m\alpha^2})}{\alpha\sqrt{\pi}} e^{-u_2^2/\alpha^2} u_2 \, du_2. \tag{1-52}$$

The interpretation of this equation is that

$$\boxed{N_2 = N_1 \exp\left(-2U/m\alpha^2\right),}$$

where N_2 represents the number of particles per unit volume in region II. The analysis shows that the fraction of the particles entering region II from region I is just $\exp -2U/m\alpha^2$ of those incident on the barrier from region I. From Eq. (52) it appears that the number of particles in region II is reduced by the same factor. The relative numbers of particles of velocity u_2 is given by the factor

$$\exp\left(-u_2^2/\alpha^2\right),$$

so the expression for the distribution of velocities is unaltered. The average kinetic energy of the particles in II is the same as in I. This result is surprising in view of the fact that the individual particles lose kinetic energy. The fact that only molecules which initially have unusually large energy associated with u can penetrate the barrier, exactly compensates for the reduction of this component of velocity at the barrier in such a way that the velocity distribution is unaltered. It should be noted that the value of α^2 is the same in both regions, and, since this is related to the average kinetic energy of a molecule, determining the temperature, the temperature of the gas which crosses the barrier is the same as the temperature of the gas in the original volume before the transfer took place. The fact that the distribution function is unaltered by a potential barrier is a property of the Maxwellian distribution of velocities.

Boltzmann's Principle for Equilibrium Between Regions of Differing Potential Energy

Boltzmann established the conditions under which regions occupied by molecules which differ in potential energy can exist in equilibrium while molecules from each region are transferring to the other. For simplicity, we assume that there is only one type of molecule in the two regions under consideration. In the first region, which we assume to be the one in which the molecules have the lower potential energy, we represent the number of molecules per unit volume by N_1. In the second region, the molecules have the potential energy U referred to the first region, and the concentration of molecules is N_2. Under equilibrium conditions, the number of molecules transferred from region I to region II must be the same as the number of molecules transferred from region II to region I. Also for equilibrium, the kinetic energy carried out of region II by the molecules leaving it must be replaced by the kinetic energy of those molecules entering this region.

Because of the potential energy difference U, there is an essential lack of symmetry in the problem. All the molecules from region II which impinge upon the boundary between the two regions with a component of velocity directed toward the boundary will be able to leave region II, because their potential energy decreases as they pass into region I, and the forces act to accelerate them toward this region. On the other hand, not all of the molecules in region I which impinge on the boundary with a component of velocity directed toward region II will have sufficient kinetic energy to carry them into this region. In this equilibrium situation, the formulae derived in the last section still apply, and the densities of the molecules in the two regions are related by the formula

$$N_2 = N_1 e^{-2U/m\alpha^2}$$

or

$$N_2 = N_1 e^{-U/kT},$$

since

$$\alpha^2 = 2kT/m.$$

This is the statement of Boltzmann's principle as applied to the two regions in equilibrium. Of course, there may be many regions differing in potential energy by various amounts and Boltzmann's principle more generally states that the number of particles per unit volume decreases with increasing potential energy according to the equation

$$N = N_0 e^{-U/kT}, \tag{1-53}$$

where U is the potential energy of a molecule measured relative to the region in which the number of molecules per unit volume is N_0, k is the gas constant per molecule (Boltzmann's constant), and T is the absolute temperature.

It is a matter of some interest that Eq. (53) has been directly verified. Particles large enough to be seen under a microscope, which differ in density from the liquid in which they are suspended, have the irregular motions which were originally observed by the botanist Brown in 1827. According to the theory of Einstein, such particles have an average translational kinetic energy equal to that of the molecules of the medium in which they are suspended. They can be considered huge gas molecules. The potential energy of these particles is $(w - b)h$, where $w = mg$ is the weight, m is the mass, b is the bouyant force of the liquid, and h is the height of the particle. For particles of the sizes observed, $(w - b)$ is so large that within a relatively small range of heights, the potential energy may vary by several times kT. The resulting decrease in the number of particles per unit volume with height has been studied, and the results for a suspension in equilibrium are those predicted by Eq. (53).

The illustration just given resembles the commonly used and somewhat idealized treatment of the earth's atmosphere. If it is assumed that the atmosphere is in equilibrium, we can deduce the concentrations of any type of molecule of mass m at any height h above the sea from a knowledge of its concentration at sea level. The relationship is

$$n = n_0 \exp(-mgh/kT). \tag{1-54}$$

It is common knowledge that T is not constant throughout the atmosphere, and exact equilibrium is impossible under such circumstances. Nevertheless, the equation gives a very satisfactory approximate representation of conditions in the atmosphere. As applied to nitrogen or oxygen, it represents approximately the rarefaction which accompanies elevation. As applied to helium, it shows that the decrease in concentration is sufficiently slow that treating the earth's gravitational field as a constant is a doubtful approximation. Hydrogen has a probability of escape from the earth's atmosphere which is likely to have influenced somewhat the abundance of this element.

For a second illustration, consider a substance in a closed container from which other matter, for simplicity, is excluded. The quantity of the substance and the temperature are so chosen that a part of the container is occupied by the liquid form of the substance with a free surface. The liquid, of course, is very much more dense than the vapor, yet the two are in equilibrium at the temperature of the system. It is possible to form this liquid only because there are attractive forces between the molecules of the substance. The potential energy of a molecule increases rapidly as it moves outward through the surface of the liquid, because work is done against these attractive forces. It is primarily this difference in potential energy between the liquid and the gas which accounts for the very great difference in the densities of a liquid and a gas in equilibrium.

The potential energy of the escaping molecules is increased at the expense of thermal kinetic energy. Evaporation is a cooling process, because only the most energetic molecules are able to escape, and the escaping molecules leave behind those of a lower average kinetic energy, thus reducing the temperature of the remaining liquid. This accounts for the heat of vaporization. For most substances, the increase of the potential energy of a molecule leaving the liquid is very considerable.

Summary

The early work on kinetic theory provided a very successful treatment of the gaseous state and a remarkably specific and concrete mechanical model to account for the general gas laws. This provided a scientific basis for the development of modern atomic theory. It was in connection with the study of Brownian motion that Perrin first determined a really satisfactory value for the mass of the molecule. In connection with kinetic theory we have spoken of the practical necessity of using statistical methods of representation. We have given a model from which various results can be derived. The statistical laws upon which our discussion is based are most successful when applied to matter which is not at too low a temperature and which is not too condensed. Nevertheless, the success of the kinetic theory as applied to permanent gases at ordinary temperatures is so spectacular that we have at one point used it as a basis for considering what happens on the molecular scale in the change from the liquid state to the gas. This illustrates a trend that the success of the kinetic theory established in atomic physics, and we shall expect further developments in this trend as, following the historical pattern, we proceed with the discussion of atomic theory.

Problems on the Kinetic Theory

1. A container, having an initial volume of 1.00 m^3, is filled with helium gas, at a temperature of 300° K, to a pressure of 1.00 × 10^5 newtons/m^2. The gas is then heated at constant pressure to a temperature of 320° K, and expansion caused by the heating takes place against this pressure.
   a. Find the volume of the gas at 320° K.
   b. How much energy had to be added to the system in the process of raising its temperature 20° K?
   c. How much has the net molecular kinetic energy of the entire assembly of molecules been increased as the temperature was increased by 20° K?
2. a. Find the length of one edge of a cube of gas which under standard conditions of temperature and presssure will contain a number of molecules equal to the population of the United States, assumed to be 200,000,000 people.
   b. A diffusion pump backed by a suitable mechanical pump will, when properly operated, reduce the pressure of gases in an enclosure to a pressure of 10^{-8} mm Hg. How many molecules per m^3 will account for this pressure at a temperature of 293° K?
   c. If by ultra-high vacuum techniques, the pressure in an enclosure is reduced to 10^{-11} mm Hg at 293° K, how many molecules per m^3 are required to account for this pressure?
3. a. Compute the mean translational kinetic energy of gas molecules at 400° K.
   b. Compute the root-mean-square (rms) speed corresponding to the energy in part (a): (1) if the gas is argon (atomic weight = 39.95 amu), and (2) if it is mercury vapor (atomic weight = 200.6 amu).
4. Compute, to three significant figures, the rms speed and the most probable speed for molecules in argon gas at 300° K.
5. If the mean-free-path in a certain gas is 1.0 mm, what fraction of the free paths is larger than 1.0 mm? What fraction is larger than 2.0 mm?
6. Discuss critically the following statements:
   a. Because of the Maxwellian distribution of velocities, each molecule of a gas has a different temperature.
   b. If one molecule has a mean-free-path L, this implies that ½ of the molecules in a given volume have values less than L, whereas ½ have free paths greater than L.

c. In a beam of molecules with nearly equal velocities, the absolute temperature T is given by $mu^2/3k$, where m is the mass of the molecule, u is the rms speed, and k is the Boltzmann constant.

7. The earth's atmosphere at sea level consists of the following constituents, in percentage by volume:

$$N_2 = 78.03,$$

$$O_2 = 20.99,$$

$$A = 0.94,$$

$$CO_2 = 0.030,$$

$$H_2 = 0.010,$$

$$H_e = 0.0004.$$

Determine the percentages by volume of the elements which contribute at least 0.1% to the composition of the atmosphere at a height of 100 km, if the atmosphere under equilibrium, conditions at a temperature of 293° K, and if the earth's gravitational field is assumed to be equal to its sea-level value throughout this height.

8. The specific heat of copper is 0.0921 and the specific heat of mercury is 0.0332. For each of these elements, determine the average gain in energy (or heat) per atom when the temperature is raised by 10° C. The specific heat of beryllium is 0.397 and that of silicon is 0.168. How do the heat capacities of a molecule based on these values compare with those of a monatomic perfect gas?

9. Compare the velocity of sound in air with the most probable speed of the nitrogen molecule at 20° C.

10. When 1 m³ of O_2 at a pressure of 1 atmosphere combines with 2.00 m³ of H_2 to form 3 m³ of water vapor, what will be the new pressure, assuming that no water vapor condenses and that the heat of formation of the compound H_2O (57,826 kg-cal/kg-mole) goes into the translational kinetic energy of the water molecules?

References on Kinetic Theory

Loeb, Leonard B., *Kinetic Theory of Gases* (New York: McGraw-Hill Book Company, 1934). (A more extensive treatment than is possible in the present chapter.)

Loeb, Leonard B., *Atomic Structure*, Part IV, Ch. 19 (New York: John Wiley and Sons, 1938). (A very useful introductory treatment.)

Sears, Francis W., *Introduction to Thermodynamics, Kinetic Theory of Gases and Statistical Mechanics* (Cambridge: Addison-Wesley, 1953). (As the title indicates, the coverage is considerably broader than the present chapter.)

2 | Laws for the Motion of Charged Particles and the Identification of Atomic Constituents

It was in connection with his work on electrical discharge in gases that J. J. Thomson in 1897 found a particle with a ratio of charge to mass which was the same for all of the gases used. This resulted in the first identification of an atomic constituent. This particle, common to all atoms, was soon called the *electron*, which name it has retained. The importance of this discovery was rather generally recognized, and other workers soon verified Thomson's results in independent experiments.

In this discussion we will use vector notation. Vector quantities are shown in **boldface** type, and both magnitude and direction are associated with such quantities. When the magnitude alone is considered, *italics* will be used. Vector equations imply as many scalar relationships as there are dimensions in the space. Readers who have had no previous experience with vector analysis might do well to interrupt the reading of the text and to study Appendix I before reading further. The unit vectors lying along the three Cartesian coordinate axes, x, y, and z, are designated by **i**, **j**, and **k** respectively.

The Behavior of a Charged Particle in a Uniform Electrostatic Field

To lay the basis for an understanding of the work of Thomson and his contemporaries, we will summarize briefly the basic laws for the motion of charged particles in electric and magnetic fields. In accordance with the implications of Thomson's discovery, we assume that there are a great number of particles all having the same electrostatic charge e, and all having the same mass m. Now, although it was quite obvious from Thomson's observations that the electron was an exceedingly minute negatively charged particle, we shall nevertheless apply to it the same laws of electricity and mechanics that were found to be successful for the large-scale phenomena previously studied in physics.

The force $\mathbf{F}$ on an electron carrying a charge $-e$ when it is placed in an electric field $\mathbf{E}$ is given by

$$\boxed{\mathbf{F} = -e\mathbf{E}.} \tag{2-1}$$

Assuming that the mass m is independent of the velocity, the acceleration is then given by Newton's second law of motion. Thus,

$$\mathbf{F}/m = \mathbf{a} = -e\mathbf{E}/m = \frac{e}{m}\nabla V, \tag{2-2}$$

where

$$\nabla V = \mathbf{i}\partial V/\partial x + \mathbf{j}\partial V/\partial y + \mathbf{k}\partial V/\partial z,$$

called the potential gradient, is expressed in volts/m. The electron is accelerated in the direction of the potential gradient.

The behavior of an electron in a uniform electrostatic field can be represented very simply. For convenience, we choose a system of coordinates in which the positive direction of the y-axis coincides with the direction of the potential gradient. Then,

$$\mathbf{a} = \frac{e}{m}\nabla V$$

$$= \mathbf{j}\frac{e}{m}\frac{dV}{dy} = \mathbf{j}\,d^2y/dt^2. \tag{2-3}$$

One integration gives

$$\mathbf{v} = \mathbf{i}v_{x_0} + \mathbf{j}\left(v_{y_0} + t\frac{e}{m}\frac{dV}{dy}\right) + \mathbf{k}v_{z_0}, \tag{2-4}$$

where

$$\mathbf{v}_0 = \mathbf{i}v_{x_0} + \mathbf{j}v_{y_0} + \mathbf{k}v_{z_0}$$

is the velocity when t is zero. A second integration gives

$$\boxed{\mathbf{s} = \mathbf{i}(v_{x_0}t + x_0) + \mathbf{j}\left(v_{y_0}t + \frac{t^2}{2}\frac{e}{m}\frac{dV}{dy} + y_0\right) + \mathbf{k}(v_{z_0}t + z_0),} \tag{2-5}$$

where $\mathbf{s}$ is the displacement of the electron from the origin, and

$$\mathbf{s}_0 = \mathbf{i}x_0 + \mathbf{j}y_0 + \mathbf{k}z_0$$

is the displacement of the electron from the origin when t is zero.

TABLE 2-1. SYMBOLS INTRODUCED IN CHAPTER 2

Symbol	Name	Quantity Designated
a		acceleration
E		electric field strength
F		force
∇	nabla	gradient operator
V		electrostatic potential
e		electronic charge
m		mass of particle (especially of electron)
i		unit vector in x-direction
j, k		unit vectors in y-, z-directions respectively
v		velocity
s		displacement
B		magnetic induction
ev		electron volts
Bev		10^9 electron volts
μ	mu	mobility (v/E)
ϕ	phi	angle
L or l		designated lengths
t		time
T		periodic time
u		particular value of velocity given by Thomson's selector
ω	omega	angular velocity
R		radius of trajectory
N		number of charge carriers per unit volume
x_0, y_0, z_0		values of the coordinates of a particle when $t = 0$
A, B, C		constants
M		mass of molecular ion

The position of the electron along the y-axis, when plotted as a function of the time, is some portion of a parabola, while the position along the other axes are linear functions of time. Thus, in general, the path or trajectory of an electron in a uniform electrostatic field is parabolic.

Magnetic Fields

The discussion of the force exerted by one magnet on another is simplified by use of a concept called the "magnetic field." Historically, the analysis of magnetic fields has followed much the same course as the analysis of electrostatic fields. The fundamental equations concerning the interaction between the poles of one magnet and the suitably defined "field" produced by the other magnet are quite similar to those set forth above in the electrostatic case. At present, however, it is customary to start with the motor rule as the basis for defining the magnetic induction vector **B**. Thus, the force on a charge $-e$ is given by

$$\boxed{\mathbf{F} = -e\mathbf{v} \times \mathbf{B},}$$

where, as before, e is the electronic charge, and $\mathbf{v} \times \mathbf{B}$ stands for the vector product of the two vectors $\mathbf{v}$ and $\mathbf{B}$, which is itself a third vector at right angles to both $\mathbf{v}$ and $\mathbf{B}$. The magnitude of the vector product is $vB \sin \theta$, where θ is the angle between the vectors $\mathbf{v}$ and $\mathbf{B}$.

An advantage of the mks system of units is that it yields simple expressions for the much used force relations. The proportionality constant in the basic force relation is unity, when all quantities are expressed in mks units. If e is expressed in coulombs, $\mathbf{v}$ in m/sec, and $\mathbf{B}$ in webers/m^2, the force is given in newtons. The negative sign, which comes into the relationship as a consequence of the electron's negative charge, may be taken into the vector product by reversing the order of the vectors $\mathbf{B}$ and $\mathbf{v}$, since $-\mathbf{B} \times \mathbf{v} = \mathbf{v} \times \mathbf{B}$. Thus, for an electron moving in a magnetic field $\mathbf{B}$ with a velocity $\mathbf{v}$, the force $\mathbf{F}$ is given by

$$\mathbf{F} = e\mathbf{B} \times \mathbf{v}. \tag{2-6}$$

Trajectory of an Electron in a Magnetic Field

An electron, projected with a velocity at right angles to a uniform magnetic field, is subject to a force at right angles both to the magnetic field and to the velocity, as indicated in the last section. Since it can be shown that power P is given by

$$P = Fv \cos \theta, \tag{2-7}$$

where θ is the angle between $\mathbf{F}$ and $\mathbf{v}$, a force at right angles to the velocity of a particle ($\cos \theta = 0$) does no work. Hence, a magnetic field causes no change in the energy of the electron, or any other charged particle. The charged particle will move with a constant speed of v, but the force at right angles to the velocity will cause a change in the direction of the velocity. The path of the particle is a circle, because the magnitude of the force is the same at all points on the path, and the curvature is constant. The magnitude of the force required to make the particle move in a circle of radius R at the constant speed v is given by

$$F = eBv = mv^2/R,$$

whence

$$e/m = v/RB. \tag{2-8}$$

The ratio e/m is thus readily obtainable when v, R, and B are known.

Solving for R, we have

$$R = mv/eB. \tag{2-9}$$

It is seen that the radius of the path is proportional to the momentum of the particle and hence R is often used as a measure of momentum.

A feature of interest in connection with Eq. (9) is that all electrons pass around a complete circle in the same time T, regardless of the value of v. For

$$T = 2\pi R/v = 2\pi m/eB, \tag{2-10}$$

and v does not appear in this expression for T. The angular velocity ω of the velocity vector itself in rad/sec is

$$\omega = \frac{2\pi}{T} = \frac{e}{m} B. \tag{2-11}$$

This is often called the "cyclotron radian frequency."

The Thomson Velocity Selector

As a means of selecting electrons of one particular speed, which could be calculated from the fields, J. J. Thomson introduced the use of electric and magnetic fields at right angles. If the electrons then have the proper velocity $\mathbf{u}$ at right angles to both fields, the magnetic force balances the electrostatic force, and the electrons therefore travel in a straight line with constant speed. The electrostatic force is

$$\mathbf{F}_e = -e\mathbf{E}.$$

The magnetic force is

$$\mathbf{F}_m = -e\mathbf{v} \times \mathbf{B}.$$

The net force is zero when $\mathbf{v} = \mathbf{u}$. Hence,

$$-e\mathbf{E} - e\mathbf{u} \times \mathbf{B} = 0$$

or

$$(\mathbf{E} + \mathbf{u} \times \mathbf{B}) \times \mathbf{B} = 0. \tag{2-12}$$

Since $\mathbf{u}$ and $\mathbf{B}$ are at right angles,

$$(\mathbf{u} \times \mathbf{B}) \times \mathbf{B} = -B^2 u, \tag{2-13}$$

and so

$$\mathbf{u} = \mathbf{E} \times \mathbf{B}/B^2, \tag{2-14}$$

since $\mathbf{u} \times \mathbf{B} = -\mathbf{E}$, by Eq. (12).

Conservation of Energy

In the electrostatic case, the forces act to produce changes of speed which create a kinetic energy exactly equal to the loss of the potential energy of the particle. In the magneto-static case, where the forces do no work, they produce changes in the direction of the velocity without altering its magnitude, so the kinetic energy remains constant as required by the principle of conservation of energy.

Although Eqs. (4) and (5) for the velocity and displacement of an electron are said to be in standard form because they give these quantities in terms of the time, it is nevertheless useful to eliminate the time in order to obtain a more easily measured quantity, such as the distance through which the charged particles have moved through the field, or alternately the potential difference through which they have fallen. These equations, by the elimination of the time, can be solved to give the speed of the electron in terms of the potential difference through which the electrons have fallen. However, the same result may be obtained directly from the conservation of energy by equating the potential energy lost by the charged particle to the kinetic energy gained. Thus,

$$eV = \tfrac{1}{2}mv^2,$$

or

$$v = \left(\frac{2eV}{m}\right)^{\frac{1}{2}}. \qquad (2\text{-}15)$$

Early Researches on the Charge to Mass Ratio for Electrons

Three important researches for determining the ratio of the charge to the mass of the electron were conducted independently, although almost simultaneously. In each of these experiments, an independent method was used.

Thomson's Method for Determining e/m

The source of the electrons in Thomson's experiments was the ionization of atoms in an electrical glow discharge. There was a considerable spread in the energy of these particles, and the crux of Thomson's method was the selection of electrons of a single velocity, which could be calculated in terms of measured quantities. For this purpose, Thomson used the crossed electric and magnetic field velocity selector described previously. In Thomson's discharge tube (Fig. 2-1), an electrode

C at one end served as a cathode. The anode A, near the middle of the arrangement, was a circular metal cylinder with a plane metal sheet at each end. A pair of small holes (one in each sheet) passed only those electrons having velocities nearly parallel to the axis of the tube, and thus defined a beam of electrons moving along the axis. The electrons then passed between a pair of parallel metal plates a and b, with a potential difference V between them, which produced a localized electric field $\mathbf{E}$ at right angles to the velocity $\mathbf{u}$ of the electrons. A magnetic field $\mathbf{B}$ was applied at right angles to both $\mathbf{u}$ and $\mathbf{E}$ in such a manner that the vector $\mathbf{E} \times \mathbf{B}$ was in the direction of $\mathbf{u}$. The crossed electric and magnetic fields thus selected electrons having the velocity $\mathbf{u}$ given by

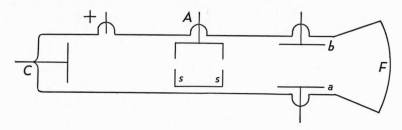

Fig. 2-1. Thomson's experimental discharge tube.

Eq. (14). These electrons, after leaving the localized electric field produced by the parallel plates, moved in the magnetic field alone. The radius R of the circular path in this region could be estimated from the length of path beyond the condenser plates and the displacement from the axis of the spot of light produced by the electrons on a fluorescent screen F. The ratio e/m for the particles was then calculated from Eq. (8). Thus,

$$e/m = u/BR = |\mathbf{E} \times \mathbf{B}|/B^3R = E/B^2R. \qquad (2\text{-}16)$$

There were some errors in Thomson's values for the fields and for the geometry of the arrangement. These combined to give a rather poor numerical value for e/m, namely 1.17×10^{11} coulombs/kg. However, the errors were the same in all the tests for the gases used, and hence Thomson was able to identify a particle having the same charge to mass ratio for any one of the gases used.

Kaufmann's Determination of e/m

The most accurate of the early values of e/m was the one obtained by Kaufmann. He used the conservation of energy for the purpose of determining the velocity of the electrons or other charged particles, which had fallen through the known potential difference V, and he combined this with the radius R of the electron beam's trajectory in a uniform magnetic field $\mathbf{B}$. The charge to mass ratio was given by

$$e/m = 2V/B^2R^2. \qquad (2\text{-}17)$$

Kaufmann's value was about 1.77×10^{11} coulombs/kg, which we know now was in error by less than 1%.

Time of Flight Measurements and the Determination of e/m

The third of the early methods was developed by Wiechert. He allowed the electrons to fall through a measured potential difference V, and acquire a speed v. He then solved the energy equation for e/m to give

$$e/m = v^2/2V. \qquad (2\text{-}18)$$

Wiechert measured the velocity of the electrons by timing their flight over a known distance with a known fraction ($\frac{1}{4}$) of the period of an oscillating circuit containing a known capacitance and inductance. His value was 1.4×10^{11} coulombs/kg, which also was considerably in error.

Further research, largely by deflection methods, established the ratio of the charge to the mass of the electron as 1.75888×10^{11} coulombs/kg. At one time, in the late 1920s, there appeared to a discrepancy between the "spectroscopic" and deflection measurements on free electrons which was greater than the indicated accuracy of either method. This, however, by further work was resolved in favor of the spectroscopic value.

Mass of the Electron

Although the electron was identified by the ratio of its charge to its mass, this information alone did not establish the mass of this particle. But there was supplementary information which gave a correct estimate of the order of magnitude of the electron's charge, for the atomic theory had developed quite extensively both in the kinetic theory of gases and in studies of chemical behavior. It was not certain that the magnitude of the electronic charge would be the same as that of the hydrogen ion in electrolysis, but this seemed likely, and later proved to be correct. The order of magnitude of e could therefore be estimated from known evidence concerning the size of the atom. Thomson had determined the charge of the negative ions produced in gases as early as 1898. The current maintained in a gas by a known electric field $\mathbf{E}$ was measured. If the drift velocity $\bar{u}$ is proportional to E, we may write

$$\bar{u} = \mu E,$$

where μ is the so-called "mobility." The current density J is then given by

$$\boxed{J = Ne\bar{u},} \tag{2-19}$$

where N is the number of charge carriers per unit volume. The number of ions in the discharge was determined by supercooling the air, whereupon moisture condensed on each ion. The droplets in a known volume were then collected and counted.

The remaining problem, that of determining $\bar{u}$ from the field strength, was solved by calculations based on information obtained by Rutherford. The idea involved in this method was to liberate electrons from zinc by photoelectric action and to collect them by an alternating electromotive force applied between the zinc plate and a collector electrode. By increasing the separation between the zinc plate and the collector sufficiently, it was possible to prevent any electrons being collected. The mobility was then determined from the known angular frequency ω of the alternating current, from the known amplitude of the electromotive force V_0, and from the least distance d required to stop the current. (Rutherford's formula was $\mu = \omega d^2 / 2V_0$, the derivation of which is left to the reader.)

By modern standards, the experimental methods we have just described lack precision, but they sufficed to demonstrate by 1903 that the charge on Thomson's particle (the electron) was between 1.33×10^{-19} and 2.16×10^{-19} coulombs. The presently accepted value of 1.6021×10^{-19} coulombs lies near the center of this range. The use of the later precision values of e and of e/m gives for the electron's mass the value

$$m = 9.107 \times 10^{-31} \text{ kg.}$$

When these magnitudes were first deduced from the evidence, they must have seemed fantastically small.

Millikan's Precision Determination of the Electronic Charge

In 1903, H. A. Wilson made an improvement in the method of determining e by forming a cloud of droplets condensed on the ions by a sudden adiabatic expansion. He allowed the cloud thus formed to settle, first under the influence of gravity alone, then under the influence of gravity plus the forces arising from an electrostatic field. From the known viscosity of air, the force could be computed. Then using the value of the electrostatic field, the charge could be deduced. Such information gave the value of e with somewhat less error than the previous methods.

It remained for Millikan to determine the charge of the electron with precision in a series of experiments carried out at the University of Chicago in the years 1904 to 1913. Millikan started by repeating the experiments of H. A. Wilson. With the aid of a microscope, however, he found that he could observe the behavior of the individual droplets. Water droplets changed in size through evaporation, and Millikan substituted the droplets of a low vapor-pressure oil formed by the aid of an "atomizer." He could estimate the weight of a droplet by timing its fall under the influence of gravity alone, using Stokes's law to obtain the viscous force resulting from its motion through the air. Then he could balance the gravitational force with a force produced by a known electrostatic field, and so he could calculate very exactly the electrostatic charge on the droplet. When the results of extended experiments of this sort were analyzed, it was found that the charges on the droplets could all be expressed as multiples of a certain definite charge, and this was interpreted as the charge of the electron. The value so obtained was very close to 1.60×10^{-19} coulombs.

Practical Relationships Based on the Properties of the Electron

In the mks system of units, the ratio of the charge to the mass of the electron is 1.75888×10^{11} (or very nearly 1.76×10^{11}) coulombs/kg. If the gradient of the potential is expressed in volts/m, the acceleration of the electron is given by

$$\mathbf{a} = \frac{e}{m} \nabla V = 1.75888 \times 10^{11} \nabla V \ (\text{m/sec}^2). \qquad (2\text{-}20)$$

Similarly, the velocity of the electron expressed as a function of the potential difference in volts through which it moves after starting from rest is

$$v = \left(\frac{2eV}{m}\right)^{1/2} = 5.9311 \times 10^5 V^{1/2} \, \text{m/sec}. \qquad (2\text{-}21)$$

Units of Energy

In general, even though mks units are inconveniently large for use in atomic problems, we use conveniently chosen submultiples based upon them. We make an exception in the case of energy. In many atomic processes the transformation of energy takes place as an electron falls through a potential difference associated with the system. A very convenient unit, therefore, is the potential energy lost by an electron as it moves between points where the electrostatic potential increases by just one volt. This unit is called the electron volt, ev. The electron is a constituent of atoms and its charge expressed in coulombs is so small that the electron volt is a convenient unit of energy. The conversion factor is the charge of the electron expressed in coulombs, and one electron volt is 1.6×10^{-19} joules. A unit 1000 times as large is useful for expressing energies associated with X-rays, and this is called the electron kilovolt, Kev. Even more popular is the use of a unit a million times as large as the electron volt, Mev. In high energy physics a still larger unit is needed, and, following American usage, we call the Bev the energy change accompanying the electron falling through 10^9 volts. Even the Bev is not nearly as large as the joule,

$$1 \text{ Bev} = 1.6 \times 10^{-10} \text{ joules.}$$

When smaller units of energy are needed, the electron millivolt, emv, or the electron microvolt, eμv, may be used.

Beginnings of Mass Spectroscopy

Isolated atoms are usually neutral, but many times in chemical substances they have "ionic character," i.e. have some charges on them. The loss of one or more electrons by a neutral atom leaves a positively charged atomic residue. The mass of these positive ions proved to be several thousand times that of the electron, and the magnitude of the positive charge was found to be equal to one or more electronic charges. It was a matter of great importance to make determinations of the charge to mass ratio for positive ions, in order that such atomic fragments might be identified from information concerning their masses.

Previously, chemical methods had resulted in rather exact determinations of atomic masses. Many of these atomic masses were almost exact multiples of the atomic mass of hydrogen, and this fact had led Prout to suggest that the mass associated with the positive charge of the ionized hydrogen atom was another of the fundamental building blocks of matter. One of the difficulties associated with explaining atomic masses in this manner was the natural existence of several elements with atomic mass numbers which were not close to being integers. For example, there was chlorine with an atomic mass of 35.46, which was almost midway between two integers.

J. J. Thomson became interested in studying these positive ions. He found that beams of them could be formed in discharge tubes by perforating the cathode. Some positive ions passing out of the discharge through this hole moved away from the cathode in the region outside of the discharge. These "positive rays," as they were first called, contained a variety of ions with a considerable spread of velocities.

An early method used by Thomson consisted in setting up electric and magnetic fields parallel to one another and at right angles to the velocity of the ions in the beam, as indicated in Fig. 2-2. The electric field deflects

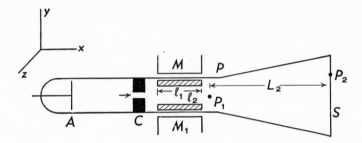

Fig. 2-2. Apparatus for the parabola method of positive ion identification.

the ions in the direction of the field. The magnetic field, on the other hand, produces a deflection at right angles both to its own direction and to the velocity. A comparison of these two deflections suffices to give information about the ions.

Let us consider the beam to be moving in the x-direction, while over a limited portion of its path (l_1) between a pair of condenser plates, a uniform electric field E_y acts in the y-direction. The time t an ion moving with a velocity v spends between these plates is then

$$t = l_1/v. \tag{2-22}$$

The acceleration of the ion is

$$a_y = neE_y/m_i, \tag{2-23}$$

where n is the number of electrons missing from the atom and m_i is the mass of the ion. The y-component of the velocity acquired in the time t in consequence of this acceleration is

$$v_y = a_y t = neE_y l_1/vm_i. \tag{2-24}$$

After leaving the region between the plates, the path of the electron will make an angle ϕ_1 with its original trajectory (which we call the axis). The tangent of this angle is given by

$$\tan \phi_1 = v_y/v = neE_y l_1/m_i v^2. \tag{2-25}$$

In the time that the electron is between the condenser plates, its displacement is

$$s_1 = a_y t^2/2 = neE_y l_1{}^2/2m_i v^2. \tag{2-26}$$

If the distance along the axis from the point P_1, at which the ion first emerges from the electric field, to the point P_2, at which it strikes a photographic plate, is L_1, the displacement y_1 of the ion on the photographic plate, measured from the axis, or the point of no deflection, is

$$y_1 = s_1 + L_1 \tan \phi_1 = E_y ne l_1 (l_1 + 2L_1)/2m_i v^2. \tag{2-27}$$

For the magnetic field, the displacement is in the z-direction. From Eq. (11), the rate of rotation of the velocity vector is

$$\omega = neB/m_i. \tag{2-28}$$

If the magnetic field extends for a distance l_2 along the axis, the time spent in the field is

$$t_2 = l_2/v. \tag{2-29}$$

Thus, the angle through which the ion velocities are turned is

$$\phi_2 = \omega t_2 = neBl_2/m_i v. \tag{2-30}$$

The displacement s_2 of the ions in the z-direction as they leave the magnetic field is given by

$$s_2 \simeq a_z t^2/2 = neBv l_2{}^2/2m_i v^2 = neB l_2{}^2/2m_i v. \tag{2-31}$$

(The approximation arises from considering the direction of the acceleration constant.) The total displacement at the photographic plate is

$$z_2 = s_2 + L_2 \tan \phi_2$$
$$= neBl_2(l_2 + 2L_2)/2m_i v, \tag{2-32}$$

where L_2 is the distance from the point of termination of the magnetic field to the photographic plate.

A given type of ion is characterized by ne/m_i. All identical ions with the velocity v strike the photographic plate with a constant displacement y_1 given by Eq. (27) and with a fixed displacement z_2 given by Eq. (32). In practice, v is not measured, and ions of a given type will have a wide spread of velocities. The unknown velocity, however, may be eliminated between Eqs. (27) and (32), giving

$$z^2 = neB^2 l_2{}^2(l_2 + 2L_2)^2 y/2m_i E l_1(l_1 + 2L_1). \tag{2-33}$$

Or, if

$$l_1 = l_2 = l \quad \text{and} \quad L_1 = L_2 = L,$$

then

$$z^2 = neB^2 l(l + 2L)y/2m_i E. \tag{2-34}$$

Now $B^2l(l + 2L)/2E$ is a constant of the apparatus as used in a given test, and ne/m_i is characteristic of the type of ion. According to Eq. (34) a given type of ion, because of the spread of velocities, gives a trace on the photographic plate in the form of a parabola. A different type of ion gives a different parabola, and by analysis of such traces it is possible to identify ions according to their charge to mass ratio.

In 1912, Thomson was able to show that neon gave at least two parabolas corresponding to the same charge number ne, and this clearly indicated that neon ions of more than one mass were present. Thomson thus identified ions of mass number 22 as well as those of mass number

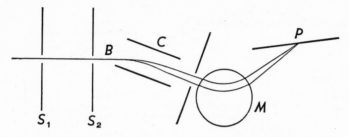

Fig. 2-3. The plan of the mass spectrograph of Aston.

20. In subsequent work by others, traces of the ion of mass number 21 were also observed. When a given chemical substance, such as neon, contains atoms of different mass numbers, these are called *isotopes*. Without abandoning the hypothesis that a second building block of matter is a particle having a mass equal to that of the positive ion which is left when the common isotope of hydrogen is ionized, it is possible to explain atomic masses like that of neon (20.183) or chlorine (35.46). One merely needs to assume that the chemical element found in nature is some appropriate mixture of isotopes, each of which has a mass that is very nearly an integer times the mass of the positive hydrogen ion (or *proton*). The exact mass unit, which has been adopted for this work, is called "the atomic mass unit" (amu), and it is defined as one-sixteenth of the mass of the oxygen isotope O^{16}.

F. W. Aston also worked at the Cavendish laboratory, first as Thomson's assistant, later as an independent research worker. The first precision mass spectrograph was built by Aston. The plan of his instrument is shown in Fig. 2-3. A beam B of ions is defined by two slits S_1 and S_2. It then passes between the plates of condenser C, where it is acted upon by crossed electric and magnetic fields. A diverging beam of ions differing in energy emerges from the velocity filter, and a portion of this passes through the stop and into the field of the electromagnet M. Here the most energetic ions of a given type, which travel in a path of rela-

tively long radius of curvature, remain within the intense field produced
by the electromagnet for a long path. The slower ions have a shorter
radius of curvature, and, because of the placement of the pole pieces
of the magnet, they remain in the field for a shorter path only. The
result is that the slightly diverging beam of ions which entered the
region between the pole pieces, leaves this region as a converging beam,
which comes to a focus as a single concentrated line on the photographic
plate P. This plate is placed at an angle so that ions of higher charge to
mass ratio strike the nearer end in a line focus, while other ions of lower
charge to mass ratio, having traveled a greater distance after leaving the

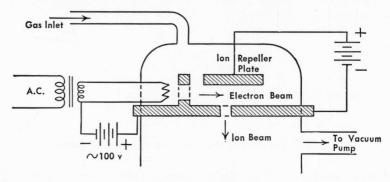

Fig. 2-4. An ion source.

electromagnet, form a line focus at points farther out on the photographic plate.

Many types of mass spectrometers for the determination of the relative
abundances of isotopes and mass spectrographs for the determination of
atomic masses have been used. Because of the importance of such
measurements, instruments for making them have been constructed and
sold commercially. It may be well to discuss some of the principles
underlying the operation of components of such equipment. In the first
place, it is necessary that the atom be obtained as a charged particle by
removing one or more electrons from its structure. It has been found
that electrons which have fallen through a potential difference of 100-300
volts are very effective in knocking electrons out of atoms of various
kinds. Fig. 2-4 shows an ion source based upon this action. The source of
electrons is a heated tungsten filament, from which electrons are accelerated by the potential difference established by a power supply,
represented in the sketch by a 100-volt battery. Electrons emerge into a
region where there exists a suitable pressure of the gas to be analyzed,
and by collision in this space, they create positive ions. These ions are
drawn out of the gas by a potential difference between an ion repeller

plate and the metal plate having a hole through which the positive ions of the beam enter the next section of the spectrograph. Here fast diffusion pumps act quickly to remove the gas that leaks into the chamber through the hole, and a good vacuum is maintained in this part of the apparatus. The ions may be given further velocity before they enter a velocity or energy selector prior to being analyzed in the field of the main magnet.

Generally, the measurement of mass is a two-step process. The energy or the velocity is first obtained by some means. Then the momentum of the ions is obtained from the curvature of the trajectory in a magnetic field. Through suitable calculations, the results of these two measurements are combined to give the charge to mass ratio, and hence an indication of the mass.

A very simple type of mass spectrometer was designed by Nier to measure the relative abundance of isotopes. It is frequently used in commerical work as a tool in chemical analysis. The ions which emerge from the source with negligible velocities are accelerated by a known voltage V to an energy

$$W = Vne = Mv^2/2. \tag{2-35}$$

The ions are then bent in a magnetic field where the equation

$$nevB = Mv^2/R \tag{2-36}$$

applies. The apparatus is designed as a long tube which is bent to a certain radius of curvature over a part of its length where the magnetic field is applied. The particles then have a known radius of curvature R if they reach the detector at the end of the tube. The detector may be simply a cup placed behind a narrow slit, the cup being connected through a galvanometer to the ground; so the galvanometer reading is a measure of the number of atoms striking it per unit time. Eliminating the velocity v from Eqs. (35), and (36) and solving for the mass M gives the result

$$\boxed{M = neB^2R^2/2V,} \tag{2-37}$$

where e is known, and n is an integer, usually one, and B, R, and V are measured. Often two types of atoms are compared. In this case

$$\boxed{M_1/M_2 = V_2/V_1,} \tag{2-38}$$

if B and R are kept constant. The accelerating voltage is varied until the detector picks up a signal, and this voltage is a measure of the mass of the particle being detected.

In the Nier mass spectrometer the energy is calculated directly from the accelerating voltage. This is a very simple procedure, but it neglects the small initial energies with which the ions enter the accelerating field. The various deflection filters are more accurate for the determination of velocity or energy, as the case may be, because their action determines the entire velocity or energy regardless of its source.

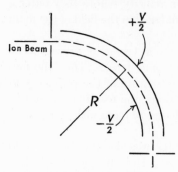

The operation of a velocity selector has been explained previously. The plan of an energy filter is shown in Fig. 2-5. The arrangement may be considered as one quadrant of a coaxial cylindrical condenser. The ions enter the region between the cylinders through a slit at a distance R from the center of curvature of the condenser plates. The force Mv^2/R, required to keep the ions in a circular path of this radius, is supplied by the electric field E. Hence,

Fig. 2-5. An energy filter.

$$neE = Mv^2/R. \tag{2-39}$$

Multiplication by R and division by the factor 2 gives the energy of the ions

$$Mv^2/2 = RneE/2. \tag{2-40}$$

This equation may be used, together with one giving the momentum of the ion in terms of the curvature of its trajectory in the magnetic field $\mathbf{B}$, for the purpose of eliminating the velocity and giving M in terms of measurable quantities.

The high precision of atomic mass determination is partly a result of a "mass doublet" technique. If oxygen and methane are put into the ion source, there are two ions of mass 16, the atomic oxygen ion O^{16+} and the molecular methane ion $CH_4{}^+$. The small difference in mass is measured and an instrument of high "dispersion" (one capable of showing differences for nearly equal masses) must therefore be used. The observed mass difference A, is also the difference between the masses of neutral particles, because the electron subtracted from each has the same rest mass. Therefore,

$$M(O^{16}) - M(C^{12}) - 4M(H^1) = A. \tag{2-41}$$

Another doublet is obtained from a mixture of ordinary and heavy hydrogen.

$$M(H^2) - 2M(H^1) = B. \tag{2-42}$$

A doubly charged ion of carbon (C^{12++}) can be obtained from an ion source. It behaves like an ion of mass 6 with a single charge as can be seen from the equations of the energy and momentum filters. It gives a doublet with the triatomic molecule of heavy hydrogen (H_3^{2+}). Measurements on this doublet give:

$$M(C^{12})/2 - 3M(H^2) = C. \tag{2-43}$$

Since $M(O^{16})$ is exactly 16 by definition of the atomic mass unit, the three equations can be solved for $M(C^{12})$, $M(H^1)$, and $M(H^2)$ separately. The magnitude of A has been found to be -0.03637 amu. Therefore, masses, which are accurate to 10^{-5} amu, can be obtained from measurements which are in error by as much as 0.03%. Masses of the various isotopes of elements have been determined by these methods.

As a result of the mass spectrometer studies, not only were many isotopes of various elements identified, but the chemical atomic masses of specimens were explained by the fractions of the total mass corresponding to the various isotopes. Typical examples are shown in Table 2-2.

TABLE 2-2. ISOTOPIC CONSTITUTION OF REPRESENTATIVE CHEMICAL ELEMENTS

Element	Mass Numbers of Isotopes	Masses δ (amu)	Content %	Atomic Mass (amu)
Ne	20	19.99872	90.51	
	21	20.99963	0.28	20.183
	22	21.99844	9.21	
Cl	35	34.97867	75.4	
				35.457
	37	36.9775	24.6	
Zn	64	63.95356	48.87	
	66	65.94667	27.62	
	67	66.9482	4.12	65.38
	68	67.9488	18.72	
	70	69.9460	0.69	

Summary

The laws for the motion of charged particles in electric and magnetic fields provided the means for identifying ions which resulted from the division of atoms into charged fragments. Thomson showed that a particle having a fixed ratio of charge to mass was found in electrical discharges in various gases. This particle, called the electron, proved to be one of those which exists in all neutral atoms. The electron had a very small mass. The positively charged residues of atoms were shown to contain almost the entire mass of the atom. These masses were nearly integral multiples of the mass of the proton. Experiments of the type initiated by Thomson, which we have discussed in this chapter, could reveal nothing concerning the distribution of the mass within the atom, and hence could provide little further information about atomic structure.

Problems

1. An electron starts from rest at the negative plate of a parallel plate condenser across which a potential difference of 1000 volts is applied. The distance between the plates is 4.00 cm. Assuming that the electric field between the plates is uniform, calculate:
   a. The acceleration of the electron.
   b. The time required for the electron to attain a speed of 5.00 Mm/sec.
   c. How far the electron has traveled in attaining this speed, and the potential difference between this point and the negative plate of the condenser.
2. Electrons are projected into the region of constant potential gradient that exists between two parallel plates. The initial velocity of the electron at the *positive* plate is 11.9 Mm/sec in a direction making an angle of 45° with the plane of the plate. If the uniform potential gradient is 5,000 volts/m, how far will the electron move away from the positive plate before turning back toward it? Where, relative to the starting point, will the electron return to the positive plate?
3. What transverse magnetic induction vector **B** acting on electrons of 300 ev energy will produce a trajectory having a radius of curvature of 0.10 m?
4. A beam of electrons moves at right angles to a magnetic induction of 0.010 webers/m². The radius of the beam's trajectory is 5.00 cm. What is the momentum of each electron in this beam?
5. Use the content of isotopes shown in Table 2-2 and calculate the expected atomic mass of chlorine from these data.
6. From the isotopic content shown in Table 2-2, calculate the expected atomic mass of zinc.
7. In a cathode ray tube, electrons emerge into an equipotential region in a cone of small angle from an anode maintained at a potential of 1000 volts relative to the cathode. If the distance from the anode to the fluorescent screen is 0.30 m, what magnetic induction vector **B** parallel to the axis of the cone will cause the electrons to be focused in a small spot on the screen?
8. What is the kinetic energy of the singly charged ion which has 10 cm for the radius of its trajectory when the mean electric intensity between the cylindrical condenser plates is 10,000 volts/m?
9. A singly charged ion is focused in a photographic plate midway between the line formed by O^{16+} and that formed by $CH_4{}^+$. What is the mass of this ion in amu?

References on the Motion of Ions in Electric and Magnetic Fields

Aston, F. W., *Isotopes* (London: Longmans, Green, 1923). (This is a standard treatment of the methods and results of mass spectroscopy.)

Dow, William G., *Fundamentals of Engineering Electronics* (New York: John Wiley, 1952). (A revision of one of the widely used early texts in the electronics field.)

Hoag, J. Barton, *Electron and Nuclear Physics*, pp. 1-47 (New York: D. Van Nostrand, 1938). (A text originally written to be used in physics courses, including laboratory.)

Loeb, Leonard B., *Atomic Structure*, pp. 5-22 (New York: John Wiley, 1938). (A good general treatment.)

Millman, Jacob, and Samuel Seely, *Electronics* (New York: McGraw-Hill Book Company, 1951). (Excellent treatment of the motion of electrons in electric and magnetic fields.)

Robertson, A. J. B., *Mass Spectrometry* (London: Methuen, 1954). (A summary including some of the more recent developments.)

3 | The Special Theory of Relativity

The development of the Special Theory of Relativity by Einstein in 1905 altered the treatment of physical phenomena in a very fundamental way. The theory was developed as a consequence of one of the great crises in physics, which came from the attempt of Michelson and Morley to obtain the answer to a very simple question: What is our own velocity relative to the medium in which light waves are propagated? Their attempt to obtain an answer to this question depended on observing the results of a race between two light beams at right angles to each other.

The Michelson-Morley Experiment

In order to understand the basis of the Michelson-Morley experiment, consider a race between two boats in a river (Fig. 3-1). One of these

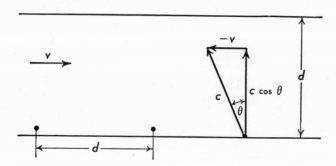

Fig. 3-1. Race between boats in a stream.

boats is to race directly across the river and back and the other is to move an equal distance upstream and then return.

TABLE 3-1. SYMBOLS USED IN CHAPTER 3

Symbol	Name	Quantity Designated
c		velocity of light in vacuum
v		mechanical speed
e		charge of the electron
m_0		rest mass of the electron
m		total mass of electron
V		electrostatic potential difference
$\mathbf{B}$		magnetic induction
t		time as measured in system assumed to be at rest
t'		time as measured in system assumed to be in motion
x		coordinate as measured in system assumed to be at rest
x'		coordinate as measured in system assumed to be in motion
T and T'		specific time intervals as defined
γ	gamma	relativistic factor $(1 - u^2/c^2)^{-\frac{1}{2}}$
W_K		kinetic energy

The width of the idealized river is d, and, between the banks, the water flows with the uniform velocity v. Each of the matched boats is capable of a speed c in still water. The boat going upstream will have a speed relative to the starting point on the bank, which is given by $c - v$, and the time taken to travel upstream is

$$t_1 = \frac{d}{c - v}. \tag{3-1}$$

The speed on the downstream trip is $c + v$, and the time is

$$t_2 = \frac{d}{c + v}. \tag{3-2}$$

Thus, the total time T' is

$$T' = t_1 + t_2 = \frac{d}{c - v} + \frac{d}{c + v} \tag{3-3}$$

$$= \frac{d(c + v) + d(c - v)}{c^2 - v^2} = \frac{2\,dc}{c^2 - v^2}. \tag{3-4}$$

In order to move directly across the stream, the other boat will have to point upstream at an angle θ given by

$$c \sin \theta = v.$$

The speed relative to the bank, therefore, is

$$c \cos \theta = (c^2 - v^2)^{\frac{1}{2}}, \tag{3-5}$$

and the total time T across and back is given by

$$T = \frac{2d}{(c^2 - v^2)^{1/2}}.$$ (3-6)

If this analogy is applied to the race between light beams, c will represent the velocity of light and v will represent the velocity through the "ether" of the "race course" mounted on the earth. The velocity of light is 3×10^8 m/sec, and the velocity of the earth in its orbit is 3×10^4 m/sec. The differences that the experiment is required to detect

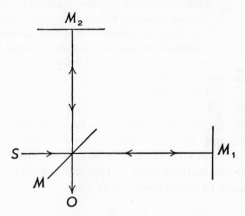

Fig. 3-2. The light paths in a Michelson interferometer.

are of the second order in the ratio of the velocities, and, to be successful, the experiment must be capable of detecting and showing changes of 1 part in 100,000,000.

For this purpose, Michelson proposed the use of the interferometer that he had invented. This is shown in Fig. 3-2. Light from the source S falls on the half-silvered mirror M. Roughly one-half of the light is transmitted to the mirror M_1 from which it is reflected. The other part of the incident light is reflected toward the mirror M_2 from which it is reflected. When the beams recombine after a second half-transmission at the mirror M, the field that the observer at O sees when he looks in the direction of the mirror M combines the light that has traveled by the two paths. If the paths are equal, the center of the field is bright. If the paths differ by one-half wavelength, the center of the field is dark.

Michelson mounted one of the mirrors on a micrometer screw and showed that observation of the shift of the interference fringes in the field was an accurate means of detecting the motion of the movable mirror corresponding to a displacement of only a fraction of a wavelength of light. A device of this precision, if carefully designed and constructed, should then be able to detect the difference in the light paths due to the earth's motion through the ether. Michelson and Morley, therefore, built a large interferometer, which they mounted on a slab of stone floating in mercury. Without disturbing the adjustment of the instrument, they could rotate it through 90° so that the two paths could be interchanged. If one of the beams is actually at a disadvantage because of the direction of motion through the ether, this should be indicated by a fringe shift in the interference pattern. Michelson and Morley failed to detect a fringe shift of an order of magnitude predicted by the theory. The results of the experiments reported by Michelson and Morley, and by subsequent workers, have been judged negative in the consensus of scientists. That is, no shift in the fringes, and, therefore, no time difference, was found. The conclusion to be drawn, then, is that light is not propagated in a medium, as sound, for example, is propagated in air.

The experiment of Michelson and Morley was so simple in conception that a negative result left a major problem of interpretation. The interference pattern itself indicates that light is accompanied by waves which produce the observed interference. All previous examples of wave motion required a material medium, and, yet, in trying to devise a model to represent the medium for light, very great difficulties were encountered. This situation was quite baffling. The Irish physicist Fitzgerald sought to resolve this difficulty by proposing that the length of the interferometer arm in the direction of the motion, contracted just the amount required to give the negative result. Obvious weaknesses of this hypothesis were that it was introduced to explain a known result and that it was not capable of direct verification. If this were in fact a law of nature, all measuring scales would shrink in the same proportion when placed against the interferometer arms for comparison. Hence, no change would be detected. Careful optical experiments showed that the change in dimensions, if it existed, was not accompanied by strains in media such as glass, which would manifest themselves by phenomena such as double refraction in the glass.

The difficulty of understanding the negative results of the Michelson-Morley experiment were so great that a major reconstruction of the basis for the description of physical phenomena was required before it could be resolved. This Einstein provided in 1905.

The Galilean Transformation

In Newtonian mechanics both space and time are treated as absolute quantities. Two observers, even though they may be in relative motion, are expected to agree on their measurements of the length of an object or the time interval between two events. In these circumstances, the relationships between the coordinates of a point in two reference systems in relative motion are very simple.

As suggested by Fig. 3-3, we assume that the coordinate system xyz is at rest. The axes of the coordinate system $x'y'z'$ are parallel to those of the xyz system, but the origin of the $x'y'z'$ system moves in the x-direction with the uniform velocity u. At a certain time the origins of the two systems will coincide, and we call this time zero. According to intuitive ideas (common sense), a man moving with the frame $x'y'z'$

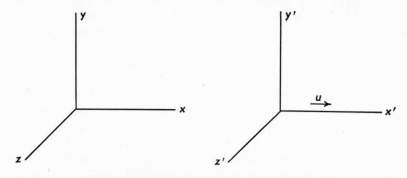

Fig. 3-3. Reference frames with relative velocity.

will agree on time measurements with a man at rest in xyz. The coordinates of a point which is fixed in the xyz system will have a coordinate x' in the moving system which decreases with respect to time at the rate u. Hence, the relationships between the coordinates are

$$
\left.
\begin{aligned}
t' &= t, \\
y' &= y, \\
z' &= z, \\
x' &= x - ut
\end{aligned}
\right\} \text{I}
$$

and
or

$$
\left.
\begin{aligned}
t &= t', \\
y &= y', \\
z &= z', \\
x &= x' + ut.
\end{aligned}
\right\} \text{II}
$$

and

These equations are called a Galilean transformation, and they are to be compared with the transformation equations introduced by Einstein to serve as the basis for the discussion of phenomena in the special theory of relativity.

The Lorentz Transformation

Let us save writing by defining the quantity which repeatedly enters the relativity theory by

$$\gamma = 1/(1 - u^2/c^2)^{\frac{1}{2}}, \qquad (3\text{-}7)$$

where u is the velocity of the transformation. For convenience, we compare a Cartesian reference frame x, y, z, which is at rest, according to our point of view, with a second reference frame which has a velocity u along the x-axis.

The Lorentz transformation for changing x, y, z and t to x', y', z', and t' is

and

$$\left.\begin{aligned}
x' &= \gamma(x - ut), \\
y' &= y, \\
z' &= z, \\
t' &= \gamma\left(t - \frac{ux}{c^2}\right);
\end{aligned}\right\}\text{III}$$

and the converse transformation is

and

$$\left.\begin{aligned}
x &= \gamma(x' + ut'), \\
y &= y', \\
z &= z', \\
t &= \gamma\left(t' + \frac{ux'}{c^2}\right),
\end{aligned}\right\}\text{IV}$$

where c represents the velocity of light in a vacuum, a constant for all observers.

These expressions resemble somewhat the previously used "Galilean transformations." The x-coordinate transforms as in the previous transformations *except that* the contraction factor γ multiplies the entire result. The expressions have a symmetry for the two observers (one in each of the two reference systems), which makes it impossible from the equations to say which frame is at rest. Einstein quickly adopted the view that absolute velocity is a physically unmeasurable quantity and that the physically significant quantity is relative velocity between two material objects or between two observers who adopt these material objects for reference. *Physical laws* are exactly the same in two reference frames in uniform relative velocity.

A very remarkable and seemingly paradoxical thing is that two observers in relative motion do not agree upon their measurements of time.

A clock in motion loses time with respect to one at rest, and this comes from the fundamentals of physics. This result is entirely independent of the type of physical process by which one attempts to measure the time. The way time changes is very similar to the way distance in the direction of the motion changes. We may emphasize this similarity by measuring time, not in seconds, but in terms of a unit so small that light travels but a single unit of distance in this unit of time. Then $c = c^2 = 1$, and a Lorentz transformation is thus changed to

$$x' = \gamma(x - ut) \tag{3-8}$$

$$t' = \gamma(t - ux) \tag{3-9}$$

$$x = \gamma(x' + ut') \tag{3-10}$$

$$t = \gamma(t' + ux'). \tag{3-11}$$

The similarity of the transformations for x and t is obvious.

The Invariance of Light Velocity

The Lorentz transformation makes it possible to understand the negative result of the Michelson-Morley experiment. Suppose that a pulse of light is emitted at the common origin of the two coordinate systems of Fig. 3-3 when $t = t' = 0$, and that, as measured in the xyz frame, it reaches the point $P(x,y,z)$ at time t, and that in the moving frame it reaches $P(x',y',z')$ at the time t'. The velocity of light as computed from these two observations is

$$c = \frac{\sqrt{x^2 + y^2 + z^2}}{t} \tag{3-12}$$

and

$$c = \frac{\sqrt{x'^2 + y'^2 + z'^2}}{t'}. \tag{3-13}$$

From the interpretation that Einstein placed on the Michelson-Morley experiment, these two measured velocities of light should be equal. Eqs. (12) and (13) may be arranged to give

$$x^2 + y^2 + z^2 - c^2t^2 = 0 \tag{3-14}$$

and

$$x'^2 + y'^2 + z'^2 - c^2t'^2 = 0. \tag{3-15}$$

The quantities on the left-hand side of Eqs. (14) and (15) are sometimes identified as the "separation," and the Lorentz transformation maintains the equality

$$x'^2 + y'^2 + z'^2 - c^2t'^2 = x^2 + y^2 + z^2 - c^2t^2. \qquad (3\text{-}16)$$

Any transformations which satisfy Eq. (16) would provide a sufficient condition for the invariance of the velocity of light. It is not necessary that the equations of transformation be those shown in III, but these equations are made plausible by their similarity to the Galilean transformation. When the relations III are substituted into the left-hand side of Eq. (16), algebraic simplification reduces this equation to the identity

$$x^2 + y^2 + z^2 - c^2t^2 = x^2 + y^2 + z^2 - c^2t^2. \qquad (3\text{-}17)$$

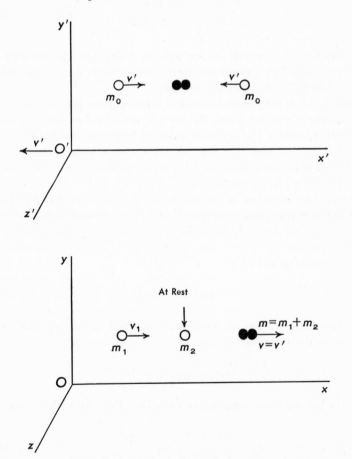

Fig. 3-4. Collision between two masses observed in different frames.

From the Lorentz transformation the relativistic law for the transformation of velocities may be derived. Differentiation of IV gives

$$dx = \gamma(dx' + u\,dt') \quad \text{and} \quad dt = \gamma\left(dt' + \frac{u}{c^2}dx'\right). \qquad (3\text{-}18)$$

Thus,

$$\frac{dx}{dt} = \frac{dx' + u\,dt'}{dt' + \dfrac{u}{c^2}dx'} = \frac{\dfrac{dx'}{dt'} + u}{1 + \dfrac{u}{c^2}\dfrac{dx'}{dt'}} \qquad (3\text{-}19)$$

and

$$v_x = \frac{v_x' + u}{1 + uv_x'/c^2}. \qquad (3\text{-}20)$$

A velocity v_x' observed in the moving frame has the velocity u of this frame added to it according to this relationship to give the velocity observed in the frame which is at rest.

With this rule for the addition of velocities, if the law of conservation of momentum is to be saved, the mass of a body must be a function of its speed. Consider the inelastic collision between two bodies. In the primed system, as shown in Fig. 3-4, the bodies of equal masses initially moving in opposite directions with equal velocities v', stick together after the impact and come to rest.

Consider an observer in an unprimed system where the relative velocity between the frames v' is chosen so that the second mass is originally at rest. The first mass then collides with it, and the two particles stick together and move to the right with the velocity v'. We assume that mass is conserved in the collision

$$m = m_1 + m_2. \qquad (3\text{-}21)$$

From the conservation of momentum applied to observation of the collision in the unprimed frame,

$$m_1 v_1 = (m_1 + m_2)v'.$$

From the law for transformation of velocities (Eq. (20) with $v_x' = u = v'$),

$$v_1 = \frac{v' + v'}{1 + v'^2/c^2} = \frac{2v'}{1 + v'^2/c^2}, \qquad (3\text{-}22)$$

and the conservation of momentum reads

$$m_1 \frac{2v'}{1 + v'^2/c^2} = (m_1 + m_2)v',$$

$$m_1 \left(\frac{2}{1 + v'^2/c^2} - 1 \right) = m_2,$$

$$m_1 \left(\frac{2}{1 + v'^2/c^2} - \frac{1 + v'^2/c^2}{1 + v'^2/c^2} \right) = m_2$$

but

$$m_2 = m_0$$

$$m_1 \left(\frac{1 - v'^2/c^2}{1 + v'^2/c^2} \right) = m_0.$$

From Eq. (22),

$$1 - \frac{v_1{}^2}{c^2} = 1 - \frac{1}{c^2} \left(\frac{2v'}{1 + v'^2/c^2} \right)^2$$

$$= 1 - \frac{1}{c^2} \frac{4v'^2}{(1 + v'^2/c^2)^2} = \frac{\left(1 + \dfrac{v'^2}{c^2}\right)^2 - \dfrac{4v'^2}{c^2}}{\left(1 + \dfrac{v'^2}{c^2}\right)^2}$$

$$= \frac{1 - \dfrac{2v'^2}{c^2} + v'^4/c^4}{(1 + v'^2/c^2)^2} = \frac{\left(1 - \dfrac{v'^2}{c^2}\right)^2}{(1 + v'^2/c^2)^2}. \qquad (3\text{-}23)$$

Hence,

$$\frac{1 + v'^2/c^2}{1 - v'^2/c^2} = \frac{1}{\sqrt{1 - u_1{}^2/c^2}}$$

and

$$m_1 = \frac{m_0}{\sqrt{1 - \dfrac{u_1{}^2}{c^2}}},$$

or in general we may write

$$m = m_0/\sqrt{1 - u^2/c^2} = \gamma m_0. \qquad (3\text{-}24)$$

This is a very fundamental relationship. It shows the way that the mass or inertia of a body changes with its speed. As usual in physics, the experiment should be made without disturbing the quantity measured. Since our analysis shows that inertia does depend upon speed, an experiment to measure inertia should determine the ratio of the force to the acceleration without changing the speed. This is possible only in case the instantaneous force is at right angles to the instantaneous velocity throughout the experiment. In this case the speed, and as a consequence the inertia, is not changed by the experiment for determining it.

One may expand

$$m = m_0 \left\{ 1 - \frac{v^2}{c^2} \right\}^{-\frac{1}{2}}$$

by the binomial theorem to obtain

$$m = m_0 \left\{ 1 + \frac{1}{2} \left(\frac{v}{c}\right)^2 + \frac{3}{8} \left(\frac{v}{c}\right)^4 + \frac{15}{48} \left(\frac{v}{c}\right)^6 + \cdots \right\}. \qquad (3\text{-}25)$$

The terms shown give the mass with sufficient accuracy when the velocity is not too large. The kinetic energy divided by the conversion factor c^2 is added to the mass of the particle. If the mass in kg is to be expressed in joules, we must multiply by the conversion factor $c^2 \simeq 9 \times 10^{16}$. This gives

$$mc^2 = m_0 c^2 \left\{ 1 + \frac{1}{2} \left(\frac{v^2}{c^2}\right) + \frac{3}{8} \left(\frac{v}{c}\right)^4 + \frac{15}{48} \left(\frac{v}{c}\right)^6 + \cdots \right\}.$$

The difference between the total energy mc^2, and the rest energy $m_0 c^2$, we call the kinetic energy W_K. Thus,

$$W_K = mc^2 - m_0 c^2 = \tfrac{1}{2} m_0 v^2 + \frac{3}{8} \frac{v^4}{c^2} m_0 + \frac{15}{48} m_0 \frac{v^6}{c^4} + \cdots$$

$$= \tfrac{1}{2} m_0 v^2 \left(1 + \frac{3}{4} \left(\frac{v}{c}\right)^2 + \frac{15}{24} \left(\frac{v}{c}\right)^4 + \cdots \right). \qquad (3\text{-}26)$$

Motion of a Particle in a Conservative Force Field

By Newton's second law,

$$F = \frac{d}{dt} (mv) = \frac{d}{dt} \left(\frac{m_0 v}{\sqrt{1 - \frac{v^2}{c^2}}} \right). \qquad (3\text{-}27)$$

This is essentially the way Newton stated his second law. It is inconsistent with $F = ma$ when relativistic corrections are made, but Eq. (27) is the correct relativistic form. Consider a particle on which a net force F does work, all of which is used to increase the kinetic energy of the particle.

$$dW = F\, ds = ds\, \frac{d}{dt}\, (mv) = \frac{ds}{dt}\, d(mv)$$

$$= vd(mv) = vd\left(\frac{m_0 v}{\sqrt{1 - \dfrac{v^2}{c^2}}}\right)$$

$$= m_0 v\, \frac{1 - \dfrac{v^2}{c^2} + \dfrac{v^2}{c^2}}{\left(1 - \dfrac{v^2}{c^2}\right)^{3/2}}\, dv = \frac{m_0 v\, dv}{\left(1 - \dfrac{v^2}{c^2}\right)^{3/2}}. \tag{3-28}$$

The kinetic energy W_K is found by integration between definite limits

$$W_K = \int_0^{v_f} \frac{m_0 v\, dv}{(1 - v^2/c^2)^{3/2}} = \frac{m_0 c^2}{(1 - v^2/c^2)^{1/2}} \Bigg]_0^{v_f}$$

$$= \frac{m_0 c^2}{(1 - v_f{}^2/c^2)^{1/2}} - m_0 c^2$$

$$= mc^2 - m_0 c^2. \tag{3-29}$$

This establishes a very reasonable result. The kinetic energy (the energy the particle has in consequence of its motion) is the total energy of the particle minus the energy that it had when at rest. If the work done to increase the kinetic energy is obtained from the motion of a charged particle through a potential difference, it may be expressed as Ve. Hence,

$$Ve = m_0 c^2 \left[\frac{1}{\left(1 - \dfrac{v^2}{c^2}\right)^{1/2}} - 1\right], \tag{3-30}$$

where the conversion factor c^2 in the right-hand member converts this mass into energy units. From this, we get

$$\frac{1}{\left(1 - \dfrac{v^2}{c^2}\right)^{1/2}} = 1 + \frac{Ve}{m_0 c^2}. \tag{3-31}$$

Next we determine the potential difference V_2 required to double the mass of the electron. If $m = 2m_0$, Eq. (29) becomes

$$2m_0 = m_0 + \frac{eV_2}{c^2}$$

or

$$V_2 = m_0c^2/e.$$

Substituting the values of m_0, c, and e, we get

$$V_2 = 511{,}600 \text{ volts.}$$

The rest mass of the electron is equivalent to 0.5116 Mev of energy. Substituting this value of m_0c^2/e into Eq. (31), we get

$$\frac{1}{\left(1 - \frac{v^2}{c^2}\right)^{1/2}} = 1 + \frac{V}{511{,}600 \text{ volts}}. \tag{3-32}$$

Solving for v, we get

$$v = c\left[1 - \frac{1}{\left(1 + \frac{V}{511{,}600 \text{ volts}}\right)^2}\right]^{1/2}. \tag{3-33}$$

Finally, substituting Eq. (32) into Eq. (24), we find that the mass of an electron effective in acceleration without a change of speed may be written

$$m = m_0\left[1 + \frac{V}{511{,}600 \text{ volts}}\right]. \tag{3-34}$$

Experimental Verifications
of the Equivalence of Mass and Energy

The Contribution of the Kinetic Energy to the Inertia

The fact that the kinetic energy of a particle increases its inertia, as predicted by the theory of relativity, has been verified in the course of a number of decisive experiments. Soon after the announcement of the theory of relativity, Bucherer performed a simple and ingenious experiment for the purpose of testing the dependence of the inertia upon the velocity. As a source of electrons, Bucherer used a radioactive sample which emitted β particles (high-speed electrons) having a spread of velocities, including some that were traveling with a speed nearly as great as that of light. This source S (Fig. 3-5) of high-speed electrons, he placed on the common axis of a pair of similar parallel circular metallic discs A and B. A potential difference was applied between the two discs, and a uniform magnetic field was set up parallel to a diameter of one of the discs. This system provides a means of selecting electrons, moving parallel to various radii of the discs, whose velocities depend on the angle θ which the radial velocity makes with the magnetic induction vector.

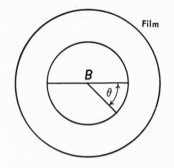

The force $\mathbf{F}_m$ exerted on an electron moving in the magnetic field $\mathbf{B}$ with a velocity $\mathbf{v}$ is given by

$$\mathbf{F}_m = e(\mathbf{v} \times \mathbf{B}),$$

whose magnitude is

$$F_m = evB \sin \theta.$$

At a given angle θ, and for electrons of the proper velocity, this force is equal and opposite to the electrostatic force $(-eE)$. Electrons not having the proper velocity hit the plates and fail to escape. Hence, the

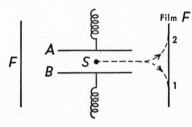

Fig. 3-5. The arrangement of apparatus in the experiment of Bucherer.

magnitude of the velocities of the electrons coming out from between the parallel discs is given by

$$v = E/(B \sin \theta). \tag{3-35}$$

After these electrons leave the region between the discs, they are deflected by the magnetic force, and in Bucherer's apparatus, they were allowed to fall on a photographic film F that surrounded the condenser plates at a fixed distance from the circumference of the discs. By reversing the direction of both the electrostatic and the magnetic fields simultaneously, the velocity selected parallel to a certain radius of the disc remained unchanged, but the deflection in the magnetic field after leaving the condenser plates was reversed. In this way Bucherer obtained two traces on the photographic film, which varied in separation with the angle θ, and from these separations, he computed the inertia of the electrons as a function of their speed.

This experiment, although ingenious and simple in principle, was not precise. The electrons were not focused into a narrow beam. Furthermore, the interpretation was complicated by the fact that the high-speed electrons were scattered when they struck the metal plates. Thus, in effect the entire interior surface area of both plates was a source of electrons, which, however, was fortunately somewhat weaker than the primary source. The uncertainties were of the order of the effect to be detected, and the experiments of Bucherer do not furnish the most decisive evidence for the correctness of the theory of relativity. The fact that Bucherer's experimental results were consistent with the formula

$$m = m_0/(1 - v^2/c^2)^{1/2}$$

had historical importance, because it was accepted as evidence which confirmed the correctness of the relativity theory.

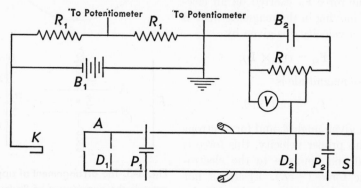

Fig. 3-6. Arrangement of apparatus in the experiment of Perry and Chaffee.

Later, in the years just prior to 1930, an experiment performed by Perry and Chaffee at Harvard University for the purpose of obtaining a precise value of e/m for electrons, incidentally gave unmistakable evidence for the contribution of the kinetic energy to the inertia. The method was a time-of-flight measurement for electrons which had fallen through a known potential difference. In this it resembled the experiment of Wiechert, but, by taking advantage of the improved methods for electrical measurements and of the development of radio frequency techniques, Perry and Chaffee were able to make their experiment more precise. A storage battery, capable of maintaining steady potential differences up to 20,000 volts, and good frequency standards were essential components of the experiment.

The apparatus used by Perry and Chaffee is shown schematically in Fig. 3-6. Electrons from a hot cathode K were accelerated as a result of the potential difference applied between this cathode and the anode A, which is a long aluminum tube. The region between K and S, along which the electrons travel, was highly evacuated. The major part of the accelerating potential was provided by a battery B_1, made up of several

1600-volt sections of the large storage battery. The positive end of the battery B_1 was grounded, and the potential supplied by this battery was measured accurately by means of a "volt box" and potentiometer arrangement. To obtain a continuous variation of the potential applied to the anode, a 2000-volt storage battery B_2 was connected across a potential divider R. The potential applied from this battery was measured by a high-quality voltmeter, the calibration of which was carefully checked. It was possible to read the applied potential to 1 or 2 parts in 10,000, even though the setting varied in the several tests by about 1 part in 1000.

A sharp beam of electrons was defined by the diaphragm D_1, and this beam was passed between the condenser plates at P_1. These condenser plates were excited by the alternating potential difference from a radio frequency oscillator. Only those electrons which passed between the plates at the two parts of the cycle when the applied potential difference was zero could pass through the diaphragm D_2, and on between the second pair of deflecting plates at P_2, which were excited by the same oscillator but were connected with such a polarity that the potential across them was 180° out-of-phase with that on the condenser at P_1. If the time taken by the electrons in the flight between P_1 and P_2 corresponded to half a cycle, or a full cycle, of the oscillator used, then the electrons which passed through P_1 when the potential difference was zero also passed through P_2 when the potential difference was zero, and their trajectory was a straight line. The distance between the two pairs of deflecting plates was 75.133 cm and the transit time was measured in terms of the known period of the oscillator. Thus, the velocity could be computed from experimental measurements. The values of the potentials adjusted to give transmission of the beam were reliable to 10 or 20 volts, and enough independent readings were taken so that the probable errors in the final averages were of the order of 5 volts.

The results of this research are summarized in Table 3-2. The first column gives the time of flight determined from the frequency of the oscillator. The second lists the mean of the potential readings obtained in numerous independent tests. The measured distance between plates P_1 and P_2 divided by the values entered in column one gives the observed velocity, entered in the third column. The potentials are in the range where relativistic effects, although not large, are appreciable. To illustrate this, we have calculated velocities by the formula of Newtonian mechanics $v = 5.9311 \times 10^5 V^{\frac{1}{2}}$, which is based on the constant $e/m_0 = 1.75888$ coul/kg. The velocities calculated by this formula are up to 2.8% higher than those observed. The electrons exhibit a corresponding increase in inertia as the kinetic energy is increased. Calculations by the relativistic formula for the velocity, also based on

TABLE 3-2. ANALYSIS OF THE EXPERIMENT OF PERRY AND CHAFFEE

| t $(10^{-8}$ sec) | V (volts) | v $(10^7$ m/sec) | | | e/m_0 coul/kg |
| | | Observed | Calculated | | |
			New-tonian	Relativ-istic	
1.2392	10,763	6.0619	6.1532	6.0577	1.7613×10^{-11}
1.2141	11,232	6.1882	6.28585	6.1810	1.7612×10^{-11}
1.06236	14,825	7.0723	7.2219	7.0641	1.7608×10^{-11}
0.99153	17,136	7.5744	7.7641	7.5689	1.7601×10^{-11}
0.94432	18,993	7.9563	8.1739	7.9472	1.7600×10^{-11}
0.92958	19,626	8.0826	8.30904	8.0734	1.7610×10^{-11}

the currently accepted value for e/m_0, are shown in the fifth column, and they follow the trend of the observed velocities perfectly. The value of e/m_0, which Perry and Chaffee derived from these observations, was 1.761 coul/kg and because we did not use this value in our calculations, the values of v calculated by the relativistic formula are all very slightly low.

On the basis of the results obtained by Perry and Chaffee, not only can there be no doubt that kinetic energy contributes to inertia, but it also is apparent that the relativistic formula at speeds of about $c/4$ accurately predicts the variation in mass.

Later, in 1940, Rogers, McReynolds, and Rogers determined the mass of high-speed electrons from a radioactive substance called RaC, for three lines of which precision values of $Br = mv/e$ had been obtained by magnetic deflection. The method was to deflect these rays in the electric field set up between two coaxial cylinders of known mean radius R. The potential difference which caused the β rays to follow the mean radius was determined by measurement. For the correct potential, the electric intensity E supplied the central force, and

$$Ee = mv^2/R.$$

Thus, combination of the two relations gives m/e directly

$$m/e = (Br)^2/ER.$$

For e/m_0 the value 1.7591×10^{11} coul/kg, obtained by Dunnington,

TABLE 3-3. VARIATION OF ELECTRONIC MASS WITH VELOCITY

v/c	V (volts)	Br (webers/m)	ER kv	m/m_0 Measured	m/m_0 Calculated
0.6337	9970	.001406	2.671	1.298	1.293
0.6961	13017	.001671	3.487	1.404	1.393
0.7496	16200	.0019315	4.341	1.507	1.511

was used. The results of the measurements are shown in Table 3-3. These results are especially interesting, because the increase in mass has become quite large, and the agreement between observed values of the mass and those calculated from the speed in the range velocities up to $0.75c$ is seen to be quite good.

Conversion of Mass into Energy

The theories of modern physics became of vital interest to the engineer as soon as it was evident that they offered vast quantities of energy which might be utilized for the benefit of society. The fact that such energies are very great is suggested by the size of the conversion factor appearing in Einstein's formula: $W = mc^2$. The suggestion that these energies might be available came from the fact that certain of the atoms existing in nature transform themselves spontaneously to other atoms and give off very energetic particles.

In 1896, Becquerel noticed that some photographic plates which had been left standing for some time with uranium on them showed "fogging" when they were developed. The phenomenon taking place in the uranium, which gave rise to the exposure of the photographic plates, was called radioactivity, and it was studied very extensively in following decades. It was discovered that three types of radiation were present. First, there were alpha particles, which were subsequently identified as high-speed helium ions. Second, there were the very high-speed electrons, called beta particles, which were previously mentioned in connection with the experiments of Bucherer, and of Rogers, McReynolds, and Rogers. Finally, there were gamma rays, which because they were not deflected by a magnetic field, were identified, at first tentatively, as energetic electromagnetic radiation.

The energies of all these types of radiation were very high, and they were conveniently expressed in millions of electron volts (Mev). Before scientists were able to build machines to produce atomic particles of these high energies, they used those existing in nature for their experiments, and the source of this energy intrigued them. Radioactivity, because of the identification of liberated helium, was interpreted as a case in which the heavy uranium atom was unstable and decomposed by breaking into two fragments, one of which was helium. Following the development of the theory of relativity, with its indication that mass and energy were interchangeable, it was proposed that in the radio-active disintegration of a substance, such as uranium, enough mass disappeared to account for the appearance of the high kinetic energy observed.

Because a small mass was equivalent to a fantastically large amount of energy, the verification of this hypothesis made accurate measurement of the masses of atomic ions a problem of great scientific importance. For this purpose it was not sufficient merely to identify the ions; in addition, differences in mass corresponding to changes in the fifth and sixth significant figures of the masses had to be measured. The precision required for this purpose made it important to adopt a precisely defined standard convention in the measurement of atomic masses. The one chosen was the one-sixteenth part of the oxygen isotope O^{16}. This is called the atomic mass unit, abbreviated amu, and its currently accepted value is 1.65985×10^{-27} kg. Thus, 1.00000 kg equals $1/1.65985 \times 10^{-27}$ amu or 6.0244×10^{26} amu.

The requirements placed upon mass spectroscopy became corresponding-ly exacting, but, through the development of methods which increased the precision by several orders of magnitude, science proved adequate to meet this challenge. When uranium decays into thorium plus an alpha particle, it is found that the mass of the uranium is greater than that of thorium plus helium. The difference in the mass is sufficient to account for the kinetic energy created in the transformation.

Summary

Einstein in founding the Special Theory of Relativity provided a necessary framework with reference to which problems of modern physics are discussed. The equivalence of mass and energy was clearly indicated, and this is the basis of important engineering developments. The simplest form of the relationship between mass and energy is

$$W = mc^2,$$

and the various equations of this chapter have been derived from this expression. Of special importance is the formula giving the variation of mass with velocity

$$m = m_0/(1 - v^2/c^2)^{1/2}.$$

Although the analysis introduced in this chapter had the objective of getting practical relationships, some one of which may be found useful in calculations of a certain type, it is often just as easy to start with one of the basic equations of this summary and to perform calculations, of the type illustrated in this chapter, directed toward securing the required information.

The conversion of a small fraction of an atom's mass into energy, illustrated in the case of radioactive decay, has now been achieved also in artificial transmutations, the rate of which can be controlled. This is developing as a source of commercial power, and the scientific facts underlying such applications are a principal interest in this introduction to modern physics.

Problems in Special Relativity

1. Starting from rest, through what potential difference must an electron fall if it is to have a 10% increase in its mass?
2. Starting from rest, through what potential difference must an electron fall if the part of its mass associated with its kinetic energy is to be three times its rest mass?
3. At what velocity does use of the Newtonian formula for kinetic energy give a 10% error?
4. What is the mass of a proton ($m_0 = 1.6724 \times 10^{-27}$ kg) after it has fallen through 1,000,000 volts of potential difference? By what fraction is its mass increased?
5. What is the speed of an electron, which, starting from rest, has fallen through a potential difference of 1,000,000 volts?
6. Assume that a 1 kg mass is standard at 20° C, and that its specific heat is 0.095. By how much will its mass increase as a result of thermal energy if the temperature is raised to 100° C?
7. One component of the cosmic rays consists of particles traveling with a speed of $0.99990c$. How does time measured on a frame moving with the particle compare with time as measured on the surface of the earth?

References on the Special Theory of Relativity

Bergman, Peter G., *Basic Theories of Physics*, Ch. 9 (New York: Prentice-Hall, 1949). (A treatment that emphasizes the physical importance of the theory.)

Eldridge, John A., *Physical Basis of Things*, Ch. 1 (New York: McGraw-Hill Book Company, 1934). (An elementary account designed to awaken the interest of the reader.)

Kaplan, Irving, *Nuclear Physics*, pp. 87-105 (Cambridge: Addison-Wesley, 1955). (An account written with a view to the applications fundamental to engineering developments.)

Leighton, Robert B., *Principles of Modern Physics*, Ch. 1 (New York: McGraw-Hill Book Company, 1959). (Basic physics is emphasized in a logically arranged treatment which departs from tradition.)

Ridenour, Louis, *Modern Physics for the Engineer*, Ch. 1 (New York: McGraw-Hill Book Company, 1954). (The chapters are written by persons with special knowledge in the respective fields.)

4 | The Origin of the Quantum Theory

Introduction

The name "quantum theory" is meant to imply that energy appears in lumps of definite size, and that in a given physical situation the changes of energy occur in finite steps or jumps. If this is true, and experience has shown that it is, one would expect to be able to detect these finite changes of energy directly in suitable experiments. This direct evidence does exist, and it constitutes the most convincing proof of the correctness of the quantum hypothesis. We will defer an account of these simple experiments to discuss the less direct evidence out of which historically the quantum theory arose.

The fields of physics to which the idea of energy changes in finite steps were first successfully applied involved averaging processes which concealed the direct evidence for the finite changes. A statistical theory based on these finite changes was used in explaining observed continuous variations in energy. The success of this theory is important, but in fairness it must be stated that this evidence alone failed to convince the majority of physicists that the existence of these quanta was a general and important principle of their science. The reader may be assured that any mental reservations which develop as he considers this theory were shared by Planck, who originated it but who was very reluctant to accept and develop all the implications of it.

The energy distribution of electromagnetic radiation in wavelength or color as a function of temperature had been indicated by qualitative observations on hot bodies since the early times in which the uses of heat were discovered, and our own experiences confirm the most obvious facts concerning it. If a body is heated only slightly above room temperature, the loss of heat from it by electromagnetic radiation is so small that it is detected with difficulty, and it is limited to such long wavelengths that our eyes do not respond to it. We sense it as warmth. The infrared radiation from heated objects is confirmed directly by photographs of hot bodies, such as flat irons, taken in complete darkness by the use of their own radiation of wavelengths too long to make them visible.

If an electric iron is accidentally heated to an abnormally high temperature, the amount of the radiation increases rapidly, and, in addition, some of the radiation is shifted into the visible in the extreme red, and the object glows with a dull red color. The filament of a lamp bulb, operated on an abnormally low potential difference, is distinctly red. As the temperature is increased by raising the power supplied to the lamp, appreciable radiation in the shorter wavelengths changes the color first to orange and then to yellow. At the same time the amount of the radiation increases very rapidly, and the lamp is a source of radiant heat. The basic problem is to determine why color depends on temperature.

This problem was analyzed theoretically by considering the radiation density in a hollow space which would exist in equilibrium with walls of the enclosure all of which were maintained at a common temperature.

TABLE 4-1. SYMBOLS USED IN CHAPTER 4

Symbol	Name	Quantity Designated
ϵ	epsilon	quantum of energy hf or $h\nu$
f		mechanical frequency
ν	nu	frequency of electromagnetic wave $\nu = c/\lambda$
p		momentum
W_m		maximum kinetic energy in harmonic motion
T_0		characteristic temperature in specific heat of solid
L		length of bounded string
a		length of edge of bounded square or cube
v_l		velocity of longitudinal waves
v_t		velocity of transverse waves
A		area
V		volume
f_m		maximum frequency in Debye's approximation formula
n, m		integers
λ	lambda	wavelength
T		temperature
k		Boltzmann's constant
h		Planck's constant
q		generalized coordinate
t		time
w		phase velocity or wave velocity
u_ν		distribution of energy, $dw/d\nu$

The equilibrium density of this radiation increases rapidly with temperature. That is, the "heat capacity" of matter-free space increases rapidly with temperature, and there is really no difficulty with this idea. The distribution in wavelength of the thermal radiation was measured experimentally, and here there was a difficulty of the most fundamental sort. Theory associated this energy with standing electromagnetic waves. The number of these in $d\lambda$ at wavelength λ increased very rapidly as the wavelength was reduced. If energy in each of these wave patterns were equally likely, all the energy of thermal radiation would appear at extremely short wavelengths. Experiment shows that none of it does. This is a discrepancy of the most obvious sort, and the conclusion that the shorter wavelengths cannot have an equal chance to accept energy is forced upon us.

According to the kinetic theory of gases, at any temperature T the characteristic energy is kT, and there are individual molecules both above and below this characteristic energy, but the number of molecules falls off quite rapidly both at the higher and the lower energies. The difficulty with the low observed energies at short wavelengths of radiation can be eliminated if it is assumed that the energy has to appear in quanta of size inversely proportional to the wavelength or directly proportional to frequency. At short wavelengths on the basis of this postulate, the quanta would get so large in comparison with kT that it is quite unlikely these wavelengths would be found in the distribution.

Similarly, a study of the specific heat of solids showed a continuous variation over a wide range of temperatures. The results, interpreted in terms of the individual atoms, indicated that the heat capacity decreased toward zero at low temperatures. If the energy acquired by the atoms goes into vibrations of definite frequency f, and if the corresponding energy quanta are of size given by

$$\epsilon = hf, \tag{4-1}$$

where h is a constant, at low temperature T the characteristic energy kT becomes so small in comparison to these quanta, that it is quite unlikely for an atom to contain one. The oscillators are raised above their states of lowest energy for such small fractions of the total time that their average heat content becomes negligible.

This is the crucial evidence which these phenomena give concerning the discrete size of these lumps of energy. The basic nature of the problem and of the nature of its solution should be clear to all readers. Some, however, will be interested in the quantitative predictions of the quantum theory. The quantitative facts are not necessary for an understanding of subsequent chapters, but they are given for the purpose of satis-

fying the curiosity of those who would like to see how the statistics give
rise to the equations.

The Concept of Action

Momentum and change of position are two of the fundamental
quantities in physics, which Newtonian mechanics emphasized. The
product of momentum and displacement was not identified as a significant quantity by Newton, who, of course, used the familiar laws of
motion as the starting point for the development of mechanics. Newton's
method of deriving the laws of mechanics is not unique. Another of the
methods for doing so involves the product of momentum and displacement, which is called action.

The definition of action may be made quite inclusive. Associated with
a coordinate q, which is used to specify the position of a particle, there
is a variable p, which is a measure of the generalized momentum. Action
is defined as the product of these two quantities. A simple illustration,
involving a coordinate and a momentum which should be familiar to
every reader is that of a mass in linear motion. The coordinate which
specifies the location of the center of mass or the position of a "particle"
may be called x, and the corresponding linear momentum p is given by

$$p = m \, dx/dt, \tag{4-2}$$

where m is the mass and t is the time. The action dA in any small element
dx of the path is simply the product

$$dA = p \, dx = m(dx)^2/dt. \tag{4-3}$$

Use of the mathematical identity $dx = (dx/dt) \, dt$ gives a useful alternate
form for expressing an element of the action

$$dA = m(dx/dt)^2 \, dt = 2W \, dt, \tag{4-4}$$

where W represents the kinetic energy $\frac{1}{2}mv^2$ as defined in Newtonian
mechanics. The units of action in the mks system are $kg \ m^2/\text{sec}$ or
joule-sec. Eqs. (3) and (4) give a quantity the integral of which over the
motion of the particle has a minimum (or at least, a rate of change which
is zero) as the path is varied. Hamilton presented this as a fundamental
principle of physics called "least action," and he was able to show that
his principle provided a suitable basis for the derivation of other mechanical laws. Even Newton's laws of motion may be drived from this
principle, and this fact serves to suggest that action, even though the
consideration of it is frequently neglected, may be an important quantity
in physics.

The Quantization of Action

The analysis of atomic systems emphasized the importance of action. Periodic phenomena were found to be associated with all atoms, and it was discovered that when the action was integrated throughout a complete period, the result was an integral multiple of a basic unit or "quantum of action." This quantum h proved to be very small:

$$h = 6.6 \times 10^{-34} \text{ joule-sec.} \tag{4-5}$$

The quantum is too small to be detected by measurements of ordinary accuracy made on the conventional objects of mechanics such as billiard balls and rifle bullets. Quantization of action was found to exist in the periodic phenomena of atomic systems, and the extremely small size of the atom was a circumstance which made the detection of this quantization an almost inevitable consequence of human curiosity about the physical behavior of things.

A little analysis will clarify the meaning and consequences of quantizing action in a periodic motion. As an illustration we use the linear simple harmonic oscillator, and choose the linear coordinate x to represent the displacement of the mass from its equilibrium position. In Eq. (4), W is then identified as the instantaneous kinetic energy of the mass in the time interval dt. If the period is denoted by T, the action is given by the integral

$$A = 2 \int_0^T W \, dt. \tag{4-6}$$

As usual in these problems we define the average value of the kinetic energy $\overline{W}$ during a period of the motion by

$$\overline{W} \equiv \frac{1}{T} \int_0^T W \, dt,$$

and the use of this in Eq. (6) gives

$$A = 2\overline{W}T. \tag{4-7}$$

If W_m is used to represent the maximum kinetic energy (which, because the force is conservative, also corresponds to the constant total energy of the oscillation), it is easily shown that

$$\overline{W} = W_m/2,$$

and, hence,

$$A = W_m T. \tag{4-8}$$

If action exists in nature only as integral multiples of the basic quantity

h, from Eq. (8), we may write

$$A = W_m T = nh, \tag{4-9}$$

where n is an integer.

That there is an important restriction on the energy of quantized systems is easily shown. If Eq. (9) is divided by the periodic time, we obtain

$$W_m = nh/T = nhf, \tag{4-10}$$

where in the final term the frequency f of the system in cycles/unit time is used for the reciprocal of the periodic time. The use of ordinary mechanics and the recognition of quantization indicates that if action appears only as integral multiples of Planck's constant h, the energy changes in quanta of size equal to Planck's constant times the frequency. This is precisely the *ad hoc* hypothesis introduced to explain the distributions of energy discussed in the introductory section.

Specific Heat of Solids

The quantum theory arose historically in connection with Planck's explanation of the distribution of thermal radiation. In its most simple form this theory was applied by Einstein to explain the variation of the specific heat of solids. Because it connects directly to the foregoing discussion, we will consider Einstein's theory for the specific heats before quantitatively discussing thermal radiation.

We have noticed that one of the great achievements of the kinetic theory was its ability to explain the energy required to heat a simple monatomic gas in terms of the increase of the translational kinetic energy of the gas molecules as a function of the temperature. A direct extension of the kinetic theory is successful in accounting for some of the observations in the case of solids.

A substance in the form of a liquid or a solid consists of atoms just as a gas does. The chief difference is in the density, and both solids and liquids have much higher numbers of atoms per unit volume (concentrations) than are found in gases and in vapors. The concentrations are so high that forces might be expected to act continuously between the atoms in solids and liquids; the observed densities should be determined primarily by equilibrium positions for the atoms in the presence of these forces.

The existence of natural cleavage planes in crystals suggests that for solids the positions of the atoms must be quite definite. Because the forces required to distort a crystal from its natural shape are large, it would be concluded that the force required to displace an atom from its equilibrium position is relatively great. Hooke's law for solids would suggest that when an atom is displaced by a small amount, the restoring force is directly proportional to the displacement of the atom from its equilibrium position.

Potential energy would be associated with the displacement of the atoms from their equilibrium positions. The existence of these equilibrium positions would not preclude the possibility of thermal motions, because the atoms, if displaced by thermal action, would vibrate about their equilibrium positions. If the vibrations are simple harmonic motions, the kinetic and potential energies, averaged over time, would be equal. The total thermal energy of an atom in a solid might be expected to equal twice that of a monatomic gas with which it is in thermal equilibrium, because, if the *kinetic* energies of the two are equal on the average, the atoms of the solid, in addition will have on the average an equal *potential* energy. Thus, for the atoms in the solid, the average energy $\overline{W}$ is given by $\overline{W} = 3kT$. For many solids the predictions of such a theory are valid at temperatures not too different from those normally prevailing in a room, while even more solids will show the predicted behavior if the measurements are made at substantially higher temperatures. These experimental results were formulated by Dulong and Petit in the statement that the product of the specific heat and the mass of a mole is a constant.

However, as any material is cooled, at a temperature depending on the substance, the heat capacity will fall below that predicted by the kinetic theory. Einstein developed a very elementary theory to account for such behavior. As the basis of his calculation, he assumed that all the atoms in a given solid would vibrate with the same frequency f_0, and that the corresponding energy quanta would be $\epsilon = hf_0$. The average energy of the oscillators at any absolute temperature was then determined by a statistical argument making use of the assumption (suggested by Boltzmann's principle) that if the number of atoms having zero energy associated with vibrations in the x-direction is N_0, the number having energy $n\epsilon$ in that "degree of freedom" will on the average be given by $N_0 e^{-n\epsilon/kT}$.

The total number of atoms can be expressed by the summation

$$N_T = N_0(1 + e^{-\epsilon/kT} + e^{-2\epsilon/kT} + \cdots + e^{-n\epsilon/kT} + \cdots)$$

$$= N_0/(1 - e^{-\epsilon/kT}). \tag{4-11}$$

The total energy in this degree of freedom of all the atoms is given by

$$W_T = ON_0 + N_0(\epsilon e^{-\epsilon/kT} + 2\epsilon e^{-2\epsilon/kT} + 3\epsilon e^{-3\epsilon/kT} + \cdots$$

$$+ n\epsilon e^{-n\epsilon/kT} + \cdots)$$

$$= N_0\epsilon e^{-\epsilon/kT}[1 + 2e^{-\epsilon/kT} + \cdots + ne^{-(n-1)\epsilon/kT} + \cdots]$$

$$= N_0\epsilon e^{-\epsilon/kT}/(1 - e^{-\epsilon/kT})^2. \tag{4-12}$$

The average energy per atom in the degree of freedom is given by

$$\overline{W} = W_T/N_T = \epsilon e^{-\epsilon/kT}(1 - e^{-\epsilon/kT})^{-1} = \epsilon(e^{\epsilon/kT} - 1)^{-1}$$

or

$$W_T = N_T\epsilon/(e^{\epsilon/kT} - 1). \tag{4-13}$$

If the atoms have three identical degrees of freedom, the result obtained should be multiplied by 3. Thus.

$$W_T = 3N_T\epsilon/(e^{\epsilon/kT} - 1).$$

An expression which should give the energy required to raise the temperature 1° K at any temperature T may be found by differentiation.

$$\frac{dW_T}{dT} = \frac{3N_T\epsilon^2}{kT^2}\frac{e^{\epsilon/kT}}{(e^{\epsilon/kT} - 1)^2}. \tag{4-14}$$

This expression may be put in various forms. By definition $\epsilon = hf_0$, and this may be substituted in Eq. (14). A more usual procedure is to define a characteristic temperature T_0, by the relationship

$$\epsilon = hf_0 = kT_0$$

or

$$T_0 = hf_0/k = \epsilon/k. \tag{4-15}$$

Hence,

$$\frac{dW_T}{dT} = 3N_Tk\left(\frac{T_0}{T}\right)^2\frac{e^{T_0/T}}{(e^{T_0/T} - 1)^2}. \tag{4-16}$$

This expression is plotted as a function of temperature in the curve designated by the name Einstein in Fig. 4-1. Plotted for comparison is

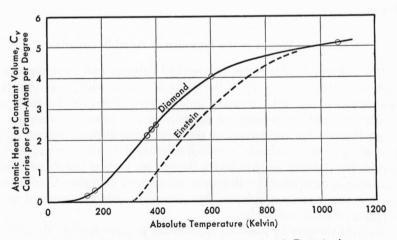

Fig. 4-1. Specific heat of diamond compared with Einstein theory.

the observed variation of specific heat for diamond. The essential correctness of Einstein's theory is supported by the fact that it gives the main features of the variation of specific heat in agreement with experiment.

Einstein's theory of specific heats supports the quantum hypothesis. At high temperatures the thermal energies readily supply the quanta $\epsilon = hf_0$ required by the oscillators, but as the temperature is reduced the quanta become so large in comparison with kT that the oscillators are excited by the addition of quanta to them for relatively small fractions of the total time. The oscillations are sometimes said to be "suppressed" at the lower temperatures.

It is significant that the determination of T_0 for various solids supports Eqs. (10) and (15). Soft materials, in which the weak restoring forces would result in low frequencies of oscillation are characterized by relatively low T_0 values. Similarly, solids with particularly massive atoms appearing near the end of the periodic table which would also have low natural oscillation frequencies, also have correspondingly low characteristic temperatures T_0.

Considering these indications of the correctness of the quantum theory as applied to the heat capacity of solids, it would appear that we could expect better quantitative agreement at the lower temperatures. The Einstein theory of specific heats shows the thermal vibrations being suppressed too abruptly as the temperature is decreased. This defect could be remedied if the theory incorporated some oscillators with lower vibrational frequencies. Debye attributed these lower frequencies to oscillations in which whole groups of atoms had related displacements in standing waves. This resulted in a truly satisfactory theory of specific heats.

Standing Waves in the Presence of Fixed Boundaries

If a uniform flexible string is stretched between two fixed supports, such as rigid pegs, the parts of the string in contact with these supports cannot move, and this condition imposes restrictions on the kinds of oscillation which are possible for this finite string. In an important class of all the possible oscillations of the string, the displacement of each part of the string is a simple harmonic function of the time with identical periods but different amplitudes for the various parts of the string. Such a manner of oscillation is called a normal mode of vibration. Considered as an example of wave motion, this situation would be described as a standing or a stationary wave.

To treat the case by methods appropriate to wave motion, the vibrations are considered to be produced by the sum of two identical sinusoidal wave trains traveling in opposite directions along the string. Each of these waves when incident upon a fixed peg is reflected with a phase change of 180°. At the peg the displacement due to the reflected wave is always just the negative of that due to the incident wave, and the algebraic sum of these two displacements, therefore, is always zero, thus satisfying the boundary condition that parts of the string in contact with the peg do not move.

For each of the two combining waves, however, there is at any instant a progressive change of phase along the string. This means that, while at selected instants of time the phase difference can be 180° everywhere along the string, so that the displacement is zero everywhere, the motion of the waves in opposite directions will result in a change of phase such that a displacement will increase as time progresses until the two waves are in phase everywhere. The sum of the two sine loops will then obviously result in a sine loop of twice the displacement which would result from either one of the combining waves.

For the displacements of a string to constitute simple harmonic motion, the combining waves must be sinusoidal, and it is not difficult to show that in simple harmonic motion the shape of the string as it vibrates is in general sinusoidal. The functions of the coordinates which are required to describe the displacements of various parts of a medium in one of the normal modes of vibration are called "eigenfunctions" (characteristic functions). This nomenclature is taken directly from the German usage. For a selected phase velocity, a given eigenfunction will correspond to a single frequency, which, therefore, may be called an "eigenfrequency."

Our problem is to determine for a given range of frequencies the number of eigenfunctions fulfilling the boundary conditions which can be fitted into the medium under consideration, in this case a flexible string of length L. This condition may be put in the form

$$\frac{2L}{\lambda} = n, \tag{4-17}$$

where λ is the wavelength in either of the combining trains of waves and n is an integer. A problem of considerable importance in many fields of physics, some of which underlie the development of modern atomic physics, is the number of these modes of vibration which lie between the wavelength λ and $\lambda + \Delta\lambda$. When λ in Eq. (17) changes by $\Delta\lambda$, n changes by Δn, where the increments satisfy the relationship

$$\frac{2L}{\lambda + \Delta\lambda} = n - \Delta n. \tag{4-18}$$

If we subtract Eq. (18) from Eq. (17), we obtain

$$\Delta n = \frac{2L}{\lambda} - \frac{2L}{\lambda + \Delta\lambda}$$

$$= \frac{2L(\lambda + \Delta\lambda - \lambda)}{\lambda(\lambda + \Delta\lambda)} = \frac{2L\,\Delta\lambda}{\lambda(\lambda + \Delta\lambda)}$$

$$\simeq \frac{2L\,\Delta\lambda}{\lambda^2}, \tag{4-19}$$

where the approximation applied to the last member is that $\Delta\lambda$ is small in comparison with λ, which implies that Δn is small compared with n.

For the transverse vibrations of a string there are two degrees of freedom corresponding to each frequency, because there are two directions at right angles to each other in which the transverse vibrations of a stretched flexible string may occur. Representing the number of degrees of freedom by m, since there are two degrees of freedom for each integer n, we have

$$\frac{\Delta m}{L} = \frac{4\,\Delta\lambda}{\lambda^2}. \tag{4-20}$$

If $\Delta\lambda$ is small compared with λ, the number of degrees of freedom per unit length of string corresponding to wavelengths between λ and $\lambda + \Delta\lambda$ is $4\,\Delta\lambda/\lambda^2$.

The simplicity of this relationship is more apparent if it is expressed in terms of the frequency f. This gives

$$f = w/\lambda,$$

where w is the phase velocity. Eliminating λ by use of Eq. (18), we get

$$2L/w = n/f, \tag{4-21}$$

and by differentiation

$$dn/f - n\,df/f^2 = 0$$

or

$$1/f = dn/n\,df,$$

which inserted into Eq. (21) gives

$$2L/w = dn/df. \tag{4-22}$$

It is seen that the number ($m = 2n$) of transverse modes of vibration is constant ($4L/w$) for each unit of frequency range. Similarly, results may be obtained for the transverse vibrations of rectangular membranes and for rectangular parallelopipeds.

In Appendix III it is shown that for a rectangular parallelopiped of volume V, the number of standing waves of a specified type in frequency range df at f is $4\pi f^2\, dfV/v^3$ or that $dN/df = 4\pi f^2 V/v^3$, where v is the velocity of propagation for the particular type of wave being considered. Allowing for two transverse modes and one longitudinal mode gives

$$dN = 4\pi V f^2\, df \left(\frac{1}{v_l^3} + \frac{2}{v_t^3}\right). \tag{4-23}$$

According to this expression the low-frequency waves with small energy quanta are relatively few. The number of allowed wave patterns increases very rapidly with frequency. When the length of the waves becomes comparable with twice the spacing of atoms in the lattice, there is a decrease in the number of allowed modes.

Instead of trying to analyze the details, Debye introduced an approximation which proved to be adequate except where very high accuracy was required. Debye recognized that the number of modes of vibration for N atoms in a lattice would be $3N$-3 or almost $3N$. He decided to use as an approximation the same number of modes distributed according to the parabolic law.

$$\frac{3N}{V} = 4\pi \left(\frac{1}{v_l^3} + \frac{2}{v_t^3}\right) \int_0^{f_m} f^2\, df$$

$$= 4\pi \left(\frac{1}{v_l^3} + \frac{2}{v_t^3}\right) \frac{f_m^3}{3}$$

or

$$f_m = \left[\frac{9}{4\pi} \frac{N}{V} \frac{1}{\left(\dfrac{1}{v_l^3} + \dfrac{2}{v_t^3}\right)}\right]^{\frac{1}{3}}, \tag{4-24}$$

which relation is used to determine f_m.

To the allowed modes of vibration of each frequency in the range from zero to f_m, Debye assumed that the principles introduced by Einstein for his oscillators of frequency f would apply, and to obtain the specific heat, the various contributions are summed. This gives

$$\frac{dW}{dT} = \sum_i k \left(\frac{T_i}{T}\right)^2 \frac{e^{T_i/T}}{(e^{T_i/T} - 1)^2}.$$

The incorporation of the distribution function Eq. (23) makes it possible to replace the summation by an integration. Thus,

$$\frac{dW}{dT} = \frac{9kN}{f_m^3} \int_0^{f_m} \frac{\left(\dfrac{hf}{kT}\right)^2 e^{hf/kT} f^2\, df}{(e^{hf/kT} - 1)^2}. \tag{4-25}$$

The "Debye temperature" is defined by $T_0 = hf_m/k$. The function appearing in the integrand is not the antiderivative of a known function, but Debye showed that, defining $x = hf/kT$,

$$\int_0^\infty \frac{x^4 e^x \, dx}{(e^x - 1)^2} = \frac{4}{15} \pi^4.$$

For a low temperature, therefore, in which the integration is extended over a large range of x,

$$\frac{dW}{dT} = \frac{12}{5} \pi^4 Nk \left(\frac{T}{T_0}\right)^3. \tag{4-26}$$

This predicted variation of specific heat according to the third power of the absolute temperature is much closer to the observations at low temperatures than was Einstein's equation. In fact the cubic law at low temperatures has been verified for quite a number of substances. The results for silicon are shown in Fig. 4-2.

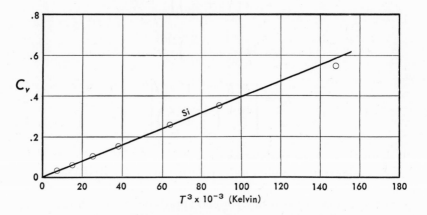

Fig. 4-2. Specific heat of silicon at low temperature.

As a concise recapitulation of the theory of specific heats we include Fig. 4-3, in which the function of Einstein is shown by the lower curve, and the function of Debye is shown by the upper curve. The extent to which Debye's theory accounts for experimental results is shown by circles which correspond to experimental values for aluminum, located on this curve through a single assignment of the Debye temperature, which is about 395° K for aluminum.

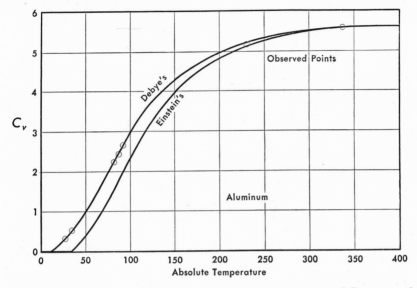

Fig. 4-3. Specific heat of aluminum compared with formulas of Einstein and Debye.

Distribution of Thermal Radiation

Planck had developed the quantum theory originally to account for the distribution of thermal radiation as a function of wavelength or frequency. Measurements on the energy distribution of the thermal radiation as a function of temperature revealed that it was possible to plot the data in such a way that one curve could be used for all temperatures. If one plots radiation density E_λ divided by the absolute temperature to the fifth power against the wavelength multiplied by the absolute temperature, all observations fall on the universal curve shown in Fig. 4-4. This result can be represented by the formula

$$E_\lambda / T^5 = f(\lambda T). \tag{4-27}$$

Theory failed to give the analytic form of the function $f(\lambda T)$ until Planck introduced the idea of quanta.

The failure of the older ideas in this connection as we have seen was a glaring one. Rayleigh introduced the idea that the number of degrees of freedom, corresponding to the number of standing wave patterns, was that computed for the transverse wave patterns derived in Appendix III. He postulated that each of the degrees of freedom should on the average have an energy kT. Hence, the energy density in the enclosure

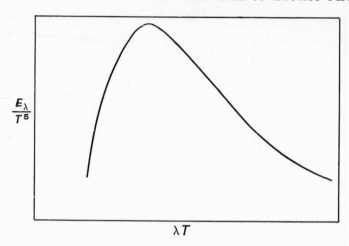

$\dfrac{E_\lambda}{T^5}$

λT

Fig. 4-4. Universal curve for distribution of radiant energy in wavelength.

should have been given by

$$u_\nu \, d\nu = 8\pi\nu^2 \, d\nu \, kT/c^3, \qquad (4\text{-}28)$$

where ν is the frequency and c is the velocity of the light waves. This formula predicts that the energy density will increase without limit as the frequency is increased. In sharp contrast with this prediction, the experimentally observed energy density falls to zero as the frequency is increased.

Planck's theory of thermal radiation was successful in accounting for the observed curve. This theory contained the following elements:

1. The energy is radiated and absorbed in discrete parcels or quanta the size ϵ of which increases with the frequency, according to the law

$$\epsilon = h\nu,$$

   where h is Planck's constant and ν is the frequency obtained from $\nu = c/\lambda$.

2. The statistics for determining the energy at any particular frequency are exactly those used by Einstein's theory for the vibrational energy of the atoms in a crystalline solid. Just as the vibrations of the atoms are suppressed at low temperatures when the thermal energy kT becomes small in comparison with hf, so here the electromagnetic oscillations are suppressed when $h\nu$ becomes large in comparison with kT.

3. The formula derived by Planck is

$$u_\nu \, d\nu = \frac{8\pi \, \nu^3 h}{c^3} \frac{d\nu}{e^{h\nu/kT} - 1}, \qquad (4\text{-}29)$$

where ν as before is the frequency as determined from the wavelength of the light. This formula was confirmed by the experimental results of Lummer and Pringsheim.

Consequences of Quantization of Radiant Energy

The fact that Planck's constant is small means that at the frequencies of man-made electromagnetic oscillators the quantization will not be so striking as to be obvious or even, in most cases, detectable. On the other hand, as the frequency increases, the size of the quanta becomes large enough to make quantization first detectable and then in suitable experiments obvious. For example, at power frequencies (60 cycles/sec), the quantum of energy is only 3.96×10^{-32} joules or 2.47×10^{-13} ev. At 6000 cycles/sec these values are multiplied by a factor of 100 to give the size of the quanta, and these certainly would not be detectable as single quanta. A broadcast frequency of 600,000 cycles/sec involves a further increase in quantum size by a factor of 100 giving 3.96×10^{-28} joules or 2.47×10^{-9} ev. Even an extremely high-frequency electromagnetic oscillator of 6×10^{10} cycles/sec, will give quanta of size 3.96×10^{-23} joules or 2.47×10^{-4} ev, and, since these are hardly detectable as single quanta, it is not surprising that the energy appears to be spread uniformly over wave fronts. If a single electron starting from rest were allowed to fall through a potential difference of 2.47×10^{-4} volts or 247 microvolts, it would have an energy equal to that in the quantum of radiation from the extremely high-frequency electromagnetic oscillator, and accurate control in the production of such energies would be difficult. In the visible at a frequency of 6×10^{14} cycles/sec, the quantum of radiation would be 2.47 ev, and thus it should be readily detectable in a suitable experiment. X-ray quanta have thousands of electron volts of energy, and gamma radiation of 10^{20} cycles/sec has a quantum of 6.6×10^{-14} joules or about 0.4 mev. Such high energy quanta should be obvious when they act upon single electrons or even single atoms.

Recapitulation of Early Developments in Quantum Theory

It seems strange that the smooth curves showing the distribution of radiant thermal energy in wavelength should require for their explanation the introduction of quanta of energy, even though these quanta, being proportional to frequency, approach zero as the wavelength tends toward infinity. Although in the section just concluded we have spoken freely of these quanta of radiant energy, it is known that Planck himself was reluctant to believe that these quanta existed in electromagnetic radiation. Planck introduced this explanation about 1900, but the general acceptance of the theory was delayed for a decade and a half or more.

In the meantime, Einstein accepted the full implications of the theory when in 1905 he used quanta of energy or photons to explain the external photoelectric effect. In the same period, Einstein also used the quantum theory in explaining the variation of the specific heat of solids, and Debye improved this theory a short time later. It was not until Bohr used the quantum hypothesis in providing a theory of atomic structure which would explain the isolated and sharply defined lines in the spectra of hydrogen that progress in the adoption of this new and strange idea was much accelerated.

Problems on Elementary Quantum Theory

1. Calculate the wavelength associated with the characteristic energy kT at the following temperatures: 100° K, 293° K, 1000° K, 10,000° K.
2. If the Debye temperatures are as follows:

Lead	80° K
Al	300° K
Si	570° K
Diamond	1500° K,

   calculate the corresponding frequencies.
3. How many standing wave patterns with wavelengths between .00100 and .00105 m can be set up inside a solid cube having an edge 1.00 meter in length? How many standing wave patterns corresponding to wavelengths between .00100 meters and .00400 meters can be set up in a cubical enclosure of the same dimensions?
4. Calculate the radiant energy between $\lambda = .00100$ m and $\lambda = .00105$ m in one cubic meter of space in equilibrium with walls at a temperature of 3000° K.
5. In this theory the fraction $1/(e^{h\nu/kT} - 1)$ may be interpreted as the number of photons which on the average occupy a single permitted standing wave.
   a. Show that at low frequencies the number of photons in the allowed standing wave is very large. What factors then account for the very low energies encountered in thermal radiation at very long wavelengths?
   b. Show that at high frequencies the corresponding standing wave pattern must contain a photon only a small fraction of the time. Is this behavior necessary to explain the shape of the curves showing the distribution of radiant energy in wavelength?
6. Determine the ratio of $h\nu$ to kT which gives a maximum for Planck's radiation distribution law (Eq. 29).
7. Assuming that Fig. 4-4 adequately represents the physical behavior of electromagnetic radiation, deduce the dependence of total radiant power on the absolute temperature. (The result required is the celebrated Stefan-Boltz-

mann radiation law, although the absence of numerical scales in Fig. 4-4 makes it impossible by this means to evaluate the proportionality constant.)

8. Eq. (29) gives the energy density of radiation in an enclosure, and this radiation is isotropic (uniformly distributed in direction). From this interpretation of Eq. (29) derive the expression for the radiant energy per unit area which would emerge each second from the interior of an enclosure through a small hole cut in one of its walls. (The measurements of Lummer and Pringsheim were made on this escaping radiation.)

9. Given the result

$$\int_0^\infty x^3(e^x - 1)^{-1}\, dx = 6\left(1 + \frac{1}{2^4} + \frac{1}{3^4} + \cdots\right)$$

$$= 6 \times 1.0823,$$

calculate the radiant energy summed over all wavelengths contained in one cubic meter of space in equilibrium with walls at a temperature of 3000° K.

References on the Origin of the Quantum Theory

Eldridge, John A., *Physical Basis of Things*, pp. 148-63 (New York: Mc-Graw-Hill Book Company, 1934).

Lewis, Wm. C. M., *A System of Physical Chemistry*, Vol. III, Appendix II, pp. 172-92 (London: Longmans, Green, 1919).

Richtmyer, F. K., *Introduction to Modern Physics*, pp. 177-247 (New York: Mc-Graw-Hill Book Company, 1928).

More Recent Treatments

Bohm, David, *Quantum Theory*, pp. 5-22 (New York: Prentice-Hall, 1951).

Slater, John C., *Modern Physics*, pp. 45-55 (New York: McGraw-Hill Book Company, 1955).

5 || First Theories of Atomic Structure

Early Ideas

J. J. Thomson identified the electron as a common constituent of all atoms, and he speculated on the way in which these negatively charged particles could be used in the structure of electrically neutral atoms. At this time the existence of discrete positive charges had not been established, and Thomson assumed that the positive charge could be distributed evenly throughout a volume. He then assumed that the positive charge required to neutralize the electrons would be distributed uniformly throughout a sphere, the volume of which was that of the atom, and that the electrons were placed at points throughout this positive distribution of charge in positions of equilibrium. This was a static model of the atom, and it has sometimes been called "Thomson's raisin pudding atomic model."

This proposal of Thomson's was by no means a solution of the problem of atomic structure. It was in fact a false start. Progress in the understanding of the atom required direct experimental evidence to start it. Ernest Rutherford attacked this problem and got the evidence which led to ideas in conformity with experience. When certain relatively heavy atoms spontaneously decompose, in the process called radioactive disintegration, they emit alpha particles. These are helium ions, emitted at very high speeds, of the order of 16,000 km/sec = 0.05 c, depending upon the heavy atom which emits them.

These fast-moving, positively charged, atomic projectiles Rutherford visualized as a tool for use in the investigation of the nature of matter. He proposed experiments in which these alpha particles could be shot through thin foils and the distribution in angle of the emerging alpha particles could be studied. Fig. 5-1 suggests a typical experi-

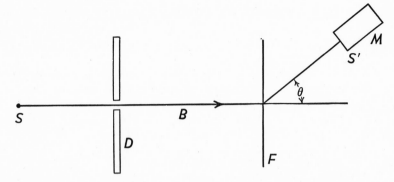

Fig. 5-1. Apparatus for study of alpha particle scattering.

mental arrangement used by Geiger and Marsden in Rutherford's laboratory. In this sketch S is a small quantity of radon used as a source of the alpha particles. D is a massive diaphragm used to stop all the particles except those passing through the aperture as a directed beam B. F represents a thin foil which is used as a target material. The detector is a zinc sulfide screen indicated at S'. When an alpha particle strikes the screen S' there is a flash of light (scintillation), and this may be seen and counted by an observer with the aid of the microscope M.

The results of such experiments showed that most of the particles pass through the film with quite small deflections but that an occasional particle is deflected through an angle of greater than 90°, as if it were reflected from the film. Such results were not very easy to understand. In the first place, for these fast-moving atomic particles, matter seems to be surprisingly transparent. Our discussion of the kinetic theory of gases has shown that the mean-free-path is really quite short, and this may be interpreted as giving molecules a collision cross section equivalent to a rigid sphere with a radius of 1-2 Å (10^{-10} meters). If the atoms in the foil were to act on the alpha particles in this manner, virtually none of the particles would be expected to emerge with practically their entire initial speed and with only a small change in direction. To the alpha particles, the atoms of the target must present a much smaller cross section than they do when they interact with each other in a gas or vapor.

The fact that a few of the particles are reflected from the film indicates that they have had practically direct collisions with something relatively massive. The fact that these direct collisions (or close interactions) are relatively infrequent is a clear indication that the mass is concentrated in very small volume. This evidence led Rutherford to

TABLE 5-1. LIST OF SYMBOLS USED IN CHAPTER 5

Symbol	Name	Quantity Designated
λ	lambda	wavelength of light
σ	sigma	wave number (wavelengths per centimeter)
ν	nu	frequency of electromagnetic radiation
n, n_1, n_2		integers
n		principal quantum number
n_r		integer quantizing radial action
l		azimuthal quantum number
m_l		magnetic quantum number
m_s		spin quantum number ($+\frac{1}{2}$ or $-\frac{1}{2}$)
R_H		Rydberg constant (for hydrogen)
A		action
W		energy
f		frequency of oscillator
T		periodic time
h		Planck's constant
ϵ_0		permittivity of free space
e^*		charge of nucleus
r		radius of electron orbit
R		radius of nuclear orbit
M		mass of nucleus
Z		atomic number

propose the nuclear model of the atom. He suggested that the positive charge of the atom and most of its mass was concentrated in a very small region, having a radius of about 0.0001 that of the atom.

The nucleus of the element of lowest atomic mass (hydrogen) would be a particle having a positive charge equal in magnitude to that of the electron, and a mass roughly 1840 times as great as the electron mass. This particle is called the proton. Other nuclei contain more than one proton, and also uncharged particles, each of which has a mass about equal to that of a proton. The number of protons in the nucleus is denoted by Z.

Atomic Spectra

An element in the form of a gas or vapor, when it is excited (energized) by passing an electrical current through it in a discharge tube, may emit a great many characteristic spectral lines. These spectra, even in the case of the simplest elements, are quite complex, and for several decades any interpretation of them was entirely lacking. Empirical data accumulated rapidly in the latter part of the nineteenth century. Bohr's theory, proposed in 1913, provided a key to the interpretation of these spectra.

Each line of a spectrum represents a single narrow band of wavelengths or a single narrow band of frequencies. The relationship between frequency ν and wavelength λ is the familiar equation

$$c = \nu\lambda, \tag{5-1}$$

where c is the phase velocity of the light in a vacuum. In spectroscopy, however, another system is generally used. Here the number of waves per centimeter is called the "wave number" σ, so $\sigma = \nu/c = 1/\lambda$. By definition, the "wave number" is the number of waves per cm, or cycles/cm.

Two of the elements that have particularly complex spectra are iron and manganese. For such elements, lines are scattered throughout all of the visible spectrum and beyond this range at frequencies both higher and lower than those corresponding to visible light. The number of lines of such elements which were observed and tabulated by 1900 extended into the thousands.

A particularly simple spectrum arises from the element of lowest atomic mass, hydrogen. Here fortunately there are only four or at most five lines which appear within the limits of visibility. These with the corresponding quantities of interest are shown in Table 5-2.

TABLE 5-2. THE BALMER SERIES FOR HYDROGEN

Line Designation	Color	Wavelength (Å)	λ/λ_∞
H_α	Red	6562	9/5
H_β	Blue	4861	16/12
H_γ	Violet	4340	25/21
H_δ	Violet	4101	36/32
H_ϵ	Extreme Violet	3970	49/45
Limit	Ultraviolet	3647	1

This is the best-known series in hydrogen, which is called the Balmer series, because it was Balmer who discovered the empirical relationship which applies to this series, namely,

$$\sigma = R_H \left\{ \frac{1}{4} - \frac{1}{n^2} \right\}, \tag{5-2}$$

where $n \geqslant 3$ is an integer, and R_H is a constant, which has come to be called Rydberg's constant. It is to be noticed that, as n increases, the lines become more closely spaced in wave number units and that there is a great concentration of lines when n becomes very large. The wave number, $\sigma_\infty = R_H/4$, is called "the series limit," and corresponds to $n = \infty$.

In 1908, Ritz observed that the sum or the difference of the wave numbers of two observed lines often gives the wave number of another spectral line. This relationship was discovered by an examination of complex spectra, but the application to hydrogen is justified. For example, the difference $\sigma(H_\beta) - \sigma(H_\alpha) = 5377$ cycles/cm should be observed as a spectral line at 5377 cycles/cm. The corresponding wavelength 1/5377 cm is in the infrared, and, at the time Ritz announced this principle, 1896, the Paschen series, in which this line appears, had already been discovered.

Table 5-2 shows the wavelengths of the first five lines, and of the series limit, for the Balmer series of hydrogen. The fourth column shows the value of the quantity

$$\lambda/\lambda_\infty = (1/\sigma)/(1/\sigma_\infty), \tag{5-3}$$

where λ and σ are respectively the wavelength and the wave number of the line and λ_∞ and σ_∞ are respectively the wavelength and the wave number of the series limit. Since, for the Balmer series of hydrogen,

$$\sigma = R_H\left(\frac{1}{2^2} - \frac{1}{n^2}\right) = \frac{n^2 - 4}{4n^2} R_H \tag{5-4}$$

and

$$\sigma_\infty = R_H/4, \tag{5-5}$$

from the substitution of Eqs. (4) and (5) into Eq. (3) we get

$$\lambda/\lambda_\infty = \frac{n^2}{n^2 - 4}, \tag{5-6}$$

from which we see that the

$$\lim_{n \to \infty} (\lambda/\lambda_\infty) = 1.$$

The formula for the Paschen series is

$$\sigma = R_H\left\{\frac{1}{3^2} - \frac{1}{n^2}\right\}$$

and setting $n = 4$ in this formula gives a result which agrees with

$$\sigma = \sigma(H_\beta) - \sigma(H_\alpha),$$

which is the line mentioned above at 5377 cycles/cm.

Quantization of Action in an Orbit

The idea of quanta was discussed in Chapter 4, and some of the early successes were reviewed. In retrospect it appears that these should have been convincing. These developments, however, did not result in an understanding and wide acceptance of quantization. We shall now consider a development which made this subject the center of scientific discussion for a decade, and which has had a lasting influence on scientific thinking. As a basis for the understanding of Bohr's theory, we calculate the action of a particle moving in uniform circular motion and apply the quantum principle to it. Since the particle moves with uniform angular velocity ω in a circle of radius r, the most convenient coordinate for specifying its position is the angle θ, which the radius connecting the center of the circle with the particle makes with a fixed line. The corresponding momentum is then identified as angular momentum $mr^2\omega$, where m is the mass of the particle. Thus, quantization results in

$$A = mr^2\omega \int_0^{2\pi} d\theta = mr^2\omega 2\pi$$

$$\boxed{= mv2\pi r = nh.}$$

(5-7)

The Bohr Atom Model

Niels Bohr spent some time working in Rutherford's laboratory, and he became familiar with the nuclear model of the atom which had been proposed by Rutherford. He also had access to the Balmer formula and other empirical formulas relating the wave numbers of spectral lines to combinations of integers. Also, he was acquainted with the quantum theory, which had been introduced by Planck more than a decade earlier. He worked on the problem of atomic structure, and, starting with hydrogen, he was able to construct a model of the atom which would account for the observed spectral lines. This initiated the development from which most of our information concerning the nature of the atom has been obtained.

As suggested by Fig. 5-2, Bohr assumed the hydrogen atom to be made up of an electron rotating about a massive, positively charged nucleus. He used ordinary electrostatics and ordinary mechanics for the system for the most part, but he was compelled to depart from the laws of classical electrodynamics which required an accelerated charge to radiate energy. He postulated that in certain favored orbits, satisfy-

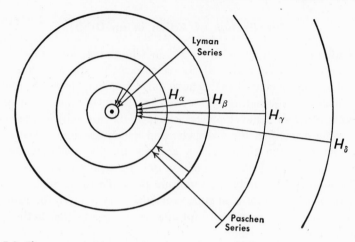

Fig. 5-2. Electron transitions and spectrum lines in Bohr's theory for hydrogen.

ing Planck's quantum condition of action, an electron could exist without radiating energy.

Following Bohr, we suppose that the electrostatic force exerted on the electron by the proton provides the force required to make the electron move in a circle of radius r. Assuming that the mass of the electron is constant and using Newton's second law, we have

$$\boxed{\frac{e^*e}{4\pi\epsilon_0 r^2} = \frac{mv^2}{r},}$$

so

$$\frac{e^*e}{4\pi\epsilon_0 r} = mv^2, \tag{5-8}$$

where ϵ_0 is the permittivity of free space, 8.85×10^{-12}, and e^* is the electrostatic charge of the nucleus. Of the circular orbits, those satisfying the quantum condition of Planck on action are

$$2\pi mvr = nh, \tag{5-7}$$

where n is a positive integer.

If we solve Eqs. (7) and (8) for r and v, we obtain

$$\boxed{r = \frac{n^2 h^2 \epsilon_0}{me^*e\pi}} \tag{5-9}$$

and

$$\boxed{v = \frac{e^*e}{2nh\epsilon_0}.} \tag{5-10}$$

Turning to the calculation of the energy, we notice that the potential energy of the system (taken as zero when the particles are infinitely separated) is

$$U = - \frac{e^*e}{4\pi\epsilon_0 r} = - \frac{(e^*e)^2 m}{4\epsilon_0^2 n^2 h^2}, \tag{5-11}$$

where the last term arises from the use of r obtained from Eq. (9). The kinetic energy in the circular orbit, for which the action is nh, is given by

$$\tfrac{1}{2}mv^2 = \frac{m}{8} \frac{(e^*e)^2}{n^2 h^2 \epsilon_0^2}, \tag{5-12}$$

where in the right-hand term v is eliminated by the use of Eq. (10). The total energy of the electron in the circular orbit, obtained through adding Eqs. (11) and (12), is

$$W = - \frac{m}{8} \frac{(e^*e)^2}{n^2 h^2 \epsilon_0^2}. \tag{5-13}$$

Using Einstein's idea that the radiant energy is equal to $h\nu$, where ν is the frequency associated with the photon, Bohr explained the lines of the spectral series as arising from the radiation of the difference of energy when an electron changes from one orbit to another of lower energy. This change in energy has the form

$$\Delta W = \frac{m}{8} \frac{(e^*e)^2}{h^2 \epsilon_0^2} \left\{ \frac{1}{n_1^2} - \frac{1}{n_2^2} \right\},$$

where $n_2 > n_1$.

Hence, using $\Delta W = h\nu$, we obtain

$$\nu = \frac{m}{8h^3} \frac{(e^*e)^2}{\epsilon_0^2} \left\{ \frac{1}{n_1^2} - \frac{1}{n_2^2} \right\}. \tag{5-14}$$

This is identical to the empirical formula for the Balmer series, if $n_1 = 2$, and $n_2 > 2$. If this expression is divided by the velocity of light (cm/sec) in vacuum, the result represented by σ gives the number of waves per centimeter.

$$\sigma = \frac{m(e^*e)^2}{8h^3 \epsilon_0^2 c} \left[\frac{1}{n_1^2} - \frac{1}{n_2^2} \right], \tag{5-15}$$

and the quantity multiplying the bracket is an expression for Rydberg's constant. If e^* is replaced by Ze, this theory should apply to any nucleus with a single electron in its force field.

Calculation of Numerical Constants for the Hydrogen Atom

For the first orbit in hydrogen, $n = 1$; hence,

$$r = \frac{(6.6 \times 10^{-34} \text{ joule-sec})^2 (8.854 \times 10^{-12} \text{ farad/m})}{\pi (9.1 \times 10^{-31} \text{ kg})(1.6 \times 10^{-19} \text{ coul})^2}$$

$$= 5.3 \times 10^{-11} \text{ m}.$$

The electron is usually found in this state, and the calculated radius agrees quite well with that obtained from kinetic theory as applied to hydrogen. The velocity is

$$v = \frac{(1.6 \times 10^{-19} \text{ coul})^2}{2(6.6 \times 10^{-34} \text{ joule-sec})(8.854 \times 10^{-12} \text{ farad/m})}$$

$$= 2.18 \times 10^6 \text{ m/sec}.$$

The orbital frequency f is

$$f = \frac{v}{2\pi r} = \frac{2.18 \times 10^6 \text{ m/sec}}{\pi (10.6 \times 10^{-11} \text{ m})}$$

$$= 6.5 \times 10^{15} \text{ cycles/sec.} \tag{5-16}$$

Since the radiated frequency is $\nu = R_H c \left\{ \dfrac{1}{n_1{}^2} - \dfrac{1}{n_2{}^2} \right\}$, $R_H c$ may be interpreted as the highest frequency $\nu_{\max}$ radiated by the hydrogen atom. This would be the value of ν when $n_1 = 1$ and $n_2 = \infty$, or $1/n_2{}^2 = 0$.

$$R_H c = \frac{(9.1 \times 10^{-31} \text{ kg})(1.6 \times 10^{-19} \text{ coul})^4}{8(6.6 \times 10^{-34} \text{ joule-sec})^3 (8.854 \times 10^{-12} \text{ farad/m})^2}$$

$$= 3.27 \times 10^{15} \text{ cycles/sec.} \tag{5-17}$$

There is no direct relationship between this highest of radiated frequencies, Eq. (17), and the highest of the rotational frequencies, Eq. (16), calculated just previously. This is in sharp contrast to radiation from an antenna, which has the frequency of the electrical oscillations.

Evidently the laws of mechanics and electricity, which apply on the large scale, are altered in a very marked way when they are applied to atomic phenomena. The system of laws as modified by quantum effects is called quantum mechanics. In his theory of the hydrogen atom, Bohr introduced several essential features of quantum mechanics. From this it was destined to develop into an extensive system, to which Bohr himself made many noteworthy contributions. He was assisted in this by noticing that the classical laws were the asymptotic form approached by quantum mechanics in the limit of large quantum numbers.

The Correspondence Principle

In classical systems, such as antennas, the electromagnetic radiation has the same frequency as that of the electrical oscillations from which it arises. Furthermore, such systems are capable of a number of natural frequencies of oscillation, the fundamental frequency and integral multiples of the fundamental which are called overtones (or "harmonics"). One of the reasons for such behavior is that the quantum of action h is too small to make itself apparent in the behavior of large-scale systems.

Bohr was able to make considerable progress in the development of quantum mechanics, because he realized that, in well-known laws of the previous physics, he had the asymptotic form of the quantum mechanical laws for large quantum numbers. For example, if the quantum numbers are made of the order of several thousand, atomic systems become of such size that they are comparable in linear dimensions to those for which the older laws physics have been established. If in a hydrogen atom $n = 1000$, the diameter of the atom is about 0.1 mm. In these circumstances the atom behaves in a way that is determined by well-known laws. The orbital frequency of the electron is given by $v/2\pi r$, which by the use of Eqs. (9) and (10) becomes

$$f_0 = \frac{m(e^*e)^2}{4\epsilon_0^2 h^3 n^3}.$$
(5-18)

Bohr's formula for the radiated frequency is

$$\nu = R_H c \left\{ \frac{1}{n_2^2} - \frac{1}{n_1^2} \right\} = R_H c \left\{ \frac{n_1^2 - n_2^2}{n_1^2 n_2^2} \right\}.$$

Consider the situation in which n_1 is very large and n_2 is just one unit smaller. The radiated frequency is given by

$$\nu = R_H c \left\{ \frac{(n_1 - n_2)(n_1 + n_2)}{n_1^2 n_2^2} \right\} \simeq 2R_H c \frac{n_1}{n_1^4} = \frac{m(e^*e)^2}{4\epsilon_0^2 h^3 n^3},$$
(5-19)

which is in agreement with the orbital frequency, just as is the rule in macroscopic systems. Furthermore, if the difference $(n_1 - n_2)$ is any small integer, the radiated frequency is a harmonic of the fundamental, and this also corresponds closely with the rules for harmonics in simple mechanical systems.

The treatment of the hydrogen spectrum has been so greatly simplified that it does not suggest the usefulness of the correspondence principle. In hydrogen, several quantum states have the same energy, and they coalesce to form a single energy level. Such energy levels are said to be multiply degenerate. The energy levels for the hydrogen atom contain such a mixture of quantum states that transitions between any two energy levels are observed. When an energy level is split into quantum states which differ in energy, as through the application of a magnetic field, it is discovered that there are "selection rules" resulting in some transitions being forbidden. The calculation of transition probabilities is an important matter on which Bohr's original theory provided no information. It was at this point that the correspondence principle proved particularly useful. It gave answers, which were qualitatively correct, although the numerical calculation of transition probabilities from the correspondence principle was never completely satisfactory.

The Spectacular Exactness of the Bohr Theory as Applied to Hydrogen Spectra

The wave numbers of the lines of the hydrogen spectrum are given empirically by the formula

$$\sigma = (109{,}677.57^6 \pm .01) \left\{ \frac{1}{n_1{}^2} - \frac{1}{n_2{}^2} \right\} \text{ (waves/cm)}. \qquad (5\text{-}20)$$

If the Rydberg constant is calculated from the atomic constants shown in Eq. (15), the agreement is as good as can be expected from the precision with which the constants are known. This is in itself a satisfactory check of Bohr's theory, but the evidence for the exactness of the theory is much stronger than this indicates. Table 5-3 shows the dependence on atomic number which spectroscopists have found in the Rydberg "constant." The simple theory of Bohr must be corrected to account for the systematic variation of the Rydberg constant with atomic number Z.

The first correction which should be put into the foregoing treatment of Bohr's theory is the fact that, according to the principles of ordinary mechanics, both the electron and the proton should rotate about their common center of mass. Because the proton is heavy rela-

TABLE 5-3. DEPENDENCE OF THE RYDBERG CONSTANT
ON THE NUCLEAR MASS *

(The number of mass units in the nucleus is indicated by the superscript.)

Nucleus	Rydberg Constant (cycles/cm)
$_1H^1$	109,677.581
$_1H^2$	109,707.419
$_1H^3$	109,717.348
$_2He^3$	109,717.344
$_2He^4$	109,722.264
$_\nu X^\infty$	$R_\infty = 109,737.31$

* Values in this table are from Bureau of Standards, Circular 467, edited by
Charlotte E. Moore except for R_∞, which is taken from *A Survey of Physical Constants*
by Bardeen and Thomson.

tive to the electron, the correction is not large, but it is appreciable.
The situation is illustrated in Fig. 5-3. According to the definition of

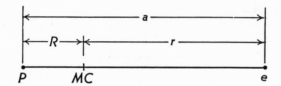

Fig. 5-3. Radii of orbits for the proton and electron.

the center of mass C, the distance R of the proton from the center of
mass is

$$R = a \frac{m}{M + m},$$

where a is the distance between the electron of mass m and the proton of
mass M. For the electron, $r = aM/(m + M)$. In the second approximation, therefore, the equations for the motion of the particles are the
following:

$$\frac{e^*e}{4\pi\epsilon_0 a^2} = \frac{MV^2}{R} \quad \text{or} \quad MV^2 = \frac{e^*eR}{4\pi\epsilon_0 a^2},$$

where V is the linear velocity of the proton and

$$\frac{e^*e}{4\pi\epsilon_0 a^2} = \frac{mv^2}{r} \quad \text{or} \quad mv^2 = \frac{e^*er}{4\pi\epsilon_0 a^2},$$

where v is the velocity of the electron.

The kinetic energy W_K now consists of two parts, since both the electron and the proton are in motion. For the proton, we have

$$(W_K)_p = \tfrac{1}{2}MV^2 = \tfrac{1}{2}M\omega^2R^2$$

$$= \tfrac{1}{2}M\omega^2a^2\left\{\frac{m}{M+m}\right\}^2 = \frac{1}{2}\frac{e^*e}{4\pi\epsilon_0a}\left\{\frac{m}{M+m}\right\}^1,$$

and for the electron, we have

$$(W_K)_e = \tfrac{1}{2}m\omega^2\left\{\frac{aM}{M+m}\right\}^2 = \frac{1}{2}\frac{e^*e}{4\pi\epsilon_0a}\left\{\frac{M}{M+m}\right\}^1.$$

The total kinetic energy is thus

$$(W_K)_p + (W_K)_e = \frac{e^*e}{8\pi\epsilon_0a} = \frac{1}{2}\left\{\frac{mM}{M+m}\right\}\omega^2a^2.$$

The angular momentum of this system is "quantized" by the relation

$$\omega MR^2 + mr^2\omega = M\omega\left\{\frac{am}{m+M}\right\}^2 + m\omega\left\{\frac{aM}{m+M}\right\}^2$$

$$= \frac{\omega(Mm)a^2}{(m+M)^2}(m+M)$$

$$= \frac{\omega Mm}{M+m}a^2 = \frac{nh}{2\pi}. \qquad (5\text{-}21)$$

Since $h/2\pi$ occurs frequently, it often is represented simply by $\hbar$. These formulas are those encountered earlier in the simple theory, except that here $\dfrac{mM}{M+m}$ replaces the actual mass m of the electron. This quantity is called the "reduced mass." Using the reduced mass in the formula for the wave number gives

$$\boxed{\sigma = \frac{m}{8}\left\{\frac{M}{M+m}\right\}\frac{(e^*e)^2}{h^3c\epsilon_0{}^2}\left\{\frac{1}{n_1{}^2} - \frac{1}{n_2{}^2}\right\}.} \qquad (5\text{-}22)$$

The factor $\left\{\dfrac{M}{M+m}\right\}$ reduces the wave numbers sufficiently to give almost perfect agreement between the theoretically computed and the observed values.

From a comparison of the Rydberg constants obtained with hydrogen and with ionized helium, it is possible to deduce the ratio of the mass of the proton to the mass of the electron. For He, the Rydberg constant is

$$R_{He} = 109{,}722.264 \text{ cyles/cm}$$

and the masses are related by the expression

$$M_{He} = 3.9717 M_H.$$

The ratio of the Rydberg constants is given by

$$\frac{R_{He}}{R_H} = \frac{1 + \dfrac{m}{M_H}}{1 + \dfrac{m}{M_{He}}} = \frac{109{,}722.26}{109{,}677.58} = \frac{1 + \dfrac{m}{M_H}}{1 + \dfrac{m}{3.9717 M_H}},$$

whence

$$\frac{M_H}{m} = 1840.$$

Since this is in almost perfect agreement with results obtained from independent evidence (like those from mass spectroscopy discussed in Chapter 2), we conclude that the Bohr theory gives results valid to about one part in 1000 on the small difference in the positions of corresponding hydrogen and helium lines. This amounts to a check in the seventh significant figure of the Rydberg constant. Thus, although none of the fundamental physical constants which combine to give the Rydberg constant, is known to this precision, the Bohr theory is successful in predicting the relative position of spectral lines to better than one part in 1,000,000. The successes of the Bohr theory pointed the way toward an understanding of atomic structure generally.

Some of the difficulty of explaining spectra in general upon the basis of the mechanical principles used by Bohr can be understood when it is realized that for ordinary helium (containing a nucleus and two electrons), the spectrum has never been derived exactly from this theory. The necessity of simplifying the general problem by the requirement of less precise information is apparent.

Extensions of Bohr's Theory

Sommerfeld, recognizing that the general motion of an electron in the central force field of a proton was elliptical, extended the analysis of Bohr to elliptic orbits. The essential step in the application of quantum mechanics to such a system was one taken independently by Sommerfeld and by Wilson. They postulated that each degree of freedom must be quantized separately. A particle moving in three-dimensional space would have three degrees of freedom, and from this circumstance three quantum numbers would be expected. It was not too difficult to identify three quantum numbers selected in such a manner that they could be applied conveniently to elliptic orbits.

There was first of all the azimuthal quantum number k arising from the quantization associated with the angular momentum in the orbit. For the elliptical orbits, there is in addition radial velocity, and the action associated with this is quantized separately. The condition is

$$\oint p_r\, dr = n_r h,$$

where n_r is an integer, p_r the radial component of momentum, and $\oint$ indicates integration over one complete cycle. The energy is then determined by the total quantum number n, where $n = n_r + k$.

According to the simple theory, the orbits lie in a plane, and the two degrees of freedom in the plane would be specified by the two quantum numbers k and n_r. There is the possibility of a third quantum number to specify the angle which the plane makes with a fixed direction in space. This was called space quantization, and a third integer was introduced for the purpose of specifying this direction. This number becomes physically significant when one direction of space is distinguished from the others as by the existence of a magnetic field in the specified direction. The quantum number k arising from the angular momentum was taken as the magnitude of a vector directed normal to the orbit. Space quantization required that the projection of this vector on the direction of the magnetic field should be the third integer introduced into the theory, and this was called the magnetic quantum number m.

Although the identification of the three quantum numbers has changed in subsequent formulations of quantum mechanics, the basic principle that three quantum numbers are associated with these three degrees of freedom has been retained. The azimuthal quantum number k has been eliminated in favor of l, very closely analogous to k, and because this notation is in current usage, l is used on the energy level diagrams. A quantum number n, called the principal quantum number, is in current use; the third of the quantum numbers is the magnetic quantum number m_l.

The three quantum numbers were not found sufficient to explain the facts observed by spectroscopists. The evidence indicated that there was another degree of freedom for each electron in the atom. Uhlenbeck and Goudsmit introduced the idea that the electron was a distribution of charge spinning on an axis, and, in consequence of this, possessing a magnetic moment. This moment can then be parallel or antiparallel to the magnetic field; so a spin quantum number m_s takes on one of two values, which according to the development of the theory were designated as $+\frac{1}{2}$ and $-\frac{1}{2}$.

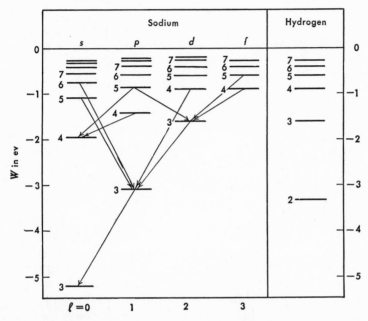

Fig. 5-4. Energy level diagrams for hydrogen and sodium.

More fundamental by far than the detailed model of atomic systems which has been constructed is the strong evidence that atoms have discrete energy levels. The energy level diagrams which have been worked out for various atoms represent very well-established facts concerning the behavior of these systems. Energy level diagrams for hydrogen and sodium are shown in Fig. 5-4. For the hydrogen atom, various elliptical and circular orbits have the same energy. Several quantum states are combined in a single energy level. For the hydrogen atom, transitions between any pair of the energy levels shown are permissible, because these levels are not really single quantum states. In the case of the sodium atom, however, a single principal quantum number n gives rise to several energy values depending upon the values of the other quantum numbers. In Fig. 5-4, the values of the principal quantum numbers are shown to identify the level. The levels shown one above the other have the same value of the quantum number l. In an allowed transition, l changes by ± 1, and the diagonal lines, representing permitted transitions, connect levels in adjacent columns of the diagram.

Limitations on Bohr's Theory of Spectra

A consequence of Sommerfeld's work was to emphasize the generalization of Bohr's quantum condition. If q_i represents a generalized coordinate, and if p_i is the corresponding momentum, the general quantum condition is that

$$\oint p_i \, dq_i = n_i h, \tag{5-23}$$

where n_i is an integer and h is Planck's constant. This relationship is useful whenever the p's can be expressed in terms of the corresponding q's, but few problems can be analyzed in this way, and Sommerfeld's treatment indicated the limitations of Bohr's theory. This type of mechanics could not be applied exactly even to the complete atom of helium, which is only the second element in the periodic table.

Guided by experimental findings, quantum mechanics developed to the point where the rules to be applied in determining the spectra even of complicated atoms were well established. Some of the rules, however, were not understood; they were not related to simple general principles through the Bohr atomic model, or its extensions as developed by Sommerfeld and others.

A noteworthy development was that of the vector model of the atom. The rules that were found to apply, particularly in connection with the splitting of the energy levels by the application of a magnetic field, clearly revealed the presence in the atom of various magnetic moments. These combined by vector rules, with quantization limiting the combinations that were allowed.

Summary

The existence in nature of a very simple atom, such as hydrogen, assisted in unraveling the mysteries of the atom. The nucleus of ordinary hydrogen was a single proton, and a single electron moved in the force field around this proton. The ordinary mechanics of such a system was not difficult to work out completely. The modifications introduced by the quantization of action were not too difficult to incorporate, and, on this basis, Bohr developed a theory that was applicable to the two-body problems of atomic physics in general. The spectrum of any ion consisting of a multiply charged nucleus with a single electron in its force field was given by Bohr's theory.

Accounting for discrete energy levels in the atom was the most notable achievement of Bohr's theory. This was accomplished through a quantization of the action. The line spectra of the various elements indicated that discrete energy levels were the general rule, and this feature of atomic theory, which was first explained in terms of the Bohr model, persisted in theories that rejected many of Bohr's assumptions.

The epoch-making influence of the Bohr theory came from the fact that it established the quantum trend in physical science. Quantum theory gained rapid acceptance as a result of the successes of the Bohr theory. Quantization of action constituted a radical departure from older mechanical laws, and the acceptance of this cleared the way for progress in the development of a mechanics suitable for the treatment of atomic phenomena.

Problems on Bohr's Theory of the Hydrogen Atom

1. a. Calculate the lowest energy of a hydrogen atom, in joules and in electron volts.
   b. What is the wavelength of the radiation emitted when an electron, at rest at a distance of 1 mm from a proton, joins the proton to form a hydrogen atom in its ground state?
2. Calculate the radius of the electronic orbit of a hydrogen atom for which $n = 2$.
3. Construct a quantitative energy level diagram for the four lowest energy states in hydrogen.
4. In a glow-discharge tube, containing hydrogen gas, electrons attain a maximum kinetic energy of 12.5 ev. What are the wavelengths of all the lines which you would expect to be radiated?
5. What is the second ionization potential of helium? (That is, after the first electron has been removed leaving the second electron in the state for which $n = 1$, what energy is required to remove this second electron?)
6. Through corrections for the motion of the nucleus, calculate the difference in the frequencies of the H_α line of the Balmer series and in the corresponding line of the spectrum of ionized helium. (The transition in this case of singly ionized helium is from the state given by $n = 6$ to that for which $n = 4$.)
7. From the energy level diagrams shown in this chapter, calculate, for each type of atom, the minimum kinetic energy which an electron must have if it is to interact with an atom and "lift" (through its own loss of kinetic energy) an

electron from its normal state in the atom to an allowed higher energy level by means of an allowed transition. The atoms which may be considered are hydrogen and sodium.

References on Bohr's Theory of the Atom

Eldridge, J. A., *Physical Basis of Things*, Chs. 14 and 15 (New York: Mc-Graw-Hill Book Company, 1934).

French, A. P., *Principles of Modern Physics*, pp. 99-122 (New York: John Wiley and Sons, 1958). (Integration of theory with a description of the crucial experiments.)

Series, G. W., *Spectrum of Atomic Hydrogen*, Chs. 1 to 5 (New York: Oxford University Press, 1958). (An excellent outline of the earlier atomic theories.)

Van Name, F. W., Jr., *Modern Physics*, Ch. 4 (New York: Prentice-Hall, 1952). (A readable elementary treatment.)

White, H. E., *Introduction to Atomic Spectra*, Chs. 1 and 2 (New York: McGraw-Hill Book Company, 1934). (A more complete treatment characteristic of specialization in spectra.)

6 | The Arrangement of Atoms in Solids and the Analysis of Crystals

Simple Crystals

The concentration of the atoms in solids is so great that it would seem natural for them to be placed in some orderly arrangement. This idea is supported by the fact that crystals occurring in nature have faces which are simple geometrical figures. Crystals can be shown to fracture (or cleave) more easily along some planes

Fig. 6-1(a). Closely packed spheres with centers in line.

than others. This suggests that the atoms are bound less strongly in some directions than in others.

If an atom is visualized as a sphere which occupies a fairly well-defined volume, it is possible to find geometrical arrangements in which the concentration is large. We may start with the problem of packing identical spheres in the greatest concentration, subject to the condition that the centers are confined to a single straight line, as shown in Fig. 6-1(a). The greatest concentration then occurs when there is a line of spheres in which each sphere touches two others, one on each side, like beads on a string. If a number of such straight strings of spheres are then arranged in the greatest concentration, with

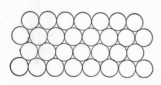

Fig. 6-1(b). Closely packed spheres with centers in a plane.

the centers of the spheres in a plane, the arrangement is that shown in Fig. 6-1(b), where the bulge of a sphere perpendicular to the line of centers fits into a depression between two spheres of the adjoining lines, one above, the other below it. Each sphere in such a plane is

111

TABLE 6-1. SYMBOLS DISTINCTIVE OF CHAPTER 6

Symbol	Name	Quantity Designated
μ	mu	index of refraction
ρ	rho	density (kg/m^3)
N		concentration of atoms (number per unit volume)
d		spacing between planes containing concentrations of atoms
(ijk)		Miller indices specifying definite planes in a crystal

The use of other symbols is generally consistent with the designations assigned in previous chapters.

surrounded by six "nearest neighbors," except the ones on the outside which are surrounded by only four or two nearest neighbors. If lines are drawn tangent to the spheres at the points of contact, a series of regular hexagons results.

Finally, if many such planes of spheres are to be stacked in such a way that the concentration of atoms in space is a maximum, the bulges at right angles to each plane of spheres will have to fit into the depressions between spheres of the adjacent planes, as shown in Fig. 6-12. The configuration described is designated as "closely packed spheres." Planes at the points of contact tangent to the surfaces form regular polyhedrons in space. Each atom on the interior is surrounded by its twelve nearest neighbors. For closely packed spheres, if the number of atoms per unit volume is known, it is possible to compute the spacing between sets of atomic planes in the configuration.

Some very common crystals have a cubic structure. For example, common salt (NaCl) forms cubic crystals, and these cubes are seen in the shape of rock-salt fragments. Here the lattice is formed by alternating Na with Cl atoms along each of the three mutually perpendicular axes of the crystal.

The elementary facts about the arrangement of the atoms in most of the simple crystals were deduced from cleavage-plane information. The spacing was determined from information concerning the configuration and the number of atoms per unit volume. The diameters of atoms, suggested by this analysis, are 1-2 Å.

The Discovery of X-rays and the Study of Their Properties

In 1895, Roentgen was studying the discharge of electricity in the residual gas within a glass tube which was quite well evacuated. The tube was encased in a closely fitting shield of thin black cardboard.

A high potential was supplied to the tube from an induction coil. In a completely darkened room, Roentgen noticed that a paper screen, which had been washed with barium platinocyanide, lighted up. The intensity of the fluorescence seemed to be the same whether or not the treated side was turned toward the discharge tube. Roentgen realized that he had discovered a very penetrating radiation which he called X-rays because of their unknown nature, and he turned to an investigation of the more important properties of this radiation.

He soon established the following facts.

1. X-rays penetrate all substances to some extent. The elements of low atomic weight are especially transparent, while elements of high atomic weight can be used as shields for protection against X-rays.

2. They cause many substances to fluoresce.

3. They cause a blackening of a photographic plate or film.

4. They are not deflected in a magnetic field, so the radiation does not consist of charged particles.

5. X-rays are generated when cathode rays in an electric discharge fall upon the anode or any other solid placed in their path.

6. The first attempts to reflect and refract them were not successful.

7. They ionize the gases through which they pass, and cause an increase in the electrical conductivity in the gas.

It should be emphasized that the first of these properties was the most unusual and, from the standpoint of immediate applications, the most interesting one of these properties. Roentgen found that the X-rays passed through a 1000-page book, and through a piece of wood 2.5 cm in thickness. A 1.5 cm thickness of aluminum absorbed them somewhat, but strangely a thin platinum foil was as absorbent as 3 or 4 mm of aluminum. The rays passed readily through skin and flesh, but they were absorbed sufficiently by bones to cast a good shadow picture on a fluorescent screen, or on a photographc plate. Within a few months, X-rays were being used to assist surgeons in their work.

Since Roentgen realized that X-rays were generated when cathode rays struck a target, he proposed as a source of X-rays an evacuated bulb contaning just enough gas to give an electrical discharge when connected to a source of high potential. The cathodes, used in early X-ray tubes were similar to those in the gas discharge tubes out of which they developed. A curved cathode for focusing the cathode rays on the target was soon introduced. The anode, which served as a target, was soon tilted at an angle of about 45° with respect to the beam, as shown in Fig. 6-2, to give a reasonable area for interception of the beam and to provide a clear path for the exit of the X-rays from the tube.

These gas tubes were the only devices used for the production of X-rays for almost two decades. During this period, the work of Thomson had indicated that the cathode rays of a gas discharge consisted of streams of electrons moving with high velocity. Work by Edison had suggested that a hot filament in a vacuum tube was a good source of electrons. It was not until 1913, however, that W. D. Coolidge eliminated the gas discharge as a source of electrons and designed an X-ray tube in which the cathode was a tungsten filament heated to a high temperature. The tube could then be evacuated as well as the then existing techniques would permit. The Coolidge tube had so many advantages that it rapidly replaced the older gas tubes.

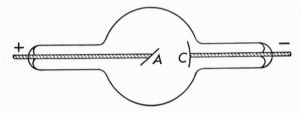

Fig. 6-2. A diagram of an X-ray tube.

Roentgen's discovery opened a new field of investigation and many ingenious workers soon entered the field. An unfortunate aspect of this interest was that these early workers were quite unaware of the radiation hazard. Severe X-ray burns were soon noticed, and several of the pioneers in the development of X-ray apparatus paid for their achievement by very much shortened lives.

The earliest measurements of X-ray intensity were made in terms of the ionization which they produced in air. The very first measurements were made by observing the rate of discharge of a gold-leaf electroscope placed near the source of X-rays. More quantitative observations were later made possible by the introduction of the "ionization chamber," the form and use of which is suggested by Fig. 6-3.

The chamber C is a metal cylinder which may be several cm in diameter. It is closed at both ends but has a window at one end for the admission of the X-rays. A collector rod AA is placed close to the axis of the cylinder, and is mounted in place by means of a rod passing through the insulating plug P. A battery B supplies a sufficient potential difference between the rod and the cylinder to cause all the ions produced by the X-rays to be collected. The rate at which ions are produced is indicated on a sensitive current-indicating device, shown on the diagram as a quadrant electrometer E.

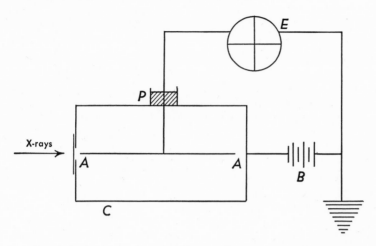

Fig. 6-3. An ionization chamber and its associated circuit.

The discussion concerning the nature of these mysterious rays had a considerable bearing on the development of physical ideas.

The Triumph of the Wave Theory in Optics

Controversy concerning the nature of the various phenomena studied in physics was not new at the time X-rays were discovered. The study of light had given rise to a similar controversy. The hypothesis that light consisted of small particles with extremely high velocity was proposed by the Greek philosophers of the classic period. Newton had supported this corpuscular theory, and his prestige was such that it remained quite popular for a century after his own contributions to optics were concluded.

The phenomena of refraction, as Newton himself suggested, could be accounted for if the component of the velocity of the light particle tangent to the glass surface it was entering remained a constant, while the component perpendicular to the glass surface was increased by an attraction of the glass for the light corpuscle. Measurements performed many years after the death of Newton, however, showed that the velocity of light in glass was less than its velocity in air. This was a severe blow to Newton's theory of refraction.

An empirical law for the propagation of light through a medium containing a gas had been observed by L. Lorenz of Copenhagen in 1880 before the discovery of X-rays. If μ represents the index of refraction and ρ the density of the gas (for any pure gas, proportional to the number of molecules per unit of volume), Lorenz found that

$$\frac{\mu^2 - 1}{(\mu^2 + 2)\rho} = \text{constant}.$$

Some years later H. A. Lorentz, using a model in which electrons were elastically bound to atoms, so that they executed forced vibrations in response to the electromagnetic waves, derived the following:

$$\frac{\mu^2 - 1}{\mu^2 + 2} = \frac{kNe^2}{3m(\nu_0^2 - \nu^2)}, \tag{6-1}$$

where e is the charge and m the mass of the electron, N is the number of atoms per unit volume, ν is the frequency of the light, ν_0 is the frequency of the free (or resonant) oscillations of the electrons accounting for the index of refraction μ, and k is a constant which depends on the units.

This formula, in addition to accounting for the experimental results of L. Lorenz, also accounts for the dispersion of light usually observed in the visible region and also explains the so-called "anomalous dispersion" of electromagnetic radiation of higher frequencies. As μ passes through unity it is quite apparent that the quantity $\mu^2 - 1$ has a relative variation which is large as compared with that of $\mu^2 + 2$, which, for approximation, may be treated as a constant. The Lorentz-Lorenz formula then shows that if $\nu_0 > \nu$, μ increases as ν is increased. Assuming that the electronic resonances responsible for the indices of refraction of most substances are in the ultraviolet, this accounts for the increase in the index of refraction for the shorter wavelengths in the visible. Furthermore, if this relationship applies for very short electromagnetic waves where $\nu_0^2 - \nu^2$ becomes negative, we may conclude that $\mu^2 - 1$ also must change sign. Hence, μ is less than unity in the region of "anomalous dispersion," as actually observed. At very high frequencies, the right-hand side of Eq. (1) approaches zero from the negative side. The resulting refractive index, slightly less than unity, means that the phase velocity of the X-rays is greater in the solid than it is in vacuum, and, as a consequence of this, X-rays may be totally reflected, if they graze a surface at less than the critical angle. It is clear, therefore, that while Newton's corpuscular theory of refraction involved contradictions, the wave theory of refraction is consistent with the observations.

The crucial experiments to show that light is accompanied by waves were those on interference and diffraction, but a critical discussion of these will be deferred. For our present purposes a knowledge of Huygens's principle offices.

The propagation of light in straight lines, as noted above, was easily explained by the corpuscular theory on the basis of the conservation of momentum. To explain this on the basis of a wave theory required a more careful consideration of the problem, and this was introduced by Huygens. He postulated that each point of a wave front could be treated as a source of light from which a spherical wave front spread with the speed of light in the forward direction. The envelope of all these various wavelets constituted the wave front at subsequent times. According to this idea, light would be propagated perpendicular to wave fronts formed by such envelopes. In the case of a continuous-plane wave front, the envelope is a plane parallel to the original wave front, and the light is propagated in straight lines. When the wave front is broken at regular intervals along its length, several envelopes may result, and where the wave is terminated, there is a possibility of Huygens's principle accounting for light spreading into the geometrical shadow.

First Attempts to Obtain Evidence Concerning the Nature of X-rays

Roentgen failed to detect evidence for the refraction or reflection of X-rays in his early experiments. Gouy performed a more precise experiment in an effort to detect refraction. By using X-rays which left the target at a very small angle (just grazing the surface), Gouy obtained a very narrow effective source. In front of this he placed a metal filament which cast a shadow on a photographic plate. A short triangular glass prism was placed on a line SP drawn from the middle of the source through the middle of the filament, as suggested in Fig. 6-4. A very small break in the shadow of the filament due to refraction in the prism should be observable on the photographic plate.

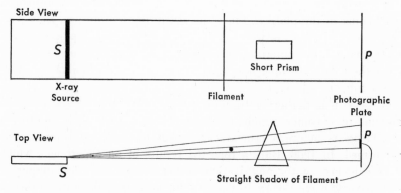

Fig. 6-4. The arrangement of the apparatus in Gouy's experiment.

None was observed and Gouy estimated that the index of refraction for the X-rays could not differ from unity by more than 0.000005.

Although Roentgen failed to detect the reflection of X-rays, Imbert and Bertin-Sans in 1896 reported results of an experiment which showed the scattering of X-rays. The plan of the experiment is shown in Fig. 6-5. The source of X-rays is at S and the direct rays are shielded from the photographic plate P, used as a detector in these experiments, by the heavy copper plate C. The position of the optically

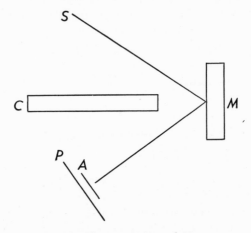

Fig. 6-5. The scattering of X-rays.

polished mirror is shown at M. Imbert and Bertin-Sans did detect radiation coming from the mirror which blackened the photographic plate P, on which the object A cast a sharp shadow. They proved that the radiation was *scattered* rather than regularly reflected, because, when they rotated the mirror M, they always obtained a blackening of the plate P. Since the scattering was diffuse, they suggested that the waves were so short that the optical polish of the plate made little difference, the radiation being diffusely scattered from the submicroscopic irregularities due to the molecular structure of the mirror surface.

A very remarkable feature in the research on X-rays was the amount of evidence which accumulated concerning their nature in the 17 years before a crucial experiment on X-ray diffraction was performed. In 1906, Barkla reported results of an experiment which gave evidence for the polarization of X-rays and therefore supported a transverse wave theory in contrast to the longitudinal wave theory which had been suggested by Roentgen.

Study of the absorption of secondary "characteristic" radiation led Barkla in 1911 to suggest the existence of X-ray spectra. It would not appear that absorption would discriminate sufficiently between X-rays of slightly different wavelength to make it a good tool for the detection of characteristic radiation. Barkla, however, developed very refined techniques. One of the ideas which he used can be discussed in connection with Fig. 6-6. X-rays coming from the source S are selected by a slit L_1 and fall upon the target material E, the

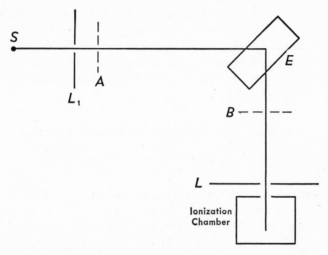

Fig. 6-6. Barkla's experiment on characteristic X-rays.

characteristic radiation of which is being investigated. If a filter screen is placed in the position A, the absorption of the filter for the original X-rays is determined. The filter is then moved to position B. The effect on the reduction of the initial radiation will be the same in this position, and any differences observed will be those due to the characteristic radiation originating in the target E. This proved to be a powerful means of detecting characteristic radiation. Barkla and his collaborators pursued this line of research for several years. They found that the mass absorption in aluminum for the characteristic radiation fell off rapidly, with increasing atomic number of the target material, along a regular curve. By 1911 Barkla was convinced that spectral series depending on atomic number were indicated by his results.

The problem in diffraction experiments was the lack of a suitable grating. Both Gouy and Forum searched for evidence of diffraction and from the failure to detect it concluded that, if X-rays were waves, their length could not be greater than 10^{-8} meters.

Before the detection of X-ray diffraction Sommerfeld reviewed the existing evidence and concluded that, if X-rays were electromagnetic in character, the wavelength should be of the order of 1 Å (10^{-10} m). The frequency is higher than that corresponding to the optical absorption bands in the ultraviolet, and on this basis the index of refraction for X-rays should be slightly less than unity. If the index of refraction is so close to unity, the failure of Roentgen to observe reflection of X-rays from a mirror surface would be understood, because a simple result of electromagnetic theory is that the reflection coefficient at a surface of separation between two media depends on the index of refraction between the two media, or on the difference in their absolute indices of refraction. The experiment of Gouy offered evidence that for X-rays the difference was small.

The Diffraction of X-rays by Natural Crystals

Crystallographers had long held rather definite ideas about the regular arrangement of atoms in the natural crystals. The regular shapes in which these crystals were formed and the existence of natural cleavage planes strongly suggested a regular arrangement of the atoms, but there was at this time no direct evidence for the manner in which individual atoms were arranged in the "elementary cell." The "elementary" or "unit cell" is the smallest section of the crystal, the periodic repetition of which produces the entire crystal.

About this time, Ewald was working in crystallography. From information on atomic mass and the known density of simple crystals he was calculating the size of a unit cell. In the course of these calculations, he consulted von Laue about one of his difficulties. Laue was impressed by the fact that the volume of the unit cell was of the order of 10^{-24} cm^3; so that the edge of an elementary cube would be 10^{-8} cm or 1 Å in length. But this was the estimated wavelength of X-rays, and Laue thought that a natural crystal, therefore, might serve as a suitable grating for X-ray diffraction.

Friedrich and Knipping, who had just completed their doctoral work with Professor Roentgen, agreed to test Laue's idea. They were aware of the fact that their X-rays were not homogeneous and that the range of wavelengths in their source might be expected to give quite complicated, and perhaps even indecisive, results. Barkla, however, had shown that when X-rays fell on a crystal containing heavy atoms, characteristic radiation resulted. Friedrich and Knipping decided to use a crystal containing a metal of intermediate atomic weight in the hope that the characteristic radiation would be diffracted. Copper sulfate crystals were easily grown and these were tried. Their first experiments were unsuccessful, because they did not have correct ideas on where to look for the diffracted rays. In their first experiment, they placed the photographic plate between the source of X-rays and the crystal. Then they tried a position alongside the crystal, and the results were negative in this case also. Finally, they successfully put the photographic plate behind the crystal so that X-rays transmitted through the crystal were

Fig. 6-7. Laue spot pattern formed by X-rays diffracted by NaCl.

received on the photographic plate. In addition to the direct transmitted beam, they found others arising from diffraction.

A Laue spot pattern for NaCl is shown as Fig. 6-7. Plates placed at various distances beyond the crystal showed that the diffracted beams traveled in straight lines. Careful experiments also gave evidence that the beams had the properties of homogeneous X-rays. These experiments provided the first evidence that X-rays had the properties of wave motion.

Experiments of Bragg

W. H. Bragg of Cambridge University had been a supporter of the corpuscular theory of X-rays. He decided to repeat Laue's experiments in an effort to show that the directions of the "diffracted beams" corresponded to particularly open channels in the array of atoms in crystals through which scattered particles could readily pass. The experiments failed of their objective, but in the course of the work a very important relationship was discovered. Bragg noticed that the X-rays were regularly reflected from the crystals, as if from mirrors. No surface had ever been polished well enough to serve as a mirror. What then were these reflectors?

Bragg looked for an explanation of these phenomena and found it in the constructive interference of waves from successive atom layers in the depth of the crystal. The explanation of the regular reflection of the X-rays provided no problem. It can be shown to result from the reflection of waves from any plane surface. The fact that on a submicroscopic scale the surface is discontinuous because it is made of atoms does not reduce the validity of the argument for regular reflection. If all points of a plane result in constructive interference of waves in a given direction, then any limited array of these points would also give constructive interference in this same direction.

To understand the reflection of certain wavelengths at definite angles, consider two successive planes in the depth of the crystal, as shown in Fig. 6-8. Here the intersections with the plane of the paper of two successive planes of atoms (each normal to the plane of the figure) are indicated by the lines A and B. A beam of X-rays $CDEF$ is incident on the surface, so the angle between either surface and any one of the rays in the beam is θ. Regular reflection from the planes A and B, respectively, results in the rays DG and FH. The ray EFH travels farther than ray CDG and, in order to have constructive interference, the difference of the paths must equal an integer times the wavelength λ of the X-rays. The difference of the distances is found

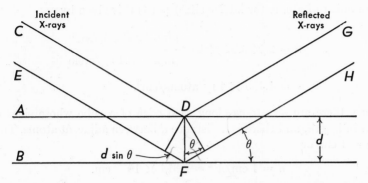

Fig. 6-8. Bragg's explanation of specular reflection at definite angles.

by dropping perpendiculars from the point D to the rays EF and FH, respectively. This gives the two small triangles with a common hypotenuse $d = DF$, where d is the separation between the planes A and B. The sum of the short sides of these triangles ($2d \sin \theta$) is the difference in the two light paths CDG and EFH. The condition for constructive interference, therefore, is that

$$n\lambda = 2d \sin \theta, \qquad (6\text{-}2)$$

where n is an integer. This is called the Bragg relation, and it is one of the most important tools in crystal analysis.

X-ray Spectroscopy

The discovery of Bragg's law for specular reflection made possible the determination of X-ray wavelengths from the computed spacings in crystals of known and simple structure.

Consider, for example, ordinary table salt. The crystalline form is that of rock salt, and the rectangular faces suggest a cubical arrangement of the atoms in the elementary cells. Each Na atom in the interior is surrounded by 6 nearest Cl atoms, and conversely. The lattice spacing can easily be computed on the assumption that the atoms are actually at the corners of a small cube. Taking the atomic weight of Cl as 35.46 and that of Na as 23.00, the molecular weight is 58.46. Avogadro's number is 6.02×10^{23}, and the number of atoms per mole of NaCl is $2 \times 6.02 \times 10^{23}$. The number of atoms per cm^3 is the number per mole, multiplied by that fraction of the molar weight which 1 cm^3 of salt represents. If the density of rock salt is taken to be 2.163 g/cm^3, the number of atoms (or lattice sites) per cm³ is given by

$$n = 2 \times 6.02 \times 10^{23} \frac{\text{atoms}}{\text{mole}} \frac{2.163 \text{ g/cm}^3}{58.46 \text{ g/mole}}$$

$$= 4.485 \times 10^{22} \text{ atoms/cm}^3.$$

Hence, there are $n^{1/3}$ atoms along each edge of a cube whose sides are 1 cm in length, and there is a distance d between adjacent atoms. Thus, $dn^{1/3} = 1$ cm, or

$$d = 1 \text{ cm}/n^{1/3} = 2.814 \times 10^{-8} \text{ cm}.$$

Uncertainties in the measurements, and in the degree of perfection of the crystals involved in the density determinations, would indicate that the result is good to only three significant figures. Siegbahn took up the problem of determining X-ray wavelengths accurately, and he needed a more precise figure. He assumed the value $d = 2.81400 \times 10^{-8}$ cm at 18° C. The additional figures were later shown to be in error, but with the precision contained in Siegbahn's measurements, a single correction factor applied to each wavelength gave required accuracy.

It is clear that there are three sets of parallel planes (one parallel to each of three of the faces that intersect at one corner of the elementary cell). Each set will contain all the atoms in the crystal. The spacing between the planes in each of these sets is just d. Other sets of equally spaced parallel planes can be chosen so that each set will contain all the atoms of the crystal, and some means of identifying these planes should be selected and discussed.

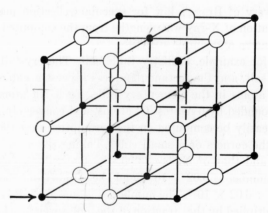

Fig. 6-9. Arrangement of the atoms in the NaCl crystal.

Consider the unit cell of the crystal as shown in Fig. 6-9. The atom at the lower left-hand corner of the front face (indicated by the arrow) may be selected as a reference. The three neighboring atoms (open circles) define a plane, and parallel to this at regular intervals are other planes that pass through certain atoms. This family of planes, too, includes all of the atoms in the crystal. This set of planes is designated as (111) for the reason that, in this set, the plane nearest to the chosen atom (but not passing through it) intersects each of the principal axes (directions defined by the three edges of a cube originating at the selected atom) at a distance along each axis that is just equal to the edge of the smallest cube with atoms at its corners.

The (111) designation is an illustration of many such designations which are known as Miller indices. Any such set of crystal planes must be chosen to pass through all the atoms. Then, since each atom of the crystal lies on some one of the set of parallel equally-spaced planes, any selected atom of the crystal will have a plane passing through it. The distance from this atom, measured along one edge of the elementary cell to the point at which the next plane of the set intersects this edge of the cell will be l/n, where l is the distance between atoms along the edge and n is a positive integer. The number n must be an integer, because the next atom must lie on some one of the set of planes, that is, it will lie on the first one of the planes, as in the illustration just given, or on the second one of them, or the third and so on. This integer n is one of the numbers used in the Miller indices.

If, for a second example, the next atom along the edge of the unit cell lies on the second plane, the distance between atoms will be divided into two equal parts by the intersection of the intervening plane, and the corresponding index is 2. The planes parallel to the faces of the elementary cell would be indicated by the Miller indices (100) or (010) or (001) indicating that, in a direction perpendicular to the planes, the intersection occurs at a distance equal to the edge of the elementary cell, while, in the two directions parallel to the edges of the cell contained in the plane, the planes being parallel do not intersect the axes at any finite distance.

As an illustration of the application of Bragg's law to the diffraction of X-rays, let us consider a beam of X-rays, containing all the various wavelengths, which strikes perpendicular to a (100) face of the NaCl crystal. For simplicity in the representation, we will consider only those X-ray beams that are reflected in the plane of the paper in Fig. 6-10. The planes responsible for these reflections are those parallel to a line which is perpendicular to the plane of the paper in the figure. This

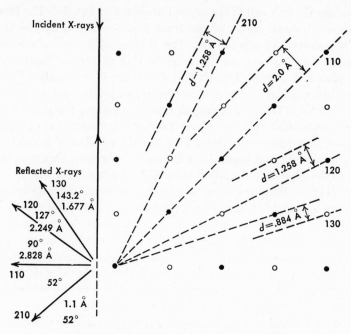

Fig. 6-10. Reflection of X-rays in NaCl.

means that, for the planes considered, one of the Miller indices (say the last one) will always be represented by a zero.

The first reflection which may be considered is that from the (100) planes. Regular reflection from these planes would mean that the direction of the X-ray was rotated through 180° or reversed on itself. The spacing between (100) planes is the length of the edge of the unit cell, and this is 2.81 Å. Thus, the Bragg relation

$$n\lambda = 2d \sin \theta = (1)\lambda = 2d \sin 90°$$

indicates that the X-rays reflected from the (100) planes in this case have a wavelength of $2d$ or 5.62 Å. There are numerous reflections of X-rays of about this wavelength from $(1NO)$ planes, where N is a large number. We will not complicate the figure by attempting to represent all of these. Rather we shall go directly to the (130) planes. These are separated by 0.884 Å and for them $\theta = 71.6°$. Hence, by Bragg's formula (1) $\lambda = 2(0.884 \text{ Å}) \sin 71.6°$ and the reflected X-rays have a wavelength of 1.677 Å. Other planes and the X-rays reflected from them are identified in the figure, and data for them are shown in Table 6-2.

TABLE 6-2. WAVELENGTHS OF THE X-RAYS REFLECTED FROM
VARIOUS PLANES IN THE CRYSTAL NaCl

Plane	θ	2d (A)	$\sin \theta$	λ (A)
100	90°	5.62	1.0000	5.62
130	71.6°	1.768	.9487	1.677
120	63.5°	2.516	.8940	2.249
110	45°	4.000	.7070	2.828
210	26.6°	2.516	.4475	1.126
310	18.5°	1.768	.3163	.559

Other grating spaces used in X-ray spectroscopy are shown in Table 6-3.

TABLE 6-3. GRATING SPACES USED IN X-RAY SPECTROSCOPY

Crystal	Chemical Composition	Grating Space (Å)
Rock salt	NaCl	2.81400
Calcite	$CaCO_3$	3.0290
Quartz	SiO_2	4.247
Potassium ferrocyanide	$K_4Fe(CN)_6$	8.408
Mica		9.93

Correction of Siegbahn Units

A knowledge of the properties of X-rays permitted the use of a ruled grating for wavelength measurement. The technique employed is to allow the X-rays to graze its surface, i.e. the angle between the beam and the surface is very small. The angle is important for two reasons. First, the critical angle for total reflection of X-rays from the grating surface is 18′. By working at angles less than this, the grating

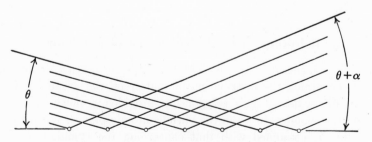

Fig. 6-11. Reflection of X-rays from a grating.

becomes a perfect reflector for X-rays. Second, the use of very small angles makes possible wavelength measurements even with ruled gratings of normal spacing, since the effective spacing of the lines is thus greatly reduced. The arrangement is shown in Fig. 6-11, where the plane of the figure is perpendicular to the lines ruled on the surface, which are indicated by the circles shown. The spacing between lines is a. The X-rays strike at an angle θ to the surface plane. After reflection, constructive interference is set up at the angle $\theta + \alpha$.

The condition for constructive interference is that

$$n\lambda = a[\cos \theta - \cos (\alpha + \theta)]. \tag{6-3}$$

Expanding the cosines in series of powers of the arguments gives

$$n\lambda = a \left[1 - \frac{\theta^2}{2} + \cdots - \left(1 - \frac{(\alpha + \theta)^2}{2} + \right) \simeq a \left[\alpha\theta + \frac{\alpha^2}{2} + \cdots \right].$$
$$\tag{6-4}$$

Even with $n = 1$, if the angles α and θ are of the order of $15' \simeq \dfrac{2\pi \times 15}{360 \times 60}$ $\simeq 0.00437$ radians, the X-ray wavelength measured will be about $1.9 \times 10^{-5}a$. Ruled gratings have spacings comparable with the wavelengths of visible light. But the X-ray wavelengths to be measured may be one ten-thousandth as large as this. Since $n\lambda$ is about $2a \times 10^{-5}$, it is clear, therefore, that this method permits the measurement even of relatively short X-rays, and in measurements of this sort, six significant figures can be obtained. Comparison of wavelengths obtained with natural crystals with those measured by use of ruled gratings revealed a discrepancy of about 0.2%. Siegbahn's assumed spacing of rock salt is, therefore, this much too low. His spacing was based upon the density of rock salt, which may be accurately measured, and upon Avogadro's number. The conclusion that Avogadro's number was in error was necessary to explain the discrepancy. Thus, X-ray diffraction provided a means of obtaining Avogadro's number with a precision which was not possible by other methods.

Diffraction in the Determination of Structures

Diffraction methods are the best available for getting definite evidence concerning the distribution of matter on the atomic and even sub-atomic scale. Bragg's relationship provided a means for determining the spacings between the various atomic planes. When this information is combined with that concerning the symmetries of the crystal, the complete structure can be deduced. The application of this method has resulted in the accumulation of data on crystal structures of many types.

Many substances form crystals with face-centered cubic structures like NaCl. A few of these, selected for illustration, together with data concerning the distance between neighboring atoms (half the length of the edge of the unit cell) are shown in Table 6-4.

TABLE 6-4. GRATING SPACINGS OF CUBIC CRYSTALS

Substance	Spacing (Å)
LiF	2.01
CsF	3.00
LiCl	2.57
MgO	2.10
MgS	2.60

Although CsF is a crystal of the NaCl type, cesium has an unusually large atomic volume, and often the simple compounds of cesium, although still forming cubic crystals, have an additional atom at the center of the cube. For example, CsCl is represented by a unit cell having eight cesium atoms at the corners of a cube 4.11 Å on each edge, while the chlorine ion is at the center of this cube at a distance of 3.56 Å from each corner. Because of this, these simple cubic structures are sometimes identified as CsCl type lattices. Other such cubic crystals

TABLE 6-5. CUBIC STRUCTURES

Substance	Lattice Spacing (Å)
CsBr	4.29
CsI	4.58
TlCl	3.84
TlBr	3.97

are listed in Table 6-5. Face-centered cubic structures have the lattice spacings shown in Table 6-6.

Particularly in metals a very common type of structure is the hexagonal close-packed. This makes use of the hexagonal arrangement of spheres in a plane to give the closest possible packing. In the plane above or below the first, spheres are also in hexagonal arrangement for close-packing, but such a plane is displaced just enough, relative to the first, so that the bulges of this plane match the depressions of

TABLE 6-6. FACE-CENTERED CUBIC STRUCTURES

Substance	Lattice Spacing (Å)
FeO	4.28
NiO	4.17
BaO	5.53
BaS	6.37
Monovalent Noble Metals	
Cu	3.61
Ag	4.08
Au	4.07
Other Metals	
Al	4.04
Ni	3.51
Pd	3.88
Pt	3.92

the first. Fig. 6-12 gives a representation of the close-packed hexagonal lattice. The distance a is measured between adjacent spheres in the plane. The distance c gives the height of the unit cell, which measures

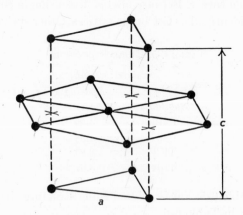

Fig. 6-12. Close-packed hexagonal structure.

the distance between alternate planes of spheres. Table 6-7 gives examples of hexagonal close-packed structures.

Since the electrons of an atom are responsible for the X-ray scattering, it is possible by a study of the distribution of the X-ray intensity

Table 6-7. Lattice Constants for Hexagonal Close-packed Structures

Lattice Spacings (Å)

Substance	a	c
Be	2.28	3.59
Mg	3.20	5.20
Zn	2.66	4.93
Cd	2.97	5.61
Ti	2.953	4.73

in a diffraction pattern to determine the distribution of the charge responsible for it. In this way, much significant information has been obtained. For example, W. L. Bragg studied the intensities in the diffraction pattern of the alkali halides and showed that in them the alkali metal had lost an electron to the halogen atoms surrounding it. Ions were known to exist in solutions, but the X-ray studies showed that they were present also in the solid state.

The molecule loses its importance in the configurations of the solid state. A sodium ion in the interior of solid NaCl is surrounded by six Cl ions, and vice versa. The coordination number is said to be six, and in crystal structure it is the coordination numbers rather than valences which are important. In lattices of the CsCl type, the coordination number is eight.

A study of the various crystals and compounds formed by a particular element suggested that there was a rather definite ionic radius. These ionic radii were important in determining whether certain arrangements would exist or not. For example, a large positive ion would be surrounded by eight negative ions, whereas a smaller positive ion would have only six. The information acquired, and the theoretical ideas which developed, enabled crystallographers to systematize their complex field.

The data of diffraction give detail obtainable in no other way. In metals and in semiconducting crystals the average distribution of charge density throughout the crystals may be deduced, and this is of great importance in understanding their behavior.

Especially in situations as complicated as those presented by alloys and solid solutions, X-ray analysis is useful. The various forms of brass have been extensively studied. A relatively simple alloy, the behavior of which has been worked out on the basis of X-ray diffraction, is $AuCu_3$. If this substance at a high temperature, with a random distribution of atoms, is quickly cooled, a face-centered cubic structure is formed, and it is found that the atom at a given lattice site is governed by probability. If, however, the material is cooled slowly, or if the solid with the disordered distribution of atoms is annealed, the gold atoms occupy the corners of the face-centered cubic and the copper atoms take their positions at the centers of the faces. This structure has been correlated with physical behavior of the alloy.

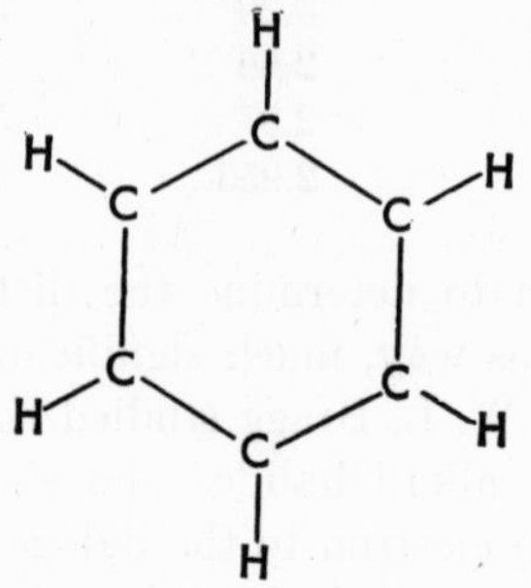

Fig. 6-13. The benzene ring.

The arrangement of atoms in molecules is of interest, and this sometimes determines the short-range order of the atoms in a crystalline solid. Faraday in 1825 isolated a substance that we have come to call benzene, and in 1867 Kekulé made the suggestion concerning its basic structure which is currently accepted. The chemical formula is C_6H_6, and Kekulé suggested that, instead of forming a chain, the

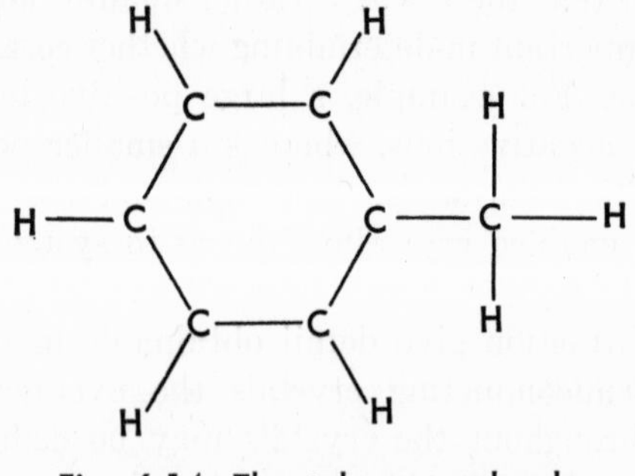

Fig. 6-14. The toluene molecule.

C atoms were arranged in the form of a closed hexagon, as suggested in Fig. 6-13. The conception of the hexagonal arrangement has been quite fruitful; it has provided simple explanations of some otherwise troublesome chemical observations.

The benzene ring is a structure upon which many organic molecules are based. Hexahydrobenzene, more commonly known as cyclohexane,

(C_6H_{12}) is formed by placing an additional H atom at each corner of the hexagon. Toluene is formed by replacing one of the H atoms of benzene by a methyl group, as shown in Fig. 6-14. Bromotoluene is formed from toluene by replacing one of the remaining H atoms present in the original benzene ring by a Br atom. This atom can be attached at any of the five remaining corners of the hexagon, but, because there is no essential difference between attaching the Br atom at either of the two corners next to the methyl group, the structures which are mirror images of one another are indistinguishable, and

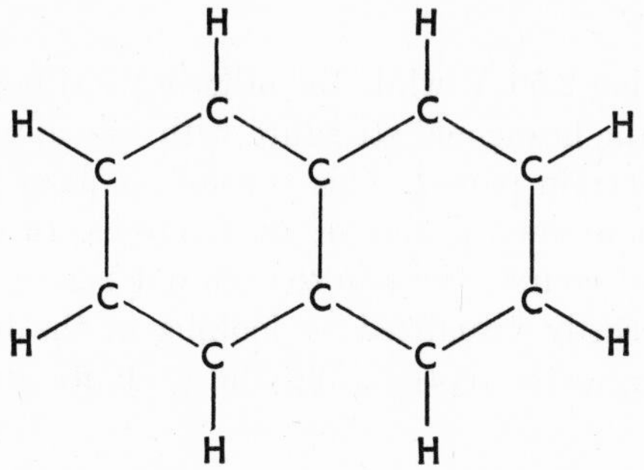

Fig. 6-15. The structure of naphthalene.

the Br atom can be placed in such a way as to form only three distinguishable chemical structures, but these three are known to the chemist. They have different shapes and they have been identified on the basis of differences in their chemical behavior, as well as in their molecular spectra. X-ray methods are ideal for such structure determinations, because they give directly the separations of the individual atoms in the structure.

The molecular structures and the crystal structures of naphthalene and anthracene are of interest when compared. The structural formula for naphthalene is shown in Fig. 6-15.

The structural formula for anthracene contains an additional benzene ring, as shown in Fig. 6-16.

When these substances are dissolved in ether, and the ether is allowed to evaporate, they recrystallize, and X-ray analysis has established that the unit cells of the two substances are those shown in Fig. 6-17.

The difference in the lengths of the OC sides for the two unit cells is 2.49 Å, and this suggests that this is the width of the benzene ring. The diamond lattice itself is a repetition of puckered hexagons, the

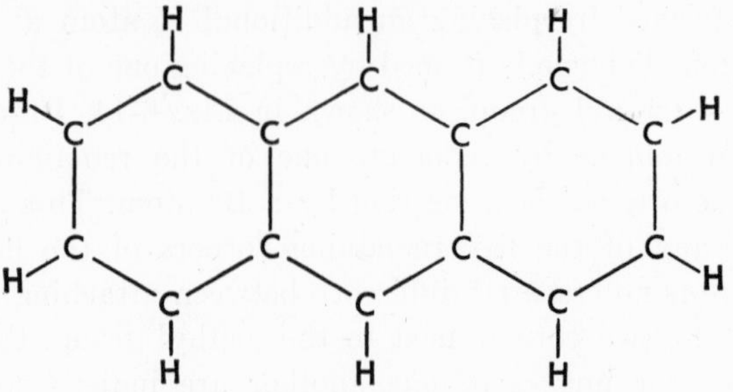

Fig. 6-16. The anthracene structure.

width of each being 2.50 Å, while the other crystalline form of carbon, graphite, shows the hexagonal structure with this approximate spacing repeated along certain planes. This suggests a fixed form and nearly constant dimensions for the ring of six C atoms. In either crystalline form of C it is, of course, possible to pick out zigzag chains of atoms. These are most easily visualized by looking at the left-hand edge of the layers of Fig. 6-18, representing the graphite structure.

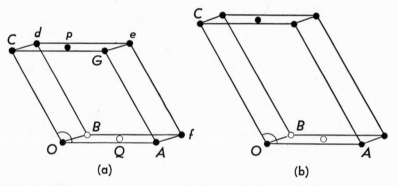

Fig. 6-17. The shapes of the unit cells in crystals of naphthalene (a) and anthracene (b).

In the diamond crystal, the distance between centers of neighboring C atoms is 1.54 Å, and the angle is 109°28′. The tetrahedral structure of the diamond crystal is shown in Fig. 6-19. Since a given atom is supported in position by four bonds equally spaced in angle, diamond is a very hard substance. It is very difficult to displace a C atom in the diamond lattice in any direction. Some one or more of the bonds is certain to provide a large restoring force when an atom is displaced in any selected direction. In graphite, on the other hand, the large

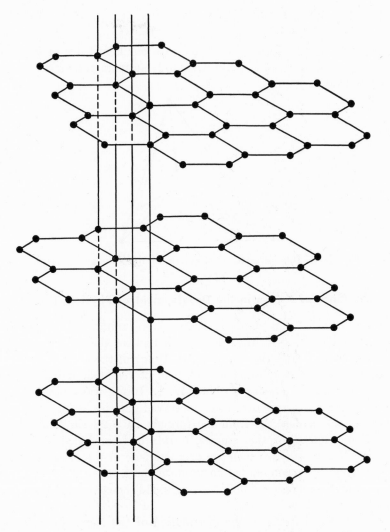

Fig. 6-18. The crystal structure of graphite.

spacing of about 3.4 Å between the planes containing the hexagons
has important consequences. First, graphite is relatively soft, because
the restoring force constant for the displacement of the atoms perpendicular to the sheets is not large, and individual atoms or groups
of atoms may be readily displaced in this direction. Second, graphite
is lamellar. The weak bonds between the sheets may be broken, and
the sheets slide quite readily over one another. Thus, graphite has
been widely used as a solid lubricant.

For the study of solids, X-rays have the advantage that they are capable of locating the individual atoms in relation to their neighbors. Without X-rays to aid in crystal analysis, our knowledge of the solid state would be far more qualitative and far more restricted than it is at present.

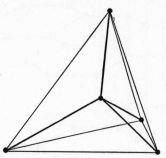

Fig. 6-19. The tetrahedral structure of the diamond crystal.

The Place of X-rays in the Development of Physical Theory

The discovery that natural crystals were suitable as diffraction gratings for use with X-rays provided a tool for the study of X-ray spectra. W. L. Bragg, the son of W. H. Bragg of the crystal structure studies, turned his attention to this field of research. Using natural crystals of known grating spacing, W. L. Bragg was able to build X-ray spectrometers, and from the observed glancing angles was able to calculate wavelengths from the formula $n\lambda = 2d \sin \theta$. We have seen that, from absorption studies, Barkla had concluded that there must be X-ray spectra which are characteristic of the element of the target which was bombarded to produce these rays. This was confirmed in the experiments of W. L. Bragg and the characteristic wavelengths were determined.

The general features of the distribution of the X-ray intensity as a function of the wavelength, when a target is bombarded by electrons first of one energy eV_1, and then by electrons of greater energy eV_2, are suggested in Fig. 6-20. The lines of the characteristic X-ray spectra are shown superimposed on a continuous spectral background. When the electron bombarding energy is raised, the line of shortest wavelength becomes apparent. This suggests the relationship between energy and wavelength which was used by Planck. As suggested in Fig. 6-21, different atoms are characterized by lines corresponding to different energies. At an energy high enough to excite characteristic spectral lines of molybdenum, tungsten shows no characteristic lines

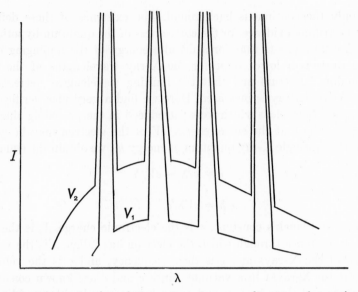

Fig. 6-20. Schematic plot of X-ray intensity as a function of wavelength. (Potential difference V_2 is much higher than V_1.)

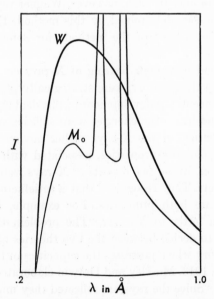

Fig. 6-21. Plot of X-ray intensity for a 35,000-volt potential difference on X-ray tubes with molybdenum and tungsten targets.

but only the continuous background. The existence of these definite lines is striking evidence for the correctness of the quantum hypothesis.

Fig. 6-20 suggests that for a definite energy of the impinging electrons there is a lower limit for the X-ray wavelengths of the corresponding spectrum and that the limiting wavelengths decrease as the electron energy is increased. Here we find a very nice verification of the quantum ideas which were introduced in the preceding chapter. If we assume that the entire energy eV of the electron may be given to produce a single X-ray quantum of energy $h\nu$, we obtain the equation

$$\nu = c/\lambda = eV/h \qquad (6\text{-}5)$$

or

$$h = eV\lambda/c, \qquad (6\text{-}6)$$

where h is Planck's constant, e is the electronic charge, V is the potential difference through which the electron has fallen, λ is the wavelength of the X-rays and ν is their frequency, and c is the velocity of light (or X-rays) in a vacuum. Since c and e are known constants of nature and since both V and λ can be measured with considerable precision, Eq. (6) provides an independent method for determining Planck's constant. The first researches (for example, those by Duane and Hunt) made to determine h by this method gave values which were about 1% too low. In 1918, however, Wagner reported the value 6.63×10^{-34} joule-sec, determined by this method. Data obtained in this way were used as one of the methods for determining Planck's constant.

There is a second important bearing of X-rays on physical theory. X-rays, because of their energy, were strategically placed to assume a very important place in the development of physical thought. Although the frequencies and hence the energies were sufficiently great to make the corpuscular nature of the X-rays rather obvious, they were not so great that the periodic properties, associated with the wave, were impossible to detect. These two aspects of X-rays were quite apparent to the early workers. They recognized that a satisfactory theory would have to incorporate both properties. For example, in 1912, W. H. Bragg wrote in a letter to *Nature:* "The problem then becomes, it seems to me, not to decide between the two theories of X-rays, but to find . . . one theory which possesses the capacities of both." In a letter dated January 30, 1913, Moseley and Darwin elaborated the idea somewhat. They said: "Since the rays are reflected they must be some kind of a pulse with an extended wave front, yet after reflection they retain their corpuscular character. Thus the energy of X-rays appears to show the contrary properties of extension over a wave front and concentration at a point."

Summary

In this chapter, we have reviewed the application of X-rays to the analysis of crystal structure. The X-rays are scattered by the electrons. The locations of constructive interference in a diffraction pattern thus give definite information concerning the positions of the individual atoms in the crystal. The intensities in the pattern give an indication of the electronic distribution. Research on the properties of solids has been greatly advanced by the use of X-rays in crystal analysis.

X-rays have contributed to our fundamental knowledge in several ways. Diffraction from ruled gratings was crucial in establishing a precise value of Avogadro's number. The frequency of X-rays is strategically placed to show both wave and corpuscular properties. Thus, X-rays provided the stimulus for one of the distinctive developments of modern physical theory.

Problems in X-rays

1. Following the usual custom, wavelengths λ in the following data are specified by their values in air. Flint glass has an index of refraction n which varies with wavelength as follows:

$\lambda(\text{Å})$	n	ν (cycles/sec)
7000	1.568	4.3×10^{14}
5500	1.577	5.46×10^{14}
4000	1.600	7.5×10^{14}

   a. From these data compute ν_0 and kN by the theory of Lorentz (where k is simply a proportionality factor put into the right-hand side of Eq. (1) so that mks units may be used).
   b. Using the constants evaluated from optical data in part (a), calculate the index of refraction of flint glass for X-rays of wavelength 1 Å.
2. A common method in X-ray spectroscopy is to rotate a crystal back and forth to vary the angle of incidence continuously. If X-rays are incident on the (100)-face of a rock-salt crystal, through what angle with respect to the original direction will the molybdenum line of 0.709 Å be reflected in this rotating crystal method?
3. Estimate Planck's constant from the observation that electrons having fallen through 62,200 volts produce X-rays of wavelengths no shorter than 0.2 Å.

4. If the critical angle of "total external reflection" of X-rays from a certain solid is 18′00″, what is the angle of refraction within the solid for X-rays incident on the surface at a grazing angle of 30′?

5. Calculate the grating spacing of KCl if this crystal has a density of 1.984 g/cm^3.

6. Determine the spacing of the (510) planes in a rock-salt crystal and that of the (430) planes.

7. X-rays of all wavelengths are incident perpendicular to the (110)-face of a rock-salt crystal. Determine the angle with respect to the initial beam and also the wavelength of X-rays which will be reflected from the (610) plane.

References on X-rays and Crystal Structure

Bragg, W. H., and W. L. Bragg, *X-rays and Crystal Structure* (New York: Harcourt, Brace, 1924). (A classic text.)

Cohen, E. R., K. M. Crowe, and J. W. M. DuMond, *The Fundamental Constants of Physics*, pp. 103-207 (New York: Interscience Publishers, 1957). (Describes use of X-rays to obtain precise values of physical constants.)

Eldridge, John A., *Physical Basis of Things*, Ch. 19 (New York: McGraw-Hill Book Company, 1934). (An interesting elementary discussion.)

Kaye, G. W. C., *X-rays* (London: Longmans, Green, 1923).

Lonsdale, K., *Crystals and X-rays* (New York: D. Van Nostrand, 1949). (A lucid specialized treatment.)

Richtmeyer, F. K., and E. H. Kennard, *Introduction to Modern Physics*, pp. 451-79 (New York: McGraw-Hill Book Company, 1947). (A good general treatment.)

Zwikker, C., *Physical Properties of Solid Materials*, pp. 20-41 (New York: Interscience Publishers, 1954). (Emphasizes crystal structure and properties.)

7 | Evidence for Corpuscular Properties Associated with Electromagnetic Radiation

If the quantum theory which Planck had introduced in connection with the distribution in energy of thermal radiation had been taken quite seriously, the energy accompanying light waves would have been considered as localized in quanta or photons for which the energy W is given by

$$W = h\nu, \qquad (7\text{-}1)$$

where ν is the frequency of the periodic phenomena in the waves as determined from the wavelength and the velocity of light. This energy, by the special theory of relativity, would be equivalent to a mass $h\nu/c^2$, and, since in free space the velocity of the photons is c, the momentum expected is

$$p = \frac{h\nu}{c^2} c = h\nu/c = h/\lambda. \qquad (7\text{-}2)$$

The photon has no rest mass, and the motion at the velocity c in free space is essential to the very nature of light. We have reviewed these facts as essential consequences of the corpuscular theory of light, which was, in spite of Planck's reluctance to accept these conclusions, a natural development. These consequences, however, were not at the time generally accepted.

The wave theory of light had gained ascendancy by the very early part of the nineteenth century. The nature of the waves, although proved to be transverse in character, was not understood. Maxwell's theoretical work on electromagnetism in the middle part of the nineteenth century provided a very attractive suggestion. His theory was that, associated with variations of the electric field in a plane-polarized

141

TABLE 7-1. LIST OF SYMBOLS USED IN CHAPTER 7

Symbol	Name	Quantity Designated
ν	nu	frequency of radiant energy
λ	lambda	wavelength
p		momentum
P		Poynting vector giving energy flux
E		electric vector
H		magnetic vector
γ	gamma	relativistic factor $(1 - v^2/c^2)^{-\frac{1}{2}}$
Δ	delta	increment of a quantity
m_0		rest mass of a particle
β	beta	phase factor: $2\pi/\lambda$
ϵ_0	epsilon sub zero	permittivity of free space
μ_0	mu sub zero	permeability of free space
I		flux of particles (number crossing unit area in unit time)

wave, and set up by them, there were variations of magnetic intensity in phase with the variations of electric intensity but in a direction making a right angle with the electric intensity. Electromagnetic waves were transverse, and the propagation was at right angles both to the electric and to the magnetic vectors. The rate of energy transfer across unit area parallel to the wave fronts was given by the Poynting vector

$$\mathbf{P} = \mathbf{E} \times \mathbf{H}. \tag{7-3}$$

Experimental verification of the existence of electromagnetic waves became an important problem in physics.

The German physicist, Hertz, in 1887 undertook this work. It was known that a condenser discharging through an inductance produced electrical oscillations. As a source, Hertz decided to use the discharge of a condenser which took place through a loop of wire when there was a breakdown at a spark gap in the loop. A similar oscillatory circuit was set up at some distance as a receiver, and Hertz showed that the spark gap in the receiver circuit could be broken down to pass a discharge when oscillations were excited in the primary circuit. It was this evidence which physics awaited to prove the correctness of Maxwell's theory and hence to complete the logical structure of the science.

In the course of his experiments, however, Hertz noticed that the behavior of the spark gap in the receiving circuit was very erratic, sometimes behaving in one way, sometimes in another. He turned aside to investigate this phenomenon and thus discovered the photoelectric effect. Hertz found that the ultraviolet light which originated in the primary spark gap, when allowed to fall on the electrodes of the secondary gap, caused it to break down much more readily than if visible light alone fell on the electrodes. Thus, in his experiments proving the electromagnetic character of the wave phenomena associated with light, Hertz discovered an effect which never has been explained on the basis of a pure electromagnetic wave picture!

Experimental Evidence Bearing on the Nature of the Photoelectric Effect

In 1888, Hallwachs discovered that a negatively charged metal plate lost its charge quite rapidly when it was exposed to ultraviolet light. This was not true for positively charged metals. As soon as the electron was discovered, Hallwachs's observation suggested that electrons were emitted when light fell on metals. In 1899, Lenard set up an apparatus for measuring the charge to mass ratio of the emitted particles, and in this way he identified them as electrons. Lenard made a second important discovery, namely that the velocity of the emitted electrons varied from zero up to some maximum value. This maximum value of the velocity was independent of the intensity of the light, but depended upon the wavelength or frequency. These results were important because of their theoretical implications.

The photoelectric effect proved interesting also because of possible applications. Although for ordinary metals visible light is found to be ineffective, Elster and Geitel showed as early as 1889 that the alkali metals, such as potassium and sodium, exhibited photoelectric emission when exposed to visible light. In 1890, they produced a vacuum photoelectric cell and, in 1892, applying the proportionality of the photoelectric emission to the incident light intensity, they used the photoelectric cell as a photometer. Also in 1892, they showed that photoelectric currents could be amplified by maintaining a suitable pressure of gas in the tube. This was accomplished by the photoelectrons which had been accelerated in the applied electric field to such energies that they were effective in ionization of the gas.

Einstein's Theory of the Photoelectric Effect

The evidence which accumulated in the studies of the photoelectric effect, when considered in the light of other developments in physics, such as Planck's quantum theory, provided a rather clear picture of what happened in this case. There was an apparent long wavelength limit for photoelectric emission. This limit depended upon the particular metal which was used as a cathode. The fact that the maximum velocity of emission from a given metal depended not on the intensity, but on the wavelength, suggested that in this case also the energy of the light was concentrated in parcels (or quanta) of size given by

$$W = h\nu.$$

In the photoelectric effect, this entire quantity of energy was given to a single electron. Thus, the quantum was annihilated although its energy was conserved in the increase of the energy of the electron. There appeared to be no way to save the unmodified wave picture in which the energy would be uniformly distributed over entire wave fronts. If this were the case, the energy associated with low intensities of light would have such a low density that the power falling on an area equal to the approximate cross section of an atom would have to accumulate for several hours before it would add up to that required for the ejection of an electron. Experiment shows that electrons are emitted as soon as light falls on a surface.

This revealed a great difficulty with the wave picture of electromagnetic radiation. Planck had actually tried to save the wave model for light by talking about the quantization in connection with the oscillators emitting the light, but the energy of the light itself he had considered to be spread uniformly over the wave front. The photoelectric effect clearly indicates that the light acts as quanta at the place where it is absorbed. Einstein saw that the treatment could be simplified if the energy of the radiation were to be considered as localized bundles throughout the entire discussion, and he introduced these quanta of light energy which have come to be called photons.

This step taken by Einstein brings us back to Newton's theory of light as corpuscles. Newton, of course, discovered interference, but this did not cause him to abandon the corpuscular theory. We can avoid this also. It is true that interference and diffraction effects suggest wave properties associated with light. We may say, however, that the function of these waves is to determine the probability of finding the photons at a particular point. The energy of the light is in the photons, and the waves accompanying these particles serve to guide them, and to determine in what quantities they will appear at definite places.

The resulting theory is less definite than a simple wave theory or a simple corpuscular theory, but it is certainly more satisfactory than a theory which is over-simplified to the extent that it contains inherent inconsistencies with experimental evidence. There appears to be no way of eliminating the properties arising from either of these simple models from our theory. Any defensible corpuscular model has associated with it wave concepts, because the momentum of the particles is determined by a wavelength. A pure wave theory will not suffice because of the incontrovertible evidence that the energy is in the form of quanta of size $h\nu$.

Einstein, in 1905, proposed his celebrated equation for the photoelectric effect. He postulated that a photon was annihilated and that its energy $h\nu$ was given to an electron within the metal. In the process of escaping from the metal, the potential energy of the electron was increased, so only a small fraction of the photon's energy appeared as kinetic energy of the electron as it left the surface of the metal. Thus, Einstein's equation for the photoelectric effect can be written,

$$mv_m^2/2 = h\nu - eV, \qquad (7\text{-}4)$$

where the term on the left-hand side represents the maximum kinetic energy observed for the electrons after emission, $h\nu$ is the energy given to the electron by the photon, and eV is the amount of energy which must be given to an electron of the metal to make it possible to overcome the attractive forces set up at the surface and thus to leave the metal.

The Einstein equation is very definite, and it is in agreement with the experience which accumulated in early studies of the photoelectric effect. It must be considered as strong evidence for the existence of light quanta. Understanding how the photon transfers its entire energy to the electron in such a way that the momentum of the electron has its major component directed out of the surface is not so simple. It must be recognized, therefore, that a simple experiment showing the action of a photon on a single free electron would have considerable value in establishing the laws which may be applied to photons.

Momentum of a Photon and the Compton Effect

The behavior of X-rays had suggested that they too might be corpuscular in nature. W. H. Bragg was reluctant to abandon the corpuscular theory of X-rays even though his relation $n\lambda = 2d \sin \theta$ is based upon the constructive interference of wave fronts from the various atomic planes of a crystal. To account for the behavior of X-rays, as Moseley and Darwin had suggested, did very definitely require both wave and particle properties.

In the "collision" between a photon and an electron *both energy* and *momentum* would be *conserved*. Let us consider the implications of this. These lead us directly to the explanation of the Compton effect. Suppose that an electron at rest is hit by a photon. Let the initial momentum of the photon be p, and let the momentum after impact be p', as shown in Fig. 7-1. Let the momentum acquired by the electron be denoted by $h\nu$, the final energy by $h\nu'$, and let the energy gained by the electron be

$$m - m_0 = m_0(\gamma - 1) = \frac{h\nu - h\nu'}{c^2},$$ (7-5)

where as before $\gamma \equiv (1 - v^2/c^2)^{-\frac{1}{2}}$.

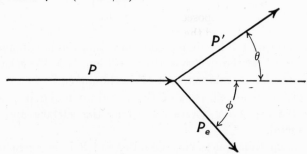

Fig. 7-1. Compton scattering of photons by electrons.

From the conservation of momentum, we may write

$$p = p' \cos \theta + p_e \cos \phi$$ (7-6)

and

$$0 = p' \sin \theta - p_e \sin \phi.$$ (7-7)

From the conservation of energy, we have

$$h\nu = h\nu' + m_0 c^2(\gamma - 1).$$ (7-8)

The momentum equations may be rewritten as

$$\frac{h\nu}{c} = \frac{h\nu'}{c} \cos \theta + m_0 v\gamma \cos \phi$$ (7-9)

and

$$0 = \frac{h\nu'}{c} \sin \theta - m_0 v\gamma \sin \phi.$$ (7-10)

Originally physicists worked with the scattered photons rather than the "recoil electrons." Let us then eliminate ϕ. Solution of Eqs. (9) and

(10) for $\cos \phi$ and $\sin \phi$ gives

$$\sin \phi = \frac{h\nu' \sin \theta}{cm_0 v \gamma} \tag{7-11}$$

and

$$\cos \phi = \frac{h(\nu - \nu' \cos \theta)}{cm_0 v \gamma}. \tag{7-12}$$

From the trigonometric identity, $1 = \sin^2 \phi + \cos^2 \phi$, we have

$$1 = \frac{h^2 \nu'^2 \sin^2 \theta}{c^2 m_0^2 v^2 \gamma^2} + \frac{h^2(\nu^2 - 2\nu\nu' \cos \theta + \nu'^2 \cos^2 \theta)}{c^2 m_0^2 v^2 \gamma^2}, \tag{7-13}$$

or

$$m_0 v^2 \gamma^2 = \frac{h^2}{\lambda'^2} \sin^2 \theta + \left\{ \frac{h}{\lambda} - \frac{h \cos \theta}{\lambda'} \right\}^2$$

$$= \left\{ \frac{h}{\lambda'} \right\}^2 + \left\{ \frac{h}{\lambda} \right\}^2 - \frac{2h^2 \cos \theta}{\lambda \lambda'}. \tag{7-14}$$

Now

$$\frac{m_0^2 v^2}{1 - v^2/c^2} \equiv \frac{m_0^2 c^2}{1 - v^2/c^2} - m_0^2 c^2. \tag{7-15}$$

Thus,

$$\left(\frac{h}{\lambda'} \right)^2 + \left(\frac{h}{\lambda} \right)^2 - \frac{2h^2 \cos \theta}{\lambda \lambda'} = m_0^2 c^2 \gamma^2 - m_0^2 c^2. \tag{7-16}$$

From the energy condition of Eq. (5), we may write

$$\frac{h}{\lambda} - \frac{h}{\lambda'} + m_0 c = m_0 c \gamma. \tag{7-17}$$

Squaring both sides of Eq. (17) and substituting in Eq. (16), we get

$$\left(\frac{h}{\lambda'} \right)^2 + \left(\frac{h}{\lambda} \right)^2 - \frac{2h^2 \cos \theta}{\lambda \lambda'} - \left(\frac{h}{\lambda} - \frac{h}{\lambda'} + m_0 c \right)^2 + m_0^2 c^2 = 0. \tag{7-18}$$

Expanding and collecting terms, we may write

$$\left(\frac{h}{\lambda'} \right)^2 - \left(\frac{h}{\lambda} \right)^2 + \left(\frac{h}{\lambda} \right)^2 - \left(\frac{h}{\lambda'} \right)^2 - \frac{2h^2 \cos \theta}{\lambda \lambda'} + \frac{2h^2}{\lambda \lambda'}$$

$$- m_0^2 c^2 + m_0^2 c^2 - 2 \left(\frac{h}{\lambda} - \frac{h}{\lambda'} \right) m_0 c = 0 \tag{7-19}$$

or

$$\boxed{\lambda' - \lambda = \frac{h}{m_0 c} (1 - \cos \theta).} \tag{7-20}$$

Now, putting in the physical constants appropriate for electrons, we get

$$\frac{h}{m_0 c} = 0.0243 \times 10^{-10} \text{ m}.$$

The wavelength of a quantum scattered by impact with a free electron at rest should be increased by

$$\Delta\lambda = 0.0243(1 - \cos\theta) \text{ Å}.$$

This has a maximum value of 0.048 Å when $\cos\theta = -1$. This shift is so small that it is hardly measurable for visible radiation, but for X-rays it is a relatively large quantity. Such an increase of wavelength of radiation by scattering was first observed by A. H. Compton who verified the derived formula for X-rays scattered at various angles from elements of low atomic number. That is, Compton himself showed that statistically, at least, the interactions of electrons with light could be accounted for by a model involving photons colliding with electrons in such a way that momentum and energy were conserved.

Compton did not observe individual impacts between individual quanta and individual electrons. The first effort to do so, which was made by Shankland, in Compton's laboratory was a failure. Since that time, however, positive results have been achieved, both by Shankland and others. Thus, we are confident that in impacts between photons and free electrons both energy and momentum are conserved, and this provides direct evidence for the corpuscular properties of radiation.

It is clear that this basic theory should apply to particles of different rest masses, and the only modification will be the use of the various rest masses for m_0 in the final equations.

When a photon strikes a particle at rest, the reaction sets the particle in motion. If the phenomenon is considered from a wave standpoint, the particle acts as a mirror, and the motion of this mirror gives a change in the wavelength of the radiation by Doppler's principle. Pure wave theory would predict a changing wavelength as the speed of the mirror is increased by the interaction. The observed result, however, consistent with quantization, is that a single photon of one energy is changed into a single photon of another energy.

The more massive particles acquire smaller speeds as a result of a collision than do lighter particles. Table 7-2 compares the maximum energy gained by an electron with the energy gained by a proton in a direct collision with a photon of the same energy. Points of interest are the very small fractions of their energy which are transferred by photons of low energy. At the other end of the energy scale, a very

TABLE 7-2. ENERGY OF RECOIL PARTICLES FOR THE COMPTON EFFECT

Photon's Energy (ev)	Electron's Energy (ev)	Proton's Energy (ev)
1,000	3.9	—
5,000	95.9	—
10,000	376.5	0.213
20,000	1,452	0.852
50,000	8,200	5.33
100,000	28,160	21.30
200,000	87,900	85.2
500,000	331,100	532.5
1,000,000	796,800	2,127.1
2,000,000	1,773,400	8,490
5,000,000	4,756,000	52,730
10,000,000	9,751,000	208,700
100,000,000	99,745,000	17,570,000

high-energy photon will have a wavelength which is negligible in comparison with the "Compton wavelength" and the scattered photon has an energy which approaches that corresponding to the Compton wavelength. In this case the particle acquires a high proportion of the energy associated with the original photon.

Radiation Pressure

Certain phenomena, of course, can be discussed in terms of either waves or corpuscles. For example, consider the energy propagation. It had been shown that the Poynting vector $\mathbf{E} \times \mathbf{H}$ represented a rate of transfer of electromagnetic energy across unit surface area in unit time. This flow of energy was related directly to the action of the electric and magnetic vectors in the wave and the forces which these vectors set up. Even in these considerations it became natural to introduce the concept of momentum associated with the electromagnetic wave. If waves are incident upon a surface, they produce a radiation pressure by virtue of their change of momentum at the surface.

The same phenomena are very simply and directly interpreted in terms of the corpuscular theory. The considerations here are identical to those involved in the kinetic theory of gases. Each photon gives its momentum to the surface as it is absorbed. If it is regularly reflected, the negative of the change in the component of its momentum normal to the surface is given to the surface, so that momentum is conserved for the system as a whole.

We illustrate this situation by considering a plane-polarized continuous electromagnetic wave of angular frequency ω. The electric and magnetic vectors are expressible by

$$\mathbf{E}_y = jE_m \cos (\omega t - \beta x), \tag{7-21}$$

where

$$\beta = 2\pi/\lambda,$$

and

$$\mathbf{H}_z = kE_m \sqrt{\frac{\epsilon_0}{\mu_0}} \cos (\omega t - \beta x) \tag{7-22}$$

and

$$|\mathbf{E}_y \times \mathbf{H}_z| = E_m{}^2 \sqrt{\frac{\epsilon_0}{\mu_0}} \cos^2 (\omega t - \beta x).$$

The average energy density is given by

$$\frac{\overline{W}}{V} = \frac{1}{2V} \int (\mu_0 H^2 + \epsilon_0 E^2)\, dV. \tag{7-23}$$

Integrating for unit surface area of the wave and over a distance in the direction of propagation equal to the wavelength, after dividing by a volume equal to the unit area times the wavelength, we obtain the correct average energy density

$$\frac{\overline{W}}{V} = \epsilon_0 E_m{}^2/2. \tag{7-24}$$

The average momentum per unit volume is obtained by dividing this by c, the velocity of light in a vacuum, and, since the force on the surface is this momentum times c, the electromagnetic radiation pressure is equal to the average energy per unit volume. Now, according to the quantum theory, the individual photons have energy $h\nu$, and the average number N_1 of these per unit volume is given by

$$N_1 = \epsilon_0 E_m{}^2/2h\nu.$$

The number arriving per unit time is given by

$$I \equiv N_1 c = \frac{\epsilon_0 E_m{}^2}{2h\nu} c.$$

Each is assumed to have the momentum $h\nu/c$, and the resulting pressure on the surface when they are absorbed is

$$p = I\frac{h\nu}{c} = \epsilon_0 E_m{}^2/2. \tag{7-25}$$

If it is noticed, that, according to Maxwell's theory, the average total energy is half potential E^2 and half kinetic H^2, the above result when expressed in terms of kinetic energy is identical to that derived for a beam of molecules, namely,

$$p = 2W_K/V.$$

Summary

Although radiation pressure can be explained in terms of electromagnetic waves, following the acceptance of Compton's results there was little doubt that the photons introduced earlier by Einstein in his explanation of the photoelectric effect had a physical existence. The reactions of electromagnetic waves with matter are most easily discussed in terms of the properties of these photons. At the same time, it is important to emphasize that the waves could not be abandoned. The energy of the corpuscle depended on periodic phenomena determined from the wavelength. The surmise of W. H. Bragg that the theory of X-rays would contain properties of both waves and corpuscles proved to be correct. Compton's results are direct evidence for the momentum of the individual particles $p = h/\lambda$, while X-ray diffraction gives a direct measure of this same wavelength λ.

Problems on the Corpuscular Action of Radiation

1. An electromagnetic oscillator radiates 1.00 kw at a frequency of 3.0×10^7 cycles/sec. If the radiation is uniformly distributed over the surface of a sphere centered at the oscillator, what is the magnitude of Poynting's vector at a distance of 100,000 m from the oscillator? What is the energy of one photon of the radiated frequency? How many photons in each second of time pass through 1.00 m² of area of the sphere of 100,000 m radius centered at the oscillator?

2. Monochromatic light of wavelength 5890 Å is incident perpendicular to a black surface which absorbs all of it and produces a radiation pressure of 10^{-9} newtons/m².
   a. What is the energy per unit volume for this radiation?
   b. How many photons/m³ would account for the energy density?

3. If energy of 3.00 ev is required to liberate any electrons from a certain metal, what is the minimum frequency of light which will be effective in producing a photoelectric effect?

4. A photon corresponding to a wavelength of 2537 Å is incident on a metal surface. It liberates an electron which moves directly away from the surface with an energy of 1.50 ev. What maximum energy required to extract the electron from the surface is consistent with these data?

5. Considering only the photon and the electron of Problem 4, what is the change of momentum between the initial and final conditions? Is the con-

servation of momentum really violated? If not, reaction with what system would you think is responsible for this change of momentum?

6. An X-ray photon which corresponds to an energy of 50,000 ev strikes an electron at rest in a direct impact and is reflected. What is the energy loss of the photon in ev? What is the change in frequency?

7. An X-ray photon which has an energy of 50,000 ev strikes an electron moving toward it with a momentum equal in magnitude to that of the incident photon, and is reflected through 180°.
   a. What is the wavelength of the photon initially?
   b. What is its wavelength after reflection?
   c. What is the gain in energy of the electron?

8. An X-ray photon which has an energy of 50,000 ev strikes an electron moving toward it with an energy of 10,000 ev and is reflected. Apply the conservation of energy and the conservation of momentum to the impact to determine the shift in the frequency of the photon.

9. If, in Problem 6, the photon is scattered at an angle of 90° with respect to its initial velocity, what is the shift of its frequency?

10. What is the angle that the electron's recoil in Problem 9 makes with the direction of the photon's initial velocity?

11. A photon having an energy of 3×10^7 ev strikes a proton at rest and it is reflected through 180°. What is the energy transferred to the proton?

References on the Corpuscular Nature of Light

Fano, U., and L. Fano, *Basic Physics of Atoms and Molecules,* Chs. 2, 3, 4, 5, 6, and 7, particularly pp. 36-9, 65-8, and 76-7 (New York: John Wiley, 1959). (The first few chapters of this book contain an original organization of the evidence supporting the atomic theory, and the pages selected show the bearing of photoelectric experiments upon the corpuscular theory of light.)

Hughes, A. L., and Lee A. DuBridge, *Photoelectric Phenomena* (New York: McGraw-Hill Book Company, 1934). (A comprehensive treatment of this restricted field.)

Loeb, Leonard B., *Atomic Structure,* Ch. 3 (New York: John Wiley, 1938).

Richtmyer, F. K., and E. H. Kennard, *Introduction to Modern Physics,* photoelectric effect, pp. 71-108. Compton effect, pp. 514-22 (New York: McGraw-Hill Book Company, 1947).

Ruark, Arthur E., and Harold C. Urey, *Atoms, Molecules and Quanta,* photoelectric effect, pp. 63ff., Compton effect, pp. 84ff. (New York: McGraw-Hill Book Company, 1930).

8 Coupled Oscillators and the Propagation of Waves Through Periodic Structures

Modern physics has developed out of the physics of Galileo and Newton, although not by a process of logical deduction from fundamental principles which were known to the founders of science. We have briefly reviewed the principles of electricity and magnetism which provide a basis for modern developments and we have summarized briefly the principles underlying mechanical vibrations. The application of the fundamental principles of electricity to the identification of the electron as a constituent of all atoms has been described. Relativistic mechanics, which became quite necessary for the discussion of electronic motion was a distinct departure from the laws of mechanics which had been systematized by Newton. Similarly, from the behavior of waves in continuous media, Rayleigh came to definite conclusions about the distribution in wavelength of thermally excited radiation. These conclusions were in error, particularly at the shorter wavelengths, because the radiant energy was quantized, and Planck by a study of the data was able to discover the principles governing the quantization.

Having discussed the identification of the electron, the development of special relativity and the origin of the quantum theory, which are all topics of modern physics, we return to review a field to which we shall apply Newtonian mechanics. The justification for delaying the discussion of coupled oscillators and wave phenomena in periodic structures is the essential complexity of the detail associated with the analysis. The reason for introducing the subject at all should be quite obvious. Matter is atomic rather than continuous in structure, and in many of the problems of physics it is quite unjustifiable to ignore this atomic structure. The X-ray evidence which we have reviewed in

TABLE 8-1. LIST OF SYMBOLS USED IN CHAPTER 8

Symbol	Name	Quantity Designated
k		restoring force constant
b		coupling constant
ω	omega	angular or radian frequency (angular velocity in the circle to which simple harmonic motion may be referred)
R		ratio of displacements y_2/y_1
μ	mu	mass per unit length of string
F		stretching force in string
a		spacing between concentrated masses
w		phase velocity
n		number of masses per wavelength λ

Chapter 6 shows unmistakably that crystals possess a regular or periodic distribution of matter in space. It would seem very strange indeed if this periodicity of the solid state could be ignored in discussing the properties of crystals or the wave phenomena in these crystals.

The essential principles which underlie the vibrations of a mechanical system are very simple and easily understood. The analysis may be made to depend upon elementary algebra or at most beginning calculus, and it is such a treatment that we review, so that it may be used as a basis for the discussion of systems having several or many concentrated masses. A study of simple vibration problems is helpful in two ways: (1) where the problems encountered are sufficiently simple to permit exact solutions, quantitatively correct information can be obtained on this basis, and (2) even when quantitative treatment is not feasible at this level, because of the complexity of the problem, by analogy with the basic problems which have been solved we can reach a qualitative understanding which is sound in principle.

There are two basic methods for obtaining information in these problems of vibratory motion in extended media. Both of these methods have been illustrated in the study of general physics. The simplest vibration problems were solved by setting down the equation for the acceleration of each oscillator and solving these for displacements consistent with given initial conditions. The complexity of the problem was increased when there were several coupled oscillators. When there was a continuous distribution of the inertia and elastance factors, as for example in the vibrations of a stretched uniform string, a second method of attack proved useful. This was to consider the vibrations as arising from trains of waves. It was then sufficient to have a description of the displacements due to the individual waves and information concerning the rate at which they were propagated.

Because of the atomic constitution of matter, to treat many problems from the vibrational viewpoint, we are compelled to consider the motions associated with individual atoms, or to treat the problem from the wave viewpoint, we are compelled to consider the propagation of waves in periodic structures. These are complicated problems, and at first thought it may seem that obtaining information about them is hopeless. Some simplifications, however, result from the fact that our primary interest is in standing waves and from the fact that it will be sufficient for us to consider simple harmonic vibrations only.

Simple Harmonic Vibrations of a Pair of Coupled Oscillators Determined by Inspection

As a simple illustration of the principles that we shall use throughout our discussion, let us consider the two oscillators suggested in Fig. 8-1. These need not be identical.

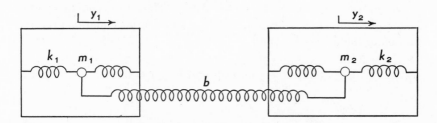

Fig. 8-1. Coupled mechanical oscillators.

The first oscillator has a mass m_1 and the second a mass m_2. Without the spring connecting the two masses, the restoring force constant for the first mass is k_1 and the similar force constant for the second mass is k_2. If the oscillators are not coupled, the differential equations of motion are

$$m_1 \frac{d^2 y_1}{dt^2} + k_1 y_1 = 0 \qquad (8\text{-}1)$$

and

$$m_2 \frac{d^2 y_2}{dt^2} + k_2 y_2 = 0. \qquad (8\text{-}2)$$

Thus, if the oscillators are uncoupled, each will execute simple harmonic motion. The radian frequency of the first oscillator (which is the angular velocity in the reference circle often used for the analysis of this problem in general physics texts) is

$$\omega_{10} = \sqrt{\frac{k_1}{m_1}}, \tag{8-3}$$

and that of the second oscillator is

$$\omega_{20} = \sqrt{\frac{k_2}{m_2}}. \tag{8-4}$$

The displacements are given by

$$y_1 = A_1 \sin (\omega_{10}t + \phi_1) \tag{8-5}$$

and

$$y_2 = A_2 \sin (\omega_{20}t + \phi_2), \tag{8-6}$$

where the amplitudes A_1 and A_2 and the phase angles ϕ_1 and ϕ_2 are entirely independent.

If now the coupling spring has one end attached to each mass, there will in general be a new equilibrium position for each of the masses. We shall simplify the treatment by agreeing to measure the displacements y_1 and y_2 from the new equilibrium positions. Then if the coupling spring has a restoring force constant of b, the differential equations for the motion of the masses become:

$$m_1 \frac{d^2y_1}{dt^2} + k_1y_1 + b(y_1 - y_2) = 0 \tag{8-7}$$

and

$$m_2 \frac{d^2y_2}{dt^2} + k_2y_2 - b(y_1 - y_2) = 0, \tag{8-8}$$

or

$$m_1\ddot{y}_1 + (k_1 + b)y_1 - by_2 = 0 \tag{8-7'}$$

and

$$m_2\ddot{y}_2 + (k_2 + b)y_2 - by_1 = 0, \tag{8-8'}$$

where $\ddot{y}$ represents the acceleration or second time derivative. From an inspection of Eqs. (7) and (8), it is clear that the only way that these can be reduced to those for simple harmonic motion is to impose the condition

$$y_2 = Ry_1, \tag{8-9}$$

where R is a suitably chosen constant. The equations for the motion then become

$$m_1\ddot{y}_1 + (k_1 + b - Rb)y_1 = 0 \tag{8-10}$$

$$m_2\ddot{y}_2 + \left(k_2 + b - \frac{b}{R}\right)y_2 = 0. \tag{8-11}$$

The radian frequencies are then expressible by

$$\omega_1' = \sqrt{\frac{k_1 + (1 - R)b}{m_1}} \tag{8-12}$$

and

$$\omega_2' = \sqrt{\frac{k_2 + \left(1 - \dfrac{1}{R}\right)b}{m_2}}. \tag{8-13}$$

In order to have Eq. (9) apply throughout the entire free oscillation, it is necessary that $\omega_1' = \omega_2'$. Hence,

$$\frac{k_1}{m_1} + \frac{1}{m_1}b - \frac{bR}{m_1} = \frac{k_2}{m_2} + \frac{1}{m_2}b - \frac{b}{m_2 R}$$

or

$$\frac{b}{m_1}R^2 - \left(\frac{k_1}{m_1} - \frac{k_2}{m_2} - \frac{b}{m_2} + \frac{b}{m_1}\right)R - \frac{b}{m_2} = 0. \tag{8-14}$$

To simplify notation we define,

$$\omega_1^2 \equiv \frac{k_1 + b}{m_1}$$

$$\omega_2^2 \equiv (k_2 + b)/m_2,$$

where ω_1 is the radian frequency of the first oscillator with the second clamped, and ω_2 is the radian frequency of the second with the first clamped in its equilibrium position. Eq. (14) then becomes

$$R = \frac{\omega_1^2 - \omega_2^2 \pm \sqrt{(\omega_1^2 - \omega_2^2)^2 + 4\dfrac{b^2}{m_1 m_2}}}{\dfrac{2b}{m_1}}. \tag{8-15}$$

If $b = 0$ the result is entirely indeterminate, and this is consistent with the direct analysis for zero coupling. Since the value of the radical is somewhat larger than $\omega_1^2 - \omega_2^2$ (on the tacit assumption that $\omega_1^2 > \omega_2^2$), we find that one of the values for R is positive and the other is negative. These values correspond to two possible simple harmonic modes of vibration and the interpretation is that in one mode the displacements are in the same sense while in the other mode they are in opposite senses.

A quantitative interpretation which is of interest is the case of small coupling, so that

$$(\omega_1{}^2 - \omega_2{}^2) \gg \frac{4b^2}{m_1 m_2}.$$

In this case,

$$R = \frac{\omega_1{}^2 - \omega_2{}^2 \pm (\omega_1{}^2 - \omega_2{}^2)\sqrt{1 + \dfrac{4b^2}{m_1 m_2 (\omega_1{}^2 - \omega_2{}^2)^2}}}{2b/m_1}$$

$$\simeq \frac{\omega_1{}^2 - \omega_2{}^2 \pm (\omega_1{}^2 - \omega_2{}^2)\left[1 + \dfrac{2b^2}{m_1 m_2 (\omega_1{}^2 - \omega_2{}^2)^2}\right]}{2b/m_1}. \qquad (8\text{-}16)$$

If the positive sign is taken,

$$R \simeq \frac{m_1(\omega_1{}^2 - \omega_2{}^2)}{b}, \qquad (8\text{-}17)$$

whereas if the negative sign is taken,

$$R \simeq -\frac{b}{m_2(\omega_1{}^2 - \omega_2{}^2)}. \qquad (8\text{-}18)$$

In the second of these modes of vibration, one point on the coupling spring appears to be fixed and the masses oscillate with simultaneous displacements in opposite directions. This is the mode having the higher of the two frequencies. For the first mode, giving the lower of the two frequencies, the mass m_2 has a relatively large displacement and the mass m_1 a smaller displacement in the same sense.

We can find the approximate frequencies by substituting the values of R in Eqs. (12) and (13). For the higher radian frequency we use the symbol ω_+, and it is given by

$$\omega_+{}^2 = \frac{k_1 + b + 1b^2/m_2(\omega_1{}^2 - \omega_2{}^2)}{m_1},$$

or

$$\omega_+ = \sqrt{\omega_1{}^2 + \frac{b^2}{m_1 m_2(\omega_1{}^2 - \omega_2{}^2)}}$$

$$= \omega_1 \sqrt{1 + \frac{b^2}{m_1 m_2 \omega_1{}^2(\omega_1{}^2 - \omega_2{}^2)}}$$

$$\simeq \omega_1 + \frac{b^2}{2m_1 m_2 \omega_1(\omega_1{}^2 - \omega_2{}^2)}. \qquad (8\text{-}19)$$

Similarly, for the lower of the two frequencies, denoted by ω_-, since $R \simeq \dfrac{m_1(\omega_1^2 - \omega_2^2)}{b}$, we obtain from Eq. (13),

$$\omega_- \simeq \sqrt{\frac{k_2 + b - \dfrac{b^2}{m_1(\omega_1^2 - \omega_2^2)}}{m_2}}$$

$$= \omega_2 \sqrt{1 - \frac{b^2}{\omega_2^2(\omega_1^2 - \omega_2^2)m_1 m_2}}$$

$$\simeq \omega_2 - \frac{b^2}{2\omega_2(\omega_1^2 - \omega_2^2)m_1 m_2}. \tag{8-20}$$

These results may be described as follows. The higher of the two frequencies for a pair of coupled oscillators is somewhat greater than the frequency of the oscillator having the higher natural frequency, which would be obtained with the oscillator of lower frequency clamped in its equilibrium position. The lower of the two frequencies for a pair of coupled oscillators is somewhat less than the frequency of the oscillator having the lower natural frequency, which would be obtained with the oscillator of higher frequency clamped in its equilibrium position.

A case of special interest to us is that in which the oscillators are identical, giving $\omega_1 = \omega_2$, etc. For this case, Eq. (15) shows that the magnitude of the displacements is always the same for the two oscillators, but that for the mode of higher frequency the simultaneous displacements are in opposite directions, while for the mode of lower frequency the displacements are in the same sense. For this special case the coupling spring is ineffective in the lower mode of vibration and

$$\omega_- = \omega_{10} = \omega_{20}.$$

On the other hand, for the higher mode of vibration $R = -1$, and Eq. (12) gives

$$\omega_+ = \sqrt{\frac{k_1 + 2b}{m_1}} = \omega_1 \sqrt{1 + \frac{b}{m_1 \omega_1^2}} \simeq 1 + \frac{b}{2m_1 \omega_1}. \tag{8-21}$$

The physical interpretation of these equations is almost as elementary as in the case of the lower mode.

Similar results might be obtained for three or more coupled oscillators. It is found that there are as many different frequencies for possible S.H.M. of the system as there are oscillators, even for identical oscillators. In the case of a coupled system of identical oscillators, the spread in the frequencies increases with the restoring force constant of the coupling springs. Instead of pursuing this matter further we turn directly to a case which has been treated conventionally by the method of wave propagation. A simple illustration is the transverse vibrations of loaded strings. This is a case which has been treated by the method of standing waves. Our approach, however, will be the elementary one which has just been used for the coupled oscillators.

The Loaded String

The basic problems in the case of transverse vibrations for a loaded string have been treated by the use of principles discussed in general physics with the aid of mathematics no more advanced than college algebra. The analysis is simplified by assuming that the transverse displacements are so small that the angle which any part of the string makes with the equilibrium position is small. This last restriction is conventional, and it is made even in more advanced treatments of the loaded string. It enables us to replace the sine of the angle the string makes with the equilibrium position by the tangent of this angle to simplify our expressions.

The physical basis of our discussion is that in the simple harmonic modes of vibration of the loaded string all parts of the system execute simple harmonic motions with the same frequency. As in the elementary treatment of vibrations the radian frequency ω is related to the mass m of the oscillating particle, and to the restoring force constant k, by the expression

$$\omega = \sqrt{\frac{k}{m}}.$$

The restoring force constant, by which we mean the absolute value of the ratio of the restoring force to the displacement giving rise to this force, is readily determined by inspection for the particles on a loaded string. Information concerning the masses and the fact that the frequency is the same for the entire system combine to enable us to determine the configurations of the loaded string corresponding to a given simple harmonic mode of vibration.

As a first illustration of the method we consider a string stretched between two fixed pegs with a force F and loaded at its midpoint with a mass which we call μL, assumed to be so large that the mass of the string itself is negligible in comparison with it. We proceed to determine the radian frequency of vibration in terms of the length of the string L, μ, and F. Fig. 8-2 illustrates this case. The mass is displaced trans-

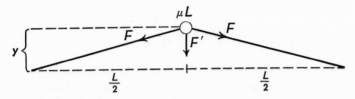

Fig. 8-2. A stretched string with a single concentrated mass at its center.

versely by the amount y and this displacement gives rise to the restoring force F' which is found by taking the sum of the y-components in the string on the two sides of the mass m. By inspection, $F' = 4Fy/L$, so $k = 4F/L$. Hence, the angular frequency ω_{11} for this case is

$$\omega_{11} = \frac{2}{L}\sqrt{\frac{F}{\mu}}.$$

Next we consider the case in which the string of length L has a mass $\mu L/2$ attached at a point at a distance of $L/4$ from each end. This situation is shown in Fig. 8-3. There are now two modes of vibration: one

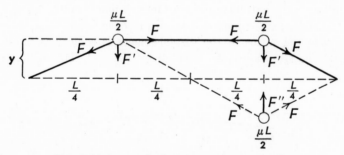

Fig. 8-3. A stretched string with two loads.

in which the masses are displaced the same amount in the same direction and one in which the equal displacements are in opposite directions. The analysis of the latter case is almost identical to the case we have already considered, and it gives the result

$$\omega_{22} = \frac{4}{L}\sqrt{\frac{F}{\mu}},$$

exactly twice the result in the preceding case, as would be expected. For identical displacements of the two masses, the restoring force on each mass is $4\dfrac{y}{L}F$, and the angular frequency therefore is

$$\omega_{12} = \frac{2}{L}\sqrt{\frac{2F}{\mu}}.$$

A comparison of corresponding frequencies is to be made later.

If along the length of the string L we have masses of $\mu L/3$ placed at a distance of $L/6$ from each end and a mass $\mu L/3$ placed in the middle of the string, the displacement of neighboring masses by the same amounts in opposite directions will give for the angular frequency

$$\omega_{33} = \frac{6}{L}\sqrt{\frac{F}{\mu}}.$$

If the middle mass remains at rest and the masses next to the two ends are displaced in opposite directions, we have the angular frequency

$$\omega_{23} = \frac{3}{L}\sqrt{\frac{3F}{\mu}}.$$

If the masses are all to be displaced in the same direction in such a way that a simple harmonic motion for each mass results, the restoring forces must be proportional to the displacement, and the problem of determining the ratios of the displacements is somewhat more complicated. The situation is represented by Fig. 8-4. The displacements

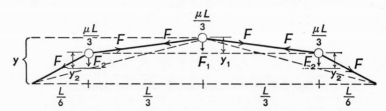

Fig. 8-4. A stretched string with three loads.

of the end masses will be the same. In this case, the restoring forces depend directly on the transverse displacement of the mass from the straight line connecting the two masses next to that for which the restoring force is calculated (or a neighboring mass with a peg in the case of the masses next to the end). These displacements are called

y_1 and y_2 as shown in Fig. 8-4. The restoring force on the central mass is $6Fy_1/L$ corresponding to the total displacement y as shown. For either of the other masses, the restoring force is $9Fy_2/L$ as shown. Another geometrical relation is necessary to complete the solution, and from the figure we see that

$$\frac{y}{3} + y_2 = y - y_1,$$

or that

$$y_2 = \frac{2y}{3} - y_1.$$

The condition for equal angular frequencies can be stated as

$$\frac{9Fy_2}{L\left(\dfrac{y}{3} + y_2\right)} = \frac{6Fy_1}{Ly}$$

or

$$\frac{2y_1}{y} = \frac{3y_2}{\dfrac{y}{3} + y_2} = \frac{3\left(\dfrac{2y}{3} - y_1\right)}{y - y_1},$$

and $y = 2y_1$.

For the radian frequency we write

$$\omega_{13} = \frac{3}{L}\sqrt{\frac{F}{\mu}}.$$

There is no essential difficulty associated with carrying this analysis further on exactly the same principles. The results which we have obtained confirm the fact that there will in general be as many modes of vibration as there are discrete masses in the distribution. Furthermore, in the limit of a uniform distribution of mass along the string we know that

$$\omega_{1\infty} = \frac{\pi}{L}\sqrt{\frac{F}{\mu}},$$

and inspection of the above results shows a very rapid approach to this limit as the number of masses is increased.

A very remarkable thing about these results is that even for relatively few masses per wavelength the simultaneous displacements of the masses are related exactly sinusoidally to distance measured along the string. We would expect this relation to apply at least approximately where the loop contains many masses, but the fact that it applies exactly in each of the cases analyzed is worth noticing.

It is not difficult to see that the periodicity in the location of the mass along the string imposes a limit on the allowed frequencies. Suppose, for example, we have a very long string with masses μa spaced at regular intervals a along the string. The mass of the string itself being negligible, the average mass per unit length of the string is μ. The stretching force in the string is F. The highest radian frequency for harmonic vibrations of the masses is the one corresponding to the displacement of neighboring masses in opposite directions. This is called the radian frequency of cut-off and it is denoted by ω_c. It can be set down at once on the basis of previous considerations

$$\omega_c = \frac{2}{a}\sqrt{\frac{F}{\mu}}. \tag{8-22}$$

Below this radian frequency are a very large number corresponding to allowed simple harmonic motions. If, as we have assumed, the string is very long, frequencies very close to zero are allowed. The loaded string, therefore, acts as a low pass filter for transverse vibrations. Below the cut-off, vibrations can be transmitted along the string without decrease in amplitude except for the effects of mechanical resistance, which for simplicity we are neglecting. Above the cut-off frequency, however, waves decrease in amplitude from mass to mass as they are transmitted along the string for the reason that the tension in the string is not sufficient to enable them to keep up with such high-frequency oscillations.

Above the cut-off frequency neighboring masses are displaced in opposite directions, but the magnitudes of these displacements decrease with constant ratio R as we move along the string. Suppose that the vibrations are excited by displacing the zeroth mass according to the equation

$$y_0 = A \sin \omega t.$$

Then, according to what has just been said,

$$y_1 = -RA \sin \omega t,$$

and

$$y_2 = R^2 A \sin \omega t.$$

The equation applying to the acceleration of the first mass is

$$(\mu a)\frac{d^2 y_1}{dt^2} = \frac{F}{a}(y_0 - y_1) + \frac{F}{a}(y_2 - y_1).$$

In addition to values for y_0, y_1, and y_2 for substitution in this equation, we need the acceleration of the first mass. This is

$$\frac{d^2y_1}{dt^2} = R\omega^2 A \sin \omega t.$$

Hence, Newton's second law applied to the motion of the first mass gives

$$R\mu a A \omega^2 \sin \omega t = \frac{F}{a}(A \sin \omega t + RA \sin \omega t) + \frac{F}{a}(R^2 A \sin \omega t + RA \sin \omega t)$$

or

$$R^2 + \left(2 - \frac{\mu a^2 \omega^2}{F}\right) R + 1 = 0. \tag{8-23}$$

Thus,

$$R = \frac{\left(\dfrac{\mu a^2 \omega^2}{F} - 2\right) \pm \sqrt{\left(\dfrac{\mu a^2 \omega^2}{F} - 2\right)^2 - 4}}{2}. \tag{8-24}$$

The ratio R is real if

$$\frac{\mu a^2 \omega^2}{F} \geq 4,$$

and the equality sign results in the previously stated cut-off frequency ω_c. The negative sign taken with the radical gives the ratio R less than 1, as we have assumed. (The positive sign would give R greater than 1, and would correspond to excitation of oscillations at some mass y_n where $n \lesssim 2$, which would result in waves moving back toward the masses of lower-numbered subscripts.) Because when ω is large enough to make $\frac{\mu a^2 \omega^2}{F}$ much greater than 4, R is considerably less than 1, the amplitude of the oscillations rapidly decreases as n increases. In this region the phase shift remains at the value π, and the amplitude decreases. The vibrations are said to be "attenuated."

Although our emphasis has been upon the conditions which lead to simple harmonic vibrations for the parts of the string, it will be informative now to interpret our results in terms of the behavior of the phase velocity for waves on the loaded string. If the string is bounded at fixed supports, twice the length of the string must be equal to the wavelength λ times an integer, or

$$2L = n\lambda \tag{8-25}$$

for the production of standing waves. For the consideration of traveling waves, the velocity w, with which the phase is propagated, must be given by

$$\boxed{w = f\lambda,}$$

(8-26)

where $f = \omega/2\pi$. Although the combination of Eqs. (25) and (26), and the information we have derived concerning the radian frequencies ω_{ik} enable us to determine the variation of phase velocity with the number of masses per wavelength, we shall give the general argument to establish this result, which we consider quite important.

The formulation of the problem is precisely the same as we have used for the discussion of attenuation above the cut-off frequency. We have concentrated masses μa spaced at intervals a along a string in which the stretching force is F. As suggested in Fig. 8-5, we consider the general

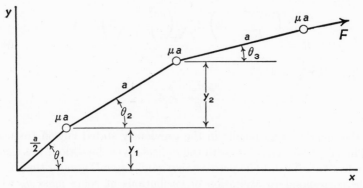

Fig. 8-5. A stretched string with n masses per wavelength.

case in which there are n masses per wavelength of a standing wave. Now,

$$w = f\lambda = \frac{na}{2\pi}\sqrt{\frac{k}{\mu a}},$$

where the restoring force used for the first mass is determined by

$$k = \frac{F(\sin\theta_1 - \sin\theta_2)}{y_1}$$

$$= \frac{F}{y_1}\left(\frac{2y_1}{a} - \frac{y_2}{a}\right)$$

$$= \frac{F}{a}\left(2 - \frac{y_2}{y_1}\right).$$

But from the sinusoidal relationship between displacements from equilibrium and distance along the string (see problem 4 at the end of this chapter), we may write

$$\frac{y_2}{y_1} = \frac{\sin\left[\dfrac{3\left(\dfrac{\pi}{2}\right)}{\lambda/2a}\right] - \sin\left[\dfrac{\left(\dfrac{\pi}{2}\right)}{\lambda/2a}\right]}{\sin\left[\dfrac{\dfrac{\pi}{2}}{\lambda/2a}\right]}$$

$$= \frac{\sin\left(\dfrac{3a\pi}{\lambda}\right) - \sin\left(\dfrac{a\pi}{\lambda}\right)}{\sin\left(\dfrac{a\pi}{\lambda}\right)}$$

$$= \frac{\sin\dfrac{3\pi}{n} - \sin\dfrac{\pi}{n}}{\sin\dfrac{\pi}{n}}$$

$$= \frac{2\cos\dfrac{1}{2}\left(\dfrac{3\pi}{n} + \dfrac{\pi}{n}\right)\sin\dfrac{1}{2}\left(\dfrac{3\pi}{n} - \dfrac{\pi}{n}\right)}{\sin\dfrac{\pi}{n}}$$

$$= \frac{2\cos 2\dfrac{\pi}{n}\sin\dfrac{\pi}{n}}{\sin\dfrac{\pi}{n}} = 2\cos 2\dfrac{\pi}{n}.$$

Thus,

$$k = \frac{F}{a}\left(2 - 2\cos\frac{2\pi}{n}\right) = \frac{4F}{a}\left(\frac{1 - \cos\dfrac{2\pi}{n}}{2}\right)$$

$$= \frac{4F}{a}\sin^2\frac{\pi}{n},$$

and

$$w = \frac{na}{2\pi} \sqrt{\frac{4F}{\mu aa} \sin^2 \frac{\pi}{n}}$$

$$= \frac{n}{\pi} \sqrt{\frac{F}{\mu}} \sin \frac{\pi}{n}$$

or

$$w = \frac{n}{\pi} w_\infty \sin \frac{\pi}{n}, \qquad (8\text{-}27)$$

where

$$w_\infty = \sqrt{\frac{F}{\mu}},$$

the phase velocity for an infinite number of masses per wavelength or for a continuous distribution of mass. Eq. (27) gives the relationship between the phase velocity and the number of masses per wavelength which was the relationship sought. A loaded string is a dispersing medium for transverse waves in much the same way that a piece of glass is for light; waves of different lengths are propagated with different velocities.

For a loaded string, the group velocity shows an even more pronounced variation with the number of masses per wavelength. Rayleigh's analysis (Appendix IV) showed that the group velocity v is related to the variation of phase velocity with wavelength by

$$v = d(w/\lambda)/d(1/\lambda) = w - \lambda \, dw/d\lambda. \qquad (8\text{-}28)$$

In this case, we have

$$w = w_\infty \frac{\lambda}{\pi a} \sin (\pi a/\lambda), \qquad (8\text{-}27')$$

and differentiation yields

$$dw/d\lambda = \frac{w_\infty}{\pi a} \left[\sin (\pi a/\lambda) - \frac{\pi a}{\lambda} \cos (\pi a/\lambda) \right].$$

Substitution of this result into Eq. (28) gives

$$v = w_\infty [\cos \pi a/\lambda] = w_\infty \cos (\pi/n). \qquad (8\text{-}29)$$

At the critical frequency, which results in two concentrated masses per wavelength, the group velocity, therefore, falls to zero.

Summary

The application of Newtonian mechanics to the problems of coupled oscillators has shown that the *number* of simple harmonic *modes of vibration* is equal to the number of the coupled *oscillating masses*. The *spread* of the *frequencies*, on the other hand, *increases* with the strength of the *coupling force* mutual to two oscillators relative to the restoring force acting on the individual oscillator. The loaded string, used as an illustration, can be treated from the standpoint of coupled oscillators to which the foregoing general conclusions apply. Such a loaded system possesses the properties of a filter which will pass some frequencies and attenuate others, and the exact system used for illustration constitutes a low-pass mechanical filter. Neglecting resistive forces, such a system passes without attenuation all vibrations below a critical cut-off frequency, and these vibrations can be treated as waves. This system attenuates all frequencies higher than that corresponding to the critical frequency. It is a matter of very considerable interest that loaded or lumped systems have a phase velocity depending on the frequency in the pass-band, and they constitute a dispersive medium. In the "stop-band," simple waves are not possible, because of the attenuation, and the attenuation depends upon the frequency.

Problems on Vibratory Systems

1. A pair of identical coupled oscillators each having an effective mass of .010 kg and each having a restoring force constant of 1.0 newtons/m are coupled by a spring having a restoring force constant of 0.01 newtons/m.
   a. Determine the radian frequency of either oscillator when the other is clamped.
   b. There are two modes of vibration in which each oscillator will execute simple harmonic motion. Describe these two modes and determine their radian frequencies.
2. A long flexible string is loaded with a bead of mass 0.0010 kg at one meter distances along its length (the mass of the string itself being negligible). The string is placed under a tension of 1.00 newton. If one end of this string is displaced harmonically at a low frequency (for example, 2 complete cycles per sec), what is the speed with which the phase of this disturbance will be propagated along the string? At what radian frequency must the end of the string be displaced in a harmonic motion if each wavelength on the string is to be 2 m?
3. A uniform flexible string has a mass of 2.00 g in a length of just 1.00 m. It is loaded at its midpoint with a concentrated mass of 2.00 g. It is then stretched between fixed pegs with a force of 1.60 newtons. All parts of this string execute simple harmonic motion with the same frequency.

a. If a snapshot were taken of the string at some instant when it is not in its equilibrium position, what mathematical function would you expect to express the displacement of the uniform portion of the string as a function of distance along the string?

b. What would you expect the snapshot to reveal concerning the configuration of the string in the neighborhood of the concentrated load?

c. What physical principles would you expect to apply in determining the frequency of this system vibrating in a single loop?

d. If you are able to do so, formulate the problem, and determine the frequency for vibration of the loaded system in a single loop.

4. A light string of length L m and under a tension of F newtons is bounded at its ends by fixed pegs. It is loaded with equal masses $\mu L/4$ at points $L/8$, $3L/8$, $5L/8$, and $7L/8$ from one end of the string.

a. Determine by inspection the shape required if all parts of the string are to vibrate in a single loop in simple harmonic motion.

b. Show also that your answers for the displacements of the *masses* are expressible by

$$y_k = y_m \sin (2k - 1)\pi/8,$$

where k is the identification of the mass numbered from one end, and y_m is a suitably chosen constant.

References on Coupled Oscillators and Wave Phenomena

(All references are somewhat more advanced than the elementary discussion given here.)

Brillouin, Leon, *Wave Propagation in Periodic Structures* (New York: Mc-Graw-Hill Book Company, 1946).

Coulson, C. A., *Waves* (Edinburgh: Oliver and Boyd, 1947; New York: Interscience Publishers, 1947).

Morse, Philip M., *Vibration and Sound*, Ch. 1 (New York: McGraw-Hill Book Company, 1948).

PART II | Configurations of Electrons

9 | Basic Ideas of Wave Mechanics

Introduction

In Part I, we reviewed the rise of atomic physics. We saw that a wave theory of light successfully explained interference and diffraction. On the other hand, we saw that it was necessary to associate photons with light waves to account for the interactions of light with matter. So, it appeared that certain light experiments required a wave theory and other light experiments required a corpuscular theory to explain them successfully.

This wave-particle dualism proved not to be confined to light alone. We will presently describe how it became necessary to associate waves with electrons to account for experiments demonstrating the diffraction of electron beams. This development of the 1920s ushered in the revolutionary theory of wave mechanics.

Wave mechanics enables us to explain and to predict atomic and solid state phenomena. It is the primary task of Part II to summarize the results of current atomic theory in several fields sufficiently diverse to suggest to the student the power of wave mechanics and to provide a basis for further study. The mathematics which we use for this purpose does not go beyond the level of an introductory course in differential equations, and much of the discussion is qualitative or only semiquantitative. Mathematical appendices supplement some of the individual sections of the text where a somewhat more quantitative treatment of an important problem might be of interest. For example, Appendix V, on the harmonic analysis of wave forms, is the mathematical basis of the present chapter, since it gives mathematical formulas to express some of the matters summarized verbally in the text. These appendices are recommended for students who wish to go a little deeper into the theory.

Origin of Wave Mechanics

We recall that Newton once proposed a corpuscular theory of light in which the particles were assumed to satisfy his own laws of motion. This theory explained the formation of shadows and Snell's laws of reflection and refraction. In other words, the corpuscular theory of Newton accounted for the facts of geometrical optics.

The wave theory of light replaced the Newtonian theory, because the former explained typical wave phenomena like interference and diffraction, whereas the latter did not explain, and even contradicted, these phenomena. The wave theory would not have been considered superior to the Newtonian theory, however, if it had not also accounted for the facts of geometrical optics. This last question was studied in detail and great generality by the Irish astronomer W. R. Hamilton about the middle of the nineteenth century. He proved that the theory of geometrical optics is a good approximation to the wave theory in a region occupied by a continuous medium whose index of refraction does not vary appreciably over distances of a few wavelengths.

To say that the theory of geometrical optics is a good approximation is equivalent to saying that all typical wave phenomena like interference and diffraction are negligible or absent. Therefore, Hamilton's work explained why the wave properties of light are ordinarily not noticed and why Newton could have thought that a beam of light is a stream of particles obeying the Newtonian laws of motion. It occurred to de Broglie in the early 1920s that what was true for light may also be true for ponderable matter; that is, it may be that material bodies are governed by wave laws but that we have failed to notice such laws in the same way that Newton, concentrating on the problems of geometrical optics, failed to appreciate the wave nature of light.

de Broglie's Postulate

In 1920, when de Broglie took up the study of theoretical physics, matter was considered to consist of atoms, which in turn were believed to have a structure based on electrons and protons. Light, on the other hand, was supposed to be an electromagnetic wave with its energy continuously distributed throughout space. This definite division in the application of the corpuscular and wave concepts was beginning to encounter difficulties.

In the first place, the facts of the photoelectric effect were never explained on the basis of a pure electromagnetic wave theory of light. Einstein, in 1905, had given his interpretation of the photoelectric effect in which the energy $h\nu$ of a quantum of light was all given to one electron, and, if this energy was sufficient to lift the electron out of the surface, photoelectric emission was possible. If $h\nu$ fell short of the energy required to expel an electron from the surface, then emission of electrons did not take place. If, as suggested by the evidence of the photoelectric effect, one turned to a corpuscular theory of light, he encountered at once the difficulty that the expression for the energy of the photon depends, not upon a simple corpuscular property, but upon a wave property. Moreover, it was still necessary to explain interference, diffraction, and other typical wave phenomena. There seemed to be no way of treating light without using both the wave and the corpuscular concepts.

On the other hand, classical mechanics was encountering difficulties in trying to explain atomic processes. Although the motion of electrons in a vacuum tube could be discussed in terms of Newtonian mechanics, when an electron was confined to the small space around an atomic nucleus, it began to exhibit behavior unlike that of a simple mechanical particle. It was true that the Bohr theory of the atom had given correct values for the wavelengths observed in the hydrogen spectrum, and had explained the general features of atomic spectra; but the results of calculations using the Bohr theory contradicted the experimental values for the ground-state energy of helium and the electronic energy levels of the hydrogen molecule. Also, the Bohr theory contained the postulate that only those orbits are allowed for which

$$\oint mv\, ds = nh, \tag{9-1}$$

where $\oint$ represents the integral once around a closed path, and this *ad hoc* assumption was itself crying for some explanation.

A crude but suggestive explanation occurred to de Broglie in 1924. He pictured a wave accompanying the electron in its orbit about the proton of a hydrogen atom. He postulated that this wave has a wavelength

$$\lambda = \frac{h}{mv}, \tag{9-2}$$

which is equivalent to assuming that the same relation between wavelength and momentum holds for both photons and particles. From Eqs.

(1) and (2), he then obtained the result

$$\oint \lambda^{-1}\, ds = n = 1, 2, 3, \cdots. \tag{9-3}$$

For example, if the orbit is circular, Eq. (3) states that the length of the circumference divided by the wavelength is a positive integer. In general, Eq. (3) means that an integral number of wavelengths fits into the closed path of the electron. This is precisely what we expect for a standing wave.

The above argument is not to be taken seriously as a final explanation of the Bohr condition, but it does suggest that there is something to the concept of material particles being guided by waves. With this motivation, de Broglie introduced the following postulate: *Consider any material particle having a definite energy W and a definite momentum p. This particle is to be represented by a plane harmonic wave whose frequency ν and wavelength λ are given by the equations*

and

$$\nu = W/h$$
$$\lambda = h/mv. \tag{9-4}$$

We write a plane harmonic wave in the form

$$\psi = A e^{j(kx - \omega t)}, \tag{9-5}$$

where $j = \sqrt{-1}$; and

$$k = 2\pi/\lambda$$
$$\omega = 2\pi\nu. \tag{9-6}$$

(This differs slightly from de Broglie's form.)

Before we discuss the experimental interpretation and the verification of de Broglie's wave mechanics, notice that the phase velocity of the wave (5) is

$$w = \frac{\omega}{k} = \frac{2\pi\, h\nu}{2\pi\, h/\lambda} = \frac{W}{p} = \frac{v}{2}, \tag{9-7}$$

if we use non-relativistic mechanics. In other words, the particle velocity is twice the phase velocity. This would appear to be a difficulty; but we must remember that the phase velocity is not actually the velocity at which the momenta and energies associated with known types of waves (e.g. ripples on water and transverse displacements of the loaded string) are transferred through space. The fact is that a plane harmonic wave with an absolutely unique frequency is a fiction. Even a wave which appears to have a unique frequency ν is actually a *superposition* of a *group* of harmonic waves each of which has a frequency almost equal to ν. This superposition of a group of waves forms a wave packet, which has a velocity given by the equation

$$\frac{d\nu}{d\left(\dfrac{1}{\lambda}\right)} = \text{group velocity.} \qquad (9\text{-}8)$$

Eq. (8) was derived and discussed in Appendix IV, and it was applied to the loaded string in Chapter 8. From Eqs. (4), we see that the group velocity is

$$\boxed{\frac{d\nu}{d\left(\dfrac{1}{\lambda}\right)} = \frac{dW}{dp} = \frac{p}{m} = v,} \qquad (9\text{-}9)$$

since $W = p^2/2m$. In other words, the group moves with a velocity equal to that of the particle itself.

Experimental Verification of de Broglie Waves

About the time that de Broglie was developing the basic concepts concerning the waves accompanying particles, experimental evidence was accumulating to support the validity of these ideas. The first experimentalists to come upon the evidence did not expect wave properties to be associated with particles, such as electrons, and they were looking for other effects when an accident and subsequent study of effects resulting from the accident made the wave properties evident.

Dr. C. J. Davisson was interested in the reflection of electrons from metal surfaces. He expected experiments of this kind to give information primarily concerning the individual atoms of which the metal was made, but the results were not extremely informative in this connection. In 1925 Dr. L. H. Germer was collaborating in this work. The best high-vacuum techniques were required for these experiments, and those used were the best known in the late 1920s and early 1930s. The point under investigation was the angular distribution of the electrons returning from a nickel target being bombarded by a collimated primary beam. There was rather general scattering of electrons in all directions, on which was superposed a prominent lobe at about the angle required by the law of regular reflection. Once while the nickel target was hot, a liquid air trap exploded and broke the tube. The target was suddenly exposed to air at atmospheric pressure and it oxidized. In order to use this target for further experiments, it was heated in a hydrogen atmosphere to reduce the oxide and was further heated in a vacuum to recondition the surface. Following this treatment the results obtained were radically altered. Instead of a general background of scattered electrons, a series of lobes appeared at rather well-defined angles. Davisson and Germer observed that the

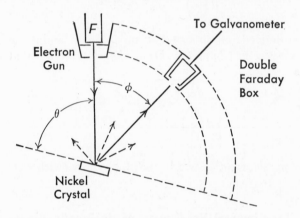

Fig. 9-1. Reflections from single crystals.

crystal size had been increased, and they interpreted this pattern as due to reflection from a number of large single crystals. Hence, they turned to the study of the reflections from a target in the form of a single crystal.

A diagram of the apparatus they constructed is shown in Fig. 9-1. Here the source of the electrons is a heated filament. The electrons are accelerated from the filament by a positive potential applied to the metal parts surrounding the filament, and a narrow beam is defined by two apertures through which the electrons pass. The electrons fall upon the single nickel crystal, which may be rotated to change the angle of incidence, and a few are reflected at various angles. The distribution in angle of the reflected electrons can be studied by collecting those which are trapped in the small opening of a double Faraday box. The angular position of the box may be varied with respect to the incident beam.

If, as predicted by de Broglie, electrons are accompanied by waves, this apparatus provides a convenient means of varying the wavelength continuously throughout the entire range of short X-ray wavelengths. According to the Bragg formula, regular reflections from crystal planes are preferred, but wavelengths reflected satisfy the relationship $n\lambda = 2d \sin \theta$, where for electrons

$$\lambda = \frac{h}{p} = \frac{12.4 \times 10^{-10} \text{ meters (volts)}^{\frac{1}{2}}}{[V \text{ (volts)}]^{\frac{1}{2}}}. \tag{9-10}$$

It is seen that $1/\lambda$ or $(V)^{\frac{1}{2}}$ plotted against the measured intensity of reflection should give a series of sharp, equally spaced maxima, where the Bragg relationship is satisfied.

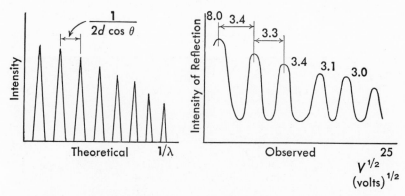

Fig. 9-2. Results of Davisson and Germer for a nickel crystal.

An experiment of this type was performed by Davisson and Germer. The normal to the crystal is set to bisect the angle ϕ between the line from the crystal to the gun and the line from the crystal to the cage. Thus, regular reflections alone are studied. The results obtained are shown in Fig. 9-2. When plotted as suggested by Eq. (10), there is a series of strong reflection peaks, which are spaced at the approximately equal increments $\Delta(V^{\frac{1}{2}})$ shown in the figure.

The apparatus of Davisson and Germer was so flexible that reflections of the Bragg type from the various sets of crystal planes could be studied. Their original paper presented results for 30 sets of electron beams for bombarding potentials below 370 volts. The results for 20 sets were precisely those expected for X-rays of the wavelengths calculated by applying the de Broglie relation to the electrons, while 9 sets were accounted for by the plane gratings formed by surface layers of atoms. Thus, even the original work suggested one of the great advantages of electron diffraction. For, whereas the scattering of X-rays is so small and the penetration so great that surface layers cannot be studied, the electrons at grazing incidence have diffraction patterns characterized entirely by the arrangement of the atoms in the surface layers. The peak for which an explanation was not at once obvious was a fairly weak one. Subsequently, the agreement of electron diffraction results with theory has been improved by incorporating into the theory the refraction of the electron beams as they enter and leave the metal.

As soon as de Broglie's theory was published, G. P. Thomson designed an experiment explicitly for the purpose of testing the validity of the wave concept. The electrons of the beam were accelerated to a relatively high energy of the order of 50,000 ev. Such energetic electrons are capable of penetrating metal foils of such thickness that they are not too fragile to place in the electron beam for use as targets.

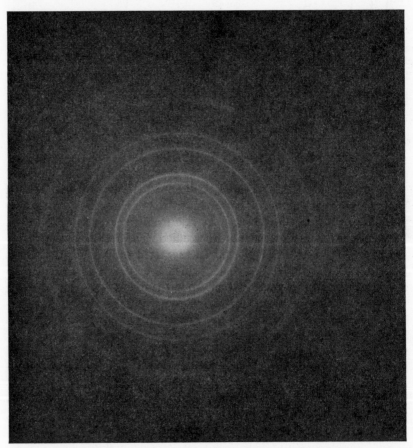

Fig. 9-3. A powder diffraction pattern for gold foil.

Such foils are ordinarily polycrystalline, and the diffraction patterns (of the so-called "powder type") obtained, consist of concentric circles. Independently, Thomson and Rupp were successful in demonstrating, by this means, the waves associated with electrons. This has become a standard research technique, and commercial equipment capable of such analysis may be purchased. Fig. 9-3 shows a powder pattern obtained by passing electrons through a gold foil. In the light of such evidence, de Broglie waves have been firmly established in scientific thinking, and electron diffraction has become commonplace. In addition, the diffraction phenomena due to de Broglie waves for other particles have been used as tools for extending our knowledge of the structure of matter.

The Schroedinger Equation

de Broglie's formulation of the wave properties associated with matter was too primitive and specialized to be used for any but the most simple applications. Schroedinger adopted the basic idea of de Broglie, and developed it into a general and powerful theory.

The general form of the differential equation which describes wave motion does not contain the wavelength. It is

$$\nabla^2 \psi - \frac{1}{w^2} \frac{\partial^2 \psi}{\partial t^2} = 0, \tag{9-11}$$

where w is the phase velocity $\lambda \nu$. Thus, it is easy to eliminate the phase velocity in favor of the wavelength and frequency. This gives

$$\nabla^2 \psi - \frac{1}{\lambda^2 \nu^2} \frac{\partial^2 \psi}{\partial t^2} = 0. \tag{9-12}$$

But by de Broglie's postulate $1/\lambda^2 = p^2/h^2$, and, thus,

$$\nabla^2 \psi - \frac{p^2}{h^2 \nu^2} \frac{\partial^2 \psi}{\partial t^2} = 0. \tag{9-13}$$

The kinetic energy W_K is related to the momentum by $W_K = p^2/2m$, and, hence,

$$p^2 = 2mW_K. \tag{9-14}$$

If the particle of mass m and total energy W is in a conservative force field, the kinetic energy is the total energy W minus the potential energy U. Thus,

$$p^2 = 2m(W - U). \tag{9-15}$$

Hence, Eq. (13) becomes

$$\nabla^2\psi - \frac{2m(W - U)}{h^2\nu^2}\frac{\partial^2\psi}{\partial t^2} = 0. \tag{9-16}$$

The assumption of a definite energy implies a definite frequency associated with the particle. For simplicity we set

$$\psi \equiv u(x,y,z)e^{-j\omega t},$$

which represents a standing wave. The second partial with respect to time is

$$\frac{\partial^2\psi}{\partial t^2} = -\omega^2 u(x,y,z)e^{-j\omega t}, \tag{9-17}$$

and Eq. (16) becomes

$$e^{-j\omega t}\left(\nabla^2 u + \frac{\omega^2}{\nu^2}\frac{2m(W - U)u}{h^2}\right) = 0. \tag{9-18}$$

Since $e^{-j\omega t}$ is not zero and since $\omega/\nu = 2\pi$, Eq. (18) implies that

$$\nabla^2 u + \frac{8\pi^2 m(W - U)u}{h^2} = 0. \tag{9-19}$$

This is called the time-independent Schroedinger equation, and it will be useful for our purposes. A somewhat more general formulation of Schroedinger's ideas is given in Appendix XI. Eq. (19) has been obtained by eliminating the phase velocity in favor of the wavelength in the second-order partial differential equation applying to wave motion and by using de Broglie's postulate to express the wavelength in terms of the mechanical quantities associated with the particle.

Born's Statistical Interpretation of ψ

Originally, both de Broglie and Schroedinger assumed that ψ had the following interpretation:

$$|\psi|^2 \simeq \text{charge density of particle.}$$

In other words, they thought that the particle itself was the wave. This interpretation led to internal contradictions of the theory. The interpretation accepted today is that

$|\psi|^2 \simeq$ probability per unit volume for finding the particle at position r at time t.

This is the interpretation made by Born. Since, if the particle exists at all, the probability for finding the particle somewhere (regardless of where it is found) must be unity, ψ must satisfy the condition

$$\boxed{\int_V |\psi(x)|^2\, dV = 1,}$$ (9-20)

where V extends over all space. A wave function ψ satisfying Eq. (20) is said to be *normalized*. Since $|e^{-j\omega t}| = 1$, the same condition is required to normalize u.

The Uncertainty Principle of Heisenberg

The representation of a particle by means of waves is not entirely definite. There are limitations on the information that it can be made to give. This is known as the uncertainty principle, and the fact that it was essential to the wave mechanical representation was first shown by Heisenberg. We have been able to identify the velocity of a particle with the group velocity of a frequency range of associated de Broglie waves. Thus, the position of the particle, identified with the position of the group, will be no more sharply defined than the boundaries of the group. Suppose, as is usually done in the theoretical discussion of mechanical problems, that velocity v of the particle is exactly known. Then the momentum of the particle, and as a consequence its wavelength, is *exactly* known. A Fourier integral analysis shows that to define a wavelength exactly requires an unmodulated pure sinusoidal wave train of infinite extension. Born's probability interpretation of the wave function states that the probability of finding the particle in a definite region is given by integrating the square of the normalized wave function over the volume defined. However, since the amplitude of the wave function is uniform throughout all space, we are led to the conclusion that, *in case the momentum is exactly known, nothing can be said about the position of the particle.* This is in sharp contrast with assumptions made in large-scale mechanics.

Conversely, since in wave mechanics the position of a particle is identified with the interference pattern which we call a group, we may ask what we must do to define the position of the group exactly. From the Fourier integral theorem we deduce the fact that the group occupies less and less space as we increase the range of wavelengths in the combining wave trains. *Thus, when the position is determined exactly, one can say nothing about the momentum.* Heisenberg's quantitative analysis of these matters led him to formulate his results in the equation:

$$\Delta p_x \, \Delta x \simeq h, \tag{9-21}$$

where the Δ's stand for the uncertainties in the quantities p_x and x, and h is Planck's constant.

This relationship can be illustrated by considering the combination of a pair of pure sine waves. For simplicity the amplitude of each sine wave may be taken as unity, and the wavelengths may be taken as λ and λ' respectively. The combination then gives

$$y = \sin 2\pi x/\lambda + \sin 2\pi x/\lambda'$$

$$= 2 \sin \pi x \left(\frac{1}{\lambda} + \frac{1}{\lambda'}\right) \cos \pi x \left(\frac{1}{\lambda} - \frac{1}{\lambda'}\right).$$

From a maximum displacement in the pattern to the next maximum displacement, the argument of the cosine factor must increase by π. Thus, for example, x must increase from 0 to $1 \left/ \left(\dfrac{1}{\lambda} - \dfrac{1}{\lambda'}\right) \right.$. Hence,

$$\Delta x = (1/\lambda - 1/\lambda')^{-1}$$

or

$$\Delta x \left(\frac{h}{\lambda} - \frac{h}{\lambda'}\right) = h.$$

If (according to de Broglie's relationship) h/λ is identified as momentum,

$$\Delta x \, \Delta p_x \simeq h.$$

This is called the indeterminacy principle or the uncertainty principle of Heisenberg. An opinion supported in contemporary physics is that this restriction is fundamental in nature, and is not merely a limitation on the reliability of our knowledge. Thus, if ΔW and Δt are the uncertainties in energy and time respectively, we can likewise show that

$$\Delta W \, \Delta t \simeq h. \tag{9-22}$$

Heisenberg justified his conclusions by the consideration of a number of idealized experiments, discussions of which are contained in many conventional treatments of quantum mechanics. If, as Heisenberg argued, because of wave mechanical limitations in nature, this is a fundamental principle, one would expect that several isolated examples of its application would have been known for decades prior to the general formulation by Heisenberg. This was in fact the case. In wave phenomena such as music, for example, it has long been known that a musical note of very short duration, that is to say a very small fraction of a period, gave no sensation of pitch. As the length of the time interval is increased, the pitch becomes more and more definitely determined. The explanation of this effect on the basis of Fourier analysis (Appendix V) had long been understood. That the known rule of acoustics $\Delta f \, \Delta t = 1$ is consistent with Heisenberg's indeterminacy principle is almost obvious. In Eq. (22) one sets $\Delta W = h \, \Delta f$, as Einstein's relationship for photons suggests. Division by h then gives

$$\Delta f \, \Delta t = 1. \tag{9-23}$$

Soon after the announcement by Heisenberg, G. W. Stewart showed that this rule of acoustics was derivable directly from the uncertainty principle, and he discussed the significance of this fact.

The resolving power of a lens is still another illustration of the uncertainty principle which was known long before Heisenberg discussed this matter. The resolving power of a lens may be specified as the smallest distance between points y_1 and y_2 in the object which can be distinguished in the image formed by the lens. If monochromatic light of wavelength λ passes through a perfect cylindrical lens of such width and focal length that the half-angle of the diverging beam of light from a line in the object is θ, the resolving power $\Delta y = \overline{y_1 y_2}$ is expressed by the known formula of physical optics

$$\Delta y = 0.50\lambda/\sin\theta, \quad (9\text{-}24)$$

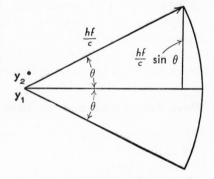

Fig. 9-4. Resolving power of a cylindrical lens.

which was derived by considering the image as an interference pattern of light waves. This could be derived from the uncertainty principle, and we will show that it is consistent with this rule. According to the Einstein theory, the momentum of a light quantum is

$$p = h/\nu c.$$

The light quantum may pass through the lens by any path in the entire angle 2θ of the beam as shown in Fig. 9-4. Thus, there is a possible uncertainty in the y-component of the momentum which is

$$\Delta p_y = (2h\nu \sin\theta)/c. \tag{9-25}$$

The corresponding uncertainty in y may be taken from Eq. (24), and when these values are multiplied, the result is

$$\Delta p_y \, \Delta y = 2h\nu \sin \theta \lambda 0.50/c \sin \theta = h,$$

consistent with the Heisenberg principle of indeterminacy.

The uncertainty principle may be illustrated in terms of the $\Delta W \, \Delta t$ product. Suppose, for example, that an electron is raised to an excited state having a mean life of 10^{-8} sec. This represents an uncertainty in the time of emission of the quantum of radiation, and this uncertainty multiplied by the uncertainty in the energy of the radiated quantum would be of the order of Planck's constant h. From this fact we deduce that

$$\Delta W = h/(10^{-8} \text{ sec}) = 6.6 \times 10^{-26} \text{ joules} = 4.06 \times 10^{-7} \text{ ev}.$$

Spectral lines, although quite sharp, thus have breadths at least as great as this. (There are other causes of the finite widths of spectral lines.)

It may seem that the Heisenberg indeterminacy principle is a limitation only on our knowledge of nature. If this were the end of the matter, it would hardly be possible to use the principle to add to our knowledge. Our presentation, however, has indicated that the principle is basic in the nature of things. By treating the principle as a law of nature, it is possible to use it successfully as a tool for analysis. This is frequently done, and will be illustrated several times in our treatment of problems by quantum mechanics.

Wave Propagation and the Uncertainties of Quantum Mechanics

Waves are not terminated so abruptly that shadows are really sharp. Very early in the development of a theory for light, a question arose concerning whether or not a wave theory could account for the observed propagation of light in straight lines. This proved to be possible, but the development showed how the waves bent into the region of the geometrical shadow. By the use of phase diagrams appropriate to the wave theory, it is not difficult to put the discussion on a quantitative basis. We may consider first the classical experiment of Young, which provided the crucial evidence for the wave nature of light.

The earliest attempts to produce the interference of light failed, because the light to be combined was obtained from "incoherent" sources. That is, there was no definite phase relationship between the light from the independent sources, in each of which the phase of the light waves was changing in an arbitrary way. In such circumstances the intensities of the light from the two sources simply added.

To overcome difficulties of this nature, as the source of the light in his experiment, Sir Thomas Young used a single narrow slit. As suggested by the opening in S_1 of Fig. 9-5, this slit was so narrow as compared with the wavelength of the light used, that Huygens's principle accounted for very considerable spreading of the light that had passed through it. This is to be considered quantitatively later in the course of this discussion. A cylindrical lens L' with the slit source of

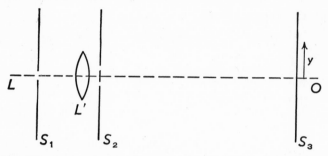

Fig. 9-5. Arrangement of apparatus in Young's experiment.

light at its principal focus is optional in the experiment, but with it, plane waves of light fall upon the screen S_2, which contains two narrow slits parallel to that in S_1. Light spreads from each of these two slits and falls upon the screen S_3. Because the light in the experiment was obtained from a single narrow source, there is a phase relationship for the light coming from the two slits. This may be discussed quantitatively in connection with the geometry shown by Fig. 9-6. If the

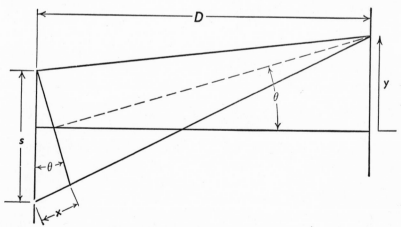

Fig. 9-6. Geometry for light paths.

plane waves of light are parallel to the screen S_2, the light at the two slits will be in phase, and when, as for the plane of symmetry of the figure, the time taken by the light in reaching a point on the third screen is the same, the light waves will be in phase at this point.

The distances y along the screen, as shown in Fig. 9-6, are measured from the plane of symmetry. In contrast to the situation shown in the figure, the distance between the slits is quite small as compared with the distance from the slits to the screen S_3. Hence, a suitable approximation is given by

$$x = s \sin \theta \simeq sy/D, \tag{9-26}$$

where x is the difference in the distances of the point at y from the two slits. If λ represents the wavelength, the light on the screen which comes from one slit differs in phase from that coming from the other by an amount

$$\phi = 2\pi x/\lambda = 2\pi sy/\lambda D \text{ radians.} \tag{9-27}$$

If the amplitude of the light coming from either slit is R, the two amplitudes may be combined as in the phase diagram of Fig. 9-7 to give the

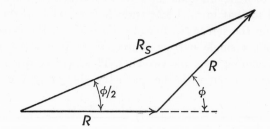

Fig. 9-7. Phase diagram for light from two slits.

resultant amplitude

$$R_s = 2R \cos (\phi/2) = 2R \cos (\pi sy/\lambda D). \tag{9-28}$$

The intensity of the light on the screen is proportional to the square of the amplitude. Thus, intensity I is given by

$$I = kR_s{}^2 = k(2R)^2 \cos^2 (\pi sy/\lambda D). \tag{9-29}$$

The interference pattern obtained by Young consisted of alternate light and dark bands. The spacing between bands is proportional to D and to the wavelength, and it is inversely proportional to the distance s between the slits.

When the retardation of phase between successive adjacent slits is just $2\pi n$, where n is an integer, a maximum of intensity is shown by the pattern on the screen. This simple analysis indicates that these peaks of constructive interference are as bright as the central maximum. Any number of equally spaced slits may be added to this arrangement. Increasing the number of slits, has one pronounced effect on the pattern. It introduces zeros of light intensity close to each maximum. For only two slits the phase shift between two adjacent slits corresponding to a zero of intensity is π. In the general case, a zero of intensity corresponds to conditions represented by a closed

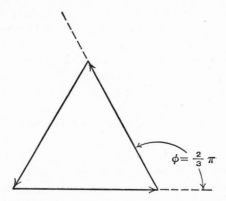

Fig. 9-8. Phase diagram for light from three slits.

figure on the phase diagram. For three slits the phase difference between adjacent sides in the phase diagram is $2\pi/3$ as shown in Fig. 9-8. For four slits the retardation of phase between light coming from adjacent slits needs to be only $2\pi/4$ or $90°$ to give a square on the phase diagram, and hence a zero of light intensity. Thus, as more slits are added, the main bright bands of constructive interference become narrower, and this in itself suggests the applicability of the uncertainty relation.

A transmission diffraction grating may be considered as an extension of Young's interference experiment to a very great number of closely spaced slits. The wave fronts corresponding to diffraction in the various orders n are the envelopes tangent to wave surfaces differing in distance by $n\lambda$ from adjacent slits. This is illustrated in

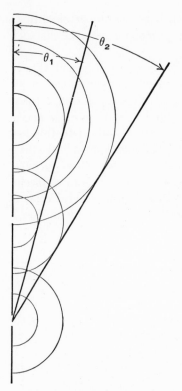

Fig. 9-9. Envelopes of wave fronts showing orders of diffraction.

Fig. 9.9. Here from the triangle shown

$$n\lambda = s \sin \theta_n, \qquad (9\text{-}30)$$

which is the simple formula for the transmission grating. The success of these formulas in accounting for optical phenomena constitutes definite evidence that light is accompanied by waves, the interference of which accounts for the distribution of intensities actually observed. This in turn would be interpreted as meaning that the light waves control the propagation of energy. If the photon postulate introduced by Einstein is accepted, the photons are guided in their motion by wave phenomena which accompany them.

The use of phase diagrams can be extended for the purpose of determining the distribution of intensity on the screen which arises from light passing through a single rectangular slit. Suppose that in Fig. 9-6, s represents the width of a single slit. Each equal element dw of the width of the slit makes the same contribution to the resulting amplitude of the light on the screen, but these contributions vary continuously in phase with the distance w from the center of the slit. If $s \ll D$, all contributions may be considered in phase at the center of the screen ($y = 0$). As y increases positively or negatively, a phase difference is introduced, and between the extreme edges of the slit separated by the distance s, this phase difference is precisely that which was computed in connection with Young's interference experiment ($\phi = 2\pi y s/\lambda D$). In this case, however, there is a continuous variation of phase from one side of the slit to the other. The contribution to the amplitude is the same for each equal width element dw, and the shift in phase across the width dw is the same in the approximation that we are using. Hence, the phase diagram constitutes an arc which is some portion of a circle, and the resultant amplitude is the chord subtended by this arc. The length of the arc is the amplitude of the resultant when $y = 0$, and we may call this A_0. The length R_t of a chord subtending an angle ϕ is

$$R_t = 2r \sin (\phi/2), \qquad\qquad (9\text{-}31)$$

where r is the radius of the circle given by

$$r = A_0/\phi,$$

and thus,

$$R_t = (2A_0/\phi) \sin (\phi/2)$$

$$= A_0 \sin (sy\pi/\lambda D)/(\pi sy/D\lambda). \qquad (9\text{-}32)$$

At $y = 0$, the resultant amplitude of the light is A_0. As y increases in either sense, this resultant amplitude decreases, at first slowly and then more rapidly, until $y = D\lambda/s$ gives the first zero of the resultant amplitude. The half-width of the diffraction pattern corresponds to an angle given by

$$\sin \theta \simeq \tan \theta = y/D = \lambda/s. \qquad (9\text{-}33)$$

For Young's interference experiment, the widths of the individual slits are not apt to be negligible in comparison to the wavelength λ of the light used, and the widths of the individual slits cause a variation in the intensity of the light in the diffraction pattern. This variation is superposed on the more rapid variation due to interference between the slits.

The uncertainties put into the theory of mechanics by the inclusion of the Heisenberg indeterminancy relation are very like those which have been discussed in connection with wave phenomena. The form of quantum mechanics in which conclusions are derived from the use of the wave model is called wave mechanics. The interference phenomena are characteristic of quantum mechanics, and they have no counterpart in ordinary theoretical mechanics, which was successfully applied to large-scale objects.

It is not difficult to discuss the experiment of Young in terms of a corpuscular theory if the uncertainty principle of Heisenberg is incorporated in it. The photons, as Einstein proposed, are considered to have energy $h\nu$ and momentum $h\nu/c = h/\lambda$. From the conservation of momentum we would expect these photons to travel in straight lines. As long as the photons have the possibility of lying at any value of y along an extended wave front, without violating the uncertainty principle, we may assert that they are moving parallel to the x-axis, and the motion of these photons, consistent with the ideas of elementary mechanics, is generally in straight lines perpendicular to the wave fronts. As soon, however, as we obtain information about the y coordinate by forcing the photons to pass through a narrow slit of width s, to satisfy Heisenberg's uncertainty principle, a spread in the y components of momenta for the various photons must arise.

$$s \, \Delta p_y = h$$

$$\Delta p_y = h/s = (h/\lambda) \sin \theta. \tag{9-34}$$

The last term is simply the total y component of momentum obtained by taking the y component of the total momentum h/λ. Eq. (34), obtained by the Heisenberg uncertainty relation is consistent with Eq. (33), as may be seen from the last two terms of Eq. (34) using y/D for $\sin \theta$ as an approximation. If s is comparable with a wavelength, the photons spread over an appreciable angle.

The fact that the corpuscular theory, to which Heisenberg's uncertainty relation has been applied, gives results consistent with the wave treatment is very suggestive. The quantum mechanics of corpuscles is equivalent to wave mechanics.

The introduction of quanta into the theory of light modifies our interpretation of phenomena in a very fundamental way. At large light intensities, the distribution of light appears to be continuous and to follow the predictions of the wave theory exactly. If the wave theory were to be accepted without modification by the quantum theory, we would expect the same relative distribution at light intensities however small. The fact that quanta are accepted as having physical existence means that the lowest finite illumination level will correspond to the reception of a single photon. This will have to be detected as an entity and not distributed over all space. The function of the waves accompanying the photon is to give the probability that it will be observed at the various points. The reception of the photons depends on statistical considerations. At low light intensities the limited number of photons to be distributed will result in a very considerable statistical fluctuation of the radiant power received at the various points. As the intensity is raised, the relative statistical fluctuations become less, and at the levels of illumination corresponding to those at which data are usually taken, the statistical fluctuations become negligible and departures of observations from the predictions of the wave theory are usually ascribed to experimental error in the measurements.

If, after the photons have passed through the slit in S_1, a single slit is made in the screen placed like S_2 of Fig. 9-5, according to a simple corpuscular theory the two slits would define a direction which the particles would follow. When, in accordance with the fundamentals of quantum mechanics, the uncertainty principle is added to the considerations, it is seen that, because the second slit again provides information about the position of the particles, there must be a further spreading of the photons beyond the second slit. This was discussed by Young in terms of the spreading of the waves beyond the second slit. According to quantum mechanics it is impossible to define an extremely narrow beam by apertures, because there must be a spreading beyond each aperture to satisfy the uncertainty principle. It might be said that the particle interacts with the slit in such a way as to create the required uncertainty in momentum.

The spreading of the photons beyond a slit would be investigated experimentally by counting the photons arriving in the various positions. The problem is essentially statistical and the intensities of the wave theory give the probabilities involved in the statistics.

The spread of momentum is associated with wave-like behavior. The fact that electrons and other particles show diffraction effects is an indication that for any form of quantum mechanics to be in conformity with experience it will have to account for the interference effects which occur when a light particle has two paths by which it may arrive at a given point.

If a second slit is added in the screen S_2 of Fig. 9-5 and the first is then covered, there will be a certain distribution of the particles passing through this slit and detected along the screen S_3. Now a pure corpuscular theory, containing no interference effects, would indicate that if both slits were open, the number of particles arriving at any point on screen S_3 could be computed by adding the two results obtained from the single slits. This is not the result of quantum mechanics as applied to elementary particles such as photons or electrons. If a counter is operating at a certain rate with one slit alone open, it is quite possible that the opening of the second slit will result in a reduction of the counting rate, and such results are readily explained by the wave theory in terms of interference effects. Quantum mechanics gives results which differ in kind from those of the older mechanics.

If one covers first one slit and then the other without ever leaving the two exposed, upon averaging he obtains the pattern of intensity predicted by the summation of the independent slits. We can call this a corpuscular pattern, although, of course, we have seen that its detail depends upon wave properties. If the two slits are uncovered at the same time, a photon may have gone by either path. It then appears to have acted as a wave, dividing and going partly by each path. Whether it is done by covering slits or by some other means, whatever establishes that the photon has gone by the one path or the other eliminates the diffraction pattern.

If one uses electrons in place of photons, the velocity of the groups representing the electrons is lower. Otherwise the phenomena are essentially the same. Rupp, using electrons grazing a surface, actually reflected electrons from a ruled grating and obtained a diffraction pattern from which the wavelength could be deduced by the use of Eq. (6-4). All of the diffraction experiments with electrons emphasize the fact that the associated waves exist and that, through constructive interference, they determine where electrons are likely to be found.

The corpuscular action of electrons has been so firmly established that, in an electronic experiment analogous to Young's, someone most certainly would suggest an experiment for showing that a given electron was to be found as a particle at one of the slits and not at the other. A remarkable thing is that quantum mechanics does not preclude this possibility. One can, for example, prove that an electron comes through one slit by shining light on the system and allowing the electron to scatter a photon. From the direction of the photon, the slit through which the electron passed can be inferred. If one could do this and still maintain the narrow peaks of the interference pattern due to two slits, he would have circumvented the uncertainty relation. In order to make an experiment of this nature definitive, however, one would have to use light of such short wavelength that, by Compton effect reaction on the electron, uncertainties in the momentum of the electron are introduced to preserve the validity of the uncertainty relation. The narrow peaks associated with the two slits would disappear and there would be the broad distribution of electrons which characterizes the passage of electrons through a single slit.

Summary

We have chosen to discuss quantum mechanics in the form that uses the fundamental properties of waves as a basis. This is called wave mechanics, and in this form of quantum mechanics physical models or analogies can be given to assist in the understanding of atomic phenomena. Just as quantities determined from waves of finite duration are limited in accuracy, there is a fundamental limitation on the accuracy with which conjugate properties such as momentum and displacement or energy and time can be specified. The Heisenberg indeterminacy principle asserts that the products of the uncertainties in two conjugate quantities is not less than Planck's constant h. This appears to be such a fundamental law of nature that it can be used very effectively as a tool in analysis. Another very useful tool is provided by eliminating phase velocity in favor of wavelength in the second-order partial differential equation of wave motion. If the wavelength associated with particles is determined in terms of their energy W and the result is substituted into the wave equation, the time factor can be canceled. The result is Schroedinger's time-independent equation

$$\nabla^2 u + 8\pi^2 m(W - U)u/h^2 = 0.$$

Born gave a statistical interpretation of the amplitude factor u by showing that it could be normalized so that the square of its magnitude when multiplied by an infinitesimal volume dV represents the probability of finding the particle in this element of volume. If the particle is an electron, the probability may be multiplied by the electronic charge, and the result will represent the time average of the charge in the element of volume.

Problems on Basic Ideas of Wave Mechanics

1. Determine the wavelength associated with the momentum of a 0.50 kg stone moving with a speed of 100 m/sec. Can you think of any experiment which would detect a wavelength of this magnitude associated with a macroscopic object?

2. Calculate the wavelength associated with an electron which has fallen through a potential difference of (a) 50 v and (b) 10 kv.

3. Calculate the wavelength associated with a proton which has fallen through a potential difference of (a) 50 v and (b) 10 kv.

4. Show that Bohr's condition for the circular orbits of hydrogen is equivalent to the statement that the circumference of the orbit is equal to an integer times the wavelength of the electron.

5. Calculate the angle at which electrons with 100 ev of energy will fulfill the Bragg condition for reflection from the 100 face of a rock salt crystal.

6. Electrons are allowed to fall through a potential difference of 50 kv and then to pass through a powdered specimen of a crystalline material. The radii of the diffraction rings observed on a screen at a distance of 30 cm from the specimen are 0.2 cm, 0.5 cm, and 1.00 cm. Assuming that these are all first order diffractions, to what spacings between planes of atoms in the crystal do they correspond?

7. What is the phase velocity of the de Broglie waves associated with an electron of 50.1 ev? With an electron of 49.9 ev? If the two de Broglie waves have equal amplitudes and move parallel through the same space, with what velocity does a point of constant amplitude in the combination of the two waves travel? Compare the latter with particle velocity computed for either.

8. An electron has a kinetic energy of 100 ev outside of a metal and it traverses a conservative force field and attains a kinetic energy of 115 ev inside the metal. Calculate the wavelength of the electron outside the metal and inside the metal. If the electron is incident on the surface of the metal at an angle of 45°, what is the angle that its velocity makes with a normal to the surface inside the metal? How does the law for the refraction of the de Broglie wave surfaces compare with Snell's law in ordinary optics?

9. a. Unmodulated oscillations of frequency 10^6 c/s are allowed to persist for 0.10 sec and are then suddenly suppressed. What is the spread in frequencies corresponding to this duration? What is the fractional uncertainty in the frequency of the terminated oscillations?

   b. Unmodulated oscillations of frequency 100 c/s are allowed to persist for 0.10 sec and are then suppressed. What is the spread in frequencies corresponding to this duration? What is the fractional uncertainty in the frequency of the terminated oscillations?

   c. If the oscillations have a frequency of 1.0 c/s, what are the corresponding uncertainties? How long would oscillations having a frequency of 1.0 c/s need to be sustained to have the same fractional uncertainty as that found in part (a)?

10. A simple harmonic oscillator has a measured frequency of $(10.000 \pm .010)$ c/s. What is the minimum time of sustained oscillation which could give an uncertainty as small as this?

11. A ball weighing 1 g is moving with a speed of (10.00 ± 0.10) m/sec. What is the minimum uncertainty of the position of its center of mass which would be consistent with basic physical limitations? Is it likely that measurements of position could be made with this accuracy even if the ball were not in motion?

12. If the position of the earth along the circumference of its orbit could be determined with an uncertainty of 4000 km, what would be the corresponding uncertainty in its momentum? Taking the mass of the earth as 6.0×10^{24} kg, the mean distance from the earth to the sun as 1.5×10^8 km, and the linear velocity of the earth in its orbit as 30 km/sec, what is the fractional uncertainty in the momentum of the earth introduced by such a measurement of the position of the earth? If the linear momentum of the earth were changed by the amount of the uncertainty found in the first part of the problem, what would be the amount by which the length of a year would be changed?

13. If the basis of de Broglie's relativistic theory $W = mc^2 = h\nu$ and the resulting expression for the phase velocity w,

$$w = c^2/v,$$

where c is the phase velocity of light in free space and v is the velocity of the particle, are used in the equation $W = h\nu$, show that the expression for the wavelength agrees with that derived in the non-relativistic theory. As the velocity of the particle becomes comparable with the speed of light, what correction should be introduced to make the formula for the wavelength deduced in the non-relativistic theory applicable in the more general case?

References on Introductory Wave Mechanics

Bohm, David, *Quantum Mechanics*, Chs. 1, 2, and 3 (New York: Prentice-Hall, 1951).

Eldridge, John A., *Physical Basis of Things*, Ch. 27 (New York: McGraw-Hill Book Company, 1934).

Slater, John C., *Modern Physics*, Ch. 9 (New York: McGraw-Hill Book Company, 1955).

10 | Standing Wave Patterns and Quantum Numbers

Introductory Note on the Solution of Problems by Wave Mechanics

Schroedinger's equation for the amplitude factor of the de Broglie waves and Born's suggestion that the amplitude factor u when squared is proportional to the probability of finding the particle represented in a unit volume at the point in space, taken together provide a method for solving the problems of atomic physics. From the standpoint of students at the undergraduate level, the fact that the equation to be solved is a second-order partial differential equation reduces the usefulness of this method, because the mathematical technique for obtaining solutions subject to appropriate boundary conditions is not assumed at this level. Furthermore, it must be admitted that, even assuming the mastery of well-known mathematical tools, it is not difficult to formulate a problem in atomic physics which is so difficult that an exact solution is not really feasible. Scientists who have applied the Schroedinger equation to the solution of atomic problems are convinced that this theoretical basis is sound, and, in spite of the limitations they encounter in applying it practically, they are generally impressed with the great usefulness of the method.

The fact that we are not seeking the most general solutions of Schroedinger's equation does in part compensate for the complexity of the equation itself. We shall treat only those cases in which the equation to be solved reduces to a single independent variable. To these ordinary differential equations the methods of calculus can be applied. Mathematical difficulties, therefore, should not prevent the understanding of the most elementary illustrations. Important results of more involved analysis will be summarized briefly, and the details of the analysis will be deferred to appendices. Finally, in the most involved applications of these methods which we shall consider, we shall resort to a roughly approximate or qualitative treatment. In some cases, approximations which appear quite crude are adequate to give results of very satisfactory accuracy, which can be justified by more elaborate and rigorous analysis.

Simple Problem of Standing Waves in One Direction

Consider an electron in a region of uniform electrostatic potential, which we call $V = 0$. This equipotential region extends from $x = 0$ to $x = a$. Going in the direction of decreasing values of x, at the plane $x = 0$ the electrostatic potential falls suddenly to an infinitely negative value, and the potential energy of the electron rises suddenly to infinity at this plane. A similar boundary condition applies at $x = a$. Within this rectangular well or "trough" the electron is allowed to move with uniform velocity in the x-direction. It is reflected at the boundaries with a sudden reversal of velocity. Since the potential energy of the electron between the boundaries is zero, the form of the Schroedinger equation which applies to it is

$$\boxed{d^2u/dx^2 + 8\pi^2 mWu/h^2 = 0,} \qquad (10\text{-}1)$$

or

$$d^2u/dx^2 + k^2u = 0, \qquad (10\text{-}1')$$

where

$$k^2 = 8\pi^2 mW/h^2. \qquad (10\text{-}1'')$$

The general solution of this second-order differential equation is

$$u = A \sin kx + B \cos kx. \qquad (10\text{-}2)$$

Since the electron cannot penetrate the potential barrier, the wave function must be zero both at $x = 0$ and at $x = a$. For Eq. (2) to be consistent with these conditions, the equations to be satisfied are

$$0 = A \sin O + B \cos O \qquad (10\text{-}3)$$

and

$$0 = A \sin ka + B \cos ka. \qquad (10\text{-}4)$$

From Eq. (3), $B = 0$, and from Eq. (4) (eliminating the trivial solution where no wave function exists),

$$\sin ka = 0.$$

Thus,

$$ka = n\pi, \qquad (10\text{-}5)$$

where n is an integer. Substitution of this value of k in Eq. (1″) and solution for the energy corresponding to a given value of n yields

$$W_n = n^2h^2/8ma^2. \qquad \bullet \qquad (10\text{-}6)$$

Thus, the sinusoidal standing waves within the trough satisfying the two boundary conditions correspond to definite energies. The amplitude of the wave function drops to zero at the boundary and remains zero outside of the trough. If $n = 1$, there are nodes at the boundaries, but no others. An internal node is added whenever n is increased by unity. Thus, n stands for the number of loops in the standing wave pattern. In this representation, the momentum is proportional to the number of wavelengths per unit distance, and the kinetic energy to the square of this quantity.

In comparison with results of the similar problem analyzed by classical mechanics, there are several distinct contrasts. In classical mechanics the particle may be at rest even though it is confined within the trough. In fact, both its position and momentum can be assumed as exactly specified. The boundaries may be moved without changing the kinetic energy of the particle. Even if the particle is in motion perpendicular to the walls of the trough, the kinetic energy can have any value regardless of the separation between the two boundaries. It is possible to move the walls of the trough without doing work on the particle. The particle is in contact with the walls for short time intervals during a collision, and at all other times the walls may be moved without any interaction with the particle. Each of these conditions is in contrast to the quantum mechanical treatment.

For a quantitative comparison we analyze by classical mechanics a similar problem of a particle in a trough. Two massive parallel plates separated by a distance x' are connected by springs in such a way that the law of force holding them together is given by

$$F_r = -kx'.$$

A particle of mass m moves from one of these plates to the other from which it is reflected without loss of energy, and it returns to the first plate for another elastic reflection there. The inertia of the plates is so large that the separation distance between them is almost constant, and one problem is to determine the average separation between the plates from data concerning the motion of the particle. If the momentum of the particle perpendicular to the walls of the trough is p_x, the change of momentum in an elastic reflection is $2p_x$. If the velocity of the particle is v_x, the number of impacts per second on each plate is $v_x/2x'$. Hence, the average force is

$$F_i = 2p_x v_x/2x' = p_x^2/mx' = 2W_k/x',$$

where W_k stands for the kinetic energy of the particle as computed by Newtonian mechanics. For equilibrium, this outward force is equated to the inward force due to the springs, and for the kinetic energy this gives

$$W_k = kx'^2/2.$$

If a similar problem is treated quantum mechanically, there is a limitation on the accuracy with which the position of the particle can be specified, and we will assume that we have no information except that the particle is between the walls of the trough with which it is assumed to react so strongly that it cannot penetrate them in any degree. As we have seen in the discussion leading to Eq. (6), the values of the kinetic energy allowed depend explicitly on the separation between the plates, quite aside from the condition imposed by the equilibrium of the system, which is basically the same in both classical and quantum mechanics. Because the kinetic energy depends explicitly on the separation between the plates as given by Eq. (6), it is possible to obtain the equilibrium separation by minimizing the total energy. As in the classical case, we assume that the infinite reflecting barriers are connected with springs such that the mutual force is $-kx'$. The total energy of the system is the sum of the kinetic energy W_n and the potential energy $kx'^2/2$. Thus,

$$W_T = n^2h^2/8mx'^2 + kx'^2/2. \tag{10-7}$$

To minimize the total energy the derivative of this is taken and set equal to zero.

$$\boxed{\frac{dW_T}{dx'} = -2n^2h^2/8mx'^3 + kx' = 0.} \tag{10-8}$$

The result is capable of direct interpretation and shows that the force the electron exerts on the boundaries is equal and opposite to that which the spring exerts on them. The fact that the value of x' satisfying Eq. (8) gives a minimum of total energy is quite easily shown by the standard methods, and this is left to the reader. The result given by Eq. (8) also indicates that motion of the boundary always involves work, which results in a change of the kinetic energy of the particle. Eq. (8) may also be interpreted in terms of energy through the substitution of Eq. (6) into Eq. (8). This gives

$$W_n = kx'^2/2. \tag{10-9}$$

In terms of the energies involved, this result checks exactly with that for W_k obtained from classical mechanics. Another interesting feature about these results is that they correspond closely to the classical analysis of the simple harmonic oscillator, because in this problem also the time average of the kinetic energy is equal to the time average of the potential energy.

If the basic problem with a *finite increase* in potential energy of the electron at the planes $x = a$ and $x = 0$ is treated by quantum mechanics, the sinusoidal waves within the trough are always obtained. For the solution outside of the trough there are two possibilities. In the first place, the total energy of the electron may be greater than the potential energy outside of the trough. In this case, the wavelength changes at the boundary of the trough, but electrons outside as well as inside are represented by sinusoidal solutions of the wave equation. There is nothing essentially new in this result; the laws of physics successfully applied to macroscopic particles would indicate that an electron with sufficient energy to surmount the barrier would sometimes be found outside of the trough. The wave mechanical solution merely confirms this expected result. In the second place, however, if the assumption is made that the total energy of the electron is less than its potential energy outside the trough, the wave mechanical solution provides a result which contrasts with previous ideas. According to the theories of macroscopic mechanics, the electron would not be expected to enter the region where its potential energy would be greater than its total energy, because its kinetic energy would be negative in this region. The solution of the wave mechanical problem shows the electron penetrating the "forbidden region" outside of the trough. Inside there are still the sinusoidal standing waves, but at the finite boundaries these waves join smoothly with a function having the form

$$u = \exp\,(-c\,\Delta x),$$

where Δx represents the distance in the x-direction measured from the boundary into the region outside of the trough. The value of the constant c, as shown in Appendix VI, depends upon the total energy of the electron and on the increase in the potential energy at the boundary.

It is important to notice that while wave mechanics permit the particles to penetrate the classically forbidden region, it is quite unlikely that a particle will penetrate deeply, because the amplitude of the wave function decreases as a negative exponential function. For electrons having total energies less than the potential energy outside the trough, the solution of the problem still gives the discrete spectrum of energy

values. The exact values of the allowed energies are influenced somewhat by the fact that the space charge arising as a result of averaging
over the electron's entire motion, is distributed over a somewhat larger
region than that occupied by the trough. By analogy with this situation,
the wave functions of electrons associated with atoms would not be
expected to have sharp outer limits on their extension.

We have just seen that a single electron within a trough can exist
in one or another of several different energy states. If the trough contains not one but several electrons, they will exert forces on one another, and the energy states might be altered. In wave mechanics,
however, it is averages which are of importance, and a good approximation may be obtained by assuming that the wave functions are those
for a single electron. The distribution of electrons among the various
allowed energy levels is a matter of considerable interest. Some of
the basic physics applying to this situation is well established.

An electron in general moves in the three dimensions of space, and
the determination of the time average of its charge distribution requires the specification of three quantum numbers. These three
quantum numbers determine the form of a standing wave pattern
with which the electron is identified. Even before the development of
wave mechanics, however, spectroscopists had found that it was impossible to account for the observed spectra of atoms by the use of
only three quantum numbers. The electron itself is inherently a two-
state system. After a consideration of rules relating to atomic spectra,
Uhlenbeck and Goudsmit introduced the idea of an electron as a distribution of charge spinning on its own axis and possessing both a
magnetic moment and a mechanical angular momentum. If the electron is in a magnetic field, the magnetic moment may be directed
either parallel or anti-parallel to this field, and the energy will depend
on the orientation. To specify this condition a fourth quantum number,
called the spin quantum number, which must be either $+\frac{1}{2}$ or $-\frac{1}{2}$,
was introduced. Furthermore, the study of atomic spectra revealed
that no two electrons could have sets of four quantum numbers which
were identical. Pauli announced this as a general principle in 1925. The
Pauli exclusion principle, as it has come to be called, states that if two
electrons in an atom have three quantum numbers identical, they
must differ in the fourth quantum number.

This information, which accumulated gradually in the field of
spectroscopy, can be applied directly to the problem of several electrons in a single trough. The energy levels will normally be filled from
the bottom up. No electron will be found in the state for which n is
zero, because to satisfy the boundary condition that the wave func-

tion falls to zero outside the trough implies that it is zero inside also, since the argument of the sine term is zero throughout the entire trough. Two electrons, differing in spin, go into the state for which n is 1, and in the absence of a magnetic field, these two electrons have the same energy. Similarly, if an additional two electrons are in the trough, they will go into the state for which n is 2, and this process will be continued until all the electrons contained in the trough are accommodated.

Electrons in a Box

The problem of electrons in a trough, which has been solved by wave mechanics, differs from the problems encountered in atomic physics in several important respects. First, in this problem the motion of the electron is unrestricted in two directions, whereas an electron associated with an atom must have its motion restricted in all three dimensions of space. Secondly, in this problem the potential function has a simple dependence on a single Cartesian coordinate, whereas for an atom the distance from a point at the center of the nucleus is the most important coordinate, and spherical coordinates in general are the most natural ones to use in problems of atomic structure. Finally, because the three coordinates in a polar system differ radically from one another, the rules of quantization arising from each of the three coordinates are expected to differ.

The analysis may be modified very easily to take account of the fact that in most problems of interest in physics, electrons are restricted to a finite volume. For example, the electron may be assumed to be contained within a cube where the potential energy is zero. For simplicity, the potential energy may be assumed to rise to infinity suddenly at the faces of the cube. If each edge of the cube has the length a, the boundary conditions may be satisfied by a relatively simple function of the Cartesian coordinates. Take the origin of the coordinates at one corner of the cube and let the axes be directed along the edges. Then the boundary conditions are satisfied by a function of the form

$$u = \sin (n_1 \pi x/a) \sin (n_2 \pi y/a) \sin (n_3 \pi z/a), \qquad (10\text{-}10)$$

where n_1, n_2, and n_3 are positive integers and are the quantum numbers applicable to the problem. Substitution of Eq. (10) into Schroedinger's equation shows that if u is to be a solution,

$$W(n_1, n_2, n_3) = (n_1{}^2 + n_2{}^2 + n_3{}^2)h^2/8ma^2. \qquad (10\text{-}11)$$

Since it is the sum of the squares of the individual quantum numbers which determines the energy, the analog of the principal quantum number in the Bohr theory of the hydrogen atom is defined by

$$n^2 = n_1{}^2 + n_2{}^2 + n_3{}^2. \tag{10-12}$$

Two states which differ in an integer assigned to any one of the three individual quantum numbers are treated as different states even though they may have the same value of n^2 and hence of the energy. The spin quantum number accounts for the doubling of the number of electrons accommodated in these states. Furthermore, a great proliferation of different quantum states having the same n, and hence the same energy, results from permutations of the individual quantum numbers. The quantum mechanical states are multiply degenerate, because more than two distinct quantum states lead to the same energy. It turns out, therefore, that, although in the problem of the trough the average number of quantum states per unit energy range decreases with energy, in the case of electrons in a cubical box the average number of quantum states per unit energy range increases. This has a qualitative correspondence to the behavior of the quantum states determined by Bohr's theory of the hydrogen atom, although the quantitative agreement is not very good, because the atom does not closely resemble a cube filled with electrons.

Discussion of the Hydrogen Atom

According to the uncertainty principle, it is impossible to specify simultaneously the position and the momentum of the electron in the hydrogen atom. A more appropriate treatment is by means of a wave function u, which represents the amplitude of a standing wave. As shown in Part I, for the total energy of the hydrogen atom, we have

$$W_T = -e^2/(4\pi r\epsilon_0) + mv^2/2 \tag{10-13}$$

$$= -e^2/(4\pi r\epsilon_0) + p^2/2m, \tag{10-13'}$$

where p represents the linear momentum, m the mass, and e the charge of the electron. Bohr's condition for quantizing action, $2\pi r \times p = nh$, may be related directly to the uncertainty principle. The interpretation in the two cases is quite different. The s states in wave mechanics have no angular momentum, because the phase does not change with angle. The uncertainty relationship for the $1s$ state may be put into the form

$$\Delta r \, \Delta p = h/2\pi. \tag{10-14}$$

The hyperbolas $rp = nh/2\pi$ may be drawn to represent possible states of the electron. Although, according to Bohr's theory for the circular orbits, only one point on each of these hyperbolas had physical significance since both the radius and the angular momentum were definite, in wave mechanics any point on each of these hyperbolas may represent the condition of an electron.

Consistent with this idea, the electron may be located close to the nucleus with a correspondingly large momentum or it may be far from the nucleus with a small momentum. The average values satisfy the equation

$$\bar{r}\bar{p} = h/2\pi$$

or

$$\bar{p} = h/2\pi\bar{r}. \tag{10-15}$$

If this value of $\bar{p}$ is used, Eq. (13′) becomes

$$W_T = -e^2/(4\pi\epsilon_0\bar{r}) + h^2/(8\pi^2 m\bar{r}^2). \tag{10-13″}$$

For testing calculated against observed values, assume that $\bar{r}$ should be assigned the value which will make the total energy a minimum. Taking the derivative of the foregoing equation and setting the result equal to zero, gives

$$d(+W_T)/d\bar{r} = +e^2/(4\pi\epsilon_0\bar{r}^2) - 2h^2/(8\pi^2 m\bar{r}^3) = 0 \tag{10-16}$$

$$d^2(+W_T)/d\bar{r}^2 = -2e^2/(4\pi\epsilon_0\bar{r}^3) + 6h^2/(8\pi^2 m\bar{r}^4), \tag{10-17}$$

whence from Eq. (16)

$$\bar{r} = h^2\epsilon_0/(\pi me^2) = a_0, \tag{10-16′}$$

which is consistent with the result (Eq. 5-9) we obtained in Part I from quantizing action in the orbit. The numerical value of a_0 is 5.3×10^{-11} m, and this is a very important atomic constant. Substitution of this value of $\bar{r}$ in Eq. (13″) gives a minimum value of $+W_n$, not a maximum, because substitution of this value in Eq. (17) shows the second derivative of $(+W_T)$ to be positive as required by calculus for a minimum.

The corresponding energy is

$$W_T = -me^4/8\epsilon_0^2 h^2$$

$$= -\frac{9.1 \times 10^{-31} \text{ kg} \times (1.6 \times 10^{-19} \text{ coulombs})^4}{8 \times (8.854 \times 10^{-12} \text{ farads/m})^2(6.62 \times 10^{-34} \text{ joule-sec})^2}$$

$$= -2.17 \times 10^{-18} \text{ joules}$$

$$= -13.59 \text{ ev.}$$

The wave function associated with this electron is spherically symmetric, and it depends only on the radius. The normalized wave function is

$$u = (\pi a_0{}^3)^{-\frac{1}{2}} \exp(-r/a_0).$$ (10-18)

Because the wave for this state is spherical, the state is designated by the notation s. The wave function of an electron in the state of lowest energy is invariably an s function, and is usually denoted by $1s$. Consistent with the discussion of the one-dimensional case, the wave function corresponding to $n = 1$ has a single loop along any radius, with a spherical node at $r = \infty$.

Uncertainties are associated with the wave mechanical representation of an electron. We cannot say with certainty where the electron is. The square of the wave function is proportional to the probability per unit volume of finding the electron at the corresponding location. It will be informative to determine the probability of the electron being in the range dr at r. The corresponding volume is $4\pi r^2\,dr$, and the magnitude of the wave function amplitude squared is given by

$$u^2 = (\pi a_0{}^3)^{-1} \exp(-2r/a_0).$$

The probability of finding the electron in a spherical shell of thickness dr at r is the product of the two factors, and hence

$$dP = 4(a_0)^{-3} r^2\,dr \exp(-2r/a_0).$$ (10-19)

The value of r at which this function comes to a maximum may be found by differentiation.

$$\frac{d}{dr}(r^2 e^{-2r/a_0}) = 0$$

or

$$(2r - 2r^2/a_0) \exp(-2r/a_0) = 0.$$ (10-20)

There is a minimum at $r = \infty$ and another at $r = 0$, and, after eliminating these two extraneous roots, the maximum is given by

$$r = a_0.$$ (10-21)

Thus, the most probable location of the electron is at a distance from the nucleus equal to the first Bohr radius. The plot of the function $r^2 \exp(-2r/a_0)$ gives the form of the average distribution of the charge of the electron as a function of the distance from the nucleus, and this

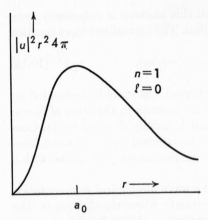

$|u|^2 r^2 4\pi$

$n=1$
$\ell=0$

$r \longrightarrow$

a_0

Fig. 10-1. Distribution of electric charge as a function of distance from the nucleus for an electron in the 1s state of hydrogen.

function is shown in Fig. 10-1. The charge is seen to be concentrated about the first Bohr radius a_0.

An electron in the second quantum state has an r-p product equal to h/π. Hence,

$$\bar{p} = h/\pi\bar{r},$$

and

$$W_T = -e^2/(4\pi\epsilon_0\bar{r}) + h^2/(2\pi^2 m\bar{r}^2).$$

The condition

$$dW_T/d\bar{r} = 0$$

yields

$$\bar{r} = 4a_0.$$

This also is consistent with the result of Bohr's theory for the radius of the second circular orbit. The wave function in this case is found to be of the form

$$u = C(1 - r/2a_0) \exp(-r/2a_0).$$

This function has a spherical symmetry with one finite spherical node (at $r = 2a_0$). This is called the 2s state.

The wave mechanical interpretation of the principal quantum number for hydrogen is apparent. It determines the number of loops in the standing wave pattern. The fact that the principal quantum number is in the denominator of the negative exponent of e means that it reduces the rate at which the wave function decreases as the distance from the nucleus increases. Thus, if n is large, the electron is relatively likely to be found far from the nucleus where its energy is large. It is the principal quantum number, which is primarily responsible for the specification of the energy of the electron.

In the case of the cubical box, we had three similar coordinates which we took to be Cartesian. There was a quantum number associated with each of these coordinates, but because the coordinates were similar, the quantum numbers were identical in their behavior. This is an especially simple case. In general, there is a quantum number which determines primarily the behavior of the wave function as one of the coordinates varies. This is illustrated by the principal quantum number, which determines primarily the change of the wave function as r varies. In spherical coordinates, however, r is an entirely different type of coordinate than the angles, and the angles themselves differ from one another. There is, in the case of the spherical coordinates, a second quantum number l, usually called the azimuthal quantum number, which determines the behavior of the wave function as the angle θ, measured with respect to the "north pole" (z-axis) of the coordinate system, varies. Associated with the third polar coordinate ϕ, there is a third quantum number m_l, usually called the magnetic quantum number, which determines the rate at which the wave function varies as ϕ is changed. As noted above, however, these three quantum numbers did not prove sufficient to account for atomic spectra, and Uhlenbeck and Goudsmit introduced the electronic spin quantum number m_s, for specifying the orientation of the electron. Appendix VII contains further discussion of the details giving rise to these quantum numbers. The main effort in this chapter has been to give illustrations of the fact that quantum numbers are related to the standing wave patterns with which the electrons are identified.

Conclusion

To account for the results of spectroscopy, four quantum numbers were found to be necessary for specifying the state of an electron in an atom. The theoretical interpretation which wave mechanics places upon these numbers is the most natural one which has been devised. Associated with wave patterns in three dimensions, three quantum numbers are required, one being associated primarily with the behavior of the standing waves in each of the spherical coordinates. The fourth quantum number specifying the orientation of the electron's spin was introduced empirically by Uhlenbeck and Goudsmit. It should be mentioned, however, that electronic spin has been placed on a satisfactory theoretical basis by Dirac, who developed a relativistic form of the wave equation. This theory of Dirac's required the electron to have a mathematical representation strongly suggesting spin. (The existence of the positron also was predicted in the same theory.)

The introduction of standing wave patterns for specifying the effective position of electrons is reasonable. The Bohr atom model certainly carried details that could not be verified by experiment. It seems likely that the time average of charge densities arising through Born's statistical interpretation of the wave functions should influence the observable results, and hence this should be capable of at least an indirect verification through experiment. We examine this matter somewhat further in the chapters that follow.

Solutions of the wave equation have been obtained in simple cases by way of illustration. Far more important than the details of these solutions is the concept of energy being determined by the standing wave pattern which gives the probability that the electron will be found in various portions of space and hence gives a distribution corresponding to the time average of the charge in various locations.

Problems on Standing Wave Patterns Associated with Electrons

1. It has been tacitly assumed that the electron in the trough has exactly zero momentum in both the y- and the z-directions. What does the uncertainty principle indicate concerning the localization of the electron in these coordinates?

2. a. If the position of the electron in the x-direction is assumed to have an uncertainty equal to the separation between the two barriers, what is the corresponding uncertainty in the momentum?
   b. If, as is frequently done, the uncertainty is considered to be the spacing between the planes at which the square of the amplitude of the wave function drops to one-half of its maximum value, what is the corresponding uncertainty in the momentum?

3. A trough contains 10 electrons in the lowest energy states consistent with the Pauli exclusion principle.
   a. What is the total energy of these electrons?
   b. What is the average energy of one electron?
   c. What must be the spacing between the two barriers to make the average energy of an electron equal to the characteristic thermal energy kT, if $T = 300° \text{ K}$?

4. If a cubical box contains 10 electrons in the lowest permitted energy states, calculate their total energy and the average energy for one electron.

5. Show by integration over all space that the function given by Eq. (18) is normalized.

6. By a normalizing integration, evaluate the constant C in the equation for the $2s$ state of hydrogen.

7. Find the force exerted by an electron in a trough, for which $n = 1$, on each of the boundaries, assuming that any increase in the energy of the electron must be supplied by work done in moving the barriers.

8. If a trough contains 10 electrons, compute the force exerted by these electrons on each boundary.

References on Standing Wave Patterns and Quantum Numbers

French, A. P., *Principles of Modern Physics*, pp. 174-204 (New York: John Wiley and Sons, 1958).

Rice, F. O., and Edward Teller, *The Structure of Matter*, pp. 1-20 (New York: John Wiley and Sons, 1949).

Sproull, R. L., *Modern Physics*, pp. 124-46 (New York: John Wiley and Sons, 1956).

11 | Basic Aspects of Atomic Behavior

Bohr's Theory of the Electron Shells

In connection with the rules of atomic energy levels, which Bohr's work in the theory of the atom revealed, it became possible to develop a theory concerning the structure of the periodic table. Bohr worked on this problem in the early 1920s. This was before the development of wave mechanics and also before Uhlenbeck and Goudsmit's introduction of electronic spin to explain the fourth quantum number. Let us recast this discussion in terms of the wave mechanics and electronic spin.

In Chapter 10 we have treated the case of standing electron waves in a cubical box. This is an approximation to an atom which is so crude that it is hardly considered seriously as an atomic model. Numerous features illustrated in connection with this simple problem, however, persist in the wave mechanical models which are successful in the treatment of the atom. In the first place, the box is of finite volume, and an atom is expected to have a finite volume even though its boundaries are less sharp than those which have been used for the box. Corresponding to the three dimensions, there are three quantum numbers, all of which are similar, and which describe the behavior of the wave pattern in these three Cartesian coordinates of ordinary space, and there is a doubling of the number of quantum states due to the two orientations of the electronic spin. Atomic systems are more nearly spherical than rectangular, and it is therefore more appropriate to use spherical polar coordinates. These three coordinates r, θ, and ϕ are all very dissimilar, and it is not surprising that the three quantum numbers describing the behavior of standing wave patterns in each of these coordinates should be found to obey quite different rules. There is a doubling of the quantum states due to the two orientations of the electronic spin indicated by the fourth quantum number. It would not be profitable to take the electrons in a box and transform to spherical coordinates, because the boundary conditions applied to the box are so unlike those which apply to the atom.

Historically, the unraveling of the mysteries of atomic behavior started with Bohr's model of the hydrogen atom and his treatment of the circular orbits. This was a theory with a single quantum number, but as we have seen in Chapter 5, the elaboration of this theory by Sommerfeld and others led almost at once to the introduction of three quantum numbers which were given a dynamical interpretation. The original interpretation gave rise to predictions in conflict with experimental evidence, and had to be modified. The introduction of the electronic spin was a great step forward, but the older dynamics was seriously in error as applied to electrons in atoms and had to be modified in a fundamental way before a really satisfactory treatment, even of the hydrogen atom, could be achieved. Certain features of the wave mechanics of the hydrogen atom are contained in Appendix VII. This discussion illustrated the association of the principal quantum number n with the radial behavior of the standing wave pattern. The quantum number l is associated with the description of the behavior of the standing wave pattern in the angle θ, and the magnetic quantum number m_l describes the behavior of the standing wave pattern in the angle ϕ. It is significant that the special theory of relativity is based on a space of four dimensions, and that Dirac by incorporating relativistic considerations arrived at the electronic spin, and this completed the theoretical basis for the description of atomic behavior applicable in regions outside of the nucleus.

The rules which the four quantum numbers (n, l, m_l, and m_s) were found to satisfy are the following:

1. n can be any positive integer. This is identified as the principal quantum number.

2. For any given value of n, l takes on all positive integral values from 0 to $n - 1$.

3. For any value of l consistent with the preceding rule, m_l may be any one of $2l + 1$ integral values, including zero, from $-l$ to $+l$.

4. The electronic spin quantum number s is $\frac{1}{2}$ and the corresponding values of m_s are $+\frac{1}{2}$ or $-\frac{1}{2}$.

As we have noticed previously, in 1925 Pauli announced the hypothesis that in a given atom no two electrons could have an identical set of the four quantum numbers n, l, m_l, and m_s. This is an analogue of the impenetrability of matter, and may be considered the basis of this previously known rule.

The periodic table shows a behavior which is easily understood on the basis of Pauli's exclusion principle applied to electrons having four quantum numbers satisfying the stated rules. In the first place, if the principal quantum number is unity, the electron is said to be in the K-shell of the atom. According to rule 2, l can then only be zero, and consequently by rule 3, m_l must be zero. Hence, from the Pauli exclusion principle, only two electrons can be in the K-shell, and these must have different values of m_s.

Electrons in the second or L-shell all have the principal quantum number equal to 2. In this case, there are considerably more possibilities, and these are tabulated below. (States having $= 0, 1, 2, 3, 4, 5, \cdots$ are conventionally designated by the letters s, p, d, f, g, h, $\cdots$.)

Conventional identification:	2s	2s	2p	2p	2p	2p	2p	2p
Quantum numbers								
l	0	0	1	1	1	1	1	1
m_l	0	0	-1	-1	0	0	$+1$	$+1$
m_s	$-\frac{1}{2}$	$+\frac{1}{2}$	$-\frac{1}{2}$	$+\frac{1}{2}$	$-\frac{1}{2}$	$+\frac{1}{2}$	$-\frac{1}{2}$	$+\frac{1}{2}$

There are thus a total of eight electrons in the completed L-shell of neon and of all of the elements of higher atomic number than neon. Between helium and neon, lithium has a single 2s electron, beryllium two of them, and for the elements from boron to neon, one 2p electron is added for each unit increase in atomic number. Although not all of the electrons permitted by an extension of this scheme are found in nature, no case violating these principles has been found.

Principles Determining the Size of Atoms

A very remarkable fact is that the atoms, although they contain numbers of electrons varying from 1 to considerably more than 90, do not differ much in the space they occupy. The increase of the nuclear charge produces a change in the radii of all the orbits in inverse proportion to the effective nuclear charge.

Although the accurate calculation of the radii of the electronic shells for specific atoms other than hydrogen is beyond the scope of this introductory treatment, and in any representative case is very tedious, it is not difficult to understand the principles which determine these radii and to make calculations which constitute a valid approximation. The accuracy of the calculation of the average displacement of any electron from the nucleus depends primarily upon the determination of the nuclear charge effective for that electron.

The effective nuclear charge is the actual nuclear charge minus the shielding factor for each electron in the atom, except the one for which the effect is being calculated. Electrostatic theory indicates an order of magnitude for the shielding effects. If, for example, we have a charge uniformly distributed over the surface of a sphere, the force this charge exerts on a charge outside of this spherical surface is just the same as that which would be caused by an equal charge concentrated at the center of the sphere. If on the other hand the charge on which the force is being determined is within a sphere the surface of which is charged uniformly, there will be no force arising from the uniform distribution of charge. There are two applications of this information directly to the atomic case. In the first place, if the electron on which the force is being considered has a displacement from the nucleus, the time average of which is very large as compared with that of another electron in the atom, this second electron will have the effect of reducing the nuclear charge by one electron. On the other hand, if the electron on which the force is being computed has an average displacement from the nucleus, the time average of which is very small with respect to that of a second electron, this second electron will not appreciably reduce the nuclear charge which is effective in creating the force on the first electron.

If the average displacements from the nucleus for the two electrons are comparable, the effect lies between zero shielding and reduction by one electronic charge. Considered qualitatively, each electron repels the other, and, by increasing the average separation between the two charges, reduces the force of repulsion which would exist if the redistribution of charges were not permitted. If the radii of the electron shells are comparable, some redistribution of charge invariably occurs.

The atom is treated as a polarizable electrical system. Even an atom, which on the average has a symmetrical distribution of charge, will show an instantaneous dipole moment arising from the motions of the individual electrons. Those in the outermost shells contribute most to the electrical dipole, and they in turn will be most easily displaced in electrostatic fields. When two atoms are brought close together, each is in the field set up by the fluctuating dipole of the other atom, and each is polarized as a result of it. There is a correlation in the positions of the electrons in two atoms which interact, and, although the electrical field of a dipole falls off with the third power of the distance from the dipole, it is this effect which is primarily responsible for the long-range forces set up by one atom on another. This, for example, is the origin of the van der Waals forces, which were mentioned in the chapter on kinetic theory.

In electrostatic theory there is a simple method for calculating forces where a redistribution of the charge is permitted as, for example, when a charge is placed on a conducting body. This is the method of images. The electronic charge in a given shell of the atom has a distribution, the time average of which is approximately spherical. To make a quantitative estimate of these effects, a conducting sphere maintained at zero potential (grounded) may be considered. When a point charge is brought into the vicinity of the grounded body, the zero potential of all points on the conducting sphere must be maintained despite the influence of the point charge which has been brought into its presence. This can be done by a single point charge of opposite sign located within the spherical surface. The location and magnitude of this "image" charge depends upon the geometry of the configuration. It is always possible, however, to cancel the effect of an external point charge by a suitably chosen internal point charge, and vice versa. Of course, the atomic shells that we consider have constant total charge. In electrostatic theory, all that is necessary to solve such a problem is to calculate the amount of the image charge and put it into the configuration, and then to put at the center of the sphere the constant charge which the sphere contains plus the negative of the image charge. In this manner, the equipotential surface is maintained and the sphere is charged by the net amount required by the given conditions. It is from the solutions of such problems in electrostatics that we get valid ideas concerning the orders of magnitude of the shielding effects.

A case of special interest is that in which the shielding charges are in the same spherical shell as the charge on which the effect is being investigated. In the case of the uniformly charged spherical shell, electrostatic theory shows that the force on a small element of charge on the surface is equal to the magnitude of the small element of charge multiplied by one-half the electric intensity close to, but outside of, the surface. This electric intensity arises from all the surface charge including the element on which the force is being calculated. For the charge contained on a finite cap of the spherical surface, the forces on the individual elements are added vectorially, and the total force is thus reduced. The shielding by electrons in the same spherical shell, therefore, would not be more than half the total charge of the other electrons contained in that shell. It should be less for at least one reason. This is that each of the electrons is a finite fraction of the total charge of a shell, and for a finite cap of a spherical surface the factor used decreases from one-half. On an empirical basis, the factor by which the electrons sharing positions in the same shell must be multiplied to account for the reduction of the nuclear charge through their shielding effects is 0.35.

For electrons in the next smaller shell, the factor is 0.85, while electrons still closer to the nucleus reduce the effective nuclear charge by nearly one electronic charge. For electrons in the next larger shell, the factor is to be taken as about 0.08, but electrons in shells still further out produce negligible shielding.

On the basis of the simple Bohr theory and the shielding considerations, it is possible to work out the radii of the various shells. From the Bohr formula, replacing Ze by the effective nuclear charge $Z_{ef}.e$, we get

$$n^2 h^2 \epsilon_0 / [\pi m (Z_{ef}.e)e].$$

The nucleus of sodium, for example, has $Z = 11$ and there are two electrons in the K-shell. Hence, the nuclear charge effective for an electron in this shell is reduced by $0.35e$ by the presence of the other electron in the shell. There are eight electrons in the completed L-shell, and from this cause the shielding is $8 \times 0.08e = 0.64e$. The sum of the two shielding effects $(0.99e)$ is almost exactly one electronic charge. (Considerations of the same kind apply, in Problem 5 at the end of the chapter, to the calculation of the frequencies for the K_α X-ray lines by the Bohr theory.) The calculation for the average displacement from the nucleus for the electrons in the K-shell, by use of the above equation, thus yields for the sodium atom the value

$$r = 0.53 \times 10^{-10}/10 \text{ m} = 0.053 \times 10^{-10} \text{ m}.$$

For each of the eight L-electrons, the effective nuclear charge would be

$$Z_{ef}.e = (11 - 0.85 \times 2 - 7 \times 0.35 - 0.08)e = 6.77e,$$

and from this effective nuclear charge the radius of the L-shell is found to be 0.31×10^{-10} m. Finally, for the single M-electron, the effective nuclear charge is

$$Z_{ef}.e = (11 - 2 - 0.85 \times 8)e = 2.2e,$$

and the radius of the L-shell (valence shell) is found to be 2.16×10^{-10} m. These results agree quite well with those of Hartree, shown in Table 11-1, which were worked out with great care by successive approximations to give self-consistent fields. The only simple calculation made for which the first figure does not agree with the table value is that for the single valence electron of sodium. In this case the error

TABLE 11-1. RADII IN ÅNGSTROM UNITS ASSOCIATED WITH
ELECTRONIC CHARGE DISTRIBUTIONS

Shell:	K	L		M			N	
Notation:	1s	2s	2p	3s	3p	3d	4s	4p
Element								
H	0.53							
He	0.30							
Li	0.20	1.50						
Be	0.143	1.19						
O	0.069	0.48	0.45					
Ne	0.061	0.41	0.38					
Na	0.050	0.32	0.28	1.55				
Cl	0.032	0.20	0.16	0.72	0.75			
Fe	0.021	0.127	0.101	0.39	0.39	0.39	1.22	
Zn	0.018	0.106	0.081	0.32	0.32	0.30	0.97	
Kr	0.015	0.09	0.067	0.25	0.25	0.25	0.74	0.86

is about 40%, whereas in all the other cases it is considerably less than 10%.

Representative electronic configurations for the various elements are shown in Table 11-1.

TABLE 11-2. ELECTRON CONFIGURATIONS IN SOME OF THE ELEMENTS

Element	K	L		M			N				O			P		
	1s	2s	2p	3s	3p	3d	4s	4p	4d	4f	5s	5p	5d	6s	6p	6d
Al	2	2	6	2	1											
Si	2	2	6	2	2											
A	2	2	6	2	6											
K							1									
Ca							2									
Sc						1	2									
Ti		Electrons in this				2	2									
Ni		block are the same				8	2									
Cu		as in argon atom.				10	1									
Zn						10	2									
Ga						10	2	1								
Ge						10	2	2								
Kr	2	2	6	2	6	10	2	6								
Rb											1					
Sr											2					
Y									1		2					
Zr									2		2					
Pd		Electrons in the core are the same							10							
Ag		as in krypton.							10		1					
Xe									10		2	6				
Cs									10		2	6		1		
La									10		2	6	1	2		
Ce									10	1	2	6	1	2		
Hf									10	14	2	6	2	2		

Ionization Potentials

The theories of electrostatics applied to atomic structure, with electrons arranged in shells, strongly suggest that the energy required to remove the most weakly bound electron (ionization potential) should show a trend from element to element, with the same period as that in the chemical properties of the periodic table. This is easily verified by an inspection of a table of ionization potentials, such as that given in Table 11-3.

TABLE 11-3. PERIODIC TABLE WITH IONIZATION POTENTIALS IN VOLTS

H							He
13.53							24.46
Li	Be	B	C	N	O	F	Ne
5.363	9.28	8.26	11.22	14.5	13.55	17.34	21.2
Na	Mg	Al	Si	P	S	Cl	A
5.12	7.61	5.96	8.12	10.9	10.3	12.95	15.68

The correlation shown, although not exact, has a very simple interpretation in terms of Coulomb's law. It turns out that for the electrons in a given shell, the reduction of the effective nuclear charge caused by the addition of an electron to that shell does not completely compensate for the addition of a proton to the nucleus. Thus, in a given row of the periodic table, the energy required to extract an electron from an atom is least for the alkali metals, where the actual nuclear charge is least, and this energy is greatest for the inert gases, where the true nuclear charge is greatest. The reason for this is that, even though electrons are added along with the protons to make the system electrically neutral, these electrons do not produce complete shielding, and the effective nuclear charge increases along the row as the actual nuclear charge increases. Hence, the alkali metals are the elements which most readily release electrons. Next to the inert gases, the halogens require the greatest amount of energy for the liberation of their electrons. This means that positive ions of inert gases are formed with relatively great difficulty. All of the positive ions formed by the extraction of outer valence electrons from atoms are stable, until they find an opportunity to recapture an electron, and thus form again the original neutral atom.

The behavior of the electrostatic charges also indicates that an electron may be added to neutral chlorine or fluorine atom to form a stable system. Although the atom at first is neutral, the electrons in the outer shell are strongly repelled by the added electron, and they are displaced in such a way that the added electron is bound to the atom by an effective nuclear charge. The electron affinities of 4.1 ev for fluorine and 3.8 ev for chlorine correlate quite well with these basic principles. Such behavior, understandable on the basis of electrostatic theory, is related to the problem of chemical valence.

The Arrangement of Atoms in Molecules

Chemical Properties

The similarity of elements having the same number of electrons in their outer shell is a clear indication of the fact that chemical valence has to do with these outermost electrons. There is a tendency for stable compounds to be formed if the combining elements have enough valence electrons to complete a shell. For example, consider table salt (NaCl). In this case, because sodium has one valence electron and chlorine has seven, there are sufficient electrons to complete a shell of eight. The ease with which sodium gives up electrons as contrasted with chlorine suggests that on the average the electron ascribed to the sodium atom might be expected to spend more of its time in the neighborhood of the chlorine than in the neighborhood of the sodium. This behavior gives rise to polarization. The dipole moments associated with many of the chemical compounds have been determined and representative values are shown in Table 11-4.

TABLE 11-4. DIPOLE MOMENTS OF GAS MOLECULES

Compounds	Dipole Moment (μ) Coulomb-meters
HCl	3.4
HBr	2.6
KCl	21.
CH_3COCH_3	9.5
NH_3	4.8

Semiquantitative Treatment of the Hydrogen Molecular Ion

For the case of a singly ionized hydrogen molecule (H_2^+) a quantitative treatment has been worked out. Since the mathematical detail constituting the basis of an exact treatment is not assumed at this level, our discussion will be only semiquantitative. It is, however, correct in principle, and the fundamentals are easily comprehended.

In the molecule of ionized hydrogen there are two protons and one electron. The protons would fly apart if their own mutual interaction constituted the only force. However, the single electron is moving about in the attractive force field set up by each of the protons. For the unexcited or normal state of the atom, the wave function in the presence of either of these protons alone is known. It is the one we justified previously by minimizing the total energy. For the hydrogen molecular ion, a solution of Schroedinger's equation which minimizes the energy is the one desired. For minimization of the energy, the protons will be separated by some distance R. To obtain a wave function for the electron in the presence of both protons, we might multiply each of the two wave functions for the electron in the presence of one or the other single proton by the same constant and add the two, taking into account the separation R between the two protons. By integrating the square of this wave function over all space, we might then determine the value of the constant which normalizes the sum of the wave functions, and makes it certain that the electron will be found somewhere in space. Between the two protons the wave functions have a relatively large value and they add. The square of this sum is proportional to the probability of finding the electron in an element of volume in this region. For this reason the electron spends a relatively great amount of time in the region between the two protons, and effectively there is a concentration of negative charge in this region.

Although the time average has the electron's charge distributed throughout space, we will be approximately correct if we assume that the point electron is placed midway between the two protons. On this basis it is easy to calculate the potential energy of the system. If in addition we could approximate the kinetic energy of the electron, we would be able to set down the total energy of the system and by minimizing it, we could get an approximate answer for the stable configuration. Consistent with the change of potential energy throughout the space, the kinetic energy of the electron is changing, and with it the wavelength of the electron. The standing wave pattern of the electron has no nodes between the protons and the pattern extends somewhat beyond each proton. We will not be much in error if we assume that in this region, the importance of which dominates the problem, the distance between the two protons is equal to seven-sixteenths of a wavelength for the electron. Thus,

$$R = 7\lambda/16 \quad \text{or} \quad \lambda = 16R/7$$

and the kinetic energy T is given by

$$T = p^2/2m = h^2/2m\lambda^2 = h^2/2m(16R/7)^2. \tag{11-1}$$

Similarly, for the potential energy V, we have

$$V = -2e^2/4\pi\epsilon_0 R - 2e^2/4\pi\epsilon_0 R + e^2/4\pi\epsilon_0 R = -3e^2/4\pi\epsilon_0 R. \quad (11-2)$$

The total energy W is then

$$W = 49h^2/512mR^2 - 3e^2/4\pi\epsilon_0 R.$$

To minimize the energy, we set the derivative equal to zero. Thus,

$$dW/dR = -49h^2/256mR^3 + 3e^2/4\pi\epsilon_0 R^2 = 0, \quad (11-3)$$

from which

$$R = \pi\epsilon_0 h^2 49/me^2 192. \quad (11-4)$$

This value of R corresponds to a minimum of energy, because d^2W/dR^2 is positive at this value of R. Substitution of the numerical values for the constants gives $R = 1.32 \times 10^{-10}$ m $= 1.32$ Å, which is correct for the order of magnitude of the internuclear distance of the hydrogen molecular ion. The experimental value is about 1.06×10^{-10} m $= 1.06$ Å.

For the total energy of the system, the calculation yields

$$W = -2.7 \times 10^{-18} \text{ joules} = -16.8 \text{ ev.}$$

This is considerably more than the binding energy of an electron in the fundamental or normal state of a single atom, as indeed it should be. Subtracting from the above result the binding energy of the neutral hydrogen atom, we obtain 3.2 ev for the energy of dissociation of the hydrogen molecular ion. The experimentally determined value is about 2.8 ev.

The Hydrogen Molecule

Symmetric and Anti-Symmetric Wave Functions

Wave mechanics represents the electrons in an atom in terms of vibratory phenomena or standing waves. A pair of hydrogen atoms when they interact with each other might be expected to show phenomena somewhat analogous to a pair of identical coupled mechanical oscillators. For the coupled mechanical oscillators, we obtained simple harmonic oscillations of relatively high frequency when the displacements were in opposite directions and harmonic oscillations of low frequency when the displacements were in the same direction.

The same principles apply to a pair of interacting hydrogen atoms. If the wave functions are in the same phase, by the superposition of the two identical wave functions, we get a symmetrical wave function giving rise to a charge distribution, which, when averaged over time, is symmetrical about the plane containing the perpendicular bisectors of the line connecting the nuclei. The situation is illustrated qualitatively in Fig 11-1. Here the contributions of the individual wave functions between the two protons are shown by the dotted curves, and the sum is shown by the solid curve. According to the probability inter-

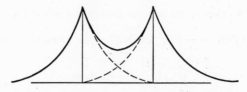

Fig. 11-1. Symmetric wave function for H_2.

pretation of wave functions, the average charge density is proportional to the square of the amplitude factor, and midway between the protons, where each wave function contributes equally to the sum, the charge density is thus four times that which would result from an electron moving in the field of either proton alone. Thus, a charge concentration

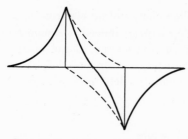

Fig. 11-2. Anti-symmetric wave function for H_2.

develops in the region between the two nuclei, and, when the resulting wave function is normalized, there is a decrease in the negative charge concentration in the regions beyond either proton. It is this development of the average charge concentration between the protons that gives rise to the valence forces for the hydrogen molecule. The binding is slightly less than twice that for the $H_2{}^+$ ion.

There is, however, another possibility. For if the combining wave functions are in opposite phase, the plane normal to the line connecting the protons and midway between them is a nodal plane. The average charge density along this plane is zero everywhere, and close to this plane the charge density is very small. The situation is illustrated in Fig. 11-2. In this case the wave function is said to be anti-symmetric, and it represents an anti-bonding condition, because the repulsion of the two protons is greater than the attraction of either proton to that portion of the electronic charge which is between them. The fact that the kinetic energy of the electron in this case is greater is also rather apparent, because the reversal of the phase of the function in the distance between the two nuclei will surely correspond to a shorter wavelength than in the preceding case, and the kinetic energy is proportional to the square of the reciprocal of this wavelength. This increases the kinetic energy of the associated electrons, and also reduces the binding energy.

The atom is an electrical system, and it is perhaps not surprising that we should have been able to apply Coulomb's law in the discussion of some of the forces between atoms. The anti-bonding states have electron displacements in the proper sense to be accounted for by the coulomb repulsions between electrons in the valence shells of the two atoms. The bonding states are characterized by electron displacements in the wrong sense to be accounted for in this manner, and this illustrates the fact that in an atom there are forces not observed between a pair of isolated charges, and they arise from quantum mechanical considerations. The bonding states illustrate this, because the wave mechanical treatment shows the electrical charge concentrating in the region between the two atoms very much as if the electrons in this case were attracting one another. This is a fair statement of the situation. If the electrons have their spins similarly oriented, the exclusion principle requires forces to arise which will oppose the encroachment of one electron into the space occupied by another. If the spins are oppositely directed, this encroachment is not forbidden by the exclusion principle, and the quantum mechanical treatment shows terms which do correspond to attractive forces. Because of the manner in which they arise in the calculations, they are sometimes called "exchange forces."

This distinction between the bonding and the anti-bonding states available to the electrons for their standing wave patterns about a molecule continues into the more complicated molecules. In the more complex molecules it is not uncommon to have some of the electrons occupying anti-bonding states while other electrons occupy bonding states to give rise to a negative total energy, which characterizes a stable molecule.

The essential features we have seen illustrated in the preceding simple examples of atoms combining to form molecules apply rather generally. In bonding states the overlapping of the wave functions causes a concentration of negative charge between the nuclei of the combining atoms, and the attraction of the nuclei for this charge provides the force which holds the atoms together. On the other hand, as the nuclei come closer together the greater concentration of the electronic charge is opposed by the fact that the wavelength associated with the electron is reduced and the associated kinetic energy is increased. This gives rise to a repulsive force which acts in addition to the electrostatic repulsion between the nuclei. When the charge distributions of the combining atoms first begin to overlap, the attractive force begins to act. (There is also a small van der Waals attraction just before the charge distributions begin to overlap, but this is not great enough to form a stable molecule at ordinary temperatures.) As the nuclei come close together, the repulsive force increases very rapidly. These facts are often represented by a plot of the potential energy of the system as a function of the distance between the combining atoms. A curve of this type is shown in Fig. 11-3. Although the analytical treatment is quite difficult when the atoms have several filled electron shells, Morse has given a mathematical formula which is an adequate approximation for many purposes. This formula can be written as

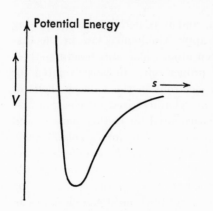

Fig. 11-3. Potential energy V of a diatomic molecule as a function of the internuclear distance r.

$$V = D_e \left[\exp \{ -2a(r - r_e) \} - 2 \exp \{ -a(r - r_e) \} \right]. \qquad (11\text{-}5)$$

Here the first term represents the repulsive force which dominates when r is less than r_e, and the second term represents the attraction which dominates when r is greater than r_e. The proof that the equilibrium distance is r_e is left as a problem (stated at the end of the chapter). In Eq. (5), D_e represents the energy required to dissociate the molecule. The fact that Eq. (5) gives a plot similar to that shown in Fig. 11-3 may easily be verified by calculating values of the energy for values of r on both sides of the minimum.

Configurations of Polyatomic Molecules

The complexities involved in applying these basic principles to polyatomic molecules are such that we will not attempt a quantitative application here. It may be of interest, however, to correlate some of the empirical information of chemistry with features of the wave mechanical representation of molecules.

One of the striking features of the wave mechanical treatment is that it gave rise to distributions for the p-electrons which showed a definite emphasis on the charge distribution of a given electronic pair along a definite direction. Thus, electronic pairs for the p-states show charge distributions along three mutually perpendicular directions. It is primarily this fact which accounts for many of the directed valences observed in chemistry.

A simple example is water (H_2O). The oxygen atom has four valence electrons in $2p$-states. This circumstance is associated with a concentration of charge distribution along three mutually perpendicular lines in the free atom and at least one of the $2p$-directions, say along the x-axis, will have to contain two paired electrons with their charge distributed along a line extending outward from the oxygen nucleus in this direction, and because this direction contains two electrons in the oxygen atom, it will not be available for the completion of bonds with the hydrogen atoms. The other p-states, in the y- and z- directions, contain single electrons. Hence, these are available for the completion

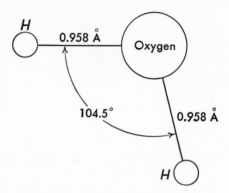

Fig. 11-4. Structure of the water molecule.

of bonds with the hydrogen atoms. A consequence is that the water molecule will be triangular in shape rather than linear. The resulting bonds are strongly polar with the electrons spending less time in the neighborhood of the protons of the hydrogen nuclei than they do in the neighborhood of the oxygen nucleus. The observed dipole moment of the water molecule (6.2×10^{-30} coulomb-meters) is a result of this. As a consequence of the triangular form of the water molecule, there are three different moments of inertia of the molecule, and these have observable consequences. Because of the strongly polar character of the bonds, the two protons will repel each other and thus distort the molecule so that the two bonds are no longer at an angle of 90°, but slightly greater. The observed angle between the bonds is about 104.5°. This structure of the water molecule is shown in Fig. 11-4.

A second, distinctly different, illustration is obtained in the case of crystals of Se and Te. For example, selenium has four valence electrons classified as $5p$. These elements at room temperature form typical crystal structures consisting of spiral chains of atoms with the double bonds joining the successive atoms extending out from a given atom along lines making approximately right angles (105° in Se and 102° in Te). The arrangement of the atoms and the bonds is suggested in Fig. 11-5. Here the shaded dark spheres represent the electronic shells of

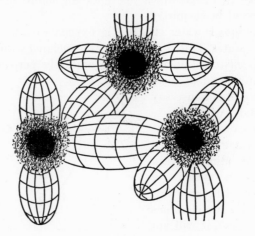

Fig. 11-5. Spiral chains of Se and Te.

the atomic cores, while the zones indicated by the curved lines contain the valence electrons associated with the atoms combining to form the crystal.

Summary

The most remarkable achievement of the modern theories of atomic structure is the general applicability of the ideas which have been introduced. Systematic behavior of atomic properties has been the subject of this chapter. The various combinations of four quantum numbers (n, l, m_l, and m_s) are sufficient to describe the electronic configurations in all of the known elements. Furthermore, the rules prescribing the allowed values of these quantum numbers apply throughout the entire periodic table.

Wave mechanics by giving a means of calculating, at least approximately, average charge densities throughout space, made possible the quantitative treatment of atomic energy levels for the more complicated atoms. The wave mechanical treatment of atoms has enabled us to make a start in a basic theoretical interpretation of chemistry. Valence electrons will be either bonding or anti-bonding depending on the relative phase of the variations in the waves which represent them. The hydrogen molecule has its two electrons in bonding states, and it shows a relatively large concentration of negative charge (on the average) at the midpoint of the line connecting the two nuclei. This accounts for the attractive force which holds the two atoms of the molecule together.

The existence of directed valences is predicted from the concentration of the negative charge along certain lines in the patterns corresponding to certain wave functions. The p-states have such a distribution of charge, and the development of the theory has shown that there is a possibility of a charge concentration along three mutually perpendicular lines. This is used to explain the triangular form of the water molecule and also the spiral chains of atoms in the crystals of certain elements.

Problems on the Periodic System of the Elements

1. a. If, contrary to fact, all the elements consistent with the Pauli exclusion principle and the rules applying to the quantum numbers, existed in nature, how many elements would be formed by starting with hydrogen and adding a number of electrons sufficient for the completion of the shell for which $n = 5$?

    b. How many elements are added by completing the shell for which $n = 6$?

2. a. Calculate the radius of the $1s$-orbit in oxygen on the basis of the Bohr theory, assuming that the effective nuclear charge is reduced by $0.35e$ because of the second electron in the same shell, and also is reduced by shielding from external electrons.

    b. Compare this result with that given in Table 11-1, and discuss the difference.

3. Make the calculation required in Problem 2 for the uranium atom for which $Z = 92$.

4. Calculate the radius of the neutral chlorine atom. How much larger is the chlorine ion that is formed by the addition of one electron?

5. On the basis of the Bohr theory, and the shielding considerations presented in this chapter, discuss the calculation of the frequencies for the K_α-lines, which arise from the transition in which n changes from 2 to 1.

6. a. Calculate the ionization potentials for the elements from Be to F inclusive on the assumption that the electron to be removed is in a hydrogen-like $2s$-state, where the effective nuclear charge is given by $eZ_{ef.} = (Z - 1.7 - 0.35N)e$, where $N = 1$ for Be, 2 for B, and so on.

    b. What are the factors which in your opinion explain the discrepancies between the experimental values in Table 11-3 and those predicted on this oversimplified theory?

7. Assuming that the charge distribution for each of two hydrogen atoms does not change as the atoms are brought together, discuss the electrostatic forces which would result from the overlapping of the charge distributions as a function of the distance separating the protons.

8. Use the approximation that Morse has given for the potential energy as a function of the internuclear distance and
   a. Show that the distance r_e is the equilibrium separation between the nuclei.
   b. What is the force constant calculated for small displacements about the equilibrium position?
9. Assume that the forces accounting for the NaCl molecule are (1) the coulomb attraction between singly charged ions of opposite sign, and (2) a repulsive force resulting from a potential energy term of the form Cr^{-8}.
   a. What value of the constant C will account for the fact that the equilibrium distance between the ions in NaCl is 2.51 Å?
   b. What is the value of the dissociation energy D_e based on these forces?
   c. What is the calculated net force at separations of 2.00 and at 3.00 Å?

References on Molecular Structure

Fano, U., and L. Fano, *Basic Physics of Atoms and Molecules*, Ch. 19-22 (New York: John Wiley and Sons, 1959).

Rice, Francis O., and Edward Teller, *The Structure of Matter*, Ch. 2 (New York: John Wiley and Sons, 1949). (An excellent non-mathematical discussion.)

Slater, John C., and Nathaniel H. Frank, *Introduction to Theoretical Physics*, Ch. 35 (New York: McGraw-Hill Book Company, 1933).

Slater, John C., *Introduction to Chemical Physics*, Ch. 23 (New York: McGraw-Hill Book Company, 1939). (A more complete treatment of the present subject.)

Sproull, Robert L., *Modern Physics—A Textbook for Engineers*, Ch. 7 (New York: John Wiley and Sons, 1956). (Treatment more quantitative than this chapter.)

12 | Electrons in Metals

One of the most important types of solids is that provided by the metallic state. The use of metals is widespread. Properties of great interest and importance for these are extremely high electrical and thermal conductivities, and also, usually, very considerable strength or toughness.

It was recognized quite early that the behavior of the valence electrons of the atoms making up the metal had much to do with these properties. Furthermore, the kinetic theory had been used with great success in explaining the properties of gases. It is not surprising, therefore, that the earliest attempts to explain the properties of metals should have involved an electron gas within the metal, which was visualized as behaving very much like an ordinary gas. The historical development of the ideas in this connection is very interesting.

The metals are crystalline. Most samples are polycrystalline, and in limited regions the atoms are arranged in a regular lattice. To explain the relatively large electrical and thermal conductivities, however, it is assumed that the electrons are free to wander throughout the lattice. Thus, each of the atoms entering the crystalline arrangement surrenders one or more electrons to the electron gas, and the atom itself exists as a singly or multiply charged ion. The ions of the lattice have definite equilibrium positions about which they oscillate with the thermal energies discussed previously, but their behavior is not distinctive. The ions do account for the heat capacity, but they are not thought to be responsible for the high electrical and thermal conductivities that characterize the metal. It is the electrons, which are free to migrate throughout the metal, that are responsible for these characteristic properties. Drude was the first to present a quantitative treatment of the conductivity on this so-called "electron gas" picture.

On the basis of this view alone, it is easy to see that the average drift motion of the electrons is very low. As an example, take silver. Since silver has a density of 10.5 g/cm³, and since silver atoms have a mass of $1.66 \times 10^{-24} \times 107.88$ g or 1.79×10^{-22} g, the number of atoms per cm³ is

$$N = (10.5 \text{ g/cm}^3)/(1.79 \times 10^{-22} \text{ g/atom}) = 5.9 \times 10^{22} \text{ atoms/cm}^3.$$

This is also the number of free electrons per cm³, if each Ag atom releases one electron. For this conductor 500 amperes/cm² would be a relatively high current density. Then since current density J is given by

$$J = Ne\bar{u},$$

where e is the electronic charge and $\bar{u}$ is the average velocity of the electrons.

$$\bar{u} = J/Ne = \frac{500 \text{ amp/cm}^2}{\left\{ \begin{array}{l} (5.9 \times 10^{22} \text{ electrons/cm}^3) \\ \times (1.6 \times 10^{-19} \text{ coulombs/electron}) \end{array} \right\}} = 0.053 \frac{\text{cm}}{\text{sec}}.$$

This drift velocity is so low as to be almost negligible in comparison with the random velocity of the electrons.

As a simplification of the problem, Drude decided to neglect the differences in speed among the electrons. His treatment resembles the first discussions of the kinetic theory of gases, in which the same approximation was made. Drude assumed that all the electrons in a metal under equilibrium conditions would travel with the same speed and that their velocity vectors would be uniformly distributed in direction. When a potential difference is applied across the metal, electrons would be accelerated in the direction of the potential gradient. Interaction with atoms in the lattice from time to time would remove the acquired drift velocity. In such interactions the electron is supposed to give to the lattice the energy it has acquired from acceleration by the field, and the velocities again become random. Such a model is capable of accounting for the high electrical conductivity of metals and also for the heating of the metal as a consequence of the current. Similarly, when a temperature gradient is applied to the metal, electrons are expected to move throughout the metal as a result of diffusion. Electrons going from the hotter parts of the metal to the colder parts would be expected to take thermal energy from the hotter parts and impart it to the lattice vibrations in the colder sections. The migrating electrons are very numerous, and a large thermal conductivity would be expected in agreement with observations.

Electrical Conductivity

Following Drude, we assume that all electrons in the metal under equilibrium conditions have the same speed v. This speed is expected to be large as compared with any drift velocities encountered in practice. We may assume, therefore, that the drift velocities will have a negligible influence on the mean-free-path of the electrons. Again for simplicity, let us decide to neglect statistical variations and to assume that all electrons travel a distance exactly equal to the mean-free-path L between interactions with the lattice. The mean time between impacts, which we call T, is given by

$$T = L/v. \tag{12-1}$$

Let the magnitude of the potential gradient in the metal be represented by $\Delta V/\Delta x$. Then, since $F = ma = e\,\Delta V/\Delta x$, the magnitude a of the acceleration of the electron is $e\,\Delta V/m\,\Delta x$, where e is the charge of the electron, and m is the mass. After an impact, the electron has on the average no drift velocity but starts again to drift in the direction of the potential gradient. The magnitude u of the velocity acquired between impacts, since the initial velocity is zero, is given by

$$u = aT = (e\,\Delta V/m\,\Delta x)(L/v), \tag{12-2}$$

and the average drift velocity $\bar{u}$ of the electrons is half of this, or

$$\bar{u} = (e\,\Delta V/2m\,\Delta x)(L/v). \tag{12-3}$$

The magnitude J of the current density is

$$J = Ne\bar{u} = Ne^2 L\,\Delta V/2mv\,\Delta x, \tag{12-4}$$

where N is the number of free electrons per unit volume.

The magnitude of the current density divided by the magnitude of the potential gradient gives the conductivity σ. Thus,

$$\sigma = Ne^2 L/2mv. \tag{12-5}$$

The reciprocal of the conductivity is the resistivity ρ. Thus,

$$\rho = 2mv/Ne^2 L. \tag{12-6}$$

At the time of Drude's work it seemed reasonable to suppose that the electrons had the thermal behavior of an ordinary gas. If this is true, then

$$mv^2/2 = 3kT/2,$$

where T is the temperature in degrees Kelvin and k is Boltzmann's constant. Thus,

$$v = (3kT/m)^{1/2}$$

and

$$\rho = 2(3mkT)^{1/2}/LNe^2. \tag{12-7}$$

Although this relationship for the resistivity has too many disposable constants to permit a crucial test of the theory, it would seem that the indicated dependence on temperature is wrong. By experiment the resistivity of pure metals is found to be almost directly proportional to the absolute temperature. This theory of metallic conduction accounts for a current proportional to the potential gradient, and thus it gives Ohm's law, but it fails to give the correct dependence of the resistivity on temperature. The relationship between thermal and electrical conductivity, however, provides additional support for the essential elements of the electronic theory of transport phenomena.

Thermal Conductivity

The problem of working out the thermal conductivity is slightly more complicated than that of working out the electrical conductivity. Consider a temperature gradient in the direction of the x-axis. The number dN of electrons per unit volume, the velocity vectors of which make angles between θ and $\theta + d\theta$ with the x-axis, as shown in Fig. 12-1, is

$$dN = N \, d\Omega/\Omega = N(2\pi \sin \theta \, d\theta)/4\pi$$

$$= N \sin \theta \, d\theta/2, \tag{12-8}$$

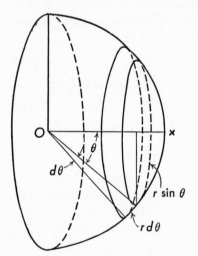

Fig. 12-1. Electrons with velocities making angles between θ and $\theta + d\theta$ with the x-axis.

where $d\Omega = (r \, d\theta)(2\pi r \sin \theta)/r^2 = 2\pi \sin \theta \, d\theta$ and $\Omega = 4\pi r^2/r^2 = 4\pi$. (The solid angle subtended at O by the element of area dA whose width is $r \, d\theta$ and whose length is $2\pi r \sin \theta$ is $d\Omega$, and the total solid angle subtended at O by the total surface area of the sphere is Ω.) It is assumed that the velocity vectors are uniformly distributed in space. Between collisions these electrons move a distance $L \cos \theta$ in the x-direction. Because the temperature gradient is dT/dx, the temperature difference between layers of atoms separated by this distance in the x-direction is

$$\Delta T = (dT/dx)L \cos \theta. \tag{12-9}$$

If one assumes that the electrons behave as a gas and that those leaving the first layer of atoms are in thermal equilibrium with those atoms, their average translational energy will be $3kT/2$. If on reaching the second layer, they come into equilibrium with it, the heat energy transferred by one electron will be

$$\Delta Q = 3kT/2 - 3k(T - \Delta T)/2 = 3k\ \Delta T/2 = 3k(dT/dx)L(\cos\ \theta)/2.$$
$$\tag{12-10}$$

The electrons under consideration have x-components of velocity $u = v \cos \theta$, and their number dN is given by Eq. (8). Let us represent the rate of transfer of heat per unit area with respect to time, or the thermal current density, by dQ/dt. The electrons under consideration contribute to the thermal current density an amount

$$d(dQ/dt) = \Delta Q\ u\ dN = 3NkLv \cos^2 \theta \sin \theta\ (dT/dx)\ d\theta/4,$$

and the total thermal current density is obtained by integrating this expression over θ

$$dQ/dt = (3NkvL\ dT/4dx)\int_0^\pi \cos^2 \theta \sin \theta\ d\theta = NkvL\ dT/2dx. \quad (12\text{-}11)$$

The coefficient of dT/dx, called the thermal conductivity, is given by

$$K = NkvL/2 = NkL(3kT/m)^{1/2}/2. \tag{12-12}$$

Although the expressions for the individual conductivities contain too many disposable constants to enable a real test of the theory to be made for the separate coefficients, the ratio of the coefficients, K/σ, is seen to be the product of the absolute temperature and some natural constants. Thus,

$$\boxed{K/\sigma = 3T(k/e)^2.} \tag{12-13}$$

The statement that the ratio of the conductivities is this function of the constants k and e and of the Kelvin temperature is known as the law of Wiedemann and Franz. For most of the good metals, the agreement of observations with this law is quite passable. There is little doubt that electrons are associated with the conduction phenomena in metals. Some of the details introduced into the theory are not in accord with the physical situation, but fortunately the ratio is not sensitive to these errors.

Lorentz attempted to improve the calculations by considering the modifications which would be introduced by a Maxwellian distribution of velocities for the electrons. Such considerations greatly complicated the calculations, but they were carried through by Lorentz. Unfortunately, the values so obtained show a greater disagreement with experiment than those obtained by Drude on the basis of his simplification of the theory. This should have led Lorentz to doubt that the velocity distribution for electrons in metals was Maxwellian. This conclusion, although it later proved to be correct, was not reached immediately.

This discrepancy between theory and experiment would have been less disturbing had there not been a pronounced inconsistency with experiments in one other important matter. The theory just presented assumed a great number of electrons behaving as a gas and having a Maxwellian distribution of velocities characteristic of the temperature. To explain the transport phenomena, the number of electrons had to be large, at least of the order of one for each atom in the lattice. Such an electron gas would make a major contribution to the specific heat of the metal, because all of these electrons would share the thermal energy. Actually, the Einstein-Debye theory of specific heats, which neglects the thermal capacity of the electrons entirely, shows very good agreement with experimental results. Thus, the electrons cannot contribute appreciably to the thermal capacity of a metal. This was a pronounced and unmistakable disagreement with the theories involving the electron gas. Clearly, something important has been ignored in this discussion of the behavior of electrons in metals.

The Sommerfeld Theory for the Behavior of Electrons in Metals

The basis for the resolution of this difficulty in the explanation of both transport phenomena and specific heat was provided by the rapid development of atomic theory, particularly the theory of atomic spectra in the early 1920s. Arnold Sommerfeld had made important contributions to the development of the theory, and in his book *Atomic Structure and Spectral Lines* had systematized the knowledge, then available. The behavior of the electrons in atoms was found to be consistent with the Pauli exclusion principle, which states that in a given atom no two electrons can have the same four quantum numbers. If any two electrons are identical in three of these quantum numbers, they must then differ in the fourth one.

One way of describing what Sommerfeld did is to say that he treated the large-scale metal crystals, or the pieces of metal which are used in the laboratory, as large molecules subject to the quantum restrictions which had been found necessary for atomic systems. This idea is sufficiently novel that it may be well to notice a few of the similarities that might make it seem worth trying. In the first place, there is the compactness of the crystal. Outermost electrons in the neighboring atoms are crowded together and thus cannot be entirely free from interactions with one another. There is even a suggestion that some crystals may be held together by valence-type forces like those encountered in the formation of molecules. Finally, there is the fact that the electrons in atomic and molecular systems do not under ordinary circumstances share the thermal energy of their environment. The atom as a whole shares this energy, but the energy state of the electron in the atom is likely to be the same over a wide range of temperatures. Similar behavior for the valence electrons in a metal would resolve the difficulty with the specific heats, if it were possible at the same time somehow to provide for the migration of the electrons throughout the volume of the metal. This did not appear to be impossible, because when atoms are crowded together in a crystal, the valence electrons are certainly acted upon by forces from all of the neighboring atoms. In many cases, the shells of charge corresponding to the valence electrons are even expected to overlap those of neighboring atoms. In such circumstances, the forces binding a given electron to the atom with which it is presumably identified in the isolated condition are very largely neutralized by forces acting on it from other neighboring atoms. Although the electron is subject to relatively strong forces, which vary from position to position in the crystal, it is quite likely that it is free to migrate and to lose its identification with a given atom of the structure almost completely. The problem, then, is to determine what the quantum numbers for electrons in the isolated atoms become when the crystal is formed. Although the problem of electrons in solids is not simple, Sommerfeld made an approximation from which quantitative deductions could be made without great difficulty.

The Sommerfeld Model

In the Sommerfeld model of a metal, as suggested by Fig. 12-2, the potential variations due to the periodicity of the lattice are neglected.

The interior of the metal is assumed to be an equipotential region. The electrostatic potential within the metal is positive with respect to the space just outside of the metal. Hence, the potential energy of an electron outside the metal is considerably greater than that of an electron inside. In normal circumstances, therefore, the valence electrons associated with the atoms contained in the lattice remain within the body of the metal.

As a diagram of this model, we may plot the potential energy of an electron against distance in one direction. According to Sommerfeld's approximation, there is no potential energy variation within

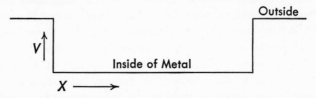

Fig. 12-2. Variation of the potential energy of an electron at the surface of a metal.

the metal, but at the surface of the metal, the potential energy rises rapidly. For some purposes the shape of the potential barrier must be considered, but this variation is confined to a very small region at the surface of the metal, and for the present it is sufficient to show this as an abrupt jump.

Thus far, the theory has no radical innovations. Sommerfeld's contribution was to introduce a method for determining the discrete energy levels within the metal, and to postulate in conformity with the Pauli exclusion principle that no more than two electrons, differing in their m_s quantum numbers, could occupy a given energy level. This introduces a large spread in the kinetic energies of the electrons.

The distribution of the allowed energies can be derived in a number of ways, differing in detail, but leading to the same major conclusions. In the first place, it would be possible to quantize the action for the back and forth motion of the electron for each of three mutually perpendicular directions in the crystal, and from the resulting allowed values of momenta to determine allowed energy levels. In the second place, and, of course, not unrelated to the first method, we could determine the energy levels from the various wavelengths of the electrons which can give rise to standing waves within the body of the metal. We choose, however, to use the uncertainty principle in an argument which is more obviously statistical in nature. The product of the uncertainty in position, as indicated by a given coordinate, and the uncertainty in the momentum associated with that coordinate is equal to Planck's constant h. If for simplicity, we consider a cube of the metal a units of length on each edge, the uncertainty relationship gives

$$a\,\Delta p_x = h,$$

$$a\,\Delta p_y = h,$$

and

$$a\,\Delta p_z = h;$$

or from the product of the three

$$\Delta p_x\,\Delta p_y\,\Delta p_z = h^3/V, \tag{12-14}$$

where $V = a^3$ is the volume of the metal. The momentum space is now divided into cells of size h^3/V, and, starting with those cells for which the momentum and energy are least, each cell is filled by placing within it two electrons differing in their m_s values.

Cells corresponding to the same energy will be those having a constant magnitude of the momentum vector. The volume of the spherical shell in momentum space corresponding to the range dp at p is obtained by multiplying the area $4\pi p^2$ of a spherical surface in this space by dp, and, since the volume of the elementary cell is h^3/V, this shell will contain

$$dn' = 4\pi p^2 V\,dp/h^3$$

cells, or twice this number, dS', of *quantum states*, each capable of accommodating an electron. Thus,

$$dS' = 8\pi p^2 V\,dp/h^3. \tag{12-15}$$

It is useful to put this result in terms of the energy W by noticing that for a free electron

$$W = p^2/2m \tag{12-16}$$

and

$$dW = p\,dp/m. \tag{12-17}$$

Hence, substituting for p and dp in Eq. (15), we get

$$dS' = 8\pi(2mW)^{\frac{1}{2}}Vm\,dW/h^3. \tag{12-18}$$

Let the number of electrons per unit volume be denoted by S. Then,

$$dS = dS'/V = 8\pi(2W)^{\frac{1}{2}}m^{\frac{3}{2}}\,dW/h^3. \tag{12-19}$$

A plot of this distribution in energy is shown by the curve indicated by the solid line of Fig. 12-3.

If it is assumed that the electrons occupy the lowest energy levels consistent with the Pauli exclusion principle, the gas is said to be degenerate, and a definite range of energies for the electrons can be determined.

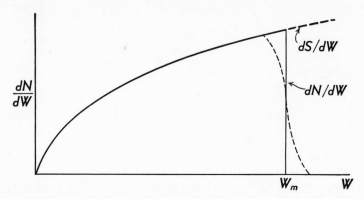

Fig. 12-3. Distribution of allowed energies for electrons in metals.

Since the metal contains N electrons per unit volume, by integration we obtain

$$N = \int_0^{W_m} dW \, dS/dW = 8\pi(2)^{1/2} m^{3/2} \int_0^{W_m} W^{1/2} \, dW / h^3,$$

where W_m is the energy of that occupied state whose energy is greater than that of any other occupied state of the degenerate gas. The integration gives

$$N = 8\pi(2m)^{3/2} W_m^{3/2} / 3h^3. \tag{12-20}$$

Hence,

$$\boxed{W_m = (3N/\pi)^{2/3} h^2 / 8m,} \tag{12-21}$$

where the energy will be in joules, if mks units are used. Putting in the values of the constants and dividing by the numerical value of the electron charge in coulombs gives

$$W_m = 3.63 \times 10^{-19} N^{2/3} \text{ (electron-volts)},$$

where N is the number of electrons per m³. An interesting feature of this result is that the normal maximum energy depends only on the number of electrons per unit volume and is independent of the size of a piece of metal. This, of course, is required for a sensible result.

Statistics of the Completely Degenerate Electron Gas

The assumption that all energy levels up to W_m are filled and none of the levels above W_m is filled gives the so-called "completely degenerate gas." It is not difficult to obtain important statistical results in this case. To find the average energy of the electrons, we multiply dS by W and integrate over the energy from zero to W_m, within which each quantum state is occupied. The result is the total energy, and, if this result is divided by the number of electrons, we obtain their average energy.

$$\overline{W} = (1/N) \int_0^{W_m} W(dS/dW)\, dW = [8\pi(2)^{1/2} m^{3/2}/Nh^3] \int_0^{W_m} W^{3/2}\, dW$$
$$(12\text{-}22)$$

$$= 16(2)^{1/2} \pi m^{3/2} W_m^{5/2}/5Nh^3. \tag{12-23}$$

Substituting the value of N obtained from Eq. (20), we have finally

$$\overline{W} = 3W_m/5. \tag{12-24}$$

Effect of Temperature on Energy Distribution of Electrons

The aforegoing analysis is very satisfactory when applied to metals for which Eq. (9) is a good approximation near the absolute zero of temperature. The modifications due to raising the temperature of the metal by a few hundred degrees Kelvin are not large. Fermi and Dirac independently contributed to the understanding of the essential facts in this case. Qualitatively, raising the temperature rounds off the sharp edge of the distribution shown by the solid line in Fig. 12-3 and makes it more like the dashed curve.

The essential difference between the Maxwell-Boltzmann statistics and those which we encounter here is that in the former case we assumed that when two particles interact, the initial states alone determine the final states into which the particles transfer. This cannot be the case here, because we have already assumed that the number of electrons in a given range of energies dW is limited to the number dS of the quantum states available. If all the states are filled, no further electrons can be put into them. We are naturally led to a statistical treatment in which the number of transitions from one energy region to another (as a result of interactions) is proportional not only to the number of electrons in the energy ranges where the initial states are supposed to lie but also to the number of *vacancies* in the ranges of energy into which the electrons are assumed to be transferred as a result of the interaction.

The probability that a state of energy W will be occupied will surely depend upon the temperature, because this has come out of Maxwell-Boltzmann statistics. It is also a function of the energy. We represent by $F(W,T)$ the probability that a state will be occupied at energy W, when the equilibrium temperature is T° K. This will also represent the proportion of the time that states are occupied under these conditions. The probability that a state will be vacant must be given by

$$1 - F(W,T),$$

and this similarly represents the fraction of the time that states are vacant. The two limiting cases which the function F approaches asymptotically have been used in previous developments. If the energy W of the state is very much less than the normal maximum energy, as given by the Sommerfeld treatment, the probability $F(W,T)$ approaches unity and $(1 - F)$ approaches zero. On the other hand, as indicated by Maxwell-Boltzmann statistics in which no restriction as a result of states occupied was considered, if the energy is high as compared with the normal maximum energy, so that the proportion of the states occupied is expected to be very low, this proportion should fall off as indicated by the factor $e^{-W/kT}$ as shown by Boltzmann's principle.

The Fermi energy level is defined as that energy at which the probability of a state being occupied is the same as that for the state being vacant. Thus, states at the Fermi energy level are occupied only 50 percent of the time. If we represent the Fermi energy by W_F, a function satisfying the three conditions we have specified is

$$F(W,T) = \frac{1}{1 + e^{(W-W_F)/kT}}, \qquad (12\text{-}25)$$

because:

1. If $W = W_F$, $F(W,T) = \frac{1}{2}$.

2. If $(W - W_F) \gg kT$, unity in the denominator is much less than the exponential, and

$$F(W,T) \simeq e^{-(W-W_F)/kT}$$

$$= e^{W_F/kT} e^{-W/kT}$$

$$= C e^{-W/kT},$$

where C is the constant factor $e^{W_F/kT}$.

3. When $(W - W_F)$ assumes a negative value such that $(W_F - W) \gg kT$, the exponential factor becomes negligible in comparison with unity, and

$$F(W,T) = 1.$$

The behavior of the Fermi fraction is sketched roughly in Fig. 12-4. As the temperature approaches absolute zero, that energy level, in the neighborhood of which half the states are occupied, is the normal maximum energy level given by Eq. (21). The Fermi level for metals does

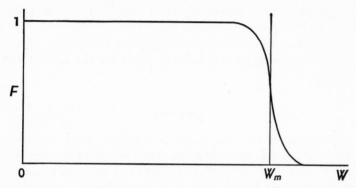

Fig. 12-4. The Fermi function for the fraction of allowed states which (on the average) are occupied.

not change rapidly with temperature, and the normal maximum energy W_m we have calculated may be used to approximate the Fermi energy at various temperatures encountered for metals in the solid state. To be technically correct, we may replace the subscript m, standing for normal maximum, by F, standing for Fermi, but we recognize that the calculations based on the normal maximum are a suitable approximation for our purposes. In terms of the speed c of the electrons, the Fermi function becomes

$$F(c) = \{1 + \exp (c^2 - c_F{}^2)/\alpha^2\}^{-1}, \qquad (12\text{-}26)$$

where in this expression c does not represent the speed of light but is variable, $\alpha = (2kT/m)^{\frac{1}{2}}$ is the most probable speed as given by formulas for the Maxwell-Boltzmann distribution at the same temperature. The most probable speed for electrons in a given metal depends upon the properties of the metal, but it is many times the speed given by α.

To determine the number dN of electrons actually found in the energy range dW at W, it is only necessary to take the expression for the number of states dS allowed in this energy range and to multiply by the value of the Fermi function for the average fraction of the available states actually occupied by electrons. Thus, we have

$$dN/dW = F(W,T) \; dS/dW = (2m)^{3/2} 4\pi W^{1/2} h^{-3} \{1 + \exp \; (W - W_F/kT\}^{-1}$$

(12-27)

or

$$dN/dc = 8\pi m^3 c^2 h^{-3} \{1 + \exp \; (c^2 - c_F^2)/\alpha^2\}^{-1}. \qquad (12\text{-}28)$$

It is easily shown that the qualitative result of applying the Fermi-Dirac statistics to electrons in metals within the range of temperatures attainable in the laboratory is to round out the sharp edges in the completely degenerate distribution previously shown at W_F. Thus, at a temperature of several hundred degrees Kelvin the distribution of electrons in energy would be that shown by the dashed curve in Fig. 12-3.

Summary

The treatment of the conduction electrons in metals by the theory of a classical gas was not successful. The free electrons were very numerous. If they had behaved as an ordinary gas, their contribution to the specific heat would have been very obvious. Analysis of the experimental results clearly indicated that the contribution of the electrons to the specific heat could not be large.

By introducing quantum laws for the electrons crowded together in metals, Sommerfeld made a major contribution. Our confidence in the idea of quantum states for the conduction electrons in metals is increased by the number of points of view which lead to essentially the same results. We have chosen to emphasize the statistical nature of the problem. Fermi and Dirac in developing the quantum statistics applicable to this problem prepared the way for the understanding of a variety of problems in atomic and solid state physics. The size of the cells into which momentum space is divided, as indicated by the application of Heisenberg's uncertainty principle, is h^3/V, where V represents the volume of the metal. Two circumstances in metals combine to cause the distinct degeneracy of the electron gas. The first of these is the small electron mass. Allowed electron energy levels, for a given size of metal, are made less numerous in a given range because of this factor. Secondly, there is the great concentration of valence electrons in the metallic crystal which requires many electrons to be contained in the restricted set of allowed energy levels. The success of applying quantum laws to electrons in metals was a great triumph for the principles which had developed in connection with atomic theory, and it established the usefulness of these laws in discussing the problems of solid state physics.

Problems Concerning Electrons in Metals

1. If the quantum states permitted for electrons within a cube are determined from the quantization of action in each direction as an electron moves across the cube, is reflected by boundaries, and finally returns to its initial position, and if each distinct quantum state, specified by the three quantum numbers can accommodate two electrons differing in m_s, work out from these principles the details of the energy distribution for 50 electrons constituting a completely degenerate electron gas, which is confined within a cubical box 5.0 Å on each edge. What is the average energy of the electrons in this distribution? What are the differences in the situation if 25 electrons are confined in a cube $5/(2^{1/3})$ Å on each edge (giving the same concentration of electrons in space)?

2. What states enumerated in Problem 1 will be eliminated if the results are to be interpreted as standing wave patterns for electrons fulfilling the boundary conditions that the amplitude of the waves should vanish at each of the boundaries? Recalculate the quantities called for in Problem 1, eliminating states as required by the boundary conditions.

3. a. If the "degeneracy" of the quantum states in a metal is removed by considering a metal crystal of length c three times its thickness a and its width b twice its thickness, what are the modifications in an expression like Eq. (10-11) for the energy in terms of the quantum numbers?

   b. If the thickness a is 1.6 Å (and the other dimensions 3.2 and 4.8 Å), determine in a manner similar to Problem 2 the energies of the states which the first 50 electrons in the rectangular box will occupy.

   c. What are the similarities and differences as compared with Problem 2?

4. a. What are the factors in Eq. (10-11) which represent the momentum quantum mechanically?

   b. What are the corresponding factors in the equation that applies to the rectangular parallelopiped with unequal edges?

   c. The energy has a different dependence on the quantum numbers identified with the different directions of part (b). Is the dependence of energy on momentum different for the different directions?

5. Calculate the normal maximum energies for the electrons in large samples of (a) aluminum and (b) of silver, on the assumption that each aluminum atom contributes three electrons to the conduction band and that each silver atom contributes just one electron to the conduction band.

6. a. Determine the numerical factor by which the normal maximum energy must be multiplied to give the average energy of a completely degenerate electron energy distribution.

   b. Determine the factor by which the normal maximum speed must be multiplied to give the average speed.

    c. Determine the factor by which the normal maximum speed must be multiplied to give the root-mean-square speed.

7. a. Assuming that tungsten has 1.22×10^{23} electrons/cm^3 in its conduction band, determine the normal maximum energy of these electrons (when the tungsten is at a low temperature).

    b. If the tungsten is raised to a temperature of 3200° K, what is the fraction of the available energy states occupied at a level 0.10 ev above and also 0.10 ev below the Fermi energy level?

    c. With the tungsten at a temperature of 3200° K, how many electrons per unit volume are there in the following energy ranges:

$$(W_m - 0.01) \text{ ev} < W < (W_m + 0.01) \text{ ev},$$

$$(W_m - 0.51) \text{ ev} < W < (W_m - 0.49) \text{ ev},$$

and

$$(W_m + 0.49) \text{ ev} < W < (W_m + 0.51) \text{ ev}.$$

8. For tungsten at 2900° K, determine what fraction of the electrons in the conduction band have energies given by $W > 1.20W_m$.

For tungsten at 2900° K, determine what fraction of the electrons in the conduction band have energies given by $W > 2.00W_m$.

For tungsten at 2900° K, determine what fraction of the electrons in the conduction band have energies given by $W > (W_m + 2.00)$ ev.

References on Electrons in Metals

Millman, Jacob, and Samuel Seely, *Electronics*, Ch. 5 (New York: McGraw-Hill Book Company, 1951). (Uses mks units in a good treatment.)

Rice, Francis O., and Edward Teller, *The Structure of Matter*, Ch. 8 (New York: John Wiley and Sons, 1949). (Excellent non-mathematical treatment.)

Slater, John C., *Introduction to Chemical Physics*, Ch. 27 (New York: McGraw-Hill Book Company, 1939). (A good systematic treatment.)

Slater, John C., "Electronic Structure of Metals," *Reviews of Modern Physics* *6*, 209 (Oct. 1934). (The ideas are developed very simply and clearly.)

Sproull, Robert L., *Modern Physics—A Textbook for Engineers*, Ch. 9 (New York: John Wiley and Sons, 1956). (Particularly good reference for electrons in metals and solid state.)

13 | Electrons in a Periodically Varying Potential Distribution

Introduction

The Sommerfeld theory of metals was a spectacular success. It accounted for the failure of conduction electrons to make a substantial contribution to the heat capacity of a metal and it accounted very well for conduction phenomena. The distribution of the energies in the conduction band was verified by the widths of the soft X-ray lines resulting from transitions of electrons from the conduction band to a vacancy in the electron shell of an atom just below the valence shell. An explanation of the thermionic emission of electrons from metals resulted from the application of the Fermi-Dirac statistics to electrons in the conduction band at elevated temperatures.

The very simplicity of this theory and the strong evidence which supported it raised one problem. The considerations basic to the theory are so general that it almost would seem as if all solids and liquids should be metals whereas actually insulators are known to exist. Upon what theoretical basis then can we account for the existence of solid insulators? Or, more specifically, what factors did Sommerfeld neglect which would account for the formation of insulators? In reviewing the theory, it is apparent that, by neglecting the periodicity of electrostatic potential within the lattice, Sommerfeld unduly simplified his theory of solids. Actually, the lattice is made up of atomic systems and the behavior of the valence electrons is profoundly altered by the presence of neighboring atoms. Our previous study of such systems has indicated that in the immediate vicinity of the nuclei, the electrostatic potential varies rapidly. One reason for the success of the Sommerfeld model was simply that the region where the potential varies rapidly is only a very small part of the total volume, and that over most of the volume within the metal the assumption of a constant electrostatic potential was a reasonable approximation. The variation of the potential energy of an electron with the distance in one direction along a row of atoms in the lattice is shown in Fig. 13-1, where the horizontal axis represents distance along a selected direction in the crystal lattice, and the vertical axis represents the potential energy U_e of an electron. The periodic variation

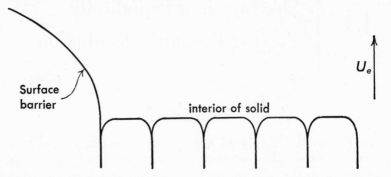

Fig. 13-1. Variation in the potential energy caused by the nuclei in a crystal lattice.

of the potential energy provides for the possibility that the electron kinetic energies in certain ranges may not be allowed.

Electron Waves in Periodic Structures

The propagation of waves in a one-dimensional, periodically loaded mechanical system was discussed in Chapter 8. There was a critical condition corresponding to a wavelength equal to twice the spacing between adjacent concentrations of mass. Neglecting friction, it was found that waves longer than twice the spacing between mass concentrations were propagated without loss of amplitude or energy. The phase velocity changed with wavelength, and the variation became quite rapid as the critical condition was approached. When the frequency was raised above the value corresponding to the critical wavelength, it was found that, even neglecting friction, there was a loss of amplitude as the vibrations traveled down the length of the array. The condition may be described qualitatively as a failure of the individual masses to keep up with the impressed vibrational frequency. The phenomena possible at such high frequencies do not correspond to true waves, because there is no distance at which the displacements are repeated exactly. The critical frequency represents a limit above which true waves are impossible, since the vibrations are reduced in amplitude (or, as we may say, they are "attenuated"). Since all waves below the critical frequency are propagated, while all those above the critical frequency are attenuated, the string with its periodic concentrations of mass may be called a "low-pass mechanical filter" (a filter which passes the low frequencies only).

The applicability of these results to waves of short wavelength in solids is quite obvious, since matter is atomic and solids are very frequently crystalline. The physical situation is often characterized by the periodic distributions of mass throughout a space lattice. The system should thus act as a low-pass filter. When the wavelengths are long (and the frequencies are correspondingly small), whole groups of atoms can be displaced in the same direction, and such low-frequency waves should be propagated. The critical frequency corresponds to the displacement of neighboring atoms in opposite directions, and at higher frequencies than this the transmission of waves is not possible.

de Broglie waves may be propagated in a crystal like that of Fig. 13-1. In this situation, there will be a concentration of the average electron-charge density in the neighborhood of each nucleus, and we must consider the propagation of the de Broglie waves through this loaded medium. On the analogy of the mechanical waves studied previously, we might expect that the longer de Broglie waves, which represent the slower electrons, would be propagated without attenuation. The first remarkable fact deduced from the interpretation of this wave picture is that, statistically at least, electrons of suitable momentum should pass through a perfect lattice unhindered.

The propagation of waves in periodic structures is, of course, an important field of study, and it does provide a suitable basis for the quantitative analysis of the behavior of electrons in solids through the calculations of properties associated with the de Broglie waves. Unfortunately, the mathematical difficulties are so great that exact solutions of problems for the various lattices encountered in nature are impossible to obtain. However, the results for actual lattices, obtained by the use of suitable approximations, can be described and justified qualitatively, as in the present discussion.

We have noticed that in most of the space occupied by the lattice, the variations of potential energy are small and that it is only in the immediate neighborhood of the nuclei that the potential variations become rapid. If the de Broglie waves of the electron have wavelengths much greater than twice the distance between adjacent atoms of the lattice, the dependence of the kinetic energy of the electron upon the momentum or the wavelength should not be much altered by the periodicity of the lattice. The waves are long enough that the average potential of the electron is effective in determining its energy. Thus, the kinetic energy of the electron is almost exactly $p^2/2m$, just as if the electrons were moving in an equipotential region. As the wavelength of the electron becomes comparable with twice the spacing between neighboring atoms, however, the kinetic energy is somewhat less than that given by $p^2/2m$. When the wavelength satisfies the Bragg

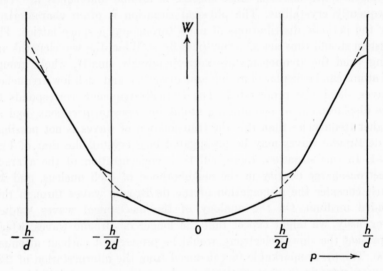

Fig. 13-2. Zone diagram for a single direction in a lattice.

relationship $n\lambda = 2d \sin \theta$ for atomic planes in the direction of propagation, standing waves are set up as a result of partial reflection from the planes, and the crystal becomes a "forbidden region" for the propagation of these electron waves. There is thus the possibility of a forbidden band of energies.

We can illustrate the behavior of the energy W as a function of the momentum p_x in a particular direction, the direction perpendicular to the (100) planes, for example, by means of what is called a "zone diagram," shown in Fig. 13-2, where the relationship $W = p^2/2m$ is represented by the dotted curve. The actual behavior of the energy as a function of the momentum is indicated by the solid curve, showing discontinuities at the values $nh/2d$ of the momentum, where n is an integer. These are the particular values of the momentum for which the de Broglie wavelengths satisfy the Bragg relationship, and these are marked by the vertical lines, which are called the "zone boundaries." It is in the neighborhood of these boundaries that the departure of the kinetic energy from the relationship $W = p^2/2m$ becomes quite pronounced. Approaching the zone boundary from the two different directions along the axis of abscissas gives two different energies. This is a very characteristic and important feature of the situation. The fact that the curve is discontinuous at the zone boundary with the two distinctly different energies indicated gives the possibility of a forbidden band of energies. Although only the particular value of the momentum which gives a wavelength corresponding to the satisfaction of the Bragg condition for the de Broglie waves is strictly

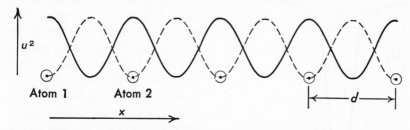

Fig. 13-3. Charge distributions of different energies for the same momentum.

excluded, there is nevertheless the possibility of an entire band of energies being forbidden. The low and the high energy states corresponding to the zone boundary are easily interpreted physically. Thus, when the Bragg relation is satisfied, the standing electron waves will have one region of charge concentration and one region of charge scarcity in the distance corresponding to the separation between adjacent atomic planes. If the charge concentrations occur midway between the atoms, where, of course, the potential energy of an electron is high, the high energy state will occur. On the other hand, if the amplitude u of the standing electron waves, and hence the charge concentration, is a maximum at the positions of the atoms in the lattice where the potential energy of an electron is low, the lower of the two energy values is expected. Fig. 13-3 suggests the two energy conditions. The solid curve corresponds to the low energy condition, and the dotted curve corresponds to the high energy case.

Approach to Band Structure Through Atomic Energy Levels

Another method of attack, alternate to the wave propagation in periodic structures, which has been used extensively by Slater and his collaborators, starts with the well-known properties of the energy

levels of the isolated atoms and considers the alteration of these as
the atoms are brought closer together. As an example to be treated
descriptively, we may start with the properties of the sodium atom.
The configuration of the unexcited sodium atom is $1s^2 2s^2 2p^6 3s^1$. The
potential energy U_e of an electron varies in such a manner around the
nucleus that electrons of different total energies are confined to different volumes extending outward from the nucleus. For the isolated
atoms, the situation may be represented graphically as shown in Fig.

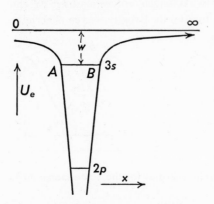

13-4. Here the potential well of
the atom by means of which it retains its electrons is shown by the
curve, and the total energies of the
various electrons are shown by
the horizontal lines at $2p$ and $3s$.
Close to the nucleus the potential
energy of an electron varies quite
rapidly, but farther from the nucleus the potential energy varies
more slowly with the distance x
from the nucleus. The $1s$-electrons
are in a state of much lower

Fig. 13-4. Electron energy levels in
the potential energy variation around
an atom.

energy than those shown in the
figure, and they are confined to a
definitely limited volume in the
immediate neighborhood of the
nucleus. The $2s$- and $2p$-electrons have such limited energy that
they too are confined to small volumes suggested by the width of the
horizontal lines in the figure. Sodium, however, in the normal state
has a single $3s$-electron, the charge of which extends into the volume
where the potential energy varies according to the law Ce^2/r, and
this variation of the potential energy is sufficiently slow that the wave
function of the $3s$-electron extends with appreciable amplitude to a
very considerable distance from the nucleus. In the isolated atom,
the time average of the distribution of charge is very definite quantity,
and the energy level of the atom in its unexcited state is quite definite.

We next consider a second identical atom of sodium brought closer
and closer to the first. In Chapter 11, we have already examined in
some detail the similar case in which two hydrogen atoms were brought
together until the wave functions of their $1s$-states overlapped. In
general, these same phenomena are repeated here. The potential energy
will be lowered along the line connecting the two nuclei for the reason
that both electrons are attracted by both nuclei. For the bonding state,

the electrons spend more time between the nuclei than they do elsewhere, because their wave functions, both having appreciable amplitude, add in this region. There is also an anti-bonding state of higher energy resulting from the subtraction of one wave function from the other. The lowering of the potential barrier between the two atoms is illustrated in Fig. 13-5. Corresponding to the situation shown in Fig. 13-5, it turns out that the wave function associated with the electron in atom 1 has an appreciable amplitude at the top T of the potential barrier between the atoms, and it is not unlikely that this electron will move from one nucleus to the other and back again. It is this interaction between the two atoms which causes the splitting of the single energy level of the isolated atom into a pair of levels character-

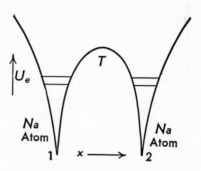

Fig. 13-5. Energy states for a pair of atoms brought close together.

izing the two interacting atoms. This splitting is consistent with the uncertainty relation in the form $\Delta W \, \Delta t \simeq h$, where Δt is the time constant which characterizes the change of a 3s-electron from one atom to the other, and ΔW is the energy difference of the two discrete energy levels. (This shows a very close correspondence to the case of identical coupled oscillators with the coupling between them varying in such a way that the two frequencies corresponding to simple harmonic modes of oscillation differ depending on the strength of the coupling.) As the atoms are brought closer together, the electrons move from one to the other in a shorter time, and the energy levels spread further apart. Ordinarily, both electrons will be found in the lower of the two energy states, and their spins will have to be oppositely directed. Both electrons spend much time between the two atoms, and the resulting concentration of negative charge between the atoms contributes an attractive force. Because of the similarity in the behavior of the two electrons, it is impossible to say definitely which electron belongs to either atom.

If more atoms are added to make a lattice, the spreading of the band of energies is determined primarily by the separation between neighboring atoms, but, just as in the analogous situation of the coupled oscillators, the number of energy levels is equal to the number of atoms, and this is described as a conservation of quantum states. Since each energy level can accommodate two electrons with oppositely directed spins, for elements liberating a single electron, the band is only half filled. Electrons can, therefore, have work done upon them by electrical forces and move temporarily into levels of higher energy without violating the quantum principles. It is quite true that those elements which contribute one electron per atom to the conduction band do form metals of excellent conductivity.

This argument would lead us to expect that, if a lattice should be formed of atoms which liberate two electrons to the valence band, the material would then be an insulator, since the valence band, filled in accordance with the Pauli exclusion principle, could then have no unoccupied levels into which any of the electrons might move. The filled band would correspond to a symmetrical distribution of the electronic velocities, so that the net current is necessarily zero. The prediction that all atoms which contribute two electrons to the valence band would form insulating crystals is false, for an inspection of the periodic table reveals that those elements which have two electrons in the outer shell form quite good metallic crystals. These include mercury, tantalum, barium, iron, cobalt, and nickel.

Evidently, there is some factor that permits electronic conduction in such elements despite their having an even number of electrons in the valence shell. This additional factor is not difficult to find. As a matter of fact, it operates also in the case of the alkali metals, for not only are the normally occupied energy levels broadened when the atoms are brought together into a lattice but the higher unoccupied levels are broadened as well. In the case of sodium, for example, the $3p$-levels, having only slightly greater energy than the $3s$-level, also are broadened, and this band overlaps the $3s$-band even at fairly large atomic spacings.

This same argument applies to the various elements having two electrons in the valence shell. These electrons normally go into the s-states, but there are p-states not too far removed in energy. The spreading of both the s- and p-levels into bands quite often results in an overlapping of the bands. This gives rise to a combined band in which only a part of the permitted states are occupied.

To illustrate the formation of an insulator, the case of carbon may be studied. The outermost electrons in the structure of the carbon atom are two valence electrons which are classified as $2p$. Somewhat more tightly bound, but also contributing in some instances to the valence of carbon are two electrons classified as $2s$. Diamond is a crystalline form of carbon, which is an insulator. In the diamond crystal, each carbon atom has four nearest neighbors, and it shares a pair of electrons, constituting a homopolar bond, with each of these neighboring atoms. The chemist G. N. Lewis developed many of the ideas concerning the homopolar bond. He suggested that electrons were shared between the atoms in such a way that a closed shell of eight electrons surrounded each atom. In the diamond crystal, there are two electrons in each of the bonds linking a central carbon atom to its four nearest neighbors, which are arranged at the corners of a regular tetrahedron, as shown by Fig. 6-19.

In such a tetrahedral structure each atom is bound in four directions in space, and the forces arising from these bonds resist the displacement of the atom in any direction. This accounts for the

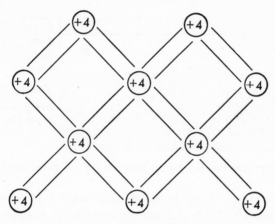

Fig. 13-6. Two-dimensional representation of the diamond lattice.

observed hardness of diamond and other crystals of the diamond structure.

Although the tetrahedral structure of the diamond lattice is not very complicated as compared with other crystalline structures, it does nevertheless give an inconveniently complicated representation for the purpose of our discussion. We will therefore simplify our representation of the diamond structure by reducing it to a plane figure in which each carbon atom is surrounded by four nearest neighbors located on the corners of a square, and the valence force is provided by a shared electron pair between each pair of atoms, which we may represent by double lines as shown in Fig. 13-6. This is a mere conventional representation, and it must be kept in mind that this figure is a simplification of the actual three-dimensional lattice, which represents as adequately as a plane figure can the relationship of each carbon atom with its four positive charges to its four nearest neighbors. The figure is seriously in error concerning the relationship of a carbon atom to its more remote neighbors. Using methods similar to Slater's, Kimball calculated the band structure of the carbon crystal. In the isolated atoms, the 2p- and the 2s-levels are distinct. As the separation between the atoms is reduced, Kimball found that the bands broaden. When the lattice constant is reduced to about 7 Å, they merge. Further reduction of the lattice constant results in the production of two well-separated energy bands containing four states per atom. The upper band is entirely empty, and the lower band is completely filled. The minimum of the energy for the lower, filled band, comes at a lattice spacing of 3.6 Å, which corresponds to the

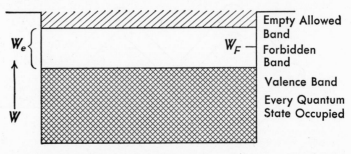

Fig. 13-7. Energy band model for an insulator (W_F = Fermi level, $W_e \gg kT$).

spacing of the carbon atoms in the diamond crystal. Because the lower band is completely filled and the upper band is completely empty, the insulating properties of diamond are to be expected. The calculated width of the forbidden energy band is about 6 or 7 ev, and at temperatures ordinarily encountered the excitation of an electron in the valence band to lift it into the conduction band is quite unlikely. Corresponding to this fact, diamond is a good insulator throughout a rather wide temperature range.

Parenthetically, it may be mentioned that a second crystalline form of carbon is graphite. Here the close spacings, somewhat like those of the diamond structure, are confined to a plane and the spacings at right angles to this plane are considerably greater, so that the bonds in this direction are weak. This accounts for the flakiness of graphite, and the larger separation in the one direction suggests an altered band structure sufficient to account for the weak electrical conductivity of graphite, which, as would be expected, differs for the different directions in the crystal.

The energy band model of an insulator—such as diamond—is shown in Fig. 13-7. Here the lower allowed band, which we may identify as the valence band, has every permissible quantum state occupied.

Above this there is a broad forbidden band, and above this there may be a band of permitted quantum states. In the case of an insulator like diamond, this second allowed band, often identified as the conduction band, is completely empty. This model accounts for the insulating properties of diamond. Although the electrons in the valence band are not so tightly bound to the individual atoms that they never move to other atoms, there is no net current, because of the essential symmetry of the motions represented by the standing wave patterns of the filled band. The application of an electric field cannot result in a current as long as the electrons are confined to the filled band. Electrons in a filled band are prevented from accepting energy from an electric field by the quantum restrictions on their motion.

Intrinsic Semiconductors

There is no sharp dividing line between conductors and insulators. If the behavior of the bands is such that the filled valence band is separated by a narrow band of forbidden energies from the second allowed band, the substance at extremely low temperatures will be an insulator, and at higher temperatures it will be a semiconductor,

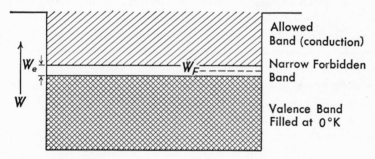

Fig. 13-8. Energy band model for an intrinsic semiconductor (W_F = Fermi level, $W_e \approx kT$).

which, because the existence of the carriers depends upon the proximity of two bands characteristic of the pure material, is called an "intrinsic semiconductor." The energy band model for this case is shown in Fig. 13-8.

The application of the Fermi-Dirac statistics to the electrons in this solid, with a Fermi level placed in the middle of the forbidden band, shows that when the width W_e of the forbidden band is not very many times larger than kT, where k is Boltzmann's constant and

T the absolute temperature, there will be an occasional vacancy in the valence band, the electron corresponding to this vacancy being found in the upper allowed (or conduction) band. In this case, conduction may take place as a result of processes ascribed to changes taking place in both of the allowed energy bands. In the first of these, as a result of the thermal vibrations of the lattice, a few electrons are given high energies corresponding to those in the upper allowed (or conduction) band. These electrons are no longer bound to individual nuclei at the lattice points. They are free to migrate throughout the lattice, and they will act as an electronic gas similar to that analyzed by Lorentz. Electrical conduction will result from the drift motion of these electrons in the direction of the potential gradient.

Conduction may also take place as a result of processes associated with the electrons in the valence band. For every electron in the conduction band, there will be a deficiency of one electron near some one of the nuclei or lattice points. In the absence of an applied potential gradient, the electrons remaining in the valence band are bound in the sense that their energy is not sufficient to take them over a barrier normally existing between two nuclei. The absence of an electron from one of the bands results in a net positive charge, which will provide an attraction force for electrons in neighboring bonds. Even though electrons in the valence band do not have energy sufficient to overcome the barrier between bonds, there will be some tunneling of electrons, and the electron deficiency will be filled by an electron jumping into it from one of the neighboring bonds. This, however, creates a new vacancy just behind it, and another of the bound electrons is likely to move to fill this second vacancy. This process repeats itself again and again. The location of the electron deficiency (sometimes called a "hole") moves in an entirely random manner.

If a potential gradient is applied to the semiconductor, the motion of the electrons in the valence band to fill an electron deficiency is no longer completely random. Electrons will move in the direction of the potential gradient into a hole, because this is the direction of decreasing potential energy, more often than they move against the potential gradient with a consequent increase in their potential energy. An electron moving from a completed bond to fill a vacancy leaves a new hole behind it. This is filled by a second electron moving into it, and the process is repeated again and again. Since on the average more electrons move in the direction of the potential gradient than against it, conduction of electricity results. This is added to the electrical conduction due to the motion of electrons in the range of energies which puts them into the conduction band, because in both cases electrons migrate in the direction of the potential gradient.

In this discussion we have been assuming that individual electrons could be identified and followed as they moved from point to point. The existence of the uncertainty relation places limitations on the extent to which we are able to do this. It may happen that one of the free electrons may collide with one of the bound electrons, exchange velocities with it, and take its place as one of the electrons bound to the nucleus. The electron liberated from the nucleus moves on in place of the original free electron, and, since the electrons are identical, such interchanges can have no effect on the conduction process. Or it may happen that a conducting electron will give up its energy near a nucleus which has an electron deficiency and be captured by it. In such an individual process, there is a loss of one conduction electron, but if equilibrium exists, such a process is balanced by thermal excitation of another electron which puts it into the conduction band. It is in a statistical sense that there is equilibrium.

The conductivity which takes place as a result of processes in both bands has been discussed in some detail, because the reader should have clearly in mind that electrons move in the direction of the potential gradient in the conduction processes taking place in both bands. In the literature treating semiconductors, however, some economy of words has been achieved through the introduction of the concept of vacancies or holes in the valence band, which act very much as positrons in an energy band in which they are free from quantum restrictions in the amounts of energy they can accept by moving in the direction of an applied electric field. In the conduction band, we specify conditions in terms of the states that the few electrons present occupy. By the same token in dealing with conditions in the valence band, it is much easier to specify conditions in terms of the few vacancies existing than to specify all of the very numerous states which are occupied. Hence, it is customary to speak of conduction by electrons in the upper allowed band and to speak of conduction by holes in the valence band.

Summary

The wave mechanical treatment of electrons in structures with periodic variations of potential has shown that the electrons in a permitted energy band can migrate throughout the lattice. A remarkable feature of this treatment is that in a perfect lattice the waves representing the electrons move unhindered. The chief restriction placed on the motion of the electrons by the periodicity of the structure in which they move is that there may be forbidden energy bands. The existence of the energy band structure for solids provides a theoretical basis for the discussion of insulators and semiconductors. The lower (or valence) band of energies in both semiconductors and insulators at the absolute zero of temperature contains all the electrons that it can without violating the Pauli exclusion principle. In insulators the separation between the top of the valence band and the bottom of the conduction band is so great that even at normal or elevated temperatures the lifting of electrons into the conduction band by thermal excitation is quite unlikely. In intrinsic semiconductors, on the other hand, the two allowed bands are separated by such a small gap that at normal temperatures thermal excitation accounts for an appreciable concentration of electrons in the conduction band.

Questions on Behavior of Electrons in Periodic Fields

1. a. Upon what physical variable does the maximum spread of the energies in an allowed band depend?
   b. Upon what physical factor does the number of energy levels in an allowed band depend?
2. When a single level becomes double as a result of the interaction of identical atoms, the spacing between the levels corresponds to the shortening of the time that an electron spends in the neighborhood of one atom without going over to the other. From the knowledge that a level splits into two which differ in energy by 0.5 ev, determine the uncertainty in the time an electron spends continuously in the neighborhood of one atom before passing to the other. This is the time constant for the transfer of the electron.
3. Show that the zone boundaries of Fig. 13-2 correspond to the Bragg condition for selective reflection of the de Broglie waves.
4. a. If the width of the forbidden band in germanium is 0.7 ev and if the Fermi level is in the middle of the gap, what is the proportion of allowed states occupied at the bottom of the conduction band at 300° K?
   b. At the top of the valence band?
5. Is it possible for a material to have different zone boundaries corresponding to electrons moving along different crystal axes? Does this consideration have any bearing on whether a material should be classified as conductor or an insulator?
6. a. If the width of the forbidden band in silicon is 1.1 ev and if the Fermi level is in the middle of the gap, at 293° K, what is the proportion of the allowed states which are occupied at the bottom of the conduction band?

b. If (contrary to fact) this probability of occupancy persisted throughout the entire conduction band, assumed to contain four quantum states per atom, what would be the concentration of conduction electrons in the crystal of silicon?

c. How does this compare with the concentration of molecules in air under standard conditions of temperature and pressure?

References on Electron Waves in Periodic Fields

Brillouin, Leon, *Wave Propagation in Periodic Structures* (New York: McGraw-Hill Book Company, 1946). (This treatment assumes that the reader is familiar with some special mathematical functions.)

Rice, Francis O., and Edward Teller, *The Structure of Matter*, Ch. 8 (New York: John Wiley and Sons, 1949). (The principles are discussed with a minimum of mathematics.)

Slater, John C., *Modern Physics*, Ch. 10 (New York: McGraw-Hill Book Company, 1955). (This discussion should be very helpful.)

Sproull, Robert L., *Modern Physics—A Textbook for Engineers*, Ch. 9 (New York: John Wiley and Sons, 1956). (The treatment is on a more quantitative level than that of this chapter.)

14 | Imperfections and Their Influence on the Properties of Crystals

The properties which are of the greatest interest in semiconductor applications result from certain imperfections in these crystals. Except for the metals, in which the band normally containing the valence electrons is only partially filled, truly perfect crystals would be electrical insulators. In Chapter 13, we have discussed the intrinsic semiconductors, in which the conduction band is separated from the valence band by a relatively small forbidden energy gap. Such a material at a temperature of absolute zero would be an insulator. It is thermal agitation which accounts for the lifting of electrons from the valence band to the conduction band to permit conductivity by electron drift in the conduction band and by deficiencies, which have come to be called holes, in the valence band. Thermal agitation on the average reduces the order of the arrangement of atoms in the lattice, and it may be classified with other lattice defects, which also reduce this order. We shall defer the quantitative discussion of lattice vibrations until after we have described other lattice defects, which, because of their static character, are more readily visualized.

Thermal Agitation and Carriers in Intrinsic Semiconductors

At a temperature of $0°$ K, an intrinsic semiconductor constitutes a highly ordered system. The lattice vibrations are suppressed. The valence band is filled and there are no electrons in the conduction band. Electrons in the valence band are executing motions of perfect symmetry, and there is no unbalanced current. At higher temperatures, thermal agitation produces the lattice vibrations which are to be discussed later, but an effect of primary importance is that a few electrons are raised from the valence band to the conduction band. This destroys the quantum requirement of perfect symmetry of electron motions and gives rise to finite conductivity as a result of uncompensated motion of charges, when a potential difference is established across the semiconductor.

In the conduction band, the electrons are in states of low kinetic energy, and their number per unit volume is so low that quantum restrictions are not very important. Maxwell-Boltzmann statistics are applicable, and the electrons are accelerated essentially as free particles.

The motion of electrons resulting in migration of deficiencies in the valence band was discussed at the end of Chapter 13 in phraseology that seemed reasonable in view of our experience with large scale phenomena. As applied to electrons in the valence band, this experience must be modified by quantum mechanical considerations. In the first place, we discussed the location of the electron deficiencies in a given bond of a given atom, and this is too definite to be allowed by the uncertainty principle, the application of which shows that an electron in the conduction band or an electron deficiency in the valence band is bound with such low energy to the localized charge which compensates for it, that on the average its charge will be spread over the volume of a sphere with a radius of several lattice spacings centered at the lattice point which holds the localized charge of sign opposite to that of the carrier. The deficiency cannot be localized too definitely without violating the uncertainty principle.

In the second place, we discussed the motion of the electrons as if they were free particles, but the physics of the situation is dominated by the fact that the electrons are in the periodic force field of the lattice and that the resulting structure of the energy bands severely limits the states of motion available to them. A given electron is not free to move as our experience based on macroscopic phenomena might lead us to believe that it would move. The concentration of electrons means that there is a real coordination of the motions of the various electrons. The deficiencies or holes in the valence band are not numerous, and these act very much as free particles with a positive charge. A little bit of formal analysis will emphasize the importance of this fact.

In a completely filled band, the electrons do not participate in conduction. Our treatment has emphasized the standing electron wave aspects of the allowed energy states of the filled band. Even when the exactness of this condition is relaxed and the electrons are simply restricted to the cells arising from the Heisenberg uncertainty principle, analysis shows that the cancellation of the currents is almost complete and that it becomes more nearly so as the size of the sample, and hence the number of electrons in the band, is increased. In a filled band, the uncanceled portion of the total current is a small fraction of the current which would arise from the motion of a single electron with one of the permitted momentum values.

The current density of a filled band containing N_a states is zero, and we may write

$$J = \sum_{i=1}^{N_a} (-e)v_i/V = (-e/V) \sum_{i=1}^{N_a} v_i = -eN_a\bar{v}/V = 0, \quad (14\text{-}1)$$

where $(-e)$ is used to represent the charge of the electron. But N_a/V is the number of electrons N_1 per unit volume and we have the familiar expression

$$J = -eN_1\bar{v} = 0, \quad\quad\quad\quad (14\text{-}2)$$

where for the filled band, as the equation shows, $\bar{v}$ is zero. For purposes of analysis, we next consider the band from which a single electron (that corresponding to the state $i = s$) is missing. To obtain the result in this case, we break the *filled band* into two parts

$$(-e/V) \sum_{i \neq s} v_i + (-e)v_s/V = 0.$$

From this equation we subtract the state $i = s$, and we obtain

$$\boxed{(-e/V) \sum_{i \neq s} v_i = ev_s/V.} \quad\quad\quad (14\text{-}3)$$

The left-hand side of this equation represents the current density due to a band with every state except one occupied. The interpretation of this equation is that a band which is complete except for one missing state is characterized by a current density which would be given by a positive charge equal to that of an electron moving with a velocity characterizing the missing state. In other words, the current due to a hole corresponds to the charge $+e$ moving with a velocity that corresponds to that of the missing state. Eq. (3) suggests the usefulness of analysis based on this property of a missing state or a hole in a nearly filled energy band.

For semiconductors in the intrinsic range, the increase in the number of carriers with temperature is the dominating effect. The rapidity of its exponential variation is quite apt to conceal other effects of the thermal vibrations.

Impurity Semiconductors

Although diamond, discussed in Chapter 13, is a good insulator, other elements of the same chemical group as carbon are common impurity-type semiconductors. The silicon atom has two $3p$-electrons in its outer shell which are bound by comparatively low energies. The two $3s$-electrons are bound somewhat more strongly, but all of these electrons in the M-shell of silicon contribute to the bonds in the diamond-type lattice which silicon forms. To take an electron from one of these homopolar bonds and put it into the empty upper energy band requires

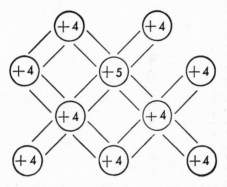

Fig. 14-1. Representation of a diamond-type lattice with one donor defect.

an energy of 1.11 ev. Thus, at all but high temperatures, silicon should be a good insulator. To produce the transition in a perfect silicon crystal to make it an intrinsic semiconductor would require raising its temperature to 450° or 500° C, and the conductivity would increase to a large value as the melting point of silicon at 1420° C is approached. It is only recently that samples of silicon pure enough to give good insulation at the lower temperatures have been produced.

Older samples of silicon showed resistivities of the order of an ohm-cm. Such a low resistivity in the diamond-type lattice of silicon is explained by the presence of impurities, for example, small proportions of elements from a neighboring column of the periodic table. If, for instance, an atom of arsenic, having three $4p$-electrons in its outer shell, replaces one of the silicon atoms in the diamond-type lattice structure, the additional electron is not needed to complete a homopolar bond. This situation is suggested in Fig. 14-1, which shows the arsenic atom located at one of the lattice points with its core charge of five protons and an extra electron not required for completing the homopolar bonds. The arsenic atom is called a donor, because it can give this added electron to wander throughout the solid. The activation energy of this process is only 54 emv (electron millivolts), and the liberation of the electron occurs readily at room temperature. The extra proton remains fixed in a core at the lattice point indicated, but the electron diffuses about in an irregular manner as a result of thermal agitation. When a potential gradient is applied to the silicon, conductivity results from the drift of these excess electrons, and, because of the negative charge of these, the conductivity is said to be of the n-type. Fig. 14-2

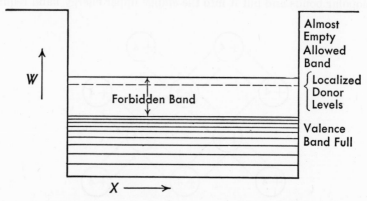

Fig. 14-2. Energy band model for an n-type semiconductor.

shows the energy band model for an n-type impurity semiconductor. Here, as previously, energy is plotted vertically, and the vertical sides of the figure represent the rise of potential energy of an electron at the surface of the solid. Above the valence band, there is a relatively wide forbidden band. Within this forbidden band, and just below the conduction band, are the localized donor levels. Loss of an electron to the conduction band leaves the donor atom positively charged. The electron migrates, but the positive donor atom is fixed in the lattice.

Conversely, if an atom of boron, having a single $2p$-electron, replaces one of the silicon atoms at a lattice point, one of the homopolar bonds will contain a single electron rather than the usual pair. This electronic deficiency in the structure makes it easy for an electron to move from one of the normal bonds to complete the bond in the neighborhood of the boron atom. The net result is that the boron atom accepts a negative electron, which is then bound in the lattice, while the vacancy (defect or hole) moves about in the structure. This process is sometimes described as removing a "hole" from an acceptor, and, the activation energy for this process being only 80 emv, an acceptor atom will be ionized a large part of the time even at room temperature. The conductivity in this case is said to be of the p-type. The fact that the resulting vacancies in the valence band behave as if they were particles having almost the same mass as an electron but having a positive charge equal in magnitude to that of an electron, should be accepted as a result of experiment. The details of the quantum mechanical calculations justifying this conclusion on theoretical grounds are not included in this treatment. Fig. 14-3 gives the energy band model of the p-type semiconductor. Electrons ionizing the acceptor levels, just

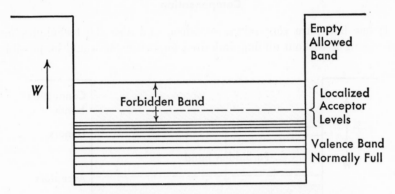

Fig. 14-3. Energy band model for the p-type semiconductor.

above the valence band, are fixed in the lattice. The vacancies in the valence band migrate.

Germanium has an outer shell consisting of two $4p$-electrons and two $4s$-electrons, and these are used in the completion of bonds in the diamond-type lattice structure. Breaking the bond in germanium is estimated to require about 700 emv, and pure germanium would be a quite high resistance material, either at or below room temperature. Laboratory samples of germanium contain impurities which give rise to conduction by processes like those discussed for silicon.

In the case of impurity semiconductors the "activation energy" is low, and if the temperature is at or above that normally prevailing in a room, a large and almost constant fraction of the impurity atoms will be ionized. The concentration of the carriers in the specimen will be almost constant, and under these circumstances, some of the less pronounced effects arising from the presence of the impurity atoms may appear.

Impurity atoms of either type, as we have indicated, replace atoms of the semiconducting element at one of the regular lattice positions.

The substitution leaves the crystal with a high degree of order. Electronic waves in the crystal, however, are influenced by the fact that an occasional atom of the lattice differs from others, and, although a perfect crystal of absolutely pure material at 0° K would offer no resistance to the movement of electrons in the conduction band, the crystals incorporating the impurity atoms contain irregularities which would cause them to offer some *residual resistance* even in the absence of thermal vibrations.

Compensation

If one had pure germanium or silicon and also the techniques for processing it without adding undesired impurities, it would be possible

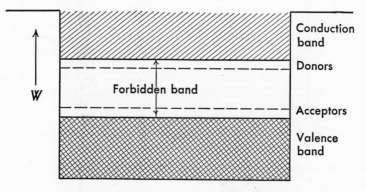

Fig. 14-4. Energy band model for a semiconductior in which there is compensation.

to start with pure material and add controlled amounts of impurities to produce desired properties. Techniques for producing remarkably pure materials in the form of single crystals have been developed, but, even in the purest of these, it is believed that the concentration of impurities is still sufficient to produce definitely measurable electrical effects. The very high resistance, attained in some samples, probably arises from a compensation of some impurities by others of the opposite type. Suppose, for example, that a sample of silicon in each small but macroscopic region of equal volume has equal numbers of donors and acceptors. The energy band model of this situation is shown in Fig. 14-4. If the donors were not present, thermal excitation of electrons from the valence band into the localized acceptor levels would leave vacancies in the valence band to account for *p*-type conduction. The donors, however, have excess electrons, and it is far more likely that these electrons would drop into the states of low energy made available to them by the existence of acceptors rather than that they should be excited into states of high energy in the conduction band. The net effect is that negative charges are distributed throughout the volume at the fixed positions of the acceptor atoms, and that positive charges are distributed throughout the volume at the fixed positions of the donor atoms. There are relatively few vacancies in the valence band and relatively few electrons in the conduction band. So far as the creation of carriers is concerned, the donors almost completely nullify the effect of the acceptors. At the high temperatures required to produce conduction in a pure crystal, the sample would become an intrinsic semiconductor, and the effect of the impurities in increasing the scattering of the carriers, while present, is not large enough to be readily detected in this case.

Optical Properties of Crystals and Luminescence

The band structure of solids provides a basis for understanding the absorption and emission of light in crystals. Light may be absorbed if the transfer of its energy to an electron can remove that electron from a level of a filled band (usually the valence band) and raise it to one of the unoccupied levels in another band, such as the conduction band, which has been discussed in connection with insulators and semiconductors. The transitions allowed are those in which the momentum of an electron changes by an amount which carries it from a point in one zone entirely across the next zone to a corresponding point in the second zone. This behavior is the basis for the construction of a so-called "reduced zone diagram," in which the portion of the curve shown in Fig. 13-2 lying between the two values $h/2d$ and h/d of the abscissas is transferred horizontally until it appears on the diagram between the abscissas $-h/2d$ and 0, and, similarly, the part of the curve shown between $-h/d$ and $-h/2d$ is transferred horizontally until it appears between 0 and $h/2d$. The selection rules allow vertical transitions on such a reduced zone diagram, and the changes of the ordinates, in dropping from the top curve vertically to the bottom one, correspond to the transformations of energy associated with an allowed transition for an electron. Such a diagram shows a range of energies between a definite minimum value and a definite maximum value which may be absorbed or emitted in the transfer of electrons between two definite bands. For a very large class of solids these energy transformations correspond to quanta associated with frequencies in the ultraviolet region of the spectrum. These are the absorption bands accounting for the optical properties to which allusion was made in Chapter 6.

Electrons may thus be transferred from the valence band to the conduction band by the interaction of ultraviolet light with the electrons in the crystal. This is a photoelectric process and the energy of the photons must lie within the absorption band. A photon is emitted when the electron drops from the conduction band to the valence band. Electrons may also be transferred from the valence band back to the conduction band through bombardment of the crystal with corpuscular radiation from nuclear reactions. In this case, a particle with a definite rest mass can give up a fraction of its kinetic energy in raising one electron from the valence to the conduction band, and then can go on to produce several other similar transitions, if its total kinetic energy is sufficient. If the energy given to an electron, in raising it from the valence to the conduction band, is converted into radiated light within 10 mμsec as the electron returns to the valence band, the phenomenon is called "fluorescence." Sometimes, however, the energy is stored within the electronic configuration of the crystal for a time which is long compared with 10 mμsec, and the phenomenon is then called "phosphorescence."

In a scintillation counter, energy from an incoming particle is used to raise electrons to excited states, from which they then return to lower energy states through the emission of the energy difference in the form of light. The resultant light pulse is quite often observable. The crystals most often used for this purpose depend for their effectiveness upon the presence of abnormalities in the crystal structure. These are often in the form of impurity atoms which are called activators. These activator atoms, or luminescence centers, usually have the effect of putting energy levels in the forbidden band, just as the donor and acceptor atoms placed localized energy levels in the forbidden band of the semiconductors that we discussed. Absorption of energy raises an electron from the valence band to the conduction band, where it is associated with a wave function extending throughout the crystal. At a luminescence center, it drops into an energy level, which is created by the presence of the activator, and then the energy is converted into visible light as the electron returns from this energy level to the valence band. To explain phosphorescence it is only necessary to provide a mechanism by which some of the energy may be stored for an appreciable time before it is allowed to reach an activator. This is usually incorporated into the model through the inclusion in the crystal of irregularities serving as "electron traps" at other sites.

The energy band model of a phosphor is shown in Fig. 14-5. Here the valence band is normally filled, but, through the action of an energetic particle, an electron is transferred to the conduction band, leaving an electronic vacancy in the valence band. The electron may go directly to a luminescence center, and, as characteristic of fluorescence, energy may be converted into light with only a short delay. Alternatively, the electron may first reach another defect of the crystal which serves as an electron trap. Here a direct transition between the level in which the electron is trapped and the valence band is forbidden by quantum selection rules. Electrons are gradually transferred from the traps to

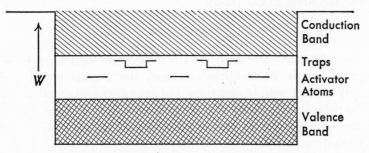

Fig. 14-5. Representation of energy states in a phosphor.

the conduction band by thermal excitation. They may then either reach one of the luminescence centers, or they may be retrapped. The energy band model of a phosphor thus accounts for the general features of the fluorescence and phosphorescence which are actually observed.

Thermal Agitation and Mobility

The foregoing discussion has introduced the fact that the application of Fermi-Dirac statistics to the electrons in the crystal accounts for the lifting of the electrons from the valence to the conduction band. By increasing the number of carriers, such excitation increases the conductivity. On the other hand, the thermal agitation of the atoms of the lattice, by increasing the disorder in the lattice, tends to decrease the conductivity. In the case of semiconductors, the increase in the number of carriers is usually the dominating effect.

In the case of metals, where the number of carriers remains a constant as the temperature changes, the influence of the temperature in increasing the resistance is clearly indicated. Even in the case of semiconductors, one of the factors upon which the conductivity depends is reduced by raising the temperature. The current density **J** is expressed by

$$\mathbf{J} = Ne\bar{u} = Ne\mu\mathbf{E}, \tag{14-4}$$

where N is the number of carriers per unit volume, each of charge e, $\bar{u}$ is the average velocity, and μ is the so-called *mobility*, defined by

$$\mu = \bar{u}/E.$$

The fact that a constant, such as mobility exists, indicates that the energy acquired by carriers from the electric field must be given to the lattice. According to Eq. (12-3),

$$\mu = eL/2mv,$$

where L is the mean-free-path and v is the average thermal speed of the electrons. In the Fermi-Dirac statistics, the average speed v does not vary rapidly with temperature, but increase of temperature would tend to reduce conductivity slightly as a result of this factor. The main influence of temperature on the resistivity of metals comes through the mean-free-path L.

In the absence of an electric field, electrons move in a random fashion as a result of interactions with the lattice vibrations. Between interactions with the lattice, an electron moves with a constant velocity until it again interacts. When an electric field is applied, the electron experiences an acceleration between collisions given by

$$\mathbf{a} = e\nabla V/m.$$

The velocity **a**t acquired in a free time t is given up in a subsequent collision. The net result is that, in a free time t, a displacement **s** given by

$$\mathbf{s} = \mathbf{a}t^2/2 \tag{14-5}$$

is added to the displacement which would have occurred in the absence of the field. The random speeds are so large that the drift velocities have negligible influence on the free times. This theory gives results identical to those of the kinetic theory of gases. The distribution of free times is a negative exponential function giving the mean free time τ as an average. If $p(t)\,dt$ represents the probability of a free time falling in the range dt at t,

$$p(t) = \frac{1}{t}\exp(-t/\tau). \tag{14-6}$$

The average drift velocity may be obtained by integration. Thus,

$$\bar{\mathbf{v}}_d = (1/\tau) \int_0^\infty \mathbf{s}(t)p(t)\, dt = (1/\tau) \int_0^\infty \mathbf{a}t^2 e^{-t/\tau}\, dt/2\tau$$

$$= (\mathbf{a}\tau/2) \int_0^\infty (t^2/\tau^2)(dt/\tau) \exp(-t/\tau)$$

$$= (\mathbf{a}\tau/2) \int_0^\infty x^2 e^{-x}\, dx = 2!(\mathbf{a}\tau/2) = e\tau \boldsymbol{\nabla} V/m. \qquad (14\text{-}7)$$

The mobility μ has been defined as the ratio of the magnitude of the average drift velocity to the magnitude of the electric intensity. Hence, from Eq. (7) the mobility is given by

$$\boxed{\mu = e\tau/m.} \qquad (14\text{-}8)$$

The current density $\mathbf{J}$ is calculated from

$$\mathbf{J} = -Ne\bar{\mathbf{v}}_d = -Ne(\tau e \boldsymbol{\nabla} V/m) = Ne\mu(-\boldsymbol{\nabla} V). \qquad (14\text{-}9)$$

The conductivity σ is defined as the ratio of the current density to the electric intensity; hence,

$$\boxed{\sigma = Ne\mu.} \qquad (14\text{-}10)$$

The resistivity ρ is the reciprocal of the conductivity. Thus,

$$\rho = 1/Ne\mu. \qquad (14\text{-}11)$$

Resistivity is inversely proportional both to carrier concentration and mobility.

Mobility as a Function of Temperature

Even a very much simplified model suggests the approximate law for the variation of resistance with temperature when the number of carriers remains virtually constant. According to classical statistics, for the vibratory motion of the atoms in the lattice, the time average of the kinetic energy and the time average of the potential energy will each be $3kT/2$. Thus, the time average of the potential energy associated with displacement in each of three mutually perpendicular directions is $kT/2$. The average potential energy associated with the x-direction, for example, is $C\overline{x^2}/2$, where x is the component of displacement of the atom from its equilibrium position, C is the constant by which the displacement of the atom must be multiplied to give the restoring force, and the bar above the x^2 indicates that the time average is taken of the square of this particular component of displacement. The root-mean-square displacement of the atom parallel to the x-axis is obtained by extracting the square root. Thus,

$$r_x = (\overline{x^2})^{1/2} = C_1 T^{1/2}. \qquad (14\text{-}12)$$

Similarly, assuming that the metal has the same properties in all directions,

$$r_y = C_1 T^{1/2} \qquad r_z = C_1 T^{1/2}.$$

The vanishing of the electrical resistance in pure and perfect metal crystals at $0°$ K, shows that the atoms, if all are in their equilibrium positions in the lattice, have zero cross section for interaction with electrons drifting through the crystal. It is natural to take the collision cross section for electrons with the lattice to be proportional to the area of a circle which has as its radius the vector sum of the root-mean-square displacements along two of the coordinate axes. According to this assumption, the collision cross section A is given by

$$A = \pi r^2 = \pi(r_x{}^2 + r_y{}^2) = 2\pi C_1{}^2 T. \qquad (14\text{-}13)$$

If, in Eq. (12-6), L is made inversely proportional to the area of Eq. (13), and if it is recognized that, according to the Fermi-Dirac statistics, the temperatures attained by metallic crystals are not likely to alter appreciably the random velocity v of Eq. (12-6), the dependence of the resistance for metals on the first power of the absolute temperature is obtained. The mobility of Eq. (10) is inversely proportional to the absolute temperature.

For semiconductors, however, the concentrations of the conduction electrons are apt to be so low that classical statistics are applicable, and the mean thermal velocity is proportional to $T^{1/2}$. The mean-free-path of Eq. (12-3) is inversely proportional to the area of Eq. (13) and to the thermal velocity of the electrons. Thus, the mobility varies as $T^{-3/2}$, and the dependence of the resistivity on temperature (by Eq. (11)), is of the form

$$\rho = C_3 T^{3/2}/Ne. \qquad (14\text{-}14)$$

For impurity semiconductors in certain ranges, N is independent of T, and ρ varies as $T^{3/2}$. In intrinsic semiconductors, the exponential dependence of N upon T dominates the variation of resistivity.

This treatment of the role of lattice vibrations is admittedly oversimplified. It ignores the fact that the forces are mutual interactions between atoms of the lattice. A crystal in equilibrium at any temperature contains elastic waves just as an evacuated enclosure contains electromagnetic waves in equilibrium with the walls. The reactions of electromagnetic energy with matter are most readily explained in terms of photons, and, similarly, the reactions of elastic lattice vibrations with electrons are most readily treated by introducing a set of phantom particles or *phonons*. Wave mechanical calculations show that the phonons in germanium behave as uncharged particles having a mass about 170 times that of an electron. The phonons are visualized as moving with the average thermal energy of translation $(3kT/2)$ and with random velocity distribution. We find the thermal speed of the electrons on the average by $mv^2/2 = 3kT/2$. Thus, at a temperature of $300°$ K, the thermal speed v_t of the electrons is about 116 km/sec, and the speed of the phonons is about 9 km/sec. The mean-free-path for electrons is about 100 mμ, and the mean-free-time is about 9×10^{-13} sec.

The model of phonons having a mass 170 times that of an electron predicts quite accurately the interactions of the electrons with the thermal vibrations of a crystal lattice. At ordinary temperatures one of the most characteristic features of the motion of electrons in a lattice is diffusion, and the model of electrons colliding with hard elastic phonons predicts such diffusion. An electron placed in a lattice with the thermally produced phonons will be forced first in one direction, then in another. Each portion of an electron's path corresponding to a free time will be a straight segment. The average length of the various linear segments is the mean-free-path. The length of each linear segment or free path is given by the product of the velocity and free time, and the model indicates that both of these factors will vary. The result is an irregular path made up of linear portions of various lengths, with their directions randomly distributed.

In the absence of an electric field, the net result of these random processes is that there is diffusion, individual particles migrating in motions that are entirely random. If a concentration gradient exists, the random motion tends to distribute the particles uniformly. This situation is accompanied by a flow of particles parallel to the direction of the gradient and proportional to its magnitude. For simplicity, one may assume that the gradient is in the x-direction, then

$$dN'/dt = -D \, dN/dx, \qquad (14\text{-}15)$$

where N' represents the number of particles crossing a unit area the normal to which is the x-direction, D is the "diffusion constant," and N is the number of particles per unit volume. Einstein's theory gave D

for an electron of charge e in terms of the Boltzmann constant k, the mobility μ and the absolute temperature.

$$D = kT\mu/e.$$

Recombination Centers

In a pure and perfect crystal, the carriers, which may be created by various processes such as thermal excitation or optical excitation, would exist for a time, which, compared with most atomic processes, is extremely long.

The long free-life of the carriers can be understood in terms of basic quantum mechanical principles. The energy to be radiated, if an electron is to be captured, is of the order of one ev. In the neighborhood of a regular lattice point, the electrostatic potential is reduced by one volt or more relative to the maxima between the atoms within a space having a diameter of about one Å. The electron would have to radiate energy and drop into the valence band within this distance along its path if it were to be captured at the site. The time a representative electron requires to traverse the lattice site is about 6×10^{-16} sec. The uncertainty principle ($\Delta W \, \Delta t = h$) shows that the time required for the radiation of the electron's energy is orders of magnitude longer than that which the electron spends in the neighborhood of the atom at a lattice point. The electrons are mainly within an energy range kT at the bottom of the conduction band, and the vacancies in the valence band structure are mainly within an energy range kT at the top of this band. The uncertainty in the energy radiated is thus about 0.05 ev. The use of this energy difference in the uncertainty principle gives for the uncertainty in the time (time constant) $T = 8 \times 10^{-14}$ sec.

It is the large mean-free-life of the carriers which accounts for the large conductivity of the actual semiconductors required in many applications. The recombination of an electron with a vacancy (thus eliminating a pair of carriers) does *not* occur each time an electron gets close enough to the positive charge associated with a vacancy to establish large electrostatic attraction. The evidence suggests that such a recapture occurs only at certain imperfections in the crystal, which we might call recombination centers. It has been established that bombarding a crystal of germanium with high energy nuclear particles produces a type of disorder that results in an increase of recombination within the crystal. A high speed nuclear particle, through direct impact with an occasional lattice atom, imparts sufficient momentum to displace it permanently to a new position, leaving behind a vacant lattice site which may serve as a recapture center. The free surface of a germanium crystal certainly has incomplete valence bonds somewhat like those produced by vacant sites within the crystal, and consistent with this fact, recapture in nearly perfect crystals is found to take place mostly at the surface. Sandblasted surfaces annihilate carriers more rapidly than etched surfaces.

Summary

The electrical properties of interest in semiconductor applications are dominated by crystalline imperfections. The carriers in germanium and silicon are due to the inclusion of impurity atoms with a chemical valence which differs from that of germanium and silicon. Carriers, whether electrons or holes, interact with vibrations of the crystal lattice rather than with the individual atoms of the lattice. The introduction of the phonon concept simplifies the treatment of these interactions. The principal effects of a limited mean-free-time between collisions with phonons are (1) the definitely limited mobility which is observed in conduction phenomena, (2) transfer of energy acquired by carriers from the electric field to the lattice, and (3) diffusion or spreading of the carriers within the material.

In an intrinsic semiconductor the number of vacancies in the valence band is equal to the number of electron carriers, because they are created in pairs. It might be thought that because of the electrostatic attraction between electrons and the positive charge associated with the absence of an electron at a vacancy, the annihilation of these pairs would proceed very rapidly. It is observed, however, that electrons and vacancies can exist in the same crystal for relatively long times without recapture of the electrons. Vacant lattice sites and sandblasted surfaces greatly increase the rate of recapture of electrons.

Problems on Imperfections in Crystals

1. a. What is the energy in ev of a photon which possesses sufficient energy to raise the most energetic electron in the valence band of silicon to the conduction band?
   b. What is the wavelength associated with this photon?
2. If electromagnetic radiation produces a uniform concentration of 10^{18} free electrons and vacancies per m^3 in a silicon crystal, calculate the conduc-

tivity of this crystal on the assumption that the mobility of electrons in silicon is 0.12 m²/volt-sec, and that the mobility of the holes is 0.025 m²/volt-sec.

3. a. If a crystal of germanium is drawn from a melt which contains 0.20 kg of germanium and 6.44 μg of antimony, what is the concentration of the donor atoms in this crystal on the assumption of uniform distribution?

   b. If all the donors are assumed to be ionized and the mobility of the electrons in germanium is 0.36 m²/volt-sec, what is the conductivity of the sample?

4. From the following data on the temperature coefficient of resistance for the various metals, determine the absolute temperature which corresponds to 0° C.

Element	Temperature (Centigrade)	Temperature coefficient of resistance
Ag	20°	0.0038
Al	25°	0.0034
Au	20°	0.0034
Cd	20°	0.0038
Co	0°	0.0033
Cu	20°	0.0038
Fe	0°	0.0062
Mg	20°	0.0040
Mo	25°	0.0033
Na	0°	0.0044
Pd	20°	0.0033
Pt	0°	0.0037
Sn	20°	0.0042
Ta	20°	0.0031
Th	0°	0.0040
W	18°	0.0045
Zn	20°	0.0037

5. a. A representative alloy has a resistivity which is higher than that of any of the elements of which it is composed. What accounts for this high resistivity?

   b. A representative alloy has a temperature coefficient of resistivity which is low compared with that of a representative pure metal. Why should this be true?

   c. If you can formulate simple explanations of parts (a) and (b) quantitatively, your answers should give numerical results correct in order of magnitude when applied to the following sets of data. Check the observed temperature coefficient against a value calculated from your interpretation of the origin of the resistivity.

Element	Atomic weight	Specific gravity	Resistivity at 20° C (ohm-m) $\times 10^8$	Temperature coefficient/°C
Cu	63.57	8.95	1.69	0.00393
Sn	118.7	7.3	11.5	0.0042
Al	26.97	2.7	2.66	0.0045
Zn	65.38	7.14	5.75	0.0037
Mn	54.93	7.2	5.0	—

Alloy	Composition	Specific gravity	Resistivity	Temperature coefficient
Bronze	Cu 88 Sn 12	8.8	18.0	0.0005
Al-brnz	Cu 97 Al 3	8.7	8.26	0.0010
Brass	Cu 70 Zn 30	8.6	8.20	0.0022
Cu-Mn	Cu 96.5 Mn 3.5	8.8	15.0	0.00022

d. What facts have you neglected which would be introduced to account for discrepancies?

6. How much gallium should have been added to the melt of Problem 3 to produce a compensated crystal?

7. If the mobility of electrons in germanium is limited to 0.36 m²/volt-sec by the lattice vibrations at 300° K, what is the expected mobility at 100° K?

References on Imperfections in Crystals

Conwell, Esther M., "Properties of Silicon and Germanium," *Proc. Inst. Radio Engrs.*, **40**, 1327 (1952).

Goldman, J. E. (ed.), *The Science of Engineering Materials*, Ch. 14, "The Physics of Semiconductors," pp. 336-57 (New York: John Wiley and Sons, 1957).

Shockley, William, *Electrons and Holes in Semiconductors*, Ch. 1 (New York: D. Van Nostrand, 1950).

Shockley, William, "Transistor Electronics: Imperfections, Unipolar and Analog Transistors," *Proc. Inst. Radio Engrs.*, **40**, 1289 (1952).

Shockley, William, J. H. Hollomon, R. Maurer, and F. Seitz, *Imperfections in Nearly Perfect Crystals* (New York: John Wiley and Sons, 1952).

15 Experimental Studies Concerning Behavior of Carriers

Introduction

In both metals and semiconductors there are carriers which drift in the electric field to produce an electric current. The fundamental distinction between metals and semiconductors is the number of these carriers per unit volume. In a representative metal there may be as many as 10^{29} electrons/m³ but in a semiconductor the concentration of the carriers may be as low as 10^{18}. This contrast in the concentration of the carriers accounts for a very great difference in the magnitude of the conductivity. In many respects the theory of phenomena in semiconductors is more simple than that of the corresponding phenomena in metals just because of this great difference in concentrations. It will be interesting to examine the experimental methods used to obtain information concerning the number and the behavior of these carriers.

The Hall Effect

A very informative tool for the investigation of these carriers is the Hall effect. This phenomenon was discovered by Edwin Hall in 1879, before the identification of the electron, but we shall, of course, use the electron theory in the discussion of it. The effect will be discussed with reference to Fig. 15-1. The flat strip or ribbon of thickness t to be investigated is represented by the rectangle $ABED$. A current in the conventional sense (a positive current) is introduced at the edge DE and is removed at the edge AB. (The conduction is due to the motion of electrons, and they are introduced at the edge AB and removed at DE.) This electric current results in establishing various equipotential

surfaces in the flat strip, and, if one terminal of a sensitive galvanometer is attached to a wire making contact with the strip at C,
a point C' on the opposite edge of the strip will be found to have the
same potential as indicated by a null reading on the galvanometer.

The Hall effect accompanies the application of a magnetic field B
perpendicular to the plane of the figure, and for definiteness we assume
that is directed out of the paper. The discussion of the Hall effect
which follows relates microscopic quantities very simply to measure-

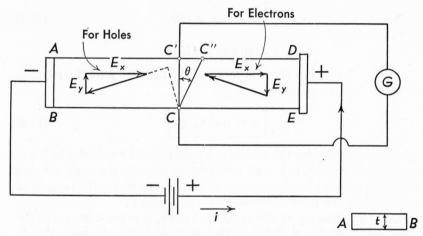

Fig. 15-1. Diagram of apparatus for Hall effect studies (the cross-sectional
area of the ribbon is $a = (AB)t$ where t is the thickness).

ments which can readily be made. The current, due to electronic motion from the left to the right, is acted upon by this magnetic field.
The force on electrons is given by $\mathbf{F} = e\mathbf{v} \times \mathbf{B}$. The result is a thrust
toward the upper edge of the ribbon. The charges deflected by the
magnetic field produce a difference of potential across the ribbon, and
the galvanometer shows a deflection. The experimenter now has two
choices for making quantitative measurements on this effect. He may
introduce a variable source of potential difference in series with the
galvanometer and adjust this until the galvanometer shows no deflection. Hall effect data are frequently taken in this manner, and such results are tabulated in the literature. Alternatively, the investigator may
move the contact C' along the edge of the strip until a point C'' is
found at which the galvanometer current vanishes. The experiment
shows that the equipotential surface has been tilted through an angle θ
by the application of the magnetic field, and when this potential dis-

tribution is established, the carriers have a drift parallel to the long edge AD of the ribbon, just as they did originally. The physics which accounts for this behavior is that an electrostatic force is set up transverse to the length of the strip which just balances the magnetic force on the carriers. Suppose that the component of the electric field parallel to the length of the filament is represented by E_x. (This quantity can be determined by rather direct measurements.) The upward component of the electric intensity is $E_y = E_x \tan \theta$. The balance of the magnetic and electrostatic forces gives the equation

$$eE_x \tan \theta = eBv \qquad (15\text{-}1)$$

from which

$$\tan \theta = Bv/E_x.$$

The drift velocity v is given in terms of the mobility μ by the relationship $v = \mu E_x$. Hence, we have

$$\boxed{\mu = (\tan \theta)/B.} \qquad (15\text{-}2)$$

In order to determine the mobility, a fundamental constant which was used in Chapter 14, it is only necessary to measure the angle through which equipotential surfaces are rotated, then to divide the tangent of this angle by the value of the magnetic induction B.

Since the geometry of the ribbon is known, it is possible also to determine the number of charge carriers per unit volume by measuring in addition the current i in the ribbon, from which a current density J is obtained through division of i by the area of cross section $a = (AB)t$ (see Fig. 15-1) of the ribbon. From the equation for current density J, we have

$$J = Nev, \qquad (15\text{-}3)$$

where N is the number of charge carriers per unit volume, e is their charge and v is their average drift speed along the ribbon. Solving for N, we obtain

$$N = J/(ev). \qquad (15\text{-}4)$$

But

$$v = \mu E,$$

so

$$N = J/(eE\mu). \qquad (15\text{-}5)$$

Substituting the value of μ obtained from Eq. (2), this becomes

$$N = JB/(eE \tan \theta). \qquad (15\text{-}6)$$

The Hall coefficient R is usually defined by

$$R = E_y/J_x B_z = E_y/(\sigma E_x)B_z, \qquad (15\text{-}7)$$

where σ is the conductivity. As illustrated in the above discussion, in the ideal case where the current density J is perpendicular to the magnetic field B, the Hall coefficient may be interpreted verbally as the ratio of the component of potential gradient in the specimen at right angles to the current density to the product of the magnitudes of the magnetic induction and the current density. From Fig. 15-1, $\tan \theta = E_y/E_x$, $R = \tan \theta/\sigma B$, and using Eq. (6),

$$\tan \theta = \frac{JB_z}{NeE_x} = \frac{\sigma B_z}{Ne},$$ (15-8)

and thus,

$$\boxed{R = 1/Ne.}$$ (15-9)

The sign of the Hall coefficient depends on the sense of the electric intensity E_y produced by the reaction of the magnetic field with the current. Positive carriers moving in one direction or negative carriers moving in the other direction make contributions to the current in the same sense. The magnetic field perpendicular to this current gives rise to a force in the same direction for either type of carrier, and in the absence of the periodic variation of potential the charges of the two different signs would move in the same sense along the y direction. Forcing positive charges upward increases the potential at the top, so that the side AD becomes positive, whereas forcing negative charges upward decreases the potential, and the side AD becomes negative. The Hall angle is positive for positive carriers and negative for negative carriers. The Hall effect gives direct evidence concerning the sign of the charges which appear to be moving.

The Hall effect was discovered before the electron was identified, and early researches showed that the Hall coefficient could have either sign. During the development of the free electron theory of metals, an effort was made to interpret the Hall coefficient in terms of that theory, but the motion of the free electrons was capable of giving only negative Hall coefficients, and the existence of the positive coefficients remained a mystery until the development of the energy band theory of semiconductors.

The concept of electronic deficiencies in an almost filled band was introduced to simplify the discussion of the phenomena occurring in p-type semiconductors. Since the phenomena observed are exactly those which would be expected on the basis of positive carriers having properties expected of the holes, for simplicity and directness they are usually discussed on this basis.

In intrinsic semiconductors the number of carriers of one sign is just equal to the number with the opposite sign. If the mobilities of the two types of carriers were exactly the same, the contributions of the positive and negative carriers to the current density would be exactly equal, and the Hall coefficient would be zero. Experiment has established that the mobility of the free, conduction-band electrons is greater than the mobility of holes, and, consistent with this observation, intrinsic semiconductors show a Hall effect which is dominated by the free electrons in the conduction band. The Hall coefficient decreases rapidly with temperature in proportion to the increase in the number of conduction electrons. Semiconductors of the n-type have Hall coefficients of the same sign at all temperatures. If the Hall coefficient of the p-type semiconductor is measured as a function of temperature, it starts at low temperatures with a high value characteristic of the few positive carriers. It decreases with temperature, at first slowly, as the number of electrons in the conduction band increases. Then it decreases rapidly, and it passes through zero as a result of the transition to the intrinsic regime, where, of course, the free electrons in the conduction band are dominant because of their higher mobility. When the Hall coefficient has attained the value characteristic of intrinsic conductivity, it has the sign characteristic of conduction by electrons, and its magnitude decreases rapidly as the number of conduction electrons is increased by raising the temperature.

The Properties of Germanium as Obtained from the Hall Effect

The number of carriers per cubic meter in germanium, to which various amounts of arsenic had been added, was determined by Hall effect measurements by Debye and Conwell. Typical results are shown in Fig. 15-2.

Here, as is customary in such work, the reciprocal of the temperature is plotted horizontally. The concentrations of carriers on the vertical axis are laid out on a logarithmic scale, but the numbers show the concentrations directly. The curve marked 1 is the one which corresponds to the purest germanium used in these tests, and the concentration of carriers varies from less than 10^{18} per m^3 at low temperatures to almost 10^{19} just before the transition to the intrinsic regime, where the logarithm of the carrier concentration becomes a linear function of $1/T$ with a high negative slope. At a temperature of $11°$ K few of the donors are ionized. Curve 2 was obtained from a specimen with a very considerable amount of arsenic added, and the carrier concentration varies from 5×10^{18} at $11°$ K to a maximum

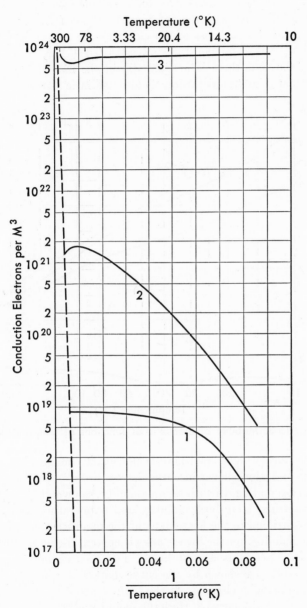

Fig. 15-2. Concentration of carriers.

of roughly 1.1×10^{21} before the transition to intrinsic conductivity. Curve 3 shows the results for high arsenic content (about 10^{24} atoms/m³). In this case, the interaction between the atoms is sufficiently great so that most of the electrons are free from the arsenic even at the lowest temperatures investigated (11°K). The curve is relatively flat, but there is a slight dip in the indicated carrier concentration at high temperatures before intrinsic conductivity takes

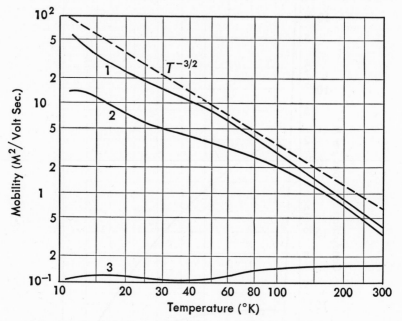

Fig. 15-3. Mobility of electrons as functions of temperature.

place. The theory developed here is not exact enough to account for this small variation shown in curve 3.

The corresponding variations of mobility, shown in Fig. 15-3, are quite interesting. Here both mobility and temperature are plotted on scales proportional to the logarithms of the quantities shown. Curve 1, giving the mobility for the lowest arsenic content, is the simplest variation shown, since it is almost linear. For intermediate arsenic content, the results are shown by the curve marked 2, where the mobility is less and the slope changes. At the highest arsenic concentration the results are shown by curve 3. Here the mobility is not a simple function of the temperature, but it increases at the higher temperatures.

For low arsenic concentration, the major factors influencing the mobility are well understood. In a perfectly regular crystal undisturbed by thermal vibrations, electrons, placed in the conduction band by photoelectric action, for example, so as not to increase thermal vibrations, would move without resistance to their motion and the mobility would be very great. Although such perfection is not attainable in practice, conductivity in single metal crystals becomes quite high at low temperature, even if superconductivity does not make it abnormally high. The resistance of metals is proportional to the temperature, and this is interpreted as meaning that it is only the thermal vibrations of the lattice with which the electrons interact. For semiconductors the density of the carriers is low and Maxwell-Boltzmann statistics should apply. Hence, the mean-thermal-speed of the carriers is proportional to the square root of the absolute temperature. For a given mean-free-path, the mean-free-time would be inversely proportional to this factor and the mobility should vary as $T^{-3/2}$. The line computed for this law is shown in Fig. 15-3, and it is seen that the germanium sample with the lowest arsenic content has a mobility closely approaching the variation calculated from the simple theory.

The low mobility shown by the curve marked 3 was obtained for the sample having a high concentration of arsenic atoms. The electrons are scattered by the lattice irregularities caused by the random distribution of arsenic atoms, and this effect, resulting in low mobility at all temperatures, is approximately independent of temperature.

A similar study emphasizing the behavior of carriers in p-type silicon was made by Pearson and Bardeen with very similar results. In the specimens used for their studies, the concentration of acceptor atoms (boron) varied from 1.5×10^{22} to $5.3 \times 10^{23}/\text{m}^3$. At the lowest temperature used ($11°$ K), the number of carriers was only about $10^{20}/\text{m}^3$ in the purest of the samples, and this increased to $8 \times 10^{22}/\text{m}^3$ before the transition to intrinsic conduction took place at $525°$ K. At higher concentrations of impurities the variation of carrier concentration with temperature was less pronounced. Points of particular theoretical interest (aside from the verification of the variation of electron (and hole) mobility with the inverse three-halves power of the absolute temperature) are:

1. Observation of mean-free-paths of electrons in silicon as large as 2×10^{-6} cm, and corresponding observations for holes about one-third as great.

2. Experimental verification of the formula $np/T^3 = 7.8 \times 10^{32}$ exp $(-12,900/T)$ for equilibrium carrier concentrations as a function of temperature. (Eq. (16-1) is a special case where, for intrinsic conductivity, $n = p = N_e$.)

3. Experimental determination of the temperature T_0 below which degeneracy of the electron gas requires the use of Fermi-Dirac statistics.

$$T_0 = (h^2/8km)(3m/n)^{\frac{2}{3}},$$

where n is the concentration of the majority carriers. At lowest concentrations $(10^{22}/m^3)$ the degeneracy temperature was $10°$ K, while at the higher concentrations (2×10^{25}) it was $250°$ K.

Hole-injection, Lifetime, and Drift in Germanium

Transistor action was discovered in the course of fundamental research on germanium by a group at the Bell Telephone Laboratories. An effort was being made to study the conductivity of a germanium crystal on a surface to which a high electric field was applied, and a pair of fine wires serving as test probes were located very close together for the measurement of local currents in the crystal. The results were not those expected, and they were most easily explained in terms of the injection at one of the probes of minority carriers, which, as a consequence of an applied potential, drifted to the other probe and profoundly modified the local conductivity in the neighborhood of this second probe.

If, for example, the germanium crystal was of the n-type, a probe which was made positive would remove electrons from the valence band of the crystal at the point of contact. These electronic deficiencies or holes would not combine directly with the electrons of the conduction band, which were present, but would be repelled by the positive charge on the probe from which they were injected and they would drift toward the negatively charged probe. Here their presence would modify the conductivity as a result of two kinds of action. In the first place, when they reached the second probe they would neutralize some of the negative space charge in the potential barrier surrounding it, and, in the second place, they would increase the number of carriers. These are important effects, which are involved in many applications, and they will be discussed in some detail in the next chapter. The point of interest at present is that transistor action showed the possibility of injecting or creating minority carriers and it provided a technique for investigating their behavior.

The invention of the transistor suggested experiments with n-type germanium in which the time of drift and also the average life of a hole might be determined by measurements involving time directly. These experiments, usually identified by the names of their originators as those of the "Haynes-Shockley type," are so simple and easily understood that they contribute definite and unmistakable evidence concerning the behavior of the carriers.

Basic Experiment for the Measurement of "Drift Mobility" of Holes in Germanium

A germanium film was cut into the form of a filament connecting two ends of enlarged cross section, as shown in Fig. 15-4, each of which served as an electrode. Emitter and collector contacts were

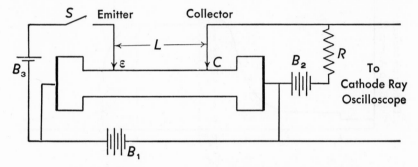

Fig. 15-4. Circuit for timing the drift of minority carriers.

made to the narrow section of the film which Haynes and Shockley called a filament. The emitter point was provided with a switch S, and the collector point was connected to the vertical plates of a cathode-ray oscilloscope with its horizontal plates connected to a source of potential difference which increased linearly as a function of the time after S was operated.

There was, of course, a certain drift of the carriers along the filament under the action of the bias battery B_1. This drift current in n-type germanium consisted mainly of electrons, but at the left-hand side some holes were injected at the electrode of large area. In the large section of germanium (with numerous carriers per unit of length), the drift was relatively slow, and conditions in this section were made to favor the neutralization of electronic deficiencies in the valence band by conduction electrons. Hence, in the main filament the drift initially present was due mainly to a drift of electrons in the conduction band. In these particular circumstances, the collector received a certain current and the cathode spot was deflected vertically a minimum amount on the cathode-ray oscilloscope. When the emitter switch S was closed, current flowed in the circuit $B_3 S \epsilon$, and this changed the potential at the emitter point immediately. A potential wave was thus sent down the filament with approximately the speed of light. This does not mean that any carriers moved with this speed, but it simply means that on the average all carriers shifted a small amount to account for a new distribution of potential. This is a behavior which is entirely analogous to what would be expected for a filament consisting of a metal or alloy. There was a displacement of the cathode spot on the vertical axis of the cathode-ray tube, which displacement was almost simultaneous with the closing of the switch. The trace

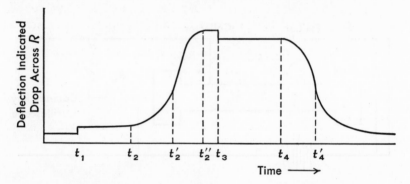

Fig. 15-5. Oscilloscope trace due to operating emitter switch.

seen on the cathode-ray tube, however, is complex, and this results from the fact that holes were injected into the germanium by the emitter. This trace is shown in Fig. 15-5.

The initial rise of the collector voltage when the switch in the emitter circuit was closed at time t_1 has already been discussed. From the circuital viewpoint, the closing of the switch caused a redistribution of the currents in the network. The resulting change in the potential drop was interpreted as the added IR drop due to current flow in the segment of the specimen to the right of the collector. This voltage drop was denoted as I_eR_d, where R_d represented the proper combination of resistances to take into account the way in which I_e divided in the two branches of the net. This was entirely analogous to the signal which would be observed in ohmic material.

The distinction between this process and that occurring when holes modify the conductivity of the germanium is of the greatest importance in understanding the behavior of semiconductors. One way of emphasizing the difference is to point out the fact that *in a sample having carriers of one type only, free electrons in the conduction band for example, it is impossible to alter the density of carriers by trying to in-*

ject or extract carriers of the same type. The reason for this is that with carriers of one type only, there is no way to compensate for the space charge of added carriers. The added space charge would result in very large fields before appreciably more carriers were added and these fields would quickly cause a readjustment of charges to the equilibrium situation, in which the space charge of the carriers is neutralized by the space charge of the lattice ions. The unbalance produced by the injection of carriers of a single type is self-annihilating in view of the space change considerations involved.

When electrons are removed from the valence band of n-type germanium, they also tend to set up a space charge, but this is quickly neutralized by flow of electrons in the conduction band. The number of carriers has been increased by the injection of the holes. The total number of conduction electrons in the specimen is thus actually increased. The conductivity is changed by the presence of the additional carriers, all of which (both holes and added conduction electrons) are subjected to the potential gradient established by the main battery, and they drift in opposite directions.

At time t_2 holes begin to arrive at the collector. In consequence, the conductivity in the vicinity of the collector is altered, and the space charge barrier giving rise to the high reverse resistance of the collector point is reduced. This results in an increase of current in the collector circuit, and this is registered as an increase in V. If all holes took exactly the same time in traveling from E to C, the rise at t_2 would be sharp—that is, there would be a step in the potential curve fully as sharp as the one at t_1. Not all holes, although they are believed to have the same mobility and are subjected to the same field, arrive at the same time. This result is due to a thermal diffusion of the holes. Earlier it was mentioned that holes in the absence of a field would wander at random through the structure. These random motions are not suppressed by the impressed electric field; a drift motion is simply superimposed on the random motion which is characteristic of the heat motions of the sample. If the central pulse of holes reaches the collector at time t_2', the average velocity is computed by $L/t_2' - t_1)$. At time t_2'' all the holes injected at the time of closing the switch have been swept by the collector, and a new equilibrium is established.

The changes occurring when the switch in the emitter circuit is opened are in every way the reverse of those we have just described. When the switch is opened, the IR drop due to the current in the emitter circuit is removed, and this signal is transmitted along the filament with the speed of light. There is a sharp drop in the vertical deflection of the trace on the cathode-ray tube screen. The removal of the current of injected holes disturbs the equilibrium, but the collector current does not respond at once, because it is still collecting the holes injected before the emitter circuit was opened. The decrease of the probe current begins quite slowly at t_4. Later at t_4', when holes drifting at the average rate have had time to arrive at the collector, the central pulse is subtracted, and there is a corresponding rapid decrease in the vertical deflection shown in the cathode-ray tube trace. The holes delayed by diffusion continue to arrive at the collector for some time, and the approach to the new equilibrium produced by the removal of the emitter current is quite gradual.

The quantitative interpretation of these experiments by Haynes and Shockley gave the following values of mobility:

$$\mu_p = 1700 \text{ cm/sec per volt/cm}$$

$$\mu_n = 3600 \text{ cm/sec per volt/cm.}$$

These values were determined with care, and the evidence presented indicated that the probable errors in the mobilities were not larger than two percent. This is of interest, because the discrepancies with corresponding values obtained from Hall effect measurements are larger than the sum of the probable errors in the two experiments. If the Hall angle θ were reduced appreciably by the presence of minority carriers, the lower mobilities obtained from Hall effect measurements through the use of Eq. (2) could be explained. The drift experiments give information which has improved our understanding of the various processes occurring in semiconductors. Another illustration is presented in the next section.

Decay of Holes in a Filament of n-type Germanium

Experiments on the filament gave evidence concerning the average lifetime of a hole in n-type germanium and conversely the lifetime of a conduction electron in p-type germanium. For this purpose, instead of a single collector probe, two were spaced a known distance apart. The holes arriving at the first collector point caused a certain increase in the conductivity while those arriving at the second collector were reduced in number by a recombination between the two points, and the increase in the conductivity by the holes of the pulse was less than at the first collector. From data obtained in this way, the reduction in the concentration of the carriers was calculated.

The time for the pulse to drift from the first to the second probe was obtained from the distance between the probes making use (1) of data on mobilities as measured in the preceding work and (2) of measurements on the potential gradient between the probes. Interesting conclusions from these studies were that the mean life of holes in n-type germanium was 0.9 μ-sec and that the mean life of free electrons in p-type germanium was 0.4 μ-sec. These times are long compared with most atomic processes, and the minority carriers persist long enough to change the conductivity by useful amounts in semiconducting devices.

Conclusion

The injection experiments show that the position of the electron deficiencies in the valence band changes as if positive charges (holes) were drifting in the direction of the electric field. The experiments on the Hall effect present even more convincing reasons for using the hole as a concept. The experimental results may be interpreted simply if positive charges are assumed to move in the magnetic and electric fields to produce the measured differences of potential. While it is possible to save the electron theory of this conduction process, it is not possible to do so without a rigorous quantum mechanical treatment of the problem, and the concepts which arise from the analysis have no advantage in plausibility over the elementary treatment of conductivity by holes, which act very much like positive electrons.

Problems on Carriers in Semiconductors

1. a. Calculate the Hall angle θ for silicon conducting by electrons only when the sample is subjected to a magnetic flux density of 0.010 webers/m².
   b. Calculate the Hall angle for silicon conducting by holes only when it is subjected to a magnetic flux density of 0.010 w/m².
   c. If a sample of silicon, when placed in a magnetic field, has a Hall angle zero, how can the result be interpreted quantitatively?
2. Compute the mobility of holes in germanium from the following data obtained in the Haynes-Shockley experiment:

Distance L between emitter and collector	1.5 mm
Potential gradient in the germanium	500. v/m
Transit time of the pulse	18 μ-sec

3. a. If a silicon-boron alloy shows a Hall coefficient of 10^{-2} m³/coulomb, what is the corresponding concentration of holes?
   b. Experiments on a silicon-boron alloy show a Hall coefficient 2×10^{-8} m³/coulomb, which appears to be constant between 70° K and 323° K. Interpret this result in terms of carrier concentration. How is the fact that these acceptors are fully ionized at a temperature of 70° K explained?

4. A sample of silicon to which no impurities are added intentionally shows a Hall coefficient of 10^{-2} m³/coulomb at $-155°$ C and a coefficient of 10^{-3} m³/coulomb for a range of some 50° near 100° C. What are the corresponding numbers of carriers?

5. The sign of the Hall coefficient in Problem 4 reverses at 290° C. Are the impurities accidentally present dominantly acceptors or donors? Give reasons for your answer. Assuming that each of the uncompensated impurity atoms contributes just one carrier at 100° C, estimate their concentration.

References on Carriers in Semiconductors

Goldman, J. E. (ed.), *The Science of Engineering Materials,* Ch. 14, "The Physics of Semiconductors" by K. Lark-Horovitz and V. A. Johnson (New York: John Wiley and Sons, 1957). (Mobility and Hall effect are discussed very well.)

Pearson, G. L., and J. Bardeen, "Electrical Properties of Pure Silicon and Silicon Alloys Containing Boron and Phosphorus," *Phys. Rev.,* **75,** 865 (1949). (This is an excellent paper for obtaining an impression of the extent of theoretical knowledge concerning carriers in semiconductors and the methods of analyzing experimental data for the purpose of extending our knowledge of basic properties.)

Shockley, William, *Electrons and Holes in Semiconductors,* Ch. 8 (New York: D. Van Nostrand, 1950). (This is the early standard reference.)

16 || Early Applications of Semiconductors

For many decades semiconductors have found increasing numbers of applications in the general field of electronics. In the early days of radio, before the development of thermionic vacuum tubes, point contact or "cat whisker" rectifiers of galena (lead sulfide) were used as detectors of radio signals. In the early 1920s Grondahl and his co-workers at the Union Switch and Signal Company developed a really practical copper oxide rectifier for power conversion. During the Second World War the development of radar in the field of ultra-high frequencies again brought crystal rectifiers back into popularity. Because of this, much work was done on the properties of silicon and germanium, and an extensive literature concerning these materials has been produced. Added impetus to fundamental studies in solid state physics was provided by the development, initiated by Shockley and his group at the Bell Telephone Laboratories, which resulted in the production of numerous types of semiconducting triodes, called *transistors*.

Variation of Resistance with Temperature for Intrinsic Semiconductors

According to the simple band model, a material in which each atom contributes two electrons to the solid structure will be an insulator unless (1) there is an overlapping of two or more bands which provides a continuous band structure which is only partially filled, and thus forms a metal; or (2) unless two allowed bands come so close together that electrons can be lifted from the normally filled valence band to the normally almost empty conduction band by thermal excitation. This latter circumstance provides the model for intrinsic semiconductors. At the absolute zero of temperature, such materials are good insulators. As the temperature of the semiconductor is increased, electrons are raised from the valence to the conduction band, and a material of low but appreciable conductivity results. Electrons in the upper band are free to move in the direction of the applied potential gradient, and the electronic deficiencies or holes left in the almost filled valence band may move in the direction of the electric field. It is because the conductivity in this case results from the fundamental nature of the allowed bands in the pure substance that the material is said to be an intrinsic semiconductor. The high resistivity results from a scarcity of carriers. Thermal agitation results in the production of these carriers, and a semiconductor in the intrinsic range is characterized by a rapid increase of the conductivity as a function of the temperature.

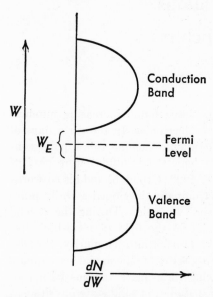

We may simplify our treatment of intrinsic semiconductors by assuming that the shapes of the conduction and valence bands are symmetrical about the Fermi level. This situation is suggested in Fig. 16-1. At a temperature of absolute zero, all the electrons are in the valence band, and the conduction band is empty. At temperatures other than absolute zero, the application of the Fermi function to the distribution of allowed levels will account for raising electrons from the valence band to the conduction band, and the number of electrons missing from the valence band as calculated will be equal to those appearing in the conduction band, if the Fermi level is taken midway between the energies corresponding to the edges of the neighboring bands. When the concentration of electrons in the conduction band is not large, this concentration is given by

Fig. 16-1. Symmetrical band structure for intrinsic semiconductors.

$$N_e = (2/h^3)(2\pi mkT)^{3/2} \exp(-W_e/2kT), \qquad (16\text{-}1)$$

where m is the effective mass of the electron in the conduction band, k is Boltzmann's constant, h is Planck's constant, T is the absolute temperature, and W_e is the width of the forbidden band of energies.

The reason for the existence of the exponential should be readily appreciated by the reader. At low densities of the carriers, the Fermi fraction is adequately approximated by an exponential involving the energy as the variable. The integral of this exponential over a range of energies is still an exponential which, in the finite limit of the range over which it is extended, will contain W_e. The slowly varying function of the temperature serving as a coefficient does not enter the argument explicitly, and its form does not need to be discussed at this point. It suffices to say that the conditions of the problem will result in a definite concentration of the carriers, and that the corresponding definite value of the coefficient is derived from a consideration of the conditions necessary to equilibrium. As usual in such cases, the exponential function dominates this expression, and for the modest relative changes in temperature usually encountered, the coefficient may be approximated by a constant. This suggests a means for experimentally determining the gap width W_e. Some property, such as conductivity, which is directly proportional to the number of carriers, and for which the dependence of the other factors on temperature is so slow that they may be treated as constants, is measured as a function of temperature. From these data the logarithm of the selected property is plotted as a function of $1/T$. The resulting graph is approximately linear, and the slope is $(- W_e/ 2k)$, and hence, from the measured value of the slope, W_e, corresponding to an activation energy, may be determined.

Thermistors

One of the earliest applications of semiconductors made use of the rapid variation of the resistance with temperature. For metals, the electrical resistance increases almost linearly with the temperature, and this is a result of the thermal vibrations interfering with the propagation of electron waves through the structure. In semiconductors the thermal vibrations of the lattice still account for the finite mobility of electrons in the structure, but the primary restriction on the electrical conductivity is the limited number of charges free to drift under the influence of an applied electric field. The number of carriers increases rapidly as a function of temperature, and the electrical resistance falls sharply as the temperature is raised.

Semiconductors used as *thermally* sensitive *resistors* are called *thermistors*. One class of applications arises directly from the fact that the change of resistance with temperature is the opposite of that in metals, and a thermistor can be used in series or parallel with a metallic conductor to compensate for the changes of resistance which take place in it as the temperature changes. Another class of applications arises from the fact that the variation of resistance with temperature can be extremely rapid. This makes thermistors useful for measurements of temperature of a highly precise type. Various metals, of course, have been used in the construction of resistance thermometers. It may happen, however, that precise indications of temperature in a very limited range are desired. Here a suitably chosen semiconductor with its rapid variation of resistance with temperature is useful. Furthermore, if only a small piece of the semiconductor is used, the response to extremely small amounts of added thermal energy will be very definite. For this reason semiconductors have been used for the detection of radiant energy. If light or other electromagnetic radiation is absorbed by a semiconductor, the energy is eventually converted into heat. The resistance of a semiconductor may therefore be used as a sensitive indication of the amount of radiant energy received by a black coating on its surface, used in raising the temperature of the semiconductor. Thermistors are used as bolometers, or devices for the detection and measurement of radiation, where high sensitivity is desired.

The Copper-Oxide Rectifier

In 1920, L. O. Grondahl was investigating the possibility of using light-sensitive cells as relays. He decided to try copper oxide formed on copper, and for this purpose, after a strip of copper had been oxidized, he clamped its oxidized surface against a strip of lead, using Micarta to transmit the pressure and insulate the clamp. When resistance measurements were made by means of a Wheatstone bridge, the results were erratic—sometimes 400 and sometimes 1200 ohms. This change bore no relation to the change of illumination, which was the point under investigation, but further investigation soon showed that it depended on the polarity of the applied electromotive force. From this discovery a good line of rectifiers was developed.

It is possible to give an energy band model to account for the rectification at the surface of contact between the copper and the copper oxide. We shall illustrate the use of these models in rectifiers of more recent origin which have the advantage of greater simplicity.

Rectification at a *p-n* Junction

It is possible to bring a p-type semiconductor into good conducting contact with an n-type semiconductor, but the resulting contact has so many imperfections that its properties are not very interesting.

Hence, the *p-n* junctions used in semiconductor applications are usually formed in a single crystal. This may be done by putting acceptors into one portion of a crystal as it is grown from a melt and donors into another part of the same crystal as the growth continues. The boundary between two such regions of the crystal is called a *p-n* junction. It exhibits behavior that is fundamental to the operation of several important semiconducting devices.

Conditions in the neighborhood of a *p-n* junction are suggested in Fig. 16-2. In the *p*-region, acceptors in fixed locations distributed

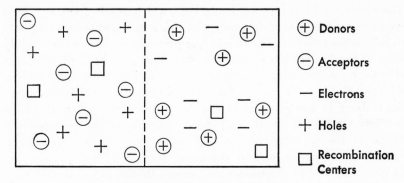

Fig. 16-2. Diagram of a *p-n* junction.

throughout the material will have electrons attached to them. The region as a whole is electrically neutral, because there is an equal concentration of holes wandering throughout the region. In the *n*-region on the other hand, each donor on the average will have released an electron and will have become a singly charged positive ion fixed in the lattice. The space charge of these ionized donors is neutralized by electrons which have random motions. In equilibrium there is no net transfer of electrons to the *p*-region and no net transfer of holes to the *n*-region. The principle of detailed balancing applies. Each process that results in the transfer of electrons to the *p*-region is balanced by an identical process proceeding in the opposite sense; so there is an equal transfer of electrons from the *p*-region to the *n*-region. Recombination is essential to the understanding of this balance, and imperfections at which recapture occurs are shown at several locations. To emphasize this condition of detailed balancing, it may be explained that, if it were possible to take a moving picture which would show all the various physical processes taking place in the semiconductor, the reversibility of all processes would give the viewer absolutely no way of telling whether the film was being run forward or backward. This situation, of course, is in striking contrast to the moving pictures of macroscopic events, where reversing the direction of the film gives effects which differ in such a pronounced manner from experience that they are positively grotesque.

When equilibrium has been established, the p-region is negative with respect to the n-region. Except for this difference of electrostatic potential, the concentration gradients would result in a net transfer of holes from the p-region to the n-region and a net transfer of electrons from the n-region to the p-region. These are electrical currents in the same sense, and, as long as they flow, equilibrium does not exist. The electrostatic charge accumulations, which result from any such transfer, quickly establish a potential difference in the sense required to reduce the transfer. The Boltzmann principle applies to the equilibrium of the two regions at different potentials, and in equilibrium the electronic concentration will be relatively large in the n-region where the potential is positive, and the hole concentration will be comparatively large in the p-region where the potential energy of the holes is relatively low. A small, high-energy fraction of the electrons will surmount the potential barrier and diffuse into the p-region, while there is a converse process for the holes. There is, of course, some loss of electrons at the recombination centers in the p-region and some loss of holes by recombination in the n-region. Detailed balancing requires that hole and electron pairs be separated through thermal action at sites where recapture also occurs, and this process will provide equal numbers of electrons to diffuse from the p-region into the n-region and to balance the number of electrons lost by recombination in the p-region. There is, of course, a converse process which results in the diffusion of holes from the n-region to the p-region.

The potential difference between the two regions is set up as a consequence of and at the expense of the component of momentum of majority carriers perpendicular to the boundary. It is only those majority carriers which have an unusually high momentum component in this direction that can be transferred through the barrier to the region on the opposite side in which they are classified as minority carriers. For any particle, this momentum persists only for a free path. Within the barrier the component of momentum, on which the establishment of the barrier depends, is quickly lost. In this process, the kinetic energy of the particle is converted into potential energy. The particles which have passed through the barrier diffuse into the equipotential region on the opposite side of the boundary. Theory has shown that the average depth L to which electrons diffuse into the p-region depends on the diffusion constant D and on the average life

T for the electrons according to the equation

$$L = (DT)^{1/2}. \tag{16-2}$$

On the basis of these principles, it is possible to make qualitatively correct plots to show the variation of the quantities of interest as functions of the distance from the p-n junction. (With certain simplifying assumptions, the quantities have been calculated from basic principles, but we will not make the present discussion quantitative.) In the first place, if we represent the number of ionized acceptors per

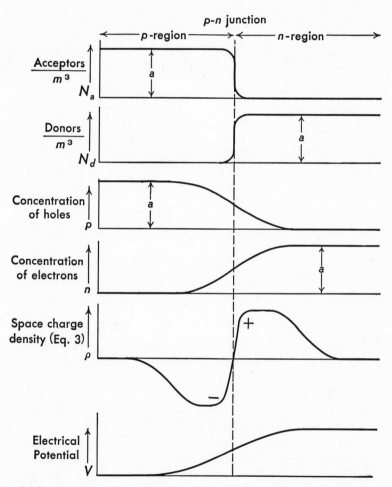

Fig. 16-3. Variation of quantities across a p-n junction. (A rearrangement of the figure given by W. Shockley in *Proc. Inst. Radio Engrs.*, **40**, 1303 (1952).)

unit volume by N_a and the number of donors per unit volume by N_d, it is clear that except for the immediate neighborhood of the boundary these quantities may be represented by constants. These two constants need not be the same, but for convenience they are represented as equal quantities in Fig. 16-3. Far from the space charge regions of the potential barrier, the concentration of electrons n in the n-region will have the same value as N_d, and in the p-region the concentration of the holes p will have the same value as N_a. In the neighborhood of

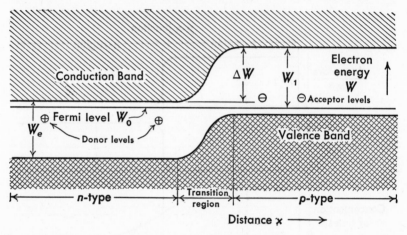

Fig. 16-4. Energy band diagram of equilibrium conditions for a p-n junction.

the junction, however, the thermal motions of the carriers will result in interdiffusion and a somewhat more gradual variation in p and n than in the plots for N_a and N_d. The space charge density ρ is given by

$$\rho = e(N_d - n - N_a + p), \tag{16-3}$$

and this quantity also is plotted in the figure. It is seen that there is a dipole charge layer in the neighborhood of the junction. (In the quantitative treatment, the potential V would be obtained by putting an expression for ρ into Poisson's equation and performing the required integrations.) The variations of the potential may be sketched qualitatively, and they are about as shown in Fig. 16-3.

Another representation of the p-n junction in equilibrium is shown in Fig. 16-4. Here the almost-filled valence band is shown as the crosshatched region at the bottom of the figure. Separated from this by the energy gap W_e is the conduction band. Localized donor levels in the n-region are indicated by the circles with the crosses in them, while the localized acceptors in the p-region are shown by the circles with the negative signs in them. Within the transition region, the energy of the electrons increases by an amount ΔW. The Fermi level, indicated by W_0 on this diagram, is between the donors and the conduction band in the n-region and between the acceptors and the valence band in the p-region.

The discussion of electric currents in the rectifier may now be placed upon a more quantitative basis. There is a current due to electrons of high kinetic energy originating in the n-region and surmounting the potential barrier in the transition region to diffuse into the p-region, a distance which on the average is L. Many of these electrons in the process of diffusion return to the n-region, but some are captured at definite sites in the p-region. This results in a transfer of electrons across the junction in the direction of the forward current as established by the concentration gradient, and it is, therefore, denoted by I_f. The principle of detailed balancing requires that in equilibrium this shall be balanced by a current of electrons which are liberated from the sites of their recapture through thermal action, and they diffuse to the junction, where they are swept into the n-region through the action of the potential gradient. This latter current we designate by I_g, where the subscript g stands for the descriptive term "generated."

When the balance is destroyed by increasing the potential barrier, fewer electrons can surmount the barrier to enter the p-region and I_f falls off rapidly, as the potential barrier is raised, as shown by the equation

$$I_f = I_g \exp\left(-e\,\Delta V/kT\right), \tag{16-4}$$

where ΔV is the change of the potential difference measured from the equilibrium condition (for which, therefore, $\Delta V = 0$), and it is positive when the potential barrier is increased. The current I_g depends on the generation of electrons in the body of the p-type material. Those generated within the diffusion distance L may be expected to diffuse to the boundary where the potential difference sweeps them into the n-region. An occasional electron generated at a distance from the boundary greater than L will, by a fortunate chain of events, also arrive at the boundary, and some of those generated within the diffusion distance will by mischance fail to reach the boundary. These processes are not altered appreciably by the applied potential difference, which our simplified treatment has assumed to be concentrated entirely at the barrier. The potential gradient within the body of the p-type material in general will be too small to alter the fact that it is the process of diffusion which accounts for the migration of electrons to the boundary. The liberation of electrons from the sites of their recapture occurs at a rate which is proportional to the concentration of holes in the p-type material. These are factors which do not vary much with the application of a modest potential difference across the junction; hence I_g can be treated as a constant.

Similar considerations apply to a high-energy fraction of holes from the p-region which can surmount the potential barrier and diffuse into the n-region where some of them are lost by recombination and account for a current I_f'. Detailed balancing requires that at equilibrium, this current should be balanced by the generated hole current I_g', which passes across the boundary in the opposite direction.

Recognizing the constancy of the currents I_g and I_g' and the exponential dependence of I_f and I_f' upon the applied potential, we are in a position to set down an expression for the current through the junction as a function of the externally applied potential ΔV. This is

$$I = I_f + I_f' - I_g - I_g'$$

$$= (I_g + I_g')[\exp(-e\,\Delta V/kT) - 1]$$

$$= I_s[\exp(-e\,\Delta V/kT) - 1], \qquad (16\text{-}5)$$

where I_s, the saturation current, is the sum of I_g and I_g'. When the height of the potential barrier is increased by the applied potential, the current through the junction, called the reverse current in the rectifier, quickly approaches this value. If, however, the applied potential difference decreases the height of the potential barrier, the forward current increases rapidly and is dominated by the exponential term in Eq. (5). Experiments with p-n junctions have confirmed the predicted variations of current with the applied potential. The physical cause of the large forward current is the concentration gradient of the carriers, which arises from the fact that the donors are most numerous on the one side and that the acceptors are most numerous on the other side. If the applied potential obliterates the potential barrier at the junction, the entire current due to the concentration gradient is observed, and thus it may have a relatively large value.

Rectification by a Metal in Contact with Silicon or Germanium

Conductivity in silicon or germanium takes place by electrons, if donor impurities dominate the sample, and by holes, if acceptor impurities dominate the sample. Even though the excess of electrons or holes may exist, a space charge may establish barriers to the migration of these carriers across boundaries as in the case of the p-n junction we have discussed. It is this fact which accounts for the rectification at silicon to metal contacts. It is well established experimentally that when a metal is placed in contact with germanium or silicon, the conductivity in one direction is high, while the conductivity in the other direction is low, even to potentials which may be of the order of several hundred volts. To explain such a marked lack of symmetry in the resistance, Shottky proposed that the space charge created a potential

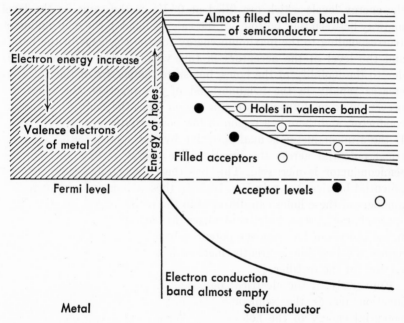

Fig. 16-5. Rectification at a junction between a semiconductor and a metal.

barrier. In the case of silicon and germanium, on which extensive work has been done, it is not difficult to make a very definite model to account for such behavior. For example, consider a p-type semiconductor in which the energy of the holes is plotted upward, and the energy of the electrons conversely is plotted downward, as shown in Fig. 16-5, in contrast to most of the figures we have drawn. At the metal-semiconductor junction, electrons from the metal diffuse into the semiconductor and fill the acceptor levels in the immediate neighborhood of the junction. This creates a negative space charge, which, because of the limited concentration of donors in the semiconductor, has appreciable width, and, to neutralize the system as a whole, a positive charge is induced on the surface of the metal. The presence of these charges accounts for rapid variations of potential in the neighborhood of the contact.

Although virtually all the acceptor levels are filled near the junction with the metal, at positions remote from the metal only half of the acceptor levels are filled, and the charge associated with the filling of these acceptors is neutralized by deficiencies of electrons (or holes) in the valance band of the semiconductor. Equilibrium is established when the Fermi level (which for the metal corresponds to the limit of the energy levels which are filled at $0°$ K) is the same as the level midway between the "bottom" of the valence band in the semiconductor (corresponding to the maximum energy for the electrons in the band) and the level of the acceptors in this vicinity. The conductivity is due to the mobility of the holes, but since the energy of the holes increases rapidly in the neighborhood of the junction, the holes are prevented from diffusing into this region from the body of the semiconductor, and there is a region of low conductivity near the junction. If the semiconductor is made positive by the application of an electrical potential across the junction, the energy of the holes in the semiconductor is increased. This has the effect of flattening out the potential barrier shown in Fig. 16-5. In these circumstances, increased numbers of these holes can diffuse into the region of the junction. The space charge of these holes neutralizes that of the filled acceptor levels in the process of lowering the potential barrier. Thus, the conductivity across the junction is greatly increased, and this is the forward direction for the rectifier.

Conversely, if the electrical potential difference applied across the junction makes the semiconductor negative, it will decrease the potential energy of the holes in the body of the semiconductor and increase the potential barrier. In this process, holes will be prevented from diffusing so close to the potential barrier, and less of the space charge of the filled acceptor levels will be neutralized. This direction of the applied potential, which increases the potential barrier at the junction, is the reverse or high resistance direction for the rectifier. This is another illustration of the principle that it is only the injection of *minority carriers* which is capable of increasing the conductivity.

Summary

In this chapter, we have described some of the more elementary applications of semiconductor physics. A characteristic property of intrinsic semiconductors is the rapid rise of conductivity with temperature. This was early used as a means of classifying semiconductors.

Junctions between two different types of materials provide the possibility of carrier distributions which lack symmetry. Carrier concentration gradients in solids may be quite large, and these, accompanied by unimpeded diffusion, result in large currents. Where the concentration gradients exist in nature, an equilibrium is established by the development of a potential gradient. Assuming the applicability of the Maxwell-Boltzmann statistics to both regions, Boltzmann's principle then gives the condition for the equilibrium of the two regions even though the densities of the carriers differ greatly. These principles are involved in the discussion of the physical processes giving rise to a rectifier action. The conductivity of a specimen may be increased by injecting minority carriers.

The p-n junction, which was used as an illustration of the physical processes, is important in electronic devices, and several such junctions may be used in combination to form a single device.

Problems on Properties of Semiconductors

1. Calculate (a) the concentration of the carriers in pure germanium at 20° C, and, from this information and the mobility of the carriers, determine (b) the conductivity of the germanium.
2. Calculate (a) the concentration of the carriers in pure silicon at 30° C, and, from this information and the mobility of the carriers, determine (b) the conductivity of the silicon.
3. A thermistor is to be made of a single germanium crystal having a cross-sectional area of 1.0 mm² and a length of 3.0 cm. The electric power supplied to the crystal is to be kept less than 0.50 mw.
   a. What is the conductivity of this germanium crystal at 50° C?
   b. What is the rate of change of conductivity with temperature at 50° C?
   c. If the galvanometer used to detect changes in current in the crystal has a resistance of 500 ohms and a current sensitivity of 1 μma, what is the sensitivity of the thermistor in detecting decreases of temperature from 50° C?
4. The saturation current in a silicon p-n junction rectifier at room temperature is 100 μma. Calculate the current when the forward voltage ΔV applied to the rectifier is 250 mv.
5. A section of p-type germanium which has 10^{22} carriers/m³, and another of the n-type which has 10^{21} electrons/m³ in the conduction band, form a p-n junction. Are these data sufficient for the calculation of any characteristic of the junction? What additional information would be required for establishing the increase in the potential energy of an electron as it moves from the n- to the p-type material under equilibrium conditions?

References on Early Applications of Semiconductors

Goldman, J. E. (ed.), *The Science of Engineering Materials,* Ch. 15, "Semiconductor Devices" by Esther M. Conwell and William J. Leivo (New York: John Wiley and Sons, 1957).

Pearson, G. L., and W. H. Brattain, "History of Semiconductor Research," *Proc. Radio Engrs.,* **43,** 1794 (1955).

Spangenberg, Karl R., *Fundamentals of Electron Devices,* pp. 171-200 (New York: McGraw-Hill Book Company, 1957).

Sproull, Robert L., *Modern Physics—A Textbook for Engineers,* pp. 325-52 (New York: John Wiley and Sons, 1956).

PART III | Nuclear Physics

17 | The Nuclear Atom

Introduction

It was not until 1911 that the nucleus was recognized as a distinct part of the atom. However, radioactivity, which is a nuclear phenomenon, was discovered by Antoine Henri Becquerel in 1896. Becquerel was studying some fluorescent ores of uranium and he found that some of the radiations given off were of a very penetrating kind. These radiations resembled X-rays, which had recently been discovered, in that they could pass through large thicknesses of opaque materials and cause blackening of a photographic plate. All ores of uranium gave off these radiations whether or not fluorescence was present. This radioactivity was also shown by thorium ores. Furthermore, it was possible to separate other radioactive elements from these ores by chemical methods. The elements radium and polonium are examples of these. They were discovered by Madame Curie who undertook this work in collaboration with her husband.

The radiations from radium and other radioactive materials were found to vary in the extent to which they could penetrate various thicknesses of absorbing material. The terms alpha, beta, and gamma radiation were used to describe three kinds of radiation, in the order of increasing penetrating power. Alpha rays are stopped by a sheet of paper of average thickness. A beam of beta rays is attenuated in passing through about one mm of aluminum. The gamma rays are so penetrating that several cm of lead may not entirely absorb them.

Measurements were made of the deflection of the radiations in electric and magnetic fields. The gamma rays were not deflected. In this respect as in others, they resemble photons of X-radiation. Penetrating photons can be designated either as gamma rays or as X-rays, de-

TABLE 17-1. LIST OF SYMBOLS USED IN CHAPTER 17

Symbol	Name	Quantity Designated
e		electronic charge
Ze		nuclear charge
E		electric field
ϵ_0	epsilon sub zero	permittivity of free space
p		impact parameter
r		polar coordinate, distance from center
θ	theta	polar coordinate, angle
U		potential energy
m		mass of a particle
v		velocity
dt		differential element of time
b		$Zze^2/[4\pi\epsilon_0(\tfrac{1}{2}mv^2)]$
ϕ	phi	angle of scattering
N		number of scattered particles
N_0		number of incident particles
n		number of scattering nuclei per unit volume
t		thickness of foil
$d\Omega$	dee omega	element of solid angle

pending upon the manner in which they are produced. When they are emitted by nuclei, they are called gamma rays. The beta rays were found to be negatively charged particles. The values of e/m found in the deflection experiments were the same as for an electron, when allowance was made for the high speed of the beta rays, which caused the relativistic mass to be appreciably higher than the rest mass of the electron.

The alpha rays were found, in magnetic deflection experiments, to be positively charged particles, and the e/m values were appropriate for helium atoms which had lost two electrons. To be certain of this identification, the helium was identified spectroscopically. A capsule of radium was placed inside a gas-discharge tube. The light from an electrical discharge in the gas showed no trace of helium initially, but the characteristic lines of this element were observed after the alpha particles had accumulated for several days.

Scattering of Alpha Particles

Many of these early discoveries were made by Ernest Rutherford. He also set out to study, in collaboration with his students, the scattering of alpha particles. It was already well known that most of the particles travel in straight lines through matter. To observe the particles which might be deflected, a narrow beam was directed at a thin foil such as a semi-transparent gold foil. The source of alpha particles was a metal button with a surface layer of radioactive atoms. From such a source, the alpha particles are emitted in all directions at random, but a narrow pencil of rays was selected by a set of defining slits. The detector was a layer of zinc sulphide on a glass plate. This screen had the property of emitting a flash of light when an alpha particle struck it. The flash was detected by observing the screen through a low-power microscope, taking advantage of the high light-sensitivity of the dark-adapted human eye.

The detector was small in area and was movable so that particles scattered from the foil could be observed at different angles to the original direction of the beam. For very small angles, many scattered alpha particles were observed, as was expected on the basis of theories current at that time. These theories predicted no scattering at all at larger angles, but some scattered alpha particles were nevertheless observed at all angles, even as large as 180°.

Since the observation of particles scattered at large angles was not in accordance with the existing theories, Rutherford worked out a theory, based upon a new model of the atom. He introduced the concept of a nucleus which is centrally located in the atom and which contains most of the mass and all of the positive charge of the atom. This nuclear model is sometimes called the Rutherford atom. The atom as a whole is, of course, electrically neutral, and the positive charge of the nucleus must be Ze, where Z is the number of electrons in the extra-nuclear structure. The nucleus is pictured as being very much smaller than the atom. Outside the nucleus, there is a region where the electric field is that produced by a point charge Ze, that is, $E = Ze/(4\pi\epsilon_0 r^2)$, where r is the distance from the center of the nucleus. The extra-nuclear electrons make no contribution to the electric field if they can be regarded as uniform spherical shells of electricity of radius greater than r. But whatever their distribution, they would have relatively small effect on the alpha particle at points very near to the nucleus.

The great strength of the nuclear electric field can be understood by working out an example. At a distance of 10^{-14} meters from the center of a lead ($Z = 82$) nucleus, the electric field is

$$E = Ze/(4\pi\epsilon_0 r^2) = (9 \times 10^9)82(1.60 \times 10^{-19})/(10^{-14})^2 \text{ mks}$$

$$= 1.2 \times 10^{21} \text{ volts/m}.$$

This may be compared with electric fields of the order of 10^8 volts/m which are the largest obtainable between parallel metal plates without cold emission of electrons from the plates. This nuclear field exerts a strong force upon the charged alpha particle whenever it penetrates to the region near the nucleus. The laws of electrostatics and classical mechanics can be used to find the angles through which the alpha particles are deflected.

Fig. 17-1 shows the path of an alpha particle which approaches a nucleus of charge Ze along a straight line which passes the nucleus at

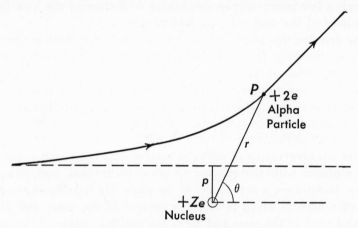

Fig. 17-1. The path of an alpha particle.

a distance p. The quantity p is called the impact parameter. The alpha particle is deflected away from the nucleus by the electrostatic force. Its path can be described in terms of the coordinates r and θ.

The potential energy U of the system is given by $U = (Ze)(ze)/(4\pi\epsilon_0 r)$, where ze is the charge on the scattered particle. For an alpha particle, $z = 2$, but the same theory may be applied to the scattering of a proton, in which case z would be unity. The initial kinetic energy of the alpha particle is $\frac{1}{2}mv_0^2$ and its kinetic energy at the point P is $\frac{1}{2}mv^2$. The initial velocity v_0 of the alpha particle is presumably a measurable quantity, but the velocity v is unknown and is less than v_0. The velocity v can be resolved into a radial component dr/dt and an angular component $r\, d\theta/dt$, and in terms of these components the kinetic energy can be expressed as

$$\tfrac{1}{2}mv^2 = \tfrac{1}{2}m[(dr/dt)^2 + (r\, d\theta/dt)^2].$$

From the law of conservation of energy, we can then write

$$\tfrac{1}{2}mv_0^2 = \tfrac{1}{2}m[(dr/dt)^2 + (r\, d\theta/dt)^2] + Zze^2/(4\pi\epsilon_0 r). \qquad (17\text{-}1)$$

This is an approximation since the kinetic energy of recoil of the scattering nucleus has been neglected. The approximation should be reasonably good for scattering by heavy nuclei such as silver and gold, but would be very bad for scattering by light elements such as hydrogen and carbon.

Angular momentum is a quantity which also is conserved in this problem. Although a force is present, it is along the line joining the nucleus and the alpha particle and thus does not contribute any torque about an axis through the nucleus. The initial angular momentum is mv_0p and the angular momentum at the point P is $m(r\, d\theta/dt)r$. Hence, if the angular momentum is conserved, we can write

$$mv_0p = mr^2(d\theta/dt). \qquad (17\text{-}2)$$

Eliminating dt between Eqs. (1) and (2), a relation between r and θ is obtained which is the equation of the path of the alpha particle. After substituting dt from Eq. (2) into Eq. (1), the latter becomes

$$\tfrac{1}{2}mv_0^2 = \tfrac{1}{2}mv_0^2[p^2(dr/d\theta)^2/r^4 + p^2/r^2] + Zze^2/(4\pi\epsilon_0 r),$$

and, when this is solved for $d\theta$, we obtain

$$d\theta = dr/\{(r^2/p)[1 - p^2/r^2 - Zze^2/(4\pi\epsilon_0 r\tfrac{1}{2}mv_0^2)]^{1/2}\}. \qquad (17\text{-}3)$$

It is customary to simplify the expression by introducing the symbol $b = Zze^2/[4\pi\epsilon_0(\tfrac{1}{2}mv_0^2)]$, where the quantity b is a length which has physical significance. If the alpha particle had approached the nucleus directly in a head-on collision ($p = 0$), it would have been undeflected from its initial line of travel and would have come to rest at a distance of r_0 from the nucleus where its initial kinetic energy would have been entirely converted into potential energy. The equation would be $\tfrac{1}{2}mv_0^2 = Zze^2/(4\pi\epsilon_0 r_0)$. The distance of closest approach r_0 in this case is thus seen to be identical with the quantity b. The simplified expression for $d\theta$ is

$$d\theta = dr/[(r^2/p)(1 - p^2/r^2 - b/r)^{1/2}]. \qquad (17\text{-}4)$$

This is a differential equation which is readily solvable by direct integration of each side. The result is

$$\theta + K = \text{arc cos}\,[1/r + b/2p^2]/[1/p^2 + b^2/4p^4]^{1/2}, \qquad (17\text{-}5)$$

where K is a constant of integration. The integration of the right-hand side is carried out in Appendix X since some substitution is required to make the integral recognizable.

Eq. (5) represents an hyperbola and Rutherford used some of the properties of the hyperbola to arrive at the angle of scattering. We may note that the quantity $1/r$ is zero when the alpha particle is at a sufficient distance from the nucleus, once when $\theta = 180°$, and again when θ is equal to the angle of scattering, denoted by ϕ. Inserting these two limiting conditions, we find that both $(180° + K)$ and $(\phi + K)$ are equal to arc cos $(b/2p^2)/(1/p^2 + b^2/4p^4)^{\frac{1}{2}}$. When two different angles have the same cosine, one is the negative of the other, that is,

$$(180° + K) = -(\phi + K) \quad \text{or} \quad K = -90° - \tfrac{1}{2}\phi$$

and

$$(180° + K) = (90° - \tfrac{1}{2}\phi) = \text{arc cos } (b/2p^2)/(1/p^2 + b^2/4p^4)^{\frac{1}{2}}. \quad (17\text{-}6)$$

Fig. 17-2 shows the trigonometric relation involved in the last formula. It is clear from the figure that an equivalent and simpler expression for

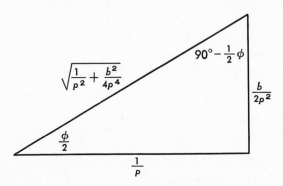

Fig. 17-2. The angles and trigonometric relations involved in Eq. (6).

the angle of scattering is

$$\boxed{\cot \tfrac{1}{2}\phi = 2p/b.} \quad (17\text{-}7)$$

This shows the dependence of the scattering angle upon the impact parameter p. The deflection is small for large impact parameters. The large deflections result from near collisions with nuclei.

Impact parameters cannot be experimentally determined and a verification of Eq. (7) is not possible for a single alpha particle. However, when a large number of alpha particles are shot into a thin foil, one can assume that all impact parameters will be involved in a geometrically determinable way, and the number of alpha particles scattered at different angles can be calculated.

Suppose that a number of alpha particles N_0 are made to strike a foil of area A and thickness t. Take n to be the number of scattering nuclei per unit volume of the foil. The number of scattering nuclei can be determined from the known density (ρ) of the material, since

$n = \rho N_A/M$, where M is the atomic weight and N_A is Avogadro's number. The number of scattering centers in the foil is nAt. Fig. 17-3 shows some of these centers.

Around each scattering center a circle of radius p has been drawn. If the initial path of an alpha particle passes inside the circle of radius p, it will be scattered at an angle greater than the angle ϕ given by Eq. (7). The number N scattered at angles greater than ϕ is calculated on the basis that the fraction scattered depends upon a ratio of areas, namely the ratio of all the areas πp^2 associated with any scattering

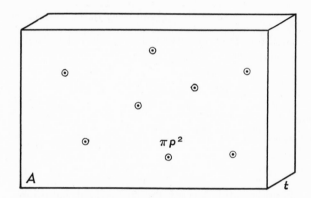

Fig. 17-3. Some of the scattering centers in a thin foil of area A and thickness t.

center to the total area of the foil. This ratio is

$$N/N_0 = \pi p^2 (nAt)/A, \tag{17-8}$$

or, expressing p in terms of ϕ,

$$N = N_0 \pi nt(b^2/4) \cot^2 \tfrac{1}{2}\phi. \tag{17-9}$$

This formula could be verified by a somewhat complicated experimental procedure.

A simple procedure is to use a detector of small area, say a, placed at a distance r from the scattering foil and at the angle ϕ with respect to the direction of the initial beam. The detector subtends a solid angle a/r^2 steradians. From the number of scattered particles observed, the number scattered per unit solid angle at the angle ϕ can be found. For comparison with this experimental result, the theoretical expression, Eq. (9), can be differentiated to obtain the number of particles $|dN|$ scattered between ϕ and $\phi + d\phi$, and this can be divided by $d\Omega$, the solid angle which lies between ϕ and $\phi + d\phi$. Thus,

$$d\Omega = 2\pi \sin \phi \, d\phi = 4\pi \sin \tfrac{1}{2}\phi \cos \tfrac{1}{2}\phi \, d\phi$$

and

$$|dN| = N_0\pi nt(b^2/4)2 \cot \tfrac{1}{2}\phi \csc^2 \tfrac{1}{2}\phi \, \tfrac{1}{2}d\phi.$$

Therefore,

$$\boxed{|dN|/d\Omega = N_0nt(b^2/16) \csc^4 \tfrac{1}{2}\phi.} \tag{17-10}$$

This is the Rutherford scattering formula. Recalling that

$$b = Zze^2/[4\pi\epsilon_0(\tfrac{1}{2}mv_0^2)],$$

it is clear that the number of scattered alpha particles observed per unit solid angle should be proportional to

   (a) $\csc^4 \tfrac{1}{2}\phi$;

   (b) t, the thickness of the scattering foil;

   (c) the square of the charge of the scattering nuclei $(Ze)^2$; and that it should be inversely proportional to

   (d) the square of the initial kinetic energy of the alpha particle, $(\tfrac{1}{2}mv_0^2)^2$.

Experimental Test of the Rutherford Equation

Table 17-2 is a summary of some measurements made by Geiger and Marsden to test the angular dependence of the alpha particles scattered by a gold foil. The first and second columns are the angles of observation ϕ and the values of $\csc^4 \tfrac{1}{2}\phi$ for those angles. The third column gives the number of scattered particles actually observed as scintillations, due allowance having already been made for changes of solid angle and for changes in the strength of the radioactive source of alpha particles. The last column is the ratio of the number observed to $\csc^4 \tfrac{1}{2}\phi$, and the constancy of this ratio is the test of the theory. These results give abundant proof of the correctness of Rutherford's law of scattering and of the nuclear picture of the structure of the atom.

A number of other experiments have confirmed the theory of alpha particle scattering. Of these, a noteworthy experiment was performed by Chadwick with scattering foils of copper, silver, and platinum. He assumed the correctness of the scattering theory, but regarded the nuclear charge Ze as an unknown to be determined for each element by observing the number of scattered particles. His results are summarized in Table 17-3, which gives for each foil the atomic number, as determined from the position of the element in the periodic table,

TABLE 17-2. A SUMMARY OF SOME MEASUREMENTS OF GEIGER AND MARSDEN
ON THE SCATTERING OF ALPHA PARTICLES BY A GOLD FOIL

ϕ	$\csc^4 \frac{1}{2}\phi$	Number of scintillations	Ratio
150°	1.15	33.1	28.8
135	1.38	43.0	31.2
120	1.79	51.9	29.0
105	2.53	69.5	27.5
75	7.25	211	29.1
60	16.0	477	29.8
45	46.6	1435	30.8
37.5	93.7	3300	35.3
30	223	7800	35.0
22.5	690	27300	39.6
15	3445	132000	38.4

and the nuclear charge in units of the electronic charge as determined
in the scattering experiment. Although, because of experimental errors,
whole numbers were not obtained, the agreement is excellent and is

TABLE 17-3. CHADWICK'S RESULTS FOR Z

	Atomic Number (chemical)	Z (scattering)
Cu	29	29.3
Ag	47	46.3
Pt	78	77.4

strong confirmation of the idea that the nuclear charge ultimately determines the chemical properties of an atom.

The "Radius of the Nucleus"

In the derivation of the scattering formula, the path of the alpha
particle was assumed to lie entirely outside the nucleus. If the path
should pass through the nucleus, the electric field would not be that of
a point charge, nor could one assume the absence of other collision
forces which would deflect the moving particle. The experimental verification of the formula can be regarded as evidence that the nuclei are
of very small size. In experiments where aluminum was used as the
scattering foil, deviations from Rutherford scattering were observed
and the term "anomalous scattering" was used to describe the effects.
Anomalous scattering was found in light elements such as aluminum
because the small nuclear charge gave less repulsive force and some

of the alpha particles approached the nucleus more closely. The results suggest that, when an alpha particle penetrates to within about 10^{-14} m of the center of the aluminum nucleus, the scattering is anomalous and that this distance is the order of magnitude of nuclear radii. The nucleus is then about ten thousand times smaller in each dimension than the atom. The exact value should not be taken too seriously, because quantum mechanics rather than classical mechanics should be used to interpret the experiments. The quantum mechanics has been applied to Coulomb scattering and the Rutherford formula was found to be exact whenever the scattering center could be regarded as a "point nucleus." However, when the finite size of the nucleus is involved, as it is when the scattering is anomalous, the classical mechanics does not give results in agreement with the quantum mechanics.

Summary

The experimental verification of the scattering formula is taken as evidence that the law of force between an alpha particle and a nucleus is the inverse square law of electrostatic repulsion. The extent to which the law of force has thus been verified can be clarified by considering a scattering problem with a different law of force.

Suppose that the incident particle is an elastic sphere of radius r_1 and that the scattering center is a similar but more massive sphere of radius

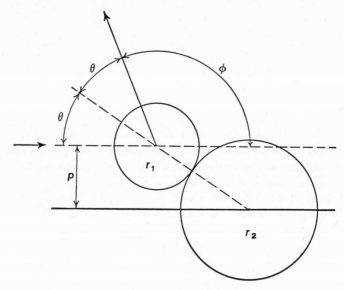

Fig. 17-4. Collision of elastic spheres.

r_2. Fig. 17-4 shows a collision between the two spheres. Again neglecting the recoil of the massive scatterer, it can be seen that the angle of scattering is $\phi = \pi - 2\theta$. The angle θ is arc sin $\{p/(r_1 + r_2)\}$, where p is the impact parameter. The expression that relates the scattering angle to the impact parameter is $p = (r_1 + r_2) \sin \theta = (r_1 + r_2) \cos \frac{1}{2}\phi$. This replaces Eq. (7). The expression for the number of particles scattered at all angles greater than ϕ is $N = N_0 \pi nt (r_1 + r_2)^2 \cos^2 \frac{1}{2}\phi$, instead of Eq. (9). The final scattering formula is

$$|dN|/d\Omega = N_0 nt (r_1 + r_2)^2/4. \tag{17-11}$$

The number of particles scattered per unit of solid angle is independent of angle, of energy, and of charge.

The dependence upon angle and energy shown by the Rutherford scattering formula is characteristic of an inverse square law, and the dependence upon Zze^2 shows that the force is electrostatic in character. The dependence upon $N_0 nt$ is apparently trivial in nature, being common to both problems, whether the force is of the long-range type, such as a coulomb force, or of the short-range type, such as the collision force between elastic spheres.

The linear dependence of the number of scattered particles upon the thickness of the layer of scattering material is found experimentally not to hold except for thin scatterers. This is interpreted to mean that particles are scattered more than once in the thicker foils. The linear dependence upon thickness is sometimes tested to insure that single scattering is being observed.

Problems

1. How closely must a 7.68 Mev alpha particle be aimed at a gold ($Z = 79$) nucleus (that is, what should be the impact parameter) in order that it shall be scattered at an angle of 90°?

(Ans.: $p = 1.48 \times 10^{-14}$ m.)

2. What fraction of the alpha particles incident upon a gold foil 3.0×10^{-5} cm thick are scattered at angles greater than 90°, if their energy is 7.68 Mev? The density and atomic weight of gold are 19.3 g/cm³ and 197.2.

(Ans.: 1.22×10^{-5}.)

3. Calculate the energy of an alpha particle which is able to penetrate to a distance of 10^{-14} m from the center of an aluminum ($Z = 13$) nucleus in a head-on collision (impact parameter = 0). Neglect the recoil of the aluminum nucleus.

(Ans.: $\frac{1}{2}mv_0^2 = 3.74$ Mev.)

4. When an alpha particle ($A = 4$) comes to rest with respect to an aluminum ($A = 27$) nucleus in a head-on collision, both particles must be moving with a total linear momentum equal to the momentum of the in-

cident alpha particle. What fraction of the initial kinetic energy is needed to conserve momentum?

(Ans.: 0.129.)

References

The student is referred to the following textbooks in nuclear physics. They should be consulted for further clarification on the topics discussed in Part III, and for references to original research papers.

Evans, R. D., *The Atomic Nucleus* (New York: McGraw-Hill Book Co., 1955).

Green, A. E. S., *Nuclear Physics* (New York: McGraw-Hill Book Co., 1955).

Halliday, D., *Introductory Nuclear Physics* (New York: John Wiley and Sons, 1955).

Kaplan, I., *Nuclear Physics* (Cambridge: Addison-Wesley, 1955).

Price, W. J., *Nuclear Radiation Detection* (New York: McGraw-Hill Book Co., 1958).

18 || Absorption of Alpha, Beta, and Gamma Rays

Our understanding of nuclear physics has not yet developed to such an extent that the subject can be presented from a basis of accepted theoretical principles. We must at first rely heavily upon experimental results, until we find, here and there, areas in which a theory seems applicable. Many experiments require the use of a detector for energetic particles. The operation of these detectors can be understood in terms of the effects produced when energetic particles are absorbed in matter.

Absorption of Massive Charged Particles

The category of massive charged particles includes helium nuclei (alpha particles), hydrogen nuclei (protons), and other particles of various charges and masses. Electrons are the lightest of the charged particles and they exhibit peculiarities which make a separate discussion advisable.

A fast charged particle, such as a proton, travels through matter in a straight line, nuclear scattering being a rare event. The kinetic energy of the particle is gradually lost to the electrons of the surrounding material. The distance traveled through matter before the kinetic energy is completely lost is called the "range" of the particle. The rate of energy loss per unit length of path $(-dW/dx)$ determines the range. To derive an exact expression for $-dW/dx$ would require the use of quantum mechanics and a considerable knowledge of atomic structure, but an approximate expression can be derived from classical principles. The derivation will serve to illustrate the mechanism of energy transfer. Fig. 18-1 shows the straight path of a moving particle of charge

ze and velocity v. A free electron at rest is situated at a distance b from the path of the particle. The diagram shows the quantities r, θ, and x, which vary as the particle moves along its path. The energy transferred to the electron is to be calculated.

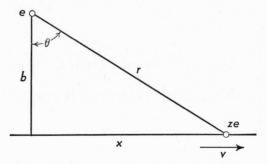

Fig. 18-1. Interaction of charged particles.

The electron is acted upon by a force $F = ze^2/4\pi\epsilon_0 r^2$. This force has two components, $F\cos\theta$ perpendicular to the path and $F\sin\theta$ parallel to the path. The component $F\sin\theta$ reverses direction during the passage of the moving particle, and its average value is zero. The component $F\cos\theta$ gives the electron a momentum p perpendicular to the path of the fast particle and this momentum can be calculated from the impulse $\int F\cos\theta\,dt$. In equation form,

$$p = \int (ze^2/4\pi\epsilon_0 r^2)\cos\theta\,dt. \tag{18-1}$$

Making the substitutions $dt = dx/v$, $r = b\sec\theta$, $x = b\tan\theta$, and $dx = b\sec^2\theta\,d\theta$, the equation becomes

$$p = (ze^2/4\pi\epsilon_0 bv)\int\cos\theta\,d\theta. \tag{18-2}$$

The integral, over all possible values of θ from $-90°$ to $+90°$, has the value 2. The kinetic energy given to the electron is

$$w = p^2/2m = (2ze^2/4\pi\epsilon_0 bv)^2/2m, \tag{18-3}$$

where w has been used for the kinetic energy given to a single electron, to distinguish it from the total kinetic energy W of the massive charged particle. This value for the energy transferred to an electron should be a fair approximation under some circumstances. The moving particle should be fast so that the distance b would not change appreciably during its passage. Also, the electron should be far enough from the

TABLE 18-1. LIST OF SYMBOLS USED IN CHAPTER 18

Symbol	Name	Quantity Designated
W		kinetic energy of a massive particle
v		velocity of the massive particle
w		energy of an electron
p		momentum of an electron
m		mass of an electron
r		polar coordinate, distance
θ	theta	polar coordinate, angle
b		distance of electron from the path
ze		charge of the moving particle
F		force
n		number of electrons per unit volume
I		energy required to produce ionization, also intensity of a beam of radiation
l		length of track
R		range of a charged particle
$h\nu$	h nu	energy of photon
μ	mu	absorption coefficient
$x_{1/2}$		half-value thickness

path of the moving particle that only small transfers of momentum and energy are involved. If the transfers are large, the incident particle cannot be pictured as continuing to move in a straight line with constant speed.

A particle traversing matter is surrounded by many electrons. The number of electrons per unit volume n can be calculated from the density ρ of the absorbing medium and is given by

$$n = \rho N_A Z/M, \qquad (18\text{-}4)$$

where M is the atomic weight, Z is the number of electrons per atom, and N_A is Avogadro's number. Those electrons which are at the distance b, between b and $b + db$, occupy a cylindrical shell of volume $2\pi lb\,db$ about a length l of the track. The energy loss to these electrons is

$$-dW = (2\pi lb\,db)n(2ze^2/4\pi\epsilon_0 bv)^2/2m. \qquad (18\text{-}5)$$

This expression should be integrated over all values of b. The result is

$$-\Delta W = (z^2 e^4 n/4\pi\epsilon_0^2 mv^2)l \ln (b_{\max}/b_{\min}). \qquad (18\text{-}6)$$

A caution is required against setting $b_{\min} = 0$ or $b_{\max} = \infty$, because either step would make the rate of energy loss infinite, and the range of the fast particle zero. Definite ranges are actually observed for these particles. The difficulty can better be discussed in terms of energies.

Since the energy w transferred to a single electron is inversely proportional to b^2, we can write

$$b_{max}/b_{min} = (w_{max}/w_{min})^{1/2}. \tag{18-7}$$

The minimum energy need not be zero, if one considers that the electrons are not free, but are actually bound in atoms. We shall set $w_{min} = I$, where I is the energy required to ionize the atom, suitably averaged over the different electrons in the atom. The maximum energy transferred to an electron is limited because the theory of elastic collisions (see Chapter 22) shows that a relatively massive particle colliding with a light one cannot impart to it a velocity greater than twice the velocity of the massive particle. Therefore,

$$w_{max} = \tfrac{1}{2}m(v_{max})^2 = \tfrac{1}{2}m(2v)^2 = 2mv^2.$$

The final expression for the rate of energy loss $-dW/dx = -\Delta W/l$ is

$$\boxed{-dW/dx = (z^2 e^4 n/8\pi\epsilon_0{}^2 mv^2)\ln(2mv^2/I).} \tag{18-8}$$

Insofar as the dependence upon variables is concerned, this formula agrees with the more accurate quantum mechanical treatment. A relativistic treatment introduces additional terms which are small unless the velocity is very near the velocity of light.

Eq. (8) shows that the rate of energy loss depends upon the nature of the absorbing medium and upon the properties of the moving particles. Because of the dependence upon the number of electrons per unit volume, liquids and solids are about a thousand times more effective than gases at standard pressure. The electrons in heavy elements are somewhat less effective than in light elements because the average binding energy of the electrons I is greater in the heavy elements. The rate of energy loss is independent of the mass of the moving particle. Although a mass m appears in the formula, it is the constant electronic mass, not the mass of the fast particle. The energy loss is a complicated function of the velocity, but slower particles lose energy more rapidly than fast particles. The dependence upon z^2 shows that a particle of charge two loses energy four times as rapidly as a particle of charge one. The equation

$$-dW/dt = z^2 f(v) \tag{18-9}$$

(independent of M) is a simplification of Eq. (8) which is adequate for some purposes. If moving particles of the same velocity are being compared, it is not necessary to know the velocity dependence $f(v)$.

Ranges of Charged Particles

The ranges of charged particles are more easily measured than the rate of energy loss. Ranges can be calculated from Eq. (8) by considering that the particle starts with initial energy W_0 at $x = 0$ and that the energy becomes zero when $x = R$, the range of the particle. The range, therefore, depends upon the initial energy of the particle.

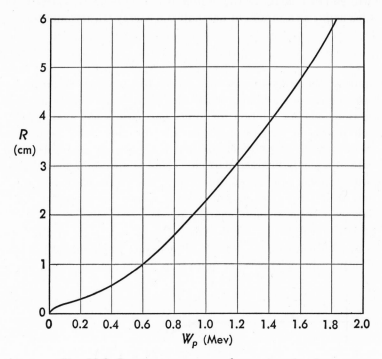

Fig. 18-2. Range-energy curve for protons in air.

It is convenient to have available range-energy relationships for different particles in different media. Fig. 18-2 is a portion of the range-energy curve for protons in air. Standard conditions for dry air are taken to be 76 cm of Hg and 15° C. Curves such as this are usually constructed from experimental results. A point on the curve is obtained by measuring the range and also determining the energy in a magnetic deflection experiment, using particles from the same source. Extrapolation of the curve into regions where measurements have not been made is based upon the theory.

The range-energy curve for deuterons in air is not found in the literature because it is assumed that the range-energy curve for protons will be used. A deuteron is compared with a proton of the same initial velocity. The deuteron has twice the energy of the proton with which it is being compared. As the velocity decreases to zero for both particles, the velocities of the two particles remain the same if "corresponding" points on the two tracks are compared. The rate of energy loss is the same for both particles because it is not mass-dependent. The deuteron with twice the initial energy and the same rate of energy loss will go twice as far as the proton of the same initial velocity, that is, twice as far as a proton of one-half the energy. In formula form

$$R_d(W) = 2R_p(\tfrac{1}{2}W).$$ (18-10)

Similarly, the range-energy relation for He³ particles is unnecessary because the range-energy curve for He⁴ particles is usually available. If the range-energy relation for alpha particles is not available, it is possible to use the range-energy curve for protons, but it is necessary to consider that a doubly charged particle loses energy at four times the rate of a singly charged particle. There is also some inaccuracy in the procedure because the capture and loss of electrons by the moving particle as it slows down is not quite the same for a doubly charged particle as it is for a singly charged particle.

It might seem that identical particles, such as a beam of alpha particles of identical energies, should all go exactly the same distance in a uniform medium. This is not quite true. There are accidental fluctua-

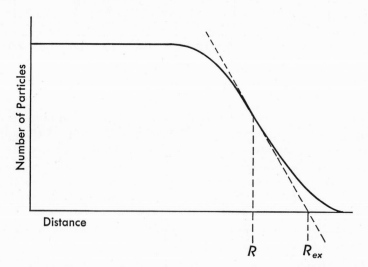

Fig. 18-3. The extrapolated range (R_{ex}) and the mean range (R).

tions in the transfer of energy to electrons, which cause some particles to go farther than others. The effect is called "straggling." Fig. 18-3 shows the number of particles in a beam as a function of the distance from the source. The distance traveled by half the particles is called the mean range. It is the mean range which is used in making up range-energy curves. An extrapolated range is obtained by drawing a tangent to the curve along its steepest portion and finding the intersection of this tangent with the x-axis. The difference between the extrapolated range and the mean range is a good indication of the amount of straggling which occurs. The difference has been exaggerated in Fig. 18-3 for illustration. The 5.30 Mev alpha particles from polonium have an extrapolated range of 3.90 cm and a mean range of 3.84 cm in air. The straggling is a relatively small effect.

Absorption of Fast Electrons

Beta rays or fast electrons have been excluded from the discussion up to this point. The electron has the same charge as a proton and the rate of energy loss in a medium would seem to be the same because the rate of energy loss was found to be independent of the mass of the moving particle. A one Mev electron has the same velocity as an 1836 Mev proton and the rate of energy loss of the two particles is not very different. Comparing an electron with a proton of the same energy, the electron has a much higher velocity. For that reason, the rate of energy loss is much smaller. Electrons, therefore, have much greater ranges than protons of the same energy. For example, a 5.30 Mev beta ray has a range close to one centimeter in solid aluminum.

Fig. 18-4 is a number-distance curve for electrons. The maximum range of the electrons is difficult to determine because of a background which is always present when the measurements are taken. The general shape of the curve is influenced by several factors, enumerated below, which do not affect more massive particles.

(1) Electrons are scattered by nuclear electric fields to a much greater extent than are heavier particles. This is primarily because they penetrate greater thicknesses of matter in which more nuclei are present. There is multiple scattering along the track of each particle which usually prevents it from achieving a large displacement in one direction, even though its length as measured along the track is not greatly affected.

(2) The heavy particles lose only a small fraction of their energy in any one collision with the electrons along their path. The beta rays,

colliding with particles of the same rest-mass, can (and sometimes do) lose a large fraction of their energy to a single electron. This tends to multiply the number of beta rays in the beam at the expense of their average energy.

(3) Electrons, during nuclear collisions, are subjected to higher accelerations than are more massive particles. There is a probability, which depends upon the acceleration, that some of the energy of the particle will be radiated as a high-energy photon. This is the same

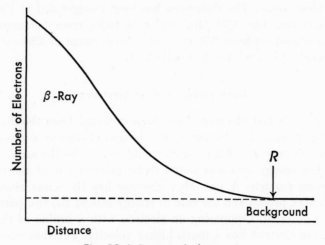

Fig. 18-4. Range of electrons.

mechanism that produces the continuous spectrum of X-rays at the target of an X-ray machine. It is the chief mechanism by which energy is lost when the energy of the electron is extremely high.

(4) The beta ray and the electron with which it collides are indistinguishable particles. In quantum mechanics, this affects the manner in which the collision must be treated. The theoretical formula for the rate of energy loss by a fast electron is quite different in form from Eq. (8), even for beta rays of non-relativistic velocities.

Absorption of Gamma Rays

The absorption of gamma rays in matter is markedly different from the absorption of fast charged particles. There is no gradual loss of energy. Those photons which do pass through a layer of matter are completely unaffected. A certain fraction of the photons are removed from the beam in rare catastrophic events. There are three kinds of events which remove photons. They are called:

(a) The photoelectric effect
(b) Compton scattering
(c) Pair production.

All three processes produce fast secondary electrons which dissipate energy along their tracks in the absorbing medium. Secondary photons are also produced in each process.

In the photoelectric effect, the entire energy of the photon is transferred to one electron in an atom of the absorber. The electron emerges from the atom with an energy w which is smaller than the energy $h\nu$ of the photon by an amount w_K that is equal to the energy required to remove it from the atom. That is,

$$w = h\nu - w_K. \tag{18-11}$$

One of several values, namely w_K, w_L, etc., may be needed depending upon which shell in the atom the electron originally occupied. A K-electron is most frequently involved. The subsequent filling of the K-shell by an electron from a higher energy state leads to emission of secondary photons which are identical with the characteristic X-ray spectrum of the absorbing element.

The Compton effect was discussed in Part I. When a photon is scattered by a free electron, its energy is shared between the recoiling electron and the scattered photon. The energy of the secondary fast electron is

$$w = hc/\lambda - hc/\lambda', \tag{18-12}$$

where the wavelength of the scattered photon λ' can be calculated from the Compton expression

$$\lambda' - \lambda = (h/m_0 c)(1 - \cos \theta). \tag{18-13}$$

The photons are scattered at various angles θ, and the recoiling electrons have accordingly various energies. The Compton electrons have a continuous distribution of energies up to a maximum value which occurs when the photon is scattered at 180° and the electron recoils in the forward direction. The electrons in the atoms of an absorbing material are not "free" electrons. If an electron is tightly bound, it does not recoil as a single particle, and the photon is scattered without change of wavelength. This ordinary scattering is important in the low energy X-ray region. At higher photon energies, the binding energy of any electron in the atom becomes negligibly small compared to the initial energy of the photon, and Compton scattering rather than ordinary scattering becomes predominant.

The first observation of pair production by Anderson in 1932 was a major scientific discovery. Anderson, using a cloud chamber to observe the tracks of charged particles, saw tracks of electrons which originated in the walls of the chamber and which occurred in pairs. A magnetic field was applied over the region occupied by the cloud chamber, causing the tracks to be bent into sections of circles. The opposite curvature of the two tracks showed that one of the particles was negative, the other positive, in charge. This verification of the opposite charges of the two electrons was historically the discovery of a new particle which is called the positive electron or positron. Electrons and positrons can be created in pairs and they can be annihilated in pairs. One is called the anti-particle of the other. The mass of the positive electron has been measured and found to be identical with the mass of the negative electron. The energy equivalent of either rest mass is equal to m_0c^2 or 0.51 Mev. The creation of the two particles requires an energy of 1.02 Mev and this is the minimum energy of a photon which can be absorbed in this way. The photon disappears in the process of pair production and its excess energy appears as kinetic energy of the two oppositely charged electrons. The energy is not always shared equally, but conservation of energy requires that

$$w_{\beta+} + w_{\beta-} = h\nu - 1.02 \text{ Mev.} \qquad (18\text{-}14)$$

The positive electron dissipates kinetic energy along its track in the ordinary way, usually coming to rest before it disappears. The positive electron, along with a negative electron in the absorber, disappear together in a process called "annihilation," the rest mass of the two particles changing to photons of equivalent energy, which are called annihilation radiation. In the common mode of annihilation, two photons each of energy 0.51 Mev are given off in opposite directions. The two photons of equal momentum in opposite directions have zero total momentum as is required by the law of conservation of momentum. There is evidence that three-photon annihilation sometimes occurs. There is also reason to believe that the electron pair, prior to annihilation, exists for an extremely short time as a hydrogen-like atom, the positive electron taking the role of the proton in an ordinary hydrogen atom. These temporary atoms are called positronium.

Apart from a knowledge of the processes involved, absorption of gamma rays can be described in terms of an absorption coefficient μ, which is defined as the fraction of the photons which are absorbed in a very thin absorber per unit thickness of absorber. The number of photons in a homogeneous beam is proportional to the intensity I

of the beam. Therefore,

$$\mu = -dI/I\ dx, \tag{18-15}$$

where dx is the thickness of the absorber. The absorption coefficient can be regarded as a constant if the plausible assumption is made that the number of photons absorbed is proportional to the thickness of the thin absorber and to the number of photons passing through it. The absorption coefficient can also be regarded as the sum of three absorption coefficients

$$\mu = \mu_1 + \mu_2 + \mu_3, \tag{18-16}$$

where μ_1 is the fraction of the photons absorbed per unit thickness of absorber as a result of photoelectric processes, and μ_2 and μ_3 are similar fractions for Compton scattering and pair production. Eq. (15) can be rewritten in the form

$$dI/I = -\mu\ dx.$$

Integration gives

$$\ln I = -\mu x + K.$$

In the absence of an absorber, $x = 0$ and the intensity is the original intensity of the beam I_0, therefore $K = \ln I_0$. Hence,

$$\ln I = -\mu x + \ln I_0$$

or

$$\ln (I/I_0) = -\mu x$$

and

$$I = I_0 e^{-\mu x}, \tag{18-17}$$

where e is the base of the natural logarithms. The intensity of a beam of gamma radiation falls off exponentially as the thickness of the absorber is increased. Any finite thickness will reduce the intensity by a calculable amount, but complete absorption does not occur.

Because the idea of a range is not applicable, it is convenient to speak of the "half-value thickness" in an absorber. The half-value thickness $x_{1/2}$ is the thickness of absorber which will reduce the beam to one-half of its initial intensity. When $x = x_{1/2}$, $I = \frac{1}{2}I_0$, and therefore,

$$\tfrac{1}{2}I_0 = I_0 e^{-\mu x_{1/2}}$$

or

$$x_{1/2} = -(\ln 0.5)/\mu = 0.693/\mu. \tag{18-18}$$

The half-value thickness can be readily calculated from the absorption coefficient, and vice versa. The nature of the exponential absorption is such that if three half-value thicknesses are used, the intensity is reduced by $(\frac{1}{2})^3 = \frac{1}{8}$. This is a convenient method of calculation when absorbers are being built up to protect personnel from sources of radiation. Some caution is required, however, because there may be several components of the radiation, each with its characteristic half-value thickness, and because secondary radiations such as scattered photons have not been considered.

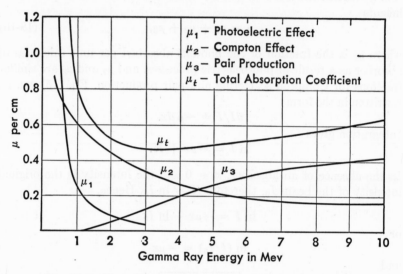

Fig. 18-5. Absorption coefficients of gamma rays in lead.

Absorption coefficients depend upon the nature of the absorbing material and upon the energy of the photons. The coefficient was regarded as a constant in integrating the absorption equation, because it does not depend upon the intensity I of the radiation nor upon the thickness x of the absorber. The dependence upon the energy of the photon is illustrated in Fig. 18-5 for lead absorbers. Photoelectric absorption is predominant at very low energies. It falls off very rapidly as the energy increases, and for energies of the order of one Mev it is less than the Compton scattering which falls off more slowly. Absorption by pair production is non-existent below 1.02 Mev and it increases not quite linearly with energy above that threshold. The total absorption coefficient, which is the sum of three partial absorption coefficients, shows a minimum at about 3 Mev. Higher energy gamma rays are more easily absorbed. The curves of Fig. 18-5 are based on theory. The theory of absorption gives the probability of occurrence in various atoms of the several absorption processes. The Klein-Nishina formula for the probability of Compton scattering is the most famous of these. The theory and experiment are considered to be in good agreement.

It was once customary to determine the energy of gamma rays by measuring the total absorption coefficient in lead. This is inaccurate, because the total absorption coefficient does not vary rapidly with energy except at low energies, and it is ambiguous because two different energies may correspond to the same absorption coefficient. The energies can be determined from the energies of the secondary electrons which they produce. The relation between electron and gamma ray energies has already been given for the three processes. There are many different methods of gamma ray spectroscopy, which differ in the means which are used to determine the energies of the secondary electrons.

The wavelengths of gamma rays can be determined by use of a diffracting crystal, making use of the Bragg relation $n\lambda = 2d \sin \theta$, as is done for X-rays. At high energies, when the wavelength is small, the Bragg reflection occurs for small angles between the face of the crystal and the incident beam. The reflected beam becomes weaker in intensity as the photon energy increases. For this reason, the method cannot be used when the photon energy is high or when the source of radiation is feeble. Because of the intensity problem, large crystals are used and they are bent to have a curved reflecting face so that the Bragg condition can be satisfied over a large region of the crystal when the incident beam is divergent. When diffraction data are available, the photon energy can be calculated from $h\nu = hc/\lambda$.

TABLE 18-2. HALF-VALUE THICKNESSES FOR 5 MEV GAMMA RAYS

H_2O	22.1	cm
Al	9.4	
Fe	2.88	
Pb	1.42	

Table 18-2 gives a few half-value thicknesses for the absorption of 5 Mev gamma rays in some common materials. They serve to illustrate the high penetrating power of gamma radiation.

Summary

Matter is not essentially impenetrable. Newton's first law applies to the fast particles in a beam. In the absence of forces between the atoms of an absorber and the fast particles, the latter continue to move in a straight line with constant momentum.

Absorbers are found to affect a beam of particles in three ways. In true absorption, a particle in the beam disappears. The photoelectric effect and the electron-pair production are true absorption processes. In scattering, a particle in the beam is deflected through an appreciable angle. Scattering may be regarded as equivalent to absorption in some circumstances, but this depends upon geometrical factors. If the beam of radiation is a narrow one, scattering through even a small angle may cause the particle to miss the detector. This is equivalent to absorption unless the particles scattered away from the detector are replaced by particles scattered toward the detector. The third absorption process is one in which the particles lose small amounts of energy repeatedly until the particle is brought to rest.

When true absorption and scattering are the absorption processes, the beam is absorbed exponentially as $I = I_0 e^{-\mu x}$ and the absorption coefficient is the important quantity. When the particle loses energy gradually, the idea of a range is applicable.

Massive charged particles are scattered as indicated in Chapter 17, but the number scattered through a significant angle is small, and no absorption coefficient need be considered. Uncharged particles do not have a range and the description is in terms of the absorption coefficient. A beam of fast electrons has an effective range, but few particles go the full distance without being scattered. For that reason, the absorption of beta rays is sometimes discussed in terms of an absorption coefficient. An absorption coefficient for beta rays has the significance of being the fraction of the beta rays which are lost by scattering per unit thickness of absorber.

Problems

1. What thickness of lead is required to reduce the intensity of a beam of 5 Mev gamma rays to 1% of its initial value?

(Ans.: 9.4 cm.)

2. For 1 Mev gamma rays, the absorption is mainly by the Compton effect process and should depend upon the number of electrons in the absorber. The half-value thickness for aluminum (density = 2.70 g/cm³, $Z = 13$, $A = 27$) is 4.1 cm. Calculate the thickness of water which would contain the same number of electrons per cm².

(Ans.: 9.6 cm. The tabulated half-value thickness of water for 1 Mev gamma rays is 9.8 cm.)

3. Find the range in air of a $_2$He^3 particle which has a kinetic energy of 3.0 Mev, making use of the range-energy curve for protons given in Fig. 18-2.

(Ans.: 1.7 cm.)

4. Suppose a photon with an initial energy of 8.0 Mev produces a Compton electron which recoils in the forward direction. Using the approximation that $\lambda \ll \lambda'$, calculate the energy of the photon scattered at 180°. What is the energy of the Compton electron?

(Ans.: 0.255 Mev, 7.75 Mev.)

19 ‖ Detection of Radiation

The operation of the instruments which are used to detect radiation depends upon the effects produced in matter by fast charged particles. This is true even for gamma ray detectors, because they are actuated by fast secondary electrons which are produced when gamma rays are absorbed in matter. Although the general mechanism of detection is the transfer of energy from the moving charged particle to the electrons in the absorbing material, three separate effects are of importance. They are:

(1) When the energy transfer removes electrons from molecules of a gas, positive and negative ions are produced and these electric charges can be separated if an electric field is applied. There are several different methods of detecting ionization in a gas.

(2) When the energy transfer raises electrons to higher energy states without entirely freeing them, de-excitation can occur with emission of photons of visible and ultraviolet light. In most liquids and solids, this de-excitation takes place in thermal collisions, without emission of photons, but there are a few exceptional substances which are classified as scintillators.

(3) A grain of silver bromide in a photographic plate can be changed to silver by a chemical reducing agent if it has been exposed to radiation which has raised an electron into a higher energy state in which it became trapped.

Photographic Plates

Photographic emulsions are used both for detecting the general level of radiation and for studying individual fast particles. The "film badge" is a photographic film protected from light, which is carried by

TABLE 19-1. LIST OF SYMBOLS USED IN CHAPTER 19

Symbol	Quantity Designated
i	electric current
R	resistance
V	potential difference
q	quantity of charge
C	capacitance

a person for two weeks, then developed. The observed blackening is a measure of the total quantity of radiation to which the person has been exposed in that time period.

Individual fast particles are found by examining an emulsion with a microscope of high magnifying power which shows the individual silver grains. A row of grains is evidence of a single charged particle. The number of grains per unit length of path sometimes identifies the particle, say as an alpha particle or as a proton. The length of the track gives the energy of the particle if a range-energy relationship is available for that particular emulsion.

The photographic technique is highly specialized. Standardized development techniques and calibration procedures are used. Special emulsions are available commercially. The silver bromide grains are thickly dispersed in a relatively small quantity of gelatin. The sensitivity of some plates is so great that a fast electron track is visible as a thin row of grains.

Collection of Ions

Ions produced in a gas by a steady beam of radiation can be collected continuously to give a steady current between the plates of an ionization chamber. The ionization chamber is similar in construction to a capacitor, with gas between the plates. The parallel plate construction is shown in Fig. 19-1, but two concentric cylinders are frequently used. The plates are usually housed in a metal box, which is

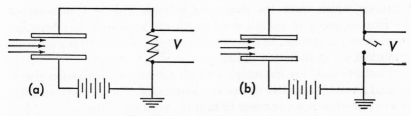

Fig. 19-1. Ionization chamber.

constructed to admit radiation from at least one direction and to keep
out undesirable air currents and to shield the plates from stray electrical effects. A battery or other voltage source is used to create an
electric field between the plates. The current which flows between plates
should be a measure of the intensity of the radiation and should not be
dependent upon the applied voltage. This is true when the applied
voltage is not too small. In weak electric fields the positive and negative ions tend to recombine inside the gas, but at higher fields with
more rapid collection there is not time for appreciable recombination
to occur. If the current which flows is large, it can be measured by
placing a galvanometer in the circuit. However, ionization currents are
frequently as small as 10^{-14} amperes or less and this is beyond the
range of sensitivity of a moving-coil galvanometer. A more sensitive
device is an electrometer, which is essentially a sensitive voltmeter, of
an electrostatic type which requires no current to operate it. There
are several types of electrometers and electrometer circuits, which have
been designed for this application. Two methods of connecting the
electrometer are commonly used. In Fig. 19-1a, the electrometer reads
the iR drop across a large resistor through which the ionization current
flows. The steady voltage is a measure of the intensity of the radiation.
In Fig. 19-1b, the voltmeter reads the rate of change of voltage across
the capacitor after the switch is opened. This is a measure of the
ionization current, since

$$dV/dt = d(q/C)/dt = (1/C)\, dq/dt = i/C, \qquad (19\text{-}1)$$

the quantity q representing the charge on one plate of an ionization
chamber of capacitance C. When only relative values of the intensity
of the radiation are of interest, the intensities are frequently recorded
in divisions per minute (dpm) on the voltmeter scale. A stop watch is
used to time the changing deflection of the voltmeter.

Personnel who work in radiation areas usually carry a pocket do-
simeter which is simply a well-insulated cylindrical capacitor in a housing which resembles a fountain pen. It is charged to a known voltage
at the beginning of the day. At the end of the day, it is connected to a
voltmeter which reads the change in voltage. This is a measure of
the total quantity of radiation to which the individual has been exposed during that time. As a matter of convenience, the voltmeter scale
is marked off in radiation units.

"Electroscopes" are instruments which combine an ionization chamber and a voltage sensitive device as a single unit. The well-known gold-
leaf electroscope is a voltmeter in that the position of the gold leaf is a
measure of the voltage difference between the leaf and the case. When it

is charged, there is an electric field which collects the ions which are produced between the leaf and the case. The gold-leaf electroscope is now seldom used, having been replaced by an improved instrument, the Lauritsen electroscope.

The Roentgen of X- or Gamma-Radiation

To set up a unit in terms of which quantities of radiation can be discussed, the roentgen has been defined as that quantity of X-rays or gamma rays which produces one electrostatic unit of ions of one sign in one cubic centimeter of an air-filled ionization chamber. One electrostatic unit is $1/(3 \times 10^9)$ coulombs of electric charge, and, since each ion has a charge of 1.60×10^{-19} coulombs, one roentgen produces 2.08×10^9 ion pairs per cm^3 of air under standard conditions of pressure and temperature. The measured ionization is produced along the tracks of fast secondary electrons, most of which originate in the walls of the chamber where photons are absorbed. To avoid a dependence upon wall materials, the roentgen is technically defined for an ideal chamber which has the sensitive volume surrounded only by air.

The intensity of radiation should be expressed in roentgens per unit time. "Milliroentgens per hour" are frequently used, as suitable units in which to express the intensities of gamma radiation which are not particularly hazardous. The electric current in an ionization chamber is proportional to the volume of the chamber when all parts of the gaseous volume are exposed to the same intensity of radiation.

It should be noted that the units discussed above are units of radiation absorption rather than radiation intensity. The distinction is not important when the absorption is proportional to the number of photons per square centimeter per second. However, the absorption coefficient would have to be considered in evaluating the true intensities.

Particle Detectors

Individual particles such as protons can be detected in an ionization chamber. The collection of ions along a short segment of a single proton track gives a very small voltage change. Fig. 19-2 shows the shape of the voltage pulse. The ion chamber C is recharged through a resistor R which is permanently connected. The rise of the pulse ΔV is nearly linear and the "rise time" depends upon the speed with which the ions are collected. The recovery is exponential with a time constant equal to CR. The pulse is amplified by use of a wide band electronic amplifier. Voltage amplification of the order of 10^6 is required to make a recordable pulse.

For fast counting, the duration of the pulse should be small. In high electric fields, the ions can be collected in times of the order of 10^{-4} sec. If pure argon or nitrogen is used in the ion chamber, collection times of the order of 10^{-6} sec can be obtained. The smaller figure is the collection time for the electrons of the ion pairs. Electrons are not collected in air because they become attached to oxygen molecules and are collected as massive negative ions.

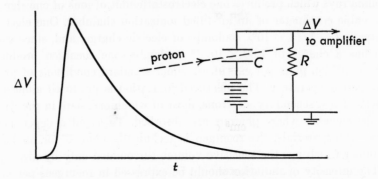

Fig. 19-2. Ionization chamber and representative single pulse.

Proportional Counter

The proportional counter is a cylindrical capacitor with a fine wire along the axis as the inner electrode. The outer cylinder is made negative with respect to the wire so that electrons which are produced by radiation will move inward. Between coaxial cylinders, the electric field varies inversely as the distance from the axis, and it is thus very strong in the immediate neighborhood of the wire. Electrons pick up enough energy in the strong field to cause further ionization when they collide with neutral gas molecules. This ionization by collision produces more electrons and if the process continues, an avalanche of electrons reaches the wire. This multiplication of electrons increases the size of the pulse. The external amplifier need not have as large a gain to make a recordable pulse. This is a considerable advantage because pulse amplifiers with gains of 10^6 are difficult to operate.

Fig. 19-3 shows the way in which pulse size varies with the voltage applied to the proportional counter. In the region where the pulse size is independent of the voltage, the instrument acts as an ordinary ionization chamber. At higher voltages, there is gas amplification, and it is possible to amplify the pulse by a factor of 100 or more without loss of

proportionality between the number of electrons in the avalanche and the amount of initial ionization. Proportional counters are usually operated at pressures below atmospheric to reduce the number of electron collisions and thereby increase the energy available for ionization in any one collision.

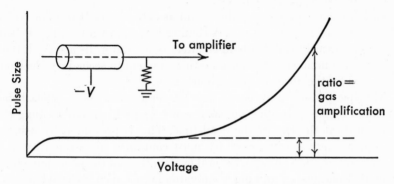

Fig. 19-3. Variation of the pulse size with voltage in a proportional counter.

Geiger Counter

A Geiger counter is exactly like a proportional counter in construction, but it is operated with higher applied voltage. The gas amplification is very high and the pulses need little further amplification, sometimes none at all. The Geiger counter is, however, more than just a proportional counter because other effects besides multiplication by electron collision become important. In a Geiger counter, ionization spreads along the entire length of the central wire. The spreading is caused by ultraviolet light, which is emitted from atoms which have been excited by electron collisions and is absorbed some distance away, with emission of photoelectrons which start new electron avalanches. As ion pairs are formed by collision, the mobile electrons are collected in a fraction of a microsecond, whereas the more massive positive ions scarcely move in that time. A cloud of positive charge accumulates in the space near the wire, and this space charge has the effect of reducing the strong electric field near the wire. When it is sufficiently reduced, no further multiplication by collision can occur. The collection of electrons ceases, but the voltage of the wire continues to change as a consequence of the motion of positive charge away from it. About 100 μsec is required for the positive charge to reach the outer cylinder.

A minimum threshold voltage is required for Geiger pulses. A good counter behaves properly over a region of about 100 v above the threshold, each pulse being initiated by an ionizing particle from the source of radiation. After each pulse there is a "dead-time" of the order of 100 μsec during which a second pulse cannot occur. The pulse size is determined by the applied voltage. At a fixed voltage the pulses are all of the same size no matter how small the amount of ionization produced by the triggering particle.

Geiger counters are especially useful as detectors of beta rays, which have tracks of low ion density. A counter with thin walls to admit beta rays is frequently called a beta counter. When the walls are thick they are called gamma counters because they respond to secondary electrons produced by the absorption of gamma rays.

Multiple pulsing may occur in a Geiger counter, each pulse being initiated by the preceding one as a result of positive ions striking the outer wall at the end of the dead-time. This is prevented by using a self-quenching gas mixture which must contain a small quantity of a polyatomic gas or a halogen. Several explanations of the effect have been offered. Counters containing a polyatomic gas such as ethyl alcohol have a finite life, because the gas is slowly decomposed by the discharge and multiple pulsing begins to occur.

The Cloud Chamber

The cloud chamber was invented by C. T. R. Wilson, as a result of his studies of the condensation of water into droplets. He found that the normal formation of fog, which occurs whenever the relative humidity exceeds 100%, depends upon the existence of dust particles as centers of condensation. In the absence of dust, spontaneous condensation does not occur until the degree of supersaturation reaches 800%. Electric charges, as ions, begin to act as centers of condensation at supersaturations in excess of 400%.

A humidity of about 700% may be achieved momentarily by a sudden expansion of a gas saturated with water vapor, in a time of the order of 0.01 sec. Tracks of fast charged particles are rendered visible by formation of water droplets along them and this sensitivity persists for times of the order of 0.1 sec.

The short sensitive-time of the cloud chamber makes for slowness in the accumulation of data. The compensating advantage is that the complete presentation of the tracks clarifies ideas about the behavior of the particles. When long range particles such as beta rays are studied, a magnetic field is used and the radius of curvature is readily computed from the curvature of the track.

Conventional cloud chambers are less used than formerly because of the development of the photographic plate technique which gives the same sort of information. A continuously sensitive cloud chamber has been invented and is now sometimes used. It consists of a vertical glass cylinder with metal top and bottom plates. The top plate is at room temperature, and the bottom plate is chilled with dry ice. Ethyl alcohol vapor is introduced at the top from saturated blotting paper. The vapor

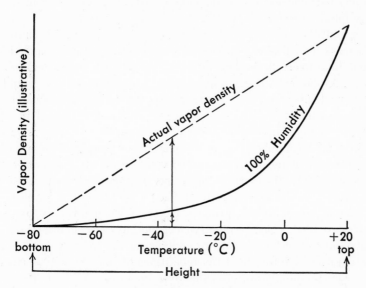

Fig. 19-4. Vapor density diagram for continuous cloud chamber.

density of alcohol as a function of temperature is plotted in Fig. 19-4, from room temperature down to $-80°$ C, the temperature attainable with dry ice. When a uniform temperature gradient is established, the abscissa can also represent the height in the chamber. The vapor density curve gives the actual vapor density near the top and bottom plates where the relative humidity is 100%. At intermediate points the actual vapor density is given by the dotted line. This is straight because diffusion should lead to a uniform concentration gradient, or perhaps the line is not quite straight if the dependence of rate of diffusion upon temperature is considered. The humidity is seen to be above 100% at all points in the chamber, and there is a region below the middle of the chamber where the relative humidity is high enough to cause condensation upon ions.

The Scintillation Technique

An alpha particle striking a zinc sulphide screen gives a flash of light which is visible to the dark-adapted human eye. Very pure zinc sulphide cannot be used. The light emission results from a certain type of imperfection in the crystalline structure, and these imperfections are made by adding small quantities of certain impurities. The early work on alpha particle scattering was done by counting flashes from such a zinc sulphide screen with the aid of a low-power magnifier.

The scintillation technique fell into disuse for a period because the counting of light flashes by eye was laborious and slow. A method was needed to convert flashes of light into pulses of electric current or voltage. A photocell, making use of the photoelectric effect, would do this in principle, but its sensitivity was too small for practical use. A new instrument, called the photomultiplier, was invented in 1936. It consists of a photocell as its first stage, followed by a system for multiplying the number of emitted electrons by a large factor. Electrons, after acceleration by about 100 volts of potential difference, can be directed onto the surface of a metal where collisions with the surface liberate secondary electrons. The number of secondary electrons can exceed the number of primary electrons when specially prepared surfaces are used. These secondary electrons have low energies, but they in turn can be accelerated toward another surface where further multiplication occurs. With about ten repetitions of this effect, it is feasible to increase the number of electrons by a factor of a million. The pulse obtained at the final collector in the photomultiplier can be further amplified by an external electronic pulse amplifier to give a pulse of recordable size. A photomultiplier tube can be converted into an alpha particle detector by coating the end of the tube, near the photoelectric surface, with a thin layer of powdered zinc sulphide which has been suitably activated.

The discovery that anthracene was a good scintillator made it possible to detect beta rays by scintillations. Because of the relatively long range of the beta rays, it is necessary to collect light from a large volume of material to obtain pulses of sufficient size. Anthracene is obtainable as a single crystal which is transparent to its emitted light. By attaching a single crystal, perhaps one cm thick, to the end of a photomultiplier tube and enclosing it in a foil just thick enough to absorb alpha particles, a beta ray counter is obtained. Although this counter is not more efficient than a Geiger counter, the pulse sizes depend upon the energies of the beta rays instead of being all of the same size, and this makes possible a certain degree of energy discrimination. The pulses can be fed into an electronic circuit, called a "kicksorter" or "pulse-height analyzer," which passes on to the recorder only those pulses which fall in a predetermined interval of size.

Gamma rays too can be counted by use of the anthracene crystal, the flashes of light being produced along the tracks of fast secondary electrons. For efficient counting, it is desirable to use a crystal which absorbs a large fraction of the gamma rays incident upon it. Single crystals of sodium iodide are commonly used. The sodium iodide is activated by adding about 0.1% of thallium iodide before growing the single crystal from the molten material. The presence of iodine (an element of high atomic number) makes the crystal a good absorber of gamma rays. The high transparency of the single crystal to light makes it possible to use very large crystals as detectors. Crystals nine inches in diameter and nine inches long are commercially available. However, one inch crystals or three inch crystals are adequate for many uses.

When a crystal is used as a detector of monoenergetic gamma rays, pulses of different sizes are obtained, the size depending upon the energy of the secondary electron produced in the crystal by absorption of the gamma ray. Photoelectrons have the full energy of the gamma rays, except for the small loss of energy in escaping from the iodine atom. Compton recoil electrons have a continuous distribution of energies. The energy is less than the energy of the initial gamma ray by an amount equal to the energy of the scattered photon. The scattered photons vary in energy as a function of the angle through which they are scattered. The two electrons of an electron pair have 1.02 Mev less

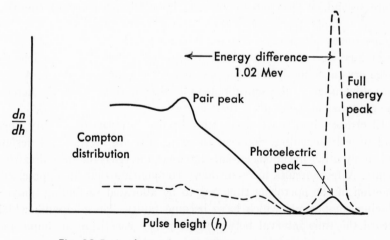

Fig. 19-5. Analysis of a scintillation counter record.

energy than the incident gamma ray. Fig. 19-5 shows the expected pulse height distribution from absorption of monoenergetic gamma rays. The ordinate dn/dh is the number of pulses per unit interval of pulse height. The solid curve is for a single small crystal. The dotted curve is for a crystal which is large enough to absorb many of the Compton scattered photons and most of the annihilation photons. A small peak appears at a position which indicates that one of the annihilation photons has been absorbed. Absorption of both annihilation photons makes a pulse which falls in the photoelectric peak. The enhancement of the full energy peak is a desirable consequence of using very large crystals.

Summary

The Geiger counter is the most sensitive detector in the sense that it responds to the smallest absorption of energy. A single ion pair is enough to initiate a pulse. However, different particles give pulses which are not distinguishable, if a mixture of particles is allowed to enter the gaseous region. With a proportional counter, on the other hand, it is possible to count particles of one kind, say alpha particles in the presence of beta rays, because the pulse size is proportional to the amount of ionization which initiated the pulse.

Geiger counters count only about 2% of the gamma rays which pass through them. This is because a count occurs only when a secondary electron enters the gaseous region. The secondary electrons are produced by absorption of gamma rays in the walls of the counter. If the walls are made thicker to absorb more gamma rays, they then absorb more secondary electrons. This limit upon the efficiency of counting does not apply to the scintillometer counting of gamma rays. The transparency of the crystal to emitted light makes it possible to count secondary electrons from a large volume of material. If a sufficiently large crystal is used, the efficiency of counting becomes 100%. A further advantage of the scintillometer is that it simultaneously detects the photons and determines their energy.

Electronic circuits are used with all pulse detectors to amplify, sort, and record the pulses. Some of these circuits are of standard design, but many other ingenious circuits have been devised for special experiments. A few circuits have so many components that an appreciable fraction of the operating time has to be allocated to finding and replacing components which have become faulty. Those circuits which record the time interval between two pulses constitute an important class. Time intervals as small as one millimicrosecond are measurable. A circuit which gives an output pulse only when two pulses in different detectors occur simultaneously is called a coincidence circuit.

The detection techniques which give a complete record of all events along the track of a single particle are especially useful in exploratory work. The cloud chamber and the photographic emulsion are used in this way. Many basic discoveries have been made with these two instruments. A third instrument called the bubble chamber is of the same type. In it, the path of a charged particle in a liquid is made visible by the formation of a track of vapor bubbles as it passes. A short sensitive period is initiated by a piston which suddenly attempts to expand the liquid.

Problems

1. The gold leaf of an electroscope is observed through a telescope which has a scale with divisions of arbitrary length in its eyepiece. Changing the applied voltage from 150 to 300 volts changes the deflection of the leaf by 55 divisions. The housing of the electroscope is a cube, 10 cm along each edge. The capacitance of the leaf is 1.0×10^{-12} farads. After being charged, the leaf collapses at the rate of one division in 9 minutes. Calculate:
   a. the ionization current in amperes,
   b. the average number of ion pairs formed per cm^3 per sec,
   c. the intensity of the radiation in milliroentgens per hour.

   (Ans.: 5.0×10^{-15} amp;

   31 ion pairs cm^{-3} sec^{-1};

   0.054 mr/hr.)

2. Comparing the amount of ionization produced in air with the energy lost by ionizing radiations, it is found that an average of 32.5 ev of energy is absorbed for each ion pair produced. Show that one roentgen is therefore equivalent to the absorption of 83 ergs per gram of air. The density of standard air is 0.001293 g/cm^3.

3. From the value 32.5 ev energy loss per ion pair formed, calculate the number of ion pairs formed along the track of a 5 Mev alpha particle. If the negative ion of each pair is collected, what total electric charge is obtained? If the charge is collected on a 30 $\mu\mu F$ capacitor, what is the voltage change?

   (Ans.: 1.54×10^5 ion pairs;

   2.46×10^{-14} coulombs;

   8.2×10^{-4} volts.)

4. A Geiger counter gives 1250 counts per second with radioactive source A and 1250 counts per second with radioactive source B. When both A and B are present, 2210 counts per second are obtained. Calculate the deadtime of the counter. This is also called the resolving time for single counts.

   (Ans.: 105 μsec.)

5. A crystal detector of 2.62 Mev gamma rays gives "full energy" pulses which, after amplification, have an average amplitude of 73.2 volts. What is the expected amplitude of pulses caused by:

a. pair production in the crystal;

b. Compton scattering through 180° in the crystal;

c. back scattering. (A so-called "back scattering" peak is caused by absorption in the crystal of photons which have been scattered through 180° in other materials.)

(Ans.: 44.7, 66.7, and 6.5 volts.)

20 || Spontaneous Transformations

Atoms were once regarded as indivisible and immutable units of matter. With the discovery of electrons and nuclei, it became clear that atoms are immutable only as long as their nuclei do not change. It is possible to remove electrons by ionizing processes, but positively charged ions remain, and these eventually return to a neutral state by picking up electrons.

That permanent changes in atoms occur spontaneously was discovered by Rutherford and Soddy. Pure elements of short life can be separated from uranium and thorium ores. As the quantity of the element diminishes with time, a second element with different chemical properties is formed. The change from the "parent" element to the "daughter" element is accompanied by the emission of alpha rays or of beta rays.

An isotope of an element can be designated by the symbol $_ZX^A$, where Z is the atomic number of the element, A is the mass number, and X is the chemical symbol appropriate to the element of that atomic number. For example, $_{92}U^{238}$ represents the common isotope of uranium. When an alpha particle is emitted, the nuclear charge is reduced by two units and the mass number by four units. The decay of uranium 238 by alpha particle emission can be represented by

$$_{92}U^{238} \rightarrow _2He^4 + _{90}Th^{234}.$$

When a beta ray is emitted, the mass number does not change. Conservation of charge requires that emission of a negative electron be accompanied by an increase by one unit of the positive charge Z of the nucleus. The decay of thorium 234, which is a negative beta ray emitter, can be represented by

$$_{90}Th^{234} \rightarrow \beta^- + _{91}Pa^{234}.$$

TABLE 20-1. LIST OF SYMBOLS USED IN CHAPTER 20

Symbol	Name	Quantity Designated
Z		atomic number
A		mass number
β^-	beta minus	fast negative electron
β^+	beta plus	fast positive electron
ν	nu	neutrino
λ	lambda	decay constant
N		number of atoms present at time t
T		half-life
I		intensity of radiation
a		rate of production of atoms
W		energy
M		exact mass of an atom
PE		potential energy
Ze		nuclear charge
ϵ_0	epsilon sub zero	permittivity of free space
r		distance from center

The daughter element has the chemical properties of element 91, which is called protactinium.

Radioactive Series

Some radioactive parent atoms decay into daughter atoms which are stable. In other cases, the daughter atoms are themselves radioactive, and are the parent atoms in another decay process. An example has already been given. Thorium 234 can be chemically separated from uranium. The sample of pure thorium emits beta rays until it has been entirely converted into protactinium 234. The latter atoms are also radioactive and successive decays are observed until a final stable product $_{82}Pb^{206}$ is formed.

The details of the series decay are illustrated in Fig. 20-1. The radium 226 isotope is found in this series. This is the well-known isotope of radium which has been much used as a source of radiation for medical purposes. At one time, uranium ores were mined solely for the purpose of extracting radium, which sold at about $25,000 a gram. A sample of radium contains all the radioactive substances below it in the series because they are formed as the radium disintegrates. Another nuclide of special interest is $_{83}Bi^{214}$ which decays in two ways, 0.04% of the atoms by alpha particle emission, the others by beta particle emission. This is called "branching."

Three radioactive series are found in natural ores. The "actinium series" starts at $_{92}U^{235}$ and ends at the stable nuclide $_{82}Pb^{207}$. Because the original parent is an isotope of uranium, forming 0.7% of normal uranium, the members of the actinium series are always found in uranium ores, but in low abundance. Thorium ores show a series beginning with $_{90}Th^{232}$ and terminating with stable $_{82}Pb^{208}$. The three natural

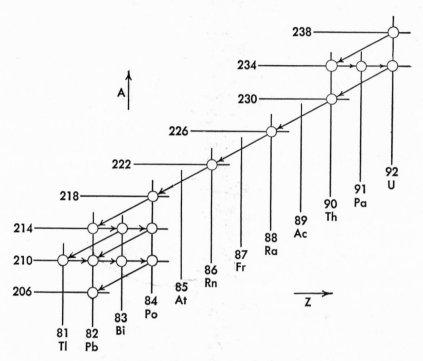

Fig. 20-1. The uranium-radium series.

series all occur in the region of heavy elements. Bismuth is the heaviest element which has any stable isotopes.

Among lighter elements, there are isolated cases of natural radioactivity. For example, potassium has been found to be weakly radioactive. This has been traced to the isotope of mass number 40 which is present as 0.012% of ordinary potassium and which emits beta rays. Sea water is weakly radioactive because of its potassium content.

All known elements have radioactive isotopes, but few of them exist in natural ores. Some of them can be produced by bombarding targets with atomic projectiles, and this will be discussed in a later chapter. There seems to be no real distinction between natural and artificial radioactivity. The remainder of this chapter will be concerned with radioactive decay in general.

Radioactive Decay

A "decay constant" λ can be defined by the formula

$$\lambda = -dN/N\,dt, \tag{20-1}$$

where N is the number of radioactive atoms present in a sample, and $-dN$ is the number which decay in the time dt. The quantity λ so defined is a mortality rate. In animal populations, the mortality rate depends upon the age of the group under consideration. The decay constant for atoms is found to be a constant which is characteristic of a particular species of atom, and this implies that no changes analogous to aging take place in atoms up until the time of their decay.

The equation $dN/N = -\lambda\,dt$ can be solved by integrating both sides, which gives

$$\ln N = -\lambda t + C.$$

The constant of integration can be evaluated by calling N_0 the number of atoms present at a time which is arbitrarily chosen as $t = 0$. Therefore, $C = \ln N_0$ and $\ln N/N_0 = -\lambda t$, or after taking antilogarithms

$$N = N_0 e^{-\lambda t}, \tag{20-2}$$

where e is the base of natural logarithms.

The half-life T of a radioactive material is defined as the time required for the number of atoms to fall to one-half of the initial number. Putting $N = N_0/2$ and $t = T$ into Eq. (2), we get

$$\tfrac{1}{2}N_0 = N_0 e^{-\lambda T}$$

or

$$T = 0.693/\lambda. \tag{20-3}$$

It is customary in radioactive tables to quote half-lives instead of decay constants. Fig. 20-2 shows a decay curve. The half-lives differ greatly for different radioactive nuclides. Half-lives as long as 10^{14} years have been reported. At the other extreme, some half-lives are too short to measure directly and the decay is practically instantaneous.

The intensity I of the radiations from a radioactive source is the number of alpha or beta particles emitted per second. This is equal to the number of atoms decaying per second $-dN/dt$, which is proportional to the number of atoms present, according to Eq. (1). Accordingly the intensity varies with time in the same way that the number of atoms varies, and

$$I = I_0 e^{-\lambda t}. \tag{20-4}$$

The decay constant of a radioactive sample can be determined experimentally, using a counter to determine the intensity of the radiations

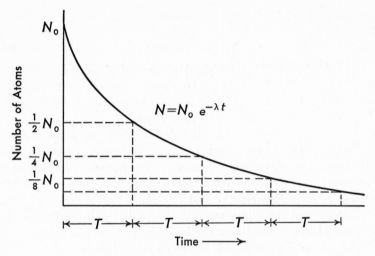

Fig. 20-2. Radioactive decay curve.

as a function of time. When the logarithm of the intensity is plotted against the time, the experimental points should lie on a straight line

$$\ln I = -\lambda t + \ln I_0. \tag{20-5}$$

The negative slope of this line is the decay constant of the sample, from which the half-life can be computed. A half-life can be determined in this way only if it is comparable to the duration of the experiment. Other methods must be used for very long and very short half-lives.

Very long half-lives can be determined by counting decay particles from a weighed quantity m of the pure substance. Eq. (1) is used to evaluate λ. The number of atoms N is equal to mN_A/A where A is the atomic weight and N_A is Avogadro's number. A count of the number of decay particles emitted per second gives $-dN/dt$. The sample must be very thin to avoid self-absorption of the decay particles. This direct determination of the decay constant gives the half-life by computation. The half-life of uranium 238 is found to be 4.50×10^9 years, and that of thorium 232, 1.39×10^{10} years. The existence of uranium and thorium ores in the earth's crust is presumably connected with their long half-lives. They have not entirely decayed in the period of several billion years that the earth may have existed.

Radium is found only in uranium ores since it is produced as a consequence of the decay of uranium. The rate of production of radium can be taken as the rate of decay of uranium. Radium decays at the same rate as it is produced in old ores where equilibrium conditions exist. Thus,

$$-(dN/dt)_U = -(dN/dt)_{Ra}$$

and

$$\lambda_U N_U = \lambda_{Ra} N_{Ra}. \tag{20-6}$$

The ratio N_U/N_{Ra} can be determined by a chemical analysis of a sample of the ore. This gives the ratio of the decay constants and the ratio of the half-lives. The half-life of uranium has already been given. The half-life of radium is found to be 1612 years.

Very short half-lives, such as the half-life of the polonium isotope of mass number 214 which is 140 μsec, were difficult to determine before the advent of fast electronic techniques. This isotope is formed by the emission of a fast electron from a bismuth isotope of mass number 214. The time interval between the fast electron which signals the formation of Po^{214} and the alpha ray which signals its decay is measured. This time interval is the life of the individual atom. The average value of the individual lives is called the "mean life." This is a little different from the half-life. It can be shown from the decay equations that the mean life is $1/\lambda$. The factor 0.693 converts a mean life to a half-life.

A radioactive material may be produced by decay of a parent or it may be produced in a target as a result of a bombardment. Considering both production and decay, a more general equation would be

$$dN/dt = a - \lambda N,$$

where a is the rate of production in atoms per unit time and λN is the rate of decay in the same units. The rate of production can be treated as a constant if the sample grows from a parent of such long life that its quantity does not change appreciably during the time under consideration, or if the sample is produced in a target under steady bombardment. If a is constant, the equation

$$dN/(a - \lambda N) = dt$$

can be solved by integrating both sides. This gives

$$(-1/\lambda) \ln (a - \lambda N) = t + C.$$

Suppose the zero of time is taken when there are no atoms present at the beginning of the bombardment. Then $N = 0$ when $t = 0$, and $C = (-1/\lambda) \ln a$. The equation becomes

$$\ln (1 - \lambda N/a) = -\lambda t$$

or, after taking antilogarithms and rearranging,

$$N = (a/\lambda)(1 - e^{-\lambda t}). \qquad (20\text{-}7)$$

Fig. 20-3 shows the growth of the radioactive material. For a bom-

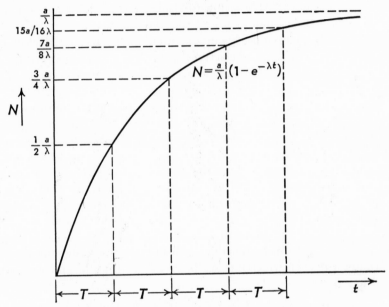

Fig. 20-3. Growth of a radioactive material for constant production rate.

bardment of infinite duration, an equilibrium condition is reached when the rate of production is equal to the rate of decay, that is when $a = \lambda N$. Fifty percent of the maximum obtainable quantity is produced in a bombardment which lasts for a time equal to the half-life of the radioactive element. There is little to be gained by prolonging the bombardment beyond about five half-lives.

Alpha Particle Emission

Radioactive decay is one of the processes in which rest mass is converted into another form of energy. An atom, initially at rest, emits a high-speed particle. There is some energy of recoil also, in an amount necessary to conserve momentum. The total energy evolution is equal to the decrease in total rest mass. An example is the decay of radium, $_{88}\text{Ra}^{226} \rightarrow {}_2\text{He}^4 + {}_{86}\text{Rn}^{222}$. The kinetic energy of the alpha particle plus that of the recoiling radon is found to be 4.88 Mev. As stated in Chapter 3, $W = Mc^2$ implies that 1 kg is equivalent to 9×10^{16} joules. Using electron-volts instead of joules, and using atomic mass units instead of kilograms, the equivalence of mass and energy can be expressed by

$$1 \text{ amu} = 931.1 \text{ Mev.} \tag{20-8}$$

The evolution of 4.88 Mev of kinetic energy means that the rest mass decreases by 0.00525 amu.

When a radium atom decays into an atom of radon, the reduction of nuclear charge releases two electrons from the extra nuclear structure of the neutral atom. However, two electrons are picked up by the alpha particle as it slows down and becomes a helium atom. The rest masses, before and after the decay, are those of the neutral atoms. A bare radium nucleus would be expected to decay with the same evolution of energy, because the change of mass is the same whether atomic or nuclear masses are used. The mass of a nucleus can be obtained from the atomic mass by subtracting the mass of Z electrons, although an approximation is involved in neglecting the small mass equivalent of the energies of the electrons in their atomic orbits.

The details of the process of alpha particle emission can also be discussed in terms of the energy of the alpha particle. Fig. 20-4 shows the potential energy PE as a function of distance between the alpha particle and the nucleus which it is leaving. At large distances, the coulomb repulsion gives

$$PE = 2Ze^2/4\pi\epsilon_0 r.$$

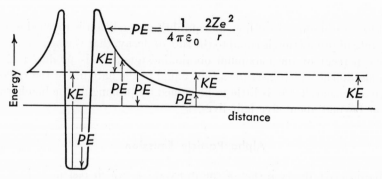

Fig. 20-4. The potential energy of an alpha particle near a nucleus.

At small distances, attractive nuclear forces cause the curve to bend downward. The shape and depth of the cup cannot be drawn exactly without a detailed knowledge of the nuclear forces. The dotted line is the energy of the emitted alpha particles, which must be constant. At very large distances, the energy is all kinetic; at some point the energy is all potential if the total energy of the alpha particle is not excessive. Closer in, there is a region where the law of conservation of energy could be satisfied only if the kinetic energy $\frac{1}{2}Mv^2$ could be negative. Inside the nucleus, there is an allowed region where the kinetic energy is again positive. According to classical mechanics, an alpha particle of that energy would not escape through the forbidden region of negative kinetic energy.

With the development of wave (or quantum) mechanics, it became possible to compute a probability that the alpha particle would pass through the barrier in a unit time. The probability of barrier penetration per unit time is equal to the decay constant λ. It was possible to bring the theoretical predictions into agreement with the experimental decay constants by making plausible assumptions about the radius of the nuclear well and about the state of the alpha particle inside the nucleus before its emission. The theory, developed by Gamov and by Condon and Gurney, was one of the great early successes of wave mechanics. The radii required by the theory are of the order of 9×10^{-15} m for the heavy nuclei which emit alpha particles.

Geiger and Nuttall showed that the half-life for an alpha emitter is primarily dependent upon the energy of the alpha particle. They did this by plotting the observed half-lives against the observed energies of decay and finding that the points fell on a smooth curve. Actually they obtained a straight line by plotting the logarithm of the decay constant against the logarithm of the range of the alpha particle in air. A slightly different straight line was found for the alpha emitters in thorium ores as compared to alpha emitters in the uranium-radium series. The strong dependence upon energy is illustrated by two of the decay constants mentioned above. The uranium isotope U^{238} gives alpha particles of 4.21 Mev kinetic energy and has a half-life of 4.50×10^9 years, whereas Po^{214} emits 7.68 Mev alpha particles and has a half-life of only 150 μsec. The wave-mechanical theory of barrier penetration is in accordance with the strong energy dependence observed.

Beta Decay Processes

Another type of radioactive decay is the spontaneous emission of a fast electron from the nucleus. This was once taken as evidence that electrons are present in nuclei. The current view is that the electron is created at the moment of emission.

The beta rays are bent in magnetic fields to obtain their momenta and the momenta are converted to energies by use of the formulas of relativistic mechanics. The energy spectra of the beta rays show continuous distributions and are in this respect unlike the energy spectra of alpha rays which show unique energies. These spectra are plotted, as shown in Fig. 20-5, in such a way that the area under the

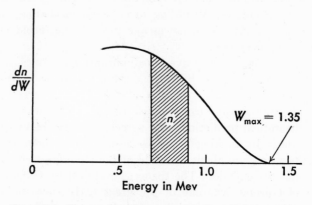

Fig. 20-5. The energy spectrum of the K^{40} beta rays.

curve represents the number of particles with energies in a corresponding energy interval.

The continuous beta ray spectrum raises a question about the law of conservation of energy in the following way. Parent atoms, which are all identical, decay into daughter atoms, which are all identical. The decrease in the rest mass is the same in every instance, and the kinetic energy evolved should be always the same. Pauli suggested a solution of the difficulty by proposing that another particle was emitted simultaneously with the electron and that the energy was shared between the two in a variable ratio. The other particle is now called the neutrino ν. It has very small (probably zero) rest mass like a photon, but, unlike a photon, it has no properties which make it readily detectable. Only recently have detectors been made sensitive enough to record a few pulses attributable to a large neutrino flux.

The energy evolved in beta decay is the sum of three energies; the kinetic energy of the fast electron, the energy of the neutrino, and the energy of recoil of the daughter atom. When the decaying atom is at rest, the momenta of the three particles must add vectorially to be zero. Experiments have been performed in which the momenta of the fast electron and the recoiling atom have been determined in magnitude and direction. The vector sum of the two was not zero, thus establishing the fact that a neutrino is emitted in a definite direction with a momentum equal and opposite to the sum of the two measured momenta.

Although the recoiling atom has a momentum which is of comparable magnitude to the momenta of the emitted particles, it is a relatively massive particle and its kinetic energy is very much less. The energy evolution can to a good approximation be taken as the sum of the energy of the electron and the neutrino. The electron has its greatest energy when the neutrino has negligible energy, and the maximum or end-point energy $\hat{W}$ of the beta ray spectrum can be taken as the total energy evolution in a disintegration. For example, the decay of potassium 40, which can be written

$$_{19}K^{40} \rightarrow \beta^- + \nu + {}_{20}Ca^{40},$$

results in a total energy evolution of 1.35 Mev, as shown in Fig. 20-5.

The decrease of rest mass is the difference between the masses of the parent atom K^{40} and the daughter atom Ca^{40}. Although the fast electron comes to rest at a considerable distance, it or another electron is needed by the daughter to become a neutral atom. Equating the decrease of rest mass to the energy evolution,

$$M_P - M_D = \hat{W}(\beta^-), \tag{20-9}$$

where M_P and M_D are the masses of the parent and daughter atoms and $\hat{W}(\beta^-)$ is the end point of the beta ray spectrum. If the mass of the daughter is known, say from mass spectrographic measurements, the mass of the parent atom can be determined from the end point of its beta ray spectrum. This is the usual method of determining atomic masses of radioactive atoms.

When radioactive nuclides began to be produced in bombardments, some of them were found to emit negative beta rays, while others emitted fast positive electrons. Examples are:

$$_6C^{14} \rightarrow \beta^- + \nu + {}_7N^{14} \qquad (T = 5600 \text{ yr})$$

and

$$_7N^{13} \rightarrow \beta^+ + \nu + {}_6C^{13} \qquad (T = 9.93 \text{ min}).$$

The energy spectrum of the positive beta rays is also continuous, implying that a neutrino is emitted in company with each fast positive electron. The two kinds of neutrino are not necessarily identical, and one of them is sometimes called an antineutrino.

Each positive beta ray is annihilated along with a negative electron, usually after it comes to rest, and two annihilation photons, each of energy 0.511 Mev, are produced. The evolution of energy in the disintegration is given by the end point of the positive beta ray spectrum, and the over-all evolution of energy is $\hat{W}(\beta^+) + 1.022$ Mev. The over-all decrease in mass is $M_P - M_D$ as before, the decrease of nuclear charge freeing an extra-nuclear electron and the annihilation process using up one negative electron, although probably not the same one. Again equating the decrease in rest mass to the energy evolution, we get

$$M_P - M_D = \hat{W}(\beta^+) + 1.022 \text{ Mev.} \qquad (20\text{-}10)$$

Obviously, the emission of positive beta rays is energetically impossible unless the mass of the parent atom exceeds that of the daughter by 1.022 Mev, or 0.001098 amu.

Emission of a positive electron reduces the nuclear charge by one unit, and the same change would take place if a negative electron is absorbed by the nucleus. Absorption of negative electrons is observed, an example being

$$_4\text{Be}^7 + e^- \rightarrow {}_3\text{Li}^7 + \nu \qquad (T = 43 \text{ days}).$$

The absorbed electron comes from the extranuclear structure, usually from the K-shell because these electrons are closer to the nucleus. The process is called "electron capture" or "K-capture." The emission of a neutrino has been verified by observing the recoil of the daughter atom. Because of the difficulty of detecting neutrinos and because of the low energy of the recoiling atoms, K-electron capture is usually observed indirectly. Following K-capture, there is a vacancy in the K-shell of the atom and an outer electron falls into it with emission of a photon of the characteristic X-ray spectrum of the element. Characteristic X-rays are readily detectable, at least for the heavier elements.

The total energy evolution is the energy of the neutrino $W(\nu)$ plus the energy $W(K)$ of the X-rays emitted when the K-shell is refilled. The decrease in rest mass is again $M_P - M_D$. Therefore,

$$M_P - M_D = W(\nu) + W(K). \qquad (20\text{-}11)$$

This equation is not very useful for determining masses, because the energies of neutrinos are not readily measurable. Neglecting $W(K)$, which is only about 0.1 Mev for the heaviest atoms, Eq. (11) shows that electron capture is energetically possible only if the mass of the parent atom is greater than the mass of the daughter. Positive beta ray emission and K-capture can be regarded as competitive processes. Among heavy elements, K-capture is more probable. The radius of the first Bohr orbit, which in quantum mechanics has the significance of an average distance between the nucleus and the K-electrons, varies inversely as Z^2. Among lighter elements, positive beta ray emission is more probable. The decay of $_4Be^7$ is exceptional, because the mass of beryllium 7 exceeds the mass of lithium 7 by only 0.88 Mev. Only K-capture occurs, positive electron emission being energetically impossible.

If two neighboring isobars $_zX^A$ and $_{z+1}X^A$ are chosen at random, it is unlikely that the two atomic masses will be exactly the same. Then the heavier of the two can decay into the lighter one, by negative electron emission if the one of lower Z is the more massive, and by K-capture if the one of higher Z is the more massive. Since it seems that these processes occur whenever they are energetically possible, a good rule would be that two neighboring isobars cannot both be stable. Examination of a table of stable isotopes shows three exceptions to this rule. The exceptions might be only apparent, because a radioactive substance with a sufficiently long half-life would appear not to be radioactive. There are many cases of stable isobars such as $_zX^A$ and $_{z+2}X^A$. Their occurrence suggests that simultaneous emission of two beta rays is highly improbable.

The first theory of beta decay was worked out by Fermi. He successfully predicted the exact shape of the continuous energy spectrum of beta rays, at least for certain cases. He predicted a strong dependence of the decay constant upon the end-point energy of the beta ray spectrum, in agreement with experimental results. Other factors which affect the decay constant are the atomic number of the decaying nucleus, and the change of nuclear angular momentum which takes place during the decay. If the parent and daughter nuclei have very different angular momenta with reference to an axis through the nucleus, the decay can be accomplished only by sending out particles for which mvr is not zero. This "off-center" emission makes the decay relatively improbable and results in a long half-life. The theory of beta decay has been modified from time to time and is still incomplete.

Gamma Ray Emission

Emission of a photon by a nucleus does not change either the atomic number or the mass number of the atom. The actual mass must, of course, decrease because of the equivalence of mass and energy. Some alpha ray and beta ray emitters also emit gamma rays, and others do not. Early work indicated that when a gamma ray is emitted it is coincident in time with the emission of a charged particle. The intensity of the gamma radiation decreases with the half-life of the particle emitter.

With the development of large electromagnets to make precision studies of the magnetic deflection of alpha particles, it became apparent that alpha emitters frequently give out several groups of different energies. For example, $_{83}Bi^{212}$, a member of the thorium series, gave groups which had kinetic energies of 6.082 and 6.043 Mev, and also other groups of weaker intensity. After adding the kinetic energies of the recoiling nuclei, the total disintegration energies were 6.199 and 6.159 Mev. When an atom decays with the smaller energy evolution, its

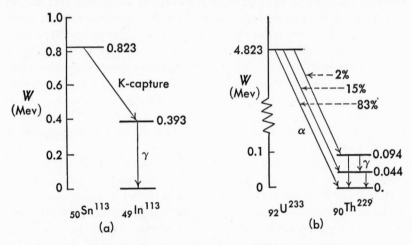

Fig. 20-6. Energy diagrams showing decay schemes.

daughter atom retains 0.040 Mev of energy which it emits as a photon. Gamma rays of this energy were observed. The experiment shows that the daughter nuclide $_{81}Tl^{208}$ has an excited state at 0.040 Mev above its ground state. Results of this sort show that nuclei, like atoms, have certain definite states of excitation. The excited states of the daughter nuclei can be found by investigating the spectra of the gamma rays, or by measuring the groups of emitted particles. In beta decay, the spectrum of the emitted particles is continuous whether or not gamma rays are emitted. The shape of the spectrum sometimes indicates that it is a superposition of two spectra with different end-points. A gamma ray, with energy equal to the difference in end-points, can be expected.

It is convenient to use energy level diagrams, such as those in Fig. 20-6, to represent radioactive decay schemes. A vertical energy scale is used and horizontal lines, one above the other, show the energy states of each nuclide. Vertical lines represent gamma ray emission and sloping lines represent the transition from one nuclear species to the other. Fig. 20-6b is an alpha decay scheme which adequately represents the available information about the decay of uranium 233. The ground state of the parent is placed at 4.823 Mev above the ground state of the daughter to show the total energy evolution in the transition.

The decay schemes suggest that the emission of the particle precedes the emission of the gamma ray. This has been verified, but the time interval is usually too short to be measurable. In rare cases, it is measurable, and sometimes the lifetime of the excited state is rather long. An example is the excited state of indium 113 which is 0.393 Mev above the ground state. It is produced by the decay of tin 113 as shown in Fig. 20-6a. Indium can be chemically separated from radioactive tin, and the indium fraction is a pure gamma ray emitter with a half-life of 105 min. Any excited state which has a measurably long half-life is called an "isomeric state." The distinction is arbitrary because it depends upon the degree of development of measuring techniques. Isomerism is understood to be characteristic of excited states which have angular momentum very different from the lower states to which they might decay.

The Curie of Radioactivity

The strength of a radioactive source should be stated in terms of the number of atoms which decay in a unit time, that is, in terms of its activity. Thus, the curie is defined as the quantity of a radioactive substance in which 3.70×10^{10} atoms decay per sec. This unit was chosen after it was observed that one gram of radium emits that number of alpha particles per second. A curie of radium is equal to a gram of radium. For substances other than radium, the number of atoms in a one-curie sample can be calculated from its decay constant, putting $-dN/dt = 3.70 \times 10^{10}$ atoms per sec. The curie unit can be used for any radioactive substance, whatever the particle emitted when the atom decays.

Summary

Atoms decay spontaneously with a decay constant λ which is characteristic of the atomic species and of its mode of decay. The decay constant is defined as $-dN/(N \, dt)$, that is, it represents the fraction of the number of atoms present which decay per unit time. The fraction of the atoms which decay in a large sample can be regarded as the probability that one atom will decay. The decay constant is then the probability per unit time that an atom will decay. A single atom has a constant probability of decay until it actually does decay, after which the probability is of course zero. What we expect of the theories of the different decay processes is that they will correctly predict the probability of decay per unit time.

The probability of getting a head when a coin is tossed is one-half. If the forces on the coin are fully understood, it should be possible to predict whether a head or a tail will show. Probabilities are used only because of our ignorance of the details of the processes which determine the result. However, in physical theories, no effort is made to understand factors which might determine when a particular atom will decay. The probability of decay is regarded as the basic physical quantity. This changed attitude toward probabilities is implicit in much of modern physics.

Problems

1. How many alpha particles and how many beta particles are emitted in the thorium series in the decay of $_{90}Th^{232}$ to $_{82}Pb^{208}$?

    (Ans.: Six alpha and four beta particles.)

2. Calculate the energy of recoil of $_{81}Tl^{208}$ when $_{83}Bi^{212}$ emits an alpha particle of kinetic energy 6.082 Mev.

    (Ans.: 0.117 Mev.)

3. Using the decay equation $N = N_0 e^{-\lambda t}$, show that the mean life is $1/\lambda$.

4. A radioactive sample contains equal numbers of atoms of two beta particle emitters, the first of half-life 6.0 min, the second of half-life 10.0 min. How long would one wait for the sample to decay if one wants 99% of the remaining atoms to be those of longer life?

    (Ans.: 99.5 min.)

5. Suppose a certain sample of uranium ore contains 120.3 g of uranium and 27.2 liters of helium at normal temperature and pressure. Calculate the age of the ore. Although uranium decays in successive steps in which alpha and beta particles are emitted, the entire sequence can be regarded as

$$_{92}U^{238} \rightarrow {}_{82}Pb^{206} + 8{}_2He^4 + 6\beta^-$$

and the half-life can be taken as that of the parent substance (4.5×10^9 yr).

    (Ans.: 1.705×10^9 yr.)

6. When N^{13} decays to C^{13} by positive electron emission, the maximum beta ray energy is 1.202 Mev. Calculate the mass of the N^{13} atom, taking the mass of the C^{13} atom to be 13.00755 amu.

    (Ans.: 13.00994 amu.)

7. When $_4Be^7$ decays to the ground state of $_3Li^7$, a 0.88 Mev neutrino is emitted. What should be the energy of recoil of the lithium 7 atom?

    (Ans.: 59 ev.)

8. Measurement has shown that radium ($_{88}Ra^{226}$) emits 3.70×10^{10} alpha particles per sec per gram of radium. Calculate its half-life from this datum.

    (Ans.: 1590 yr.)

9. Calculate the mass in grams of one curie of polonium 210, an alpha emitter with a half-life of 138 days.

    (Ans.: 2.22×10^{-4} g.)

21 | Nuclear Reactions

When a radioactive source is enclosed in a calorimeter, the temperature rises because the energy of the absorbed radiation is converted into heat. Useful quantities of heat are not produced by ordinary sources, and there seems to be no way to increase the rate of evolution of heat by controlling the rate of disintegration. Decay constants have been found to be unaffected by controllable conditions such as pressure and temperature.

The control of energy evolution was found to be possible when Rutherford discovered that reactions take place as a result of nuclear collisions. This discovery followed in a natural way from the studies of alpha particle scattering. Energetic protons, the nuclei of ordinary hydrogen, were identified among the scattered alpha particles. They were found to result from the passage of alpha particles through nitrogen. The nuclear reaction can be written as

$$_7N^{14} + {}_2He^4 \rightarrow {}_1H^1 + {}_8O^{17}$$

or

$$N^{14}(\alpha,p)O^{17}.$$

The production of oxygen, with $Z = 8$, can be inferred from the law of conservation of charge. If the law of conservation of mass number is also assumed, the isotope of oxygen is identified. These conservation laws have been verified in other nuclear reactions. From the original discovery in 1919, until 1932, the known nuclear reactions were all of the (α,p) type. Other targets were found to emit protons during bombardment with alpha particles from natural radioactive sources.

The advantage of bombarding targets with positive ions from high voltage accelerators was generally recognized. A current as small as 1 μamp of singly charged particles delivers 6.24×10^{12} particles per

TABLE 21-1. LIST OF SYMBOLS USED IN CHAPTER 21

Symbol	Name	Quantity Designated
M		rest mass of an atom
W		kinetic energy
Q		increase of kinetic energy or decrease of rest mass
p		momentum
θ	theta	angle at which particle is emitted
N		number of particles or reactions
n		number of target nuclei per unit volume
σ	sigma	cross section
r		nuclear radius

second. As a source of high speed particles, this is equivalent to 170 curies and is about a thousand times more than the emission from the sources of alpha particles which are usually available. A further advantage is that the accelerated particles can impinge on a small area of target from one direction, whereas particles from a radioactive source are emitted in all directions. Several large machines to accelerate positive ions were developed in this period, among them the cyclotron by Lawrence, the electrostatic generator by Van de Graaff and Herb, and the voltage multiplier by Cockcroft and Walton.

In 1932, Cockcroft and Walton made the first use of a high voltage machine to produce a nuclear reaction. Hydrogen nuclei from an ion source were accelerated by a potential difference of 700 kv and then were allowed to fall on a lithium target. Alpha particles of 9.0 Mev energy were produced in the target, the reaction being

$$_3\text{Li}^7 + {}_1\text{H}^1 \rightarrow {}_2\text{He}^4 + {}_2\text{He}^4.$$

This was the first (p,α) reaction. It happens in this case that the residual nucleus is an alpha particle also. A (p,α) reaction has been produced in a number of target materials. Targets of the light elements are preferable, to minimize the force of electrostatic repulsion between the target nuclei and the positively charged bombarding particles.

With the discovery of heavy hydrogen (called deuterium), another bombarding particle became available. The isotope H^2 is present to about one part in 5000 in natural hydrogen, from which it can be separated. When pure deuterium gas is used in the ion source of a high voltage machine, a beam of deuterons is obtained at the target. Reactions of the (d,p) and (d,α) type occur in many targets. Deuterons are sometimes produced in a reaction, for example in $Be^9 (p,d)$, but they are especially effective as bombarding particles.

Energy Evolution in Nuclear Reactions

The exact masses of the atoms involved in a nuclear reaction are frequently available from mass spectrographic determinations. For the (p,α) reaction in lithium 7, the exact atomic masses are:

$$Li^7—7.01822 \text{ amu,}$$

$$H^1—1.00814 \text{ amu,}$$

and

$$He^4—4.00388 \text{ amu.}$$

The total mass of the two atoms which enter the reaction is 8.02636 amu, and the rest mass afterwards is 8.00776 amu. The total decrease in rest mass is 0.01860 amu. If nuclear masses instead of atomic masses are used, the change in mass is the same. The observed kinetic energy of the particles shows an increase in the reaction. The two alpha particles have about the same energy, 9.0 Mev, and the energy of the incident proton is 0.7 Mev. The increase of kinetic energy is 17.3 Mev. If the observed increase of kinetic energy is equated to the decrease of rest mass, then 0.01860 amu = 17.3 Mev, or 1 amu = 931 Mev. This is an experimental verification of the mass-energy equivalence expressed by $W = Mc^2$.

The increase of kinetic energy, or decrease of rest mass, is called the "Q-value" of the reaction. In equation form,

$$Q = M_1 + M_2 - M_3 - M_4 \tag{21-1}$$

and

$$Q = W_3 + W_4 - W_1 - W_2, \tag{21-2}$$

where the subscripts refer to the target nucleus, the bombarding particle, the emitted particle, and the residual nucleus, in that order. The energy W_1 is equal to zero in any practical situation. The Q-value is customarily placed to the right in a decay equation, to balance the exact masses. Some examples are:

$$_3Li^7 + _1H^1 \rightarrow _2He^4 + _2He^4 + Q \text{ (17.3 Mev),}$$

$$_9F^{19} + _1H^2 \rightarrow _2He^4 + _8O^{17} + 10.03 \text{ Mev,}$$

and

$$_6C^{12} + _2He^4 \rightarrow _1H^1 + _7N^{15} - 4.96 \text{ Mev.}$$

A reaction is called *exoergic* or *endoergic*, depending upon whether the Q-value is positive or negative, respectively, for that particular reaction.

Q-values can be calculated from the exact atomic masses when they are known, or they can be calculated from the observed increase of kinetic energy in a reaction. The energy W_3 of an emitted particle can be determined from its range, from its radius of curvature in a magnetic field, from its deflection in an electric field, or from the size of a pulse in a scintillation or ionization counter. The bombarding energy W_2 is known from the voltage used to accelerate the particle. The energy of recoil W_4 of the residual nucleus is usually not meas-

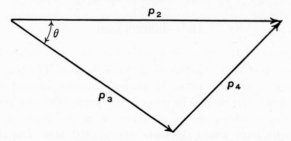

Fig. 21-1. Conservation of momentum in a nuclear reaction.

ured. It can be calculated from the energies of the other two particles by making use of the law of conservation of momentum. Fig. 21-1 shows the relations of the momentum vectors when the particle of momentum p_3 is observed at an angle θ to the direction of the incident beam. From the law of cosines,

$$p_4{}^2 = p_2{}^2 + p_3{}^2 - 2p_2 p_3 \cos \theta.$$

Using the non-relativistic relation between the momentum and the energy, $W = p^2/2M$, this becomes

$$2M_4 W_4 = 2M_2 W_2 + 2M_3 W_3 - 2(2M_2 W_2)^{1/2}(2M_3 W_3)^{1/2} \cos \theta$$

and

$$W_4 = (M_2/M_4)W_2 + (M_3/M_4)W_3 - (2/M_4)(M_2 M_3 W_2 W_3)^{1/2} \cos \theta.$$

$$(21\text{-}3)$$

The ratios of the masses must be known to obtain the recoil energy, but they need be known only to the percent accuracy of the energy measurements. If the ratios of mass numbers are used, the error is not greater than 1%. The value of W_4 can be substituted into Eq. (2) to get the

"Q-value equation." Thus,

$$Q = W_3(M_4 + M_3)/M_4 - W_2(M_4 - M_2)/M_4$$
$$- (2/M_4)(M_2 M_3 W_2 W_3)^{1/2} \cos \theta. \quad (21\text{-}4)$$

This equation is used to calculate Q-values from the measurements of the energies in a nuclear reaction. It can also be used, when the Q-value is known, to calculate the energy W_3 of the particles emitted at any angle to the direction of the incident beam. Used in this way, it is a quadratic equation in $(W_3)^{1/2}$, which can be solved by the standard method. As a general trend, the emitted particles have their maximum energy in the forward direction and progressively less energy as the angle is increased.

In many experiments the emitted particles are observed at 90° to the bombarding beam. With this restriction ($\theta = 90°$), the energy of an emitted particle is

$$W_3 = W_2(M_4 - M_2)/(M_4 + M_3) + QM_4/(M_4 + M_3). \quad (21\text{-}5)$$

The particle produced in a reaction gets a fraction of the bombarding energy and a fraction of the energy released in the reaction. If, however, the Q-value is negative, no particles are observed at 90° except at high bombarding energies. The value of W_2 at which emission of particles becomes energetically possible is called the threshold of the reaction. Thresholds are characteristic of reactions which have negative Q-values. The threshold for observation of the reaction at 90° is at a somewhat higher energy than for observations in the forward direction.

The Cross Section of a Reaction

The quantitative measure of radioactivity is the decay constant, which is defined as the probability that an atom will decay in unit time. Nuclear reactions can be described in terms of the probability that a reaction will occur per unit length of path of a bombarding particle. This can be expressed as $N_2/(N_1 \, dx)$, where N_2 is the number of nuclear reactions and the denominator is the total length of track when N_1 bombarding particles pass through a target of thickness dx. However, the probability of a reaction should be proportional to the density of target material, which can be expressed as the number n of target nuclei per unit volume of target. Then $N_2/(N_1 \, dx)$ is proportional to n or

$$\boxed{N_2 = \sigma N_1 n \, dx,} \quad (21\text{-}6)$$

where σ is a constant of proportionality called the cross section of the reaction. The cross section is defined by this equation. It has the dimensions of an area.

The cross section of a reaction can be compared with the actual area πr^2 presented by a nucleus to a bombarding particle. The total area of all the target nuclei in a thin foil of area A and thickness dx is $\pi r^2 nA\ dx$. On the assumption that bombarding particles can be aimed at the foil but not at the individual nuclei:

(no. of collisions/no. of particles) = (area of nuclei/area of foil)

or

$$(N_c/N_1) = \pi r^2 nA\ dx/A,$$

where N_c is the number of collisions. Therefore,

$$N_c = \pi r^2 N_1 n\ dx. \tag{21-7}$$

It would seem that the number of nuclear reactions would not be greater than the number of collisions. The cross section of a reaction might be expected to be less than the area presented by a nucleus to an incoming particle, although perhaps of that order of magnitude in some cases. Cross sections are frequently found to be of the order of 10^{-24} cm^2. A unit of cross section equal to 10^{-24} cm^2 is sometimes used and is called the "barn."

A cross section is determined experimentally by counting the number of disintegration particles N_2 emitted from a target in a certain time. The number of bombarding particles N_1 is calculated from the number of coulombs in the beam striking the target in the same time. The number of nuclei per unit volume n can be calculated from the ordinary density, using Avogadro's number.

Thin targets are used for determinations of the cross section and for precise measurements of the Q-value. A thin layer is usually deposited upon a backing material which is known not to emit particles during bombardment. A target is called "thick" if the charged bombarding particle loses all of its energy and comes to rest inside the target material. Reactions are produced at all bombarding energies, equal to or less than the initial energy. Thick targets are used when the only object is to get the maximum number of disintegrations.

The cross section of a reaction is strongly dependent upon the energy of the bombarding particle. Several types of dependence are found. When the bombarding particle is positively charged, the cross section increases with energy as shown in Fig. 21-2. Low energy particles do not reach the target nuclei because of electrostatic repulsion. The shape of the curve is related to the probability of barrier penetration.

At high energies the incoming particle goes over the barrier rather than through it.

When the Q-value of a reaction is negative, the required decrease in kinetic energy cannot occur unless the initial kinetic energy exceeds a

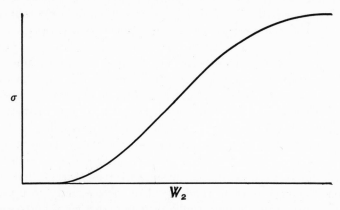

Fig. 21-2. The dependence of the cross section upon the kinetic energy W_2 when the bombarding particle is positively charged.

certain value. The cross section curve shows a threshold at that energy. Below this threshold, the cross section of the reaction is zero.

Induced Radioactivity

The residual atom produced in a nuclear reaction is often a stable isotope which has been found by mass spectroscopists to be present in a normal sample of the element. On the other hand, they are often atoms of a new kind not found in natural samples. Two examples, chosen at random, are:

$$_{7}N^{14} + {}_{1}H^{1} \rightarrow {}_{2}He^{4} + {}_{6}C^{11}$$

and

$$_{5}B^{11} + {}_{2}He^{4} \rightarrow {}_{1}H^{1} + {}_{6}C^{14}.$$

The stable isotopes of carbon are C^{12} and C^{13}. Carbon 11 is found to decay by emission of positive beta rays with a half-life of 20.5 min. Carbon 14 is a negative beta ray emitter with a half-life of 5580 yr. Many hundreds of radioactive species have been discovered in this way. No doubt there are many other radioactive nuclides which have not yet been discovered because they are not produced as residual nuclei in any known type of nuclear reaction.

The manner in which radioactivity builds up in a target under bombardment has been discussed in Chapter 20. After bombardment ceases, decay occurs in the usual way. If the half-life is long enough, a chemical analysis of a target will identify the radioactive element. The amounts separated are too small to be weighable, but some of the stable element can be added, then precipitated out, and the radioactivity will go with the precipitate if the identification is correct.

The atomic mass of a radioactive species determines the Q-value of the reaction which produced it. The Q-value can be obtained from the measured kinetic energies of the particles. Of the four rest masses involved, three will usually be known, and the fourth can be calculated from the Q-value. The method has been carried even further. After enough nuclear reactions were studied, it became possible to arrange sets of simultaneous equations, in each of which the decrease in rest mass was expressed in terms of the measured Q-value. Solution of these equations gave all of the masses involved, except that of the common isotope of oxygen which is taken to be exactly 16 amu. The masses of the stable atoms could be compared with mass-spectrographic values. Serious discrepancies were found at first, but these have been resolved by more precise mass determinations.

It is a matter of interest that no new stable nuclides have been discovered as residual nuclei. In some distant past, conditions were apparently favorable for producing all kinds of stable atoms. These conditions were probably also favorable for the production of radioactive atoms. The radioactive atoms have decayed, unless they had half-lives of the order of 10^9 years and longer.

Nuclear Energy States

Each nuclear species has a set of distinctive energy states in which it can exist. Only the state of lowest energy is stable. The nucleus usually transforms from its states of high energy to its states of lower energy by photon emission. Excited states of nuclei affect the progress of nuclear reactions in several ways, depending upon whether the excited state belongs to the target nucleus, the residual nucleus, or the compound nucleus, which is formed by capture of the incident particle.

Lithium 7 is a stable isotope of lithium which is frequently used as a target material. It has an excited state 0.477 Mev above its ground state. When bombarded by fast particles such as protons, some nuclei are raised to the excited state, the energy being supplied by the fast protons. Gamma rays of 0.477 Mev energy are observed during the bombardment. This process can be regarded as a nuclear reaction, in which the emitted particle is the same in kind but not in energy as the bombarding particle. The reaction can be written

$$_3\text{Li}^7 + {}_1\text{H}^1 \rightarrow {}_1\text{H}^1 + ({}_3\text{Li}^7)^* - 0.477 \text{ Mev,}$$

where the asterisk is used to indicate that the nucleus is in an excited state. With targets of high nuclear charge, the capture and re-emission of the incident particle is less probable. A process called "coulomb excitation," in which the incident charged particle is scattered in the coulomb field, with loss of energy, puts the target nucleus in its excited state. Gamma rays are emitted and their energy gives the height above the ground state of the excited level. Much information about the low-lying excited states of stable nuclei has been accumulated in this way.

The residual nucleus, formed in a nuclear reaction, is sometimes in its ground state and sometimes in one of its excited states. For example, the (d,p) reaction in carbon 12 may be either

$$_6\text{C}^{12} + {}_1\text{H}^2 \rightarrow {}_1\text{H}^1 + {}_6\text{C}^{13} + Q_1$$

or

$$_6\text{C}^{12} + {}_1\text{H}^2 \rightarrow {}_1\text{H}^1 + ({}_6\text{C}^{13})^* + Q_2.$$

Proton groups of two different energies are emitted. The two Q-values, determined from the energies of the emitted particles and the bombarding energy, are $+2.72$ Mev and -0.37 Mev. The difference is caused by the greater rest mass of the atom which has the greater energy. The extra rest mass, expressed in energy units, is 3.09 Mev. Gamma rays of this energy, which are emitted during the transition to the ground state, are observed. Excited states of residual nuclei can be found, either by studying the groups of particles emitted during a reaction, or by studying the gamma rays which accompany them.

A nuclear reaction can often be regarded as a sequence of two separate events, first the capture of the incident particle by the target nucleus to form a compound nucleus, and then the decay of the compound nucleus by particle emission. For example, the (d,p) reaction in carbon 12 can be written as

$$_6\text{C}^{12} + {}_1\text{H}^2 \rightarrow ({}_7\text{N}^{14})^* \rightarrow {}_1\text{H}^1 + {}_6\text{C}^{13}.$$

Ordinary nitrogen 14 is stable, but the compound nucleus formed in this reaction is an excited state of nitrogen 14. Considering the first step only,

$$_6\text{C}^{12} + {}_1\text{H}^2 \rightarrow ({}_7\text{N}^{14})^* + Q_1;$$

the kinetic energy of the compound nucleus can be determined from the law of conservation of momentum. That is,

$$p_c = p_2,$$

where p_2 is the momentum of the bombarding particle, and p_c is the momentum of the compound nucleus. Since $W = p^2/2M$, we have

$$M_c W_c = M_2 W_2.$$

The kinetic energy of the compound nucleus is

$$W_c = W_2 M_2/(M_1 + M_2),$$

where $(M_1 + M_2)$ has been used as a sufficiently close approximation to M_c. The increase in the kinetic energy is $W_c - W_2 = -W_2 M_1/(M_1 + M_2)$, and the decrease in the rest mass is $M_1 + M_2 - M_c$. The two quantities can be equated, if they are expressed in the same units; thus,

$$\boxed{M_c = M_1 + M_2 + W_2 M_1/(M_1 + M_2).} \qquad (21\text{-}8)$$

At any particular bombarding energy, the mass of the compound nucleus can be calculated from this equation. If the mass of this nucleus in its ground state also is known, its excess mass and therefore its energy of excitation can be found. It is a matter of observation, and also of theory, that there is a high probability of forming the compound nucleus when its energy of excitation is equal to the energy of one of the permissible excited states of that nucleus. Fig. 21-3 shows the yield of protons from the $C^{12}(d,p)$ reaction plotted against the bombarding energy W_2. The curve shows the general trend for the cross section of a reaction illustrated in Fig. 21-2, but there are peaks in the yield curves at 0.92, 1.16, and 1.23 Mev. At these bombarding energies, the mass of the compound nucleus is equal to the mass of nitrogen 14 in one of its permissible excited states. The high proton yield at these energies is a consequence of the high probability of formation of the compound nucleus. It should not be concluded that a compound nucleus is formed in all nuclear reactions. However, when peaks or "resonances" are observed in a yield curve, they are to be interpreted as evidence of excited states of a compound nucleus.

A compound nucleus may decay by particle emission, as in the above example, or it may decay by emission of gamma rays. Usually, particle emission has a much higher probability per unit time, and gamma rays are not observed. When particle emission is slow for any reason, gamma rays are observed and the reaction is called "simple capture." Examples of simple capture are

$$_6C^{13} + _1H^1 \rightarrow \gamma + _7N^{14}$$

and

$$_3Li^7 + _2He^4 \rightarrow \gamma + _5B^{11}.$$

In these reactions, the compound neucleus is the same as the residual nucleus.

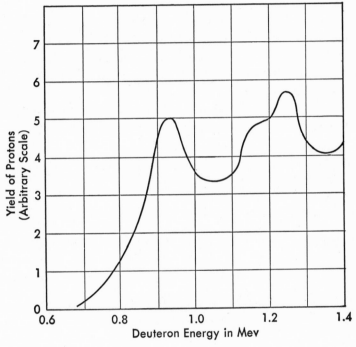

Fig. 21-3. Yield curve for the $C^{12}(p,d)$ reaction.

Resonances, such as those shown in Fig. 21-3, often have a measurable breadth, which suggests that the excited states are not well defined in energy. The breadth of the resonance, measured half-way between its peak and its base, is—after multiplying by $M_1/(M_1 + M_2)$ —a measure of the uncertainty in the energy of the state of the system. This uncertainty is related to a time interval Δt by Heisenberg's uncertainty principle $\Delta W \ \Delta t = h/2\pi$. The quantity Δt is interpreted as the mean life of the compound nucleus in its excited state. In quantum mechanics it is not possible to specify exactly the energy of a state which can exist only for a very short time. By measuring widths, lifetimes of the order of 10^{-20} sec can be inferred.

Summary

When one nucleus collides with another, nuclear reactions may occur. Without reference to experimental work it is possible to write down a vast number of reactions. Whether or not a conceivable reaction will actually occur is another problem. When a reaction is found, it is customary to express the probability of its occurrence in terms of a cross section for that reaction.

Some types of reaction, such as the (α,p), (p,α), (d,p), and (d,α) reactions, frequently have large cross sections. Some other conceivable reactions possibly occur with small cross sections so that they are not readily detectable. Still others do not occur at all because some conservation law would be violated.

Among the conservation laws which are never violated in any nuclear reaction are the laws of conservation of:

(1) Electric charge
(2) Mass-energy
(3) Linear Momentum
(4) Angular Momentum
(5) Mass number.

There are several other conservation laws of more subtle character.

Problems

1. Calculate the heat evolved in cal/hr in a container enclosing one curie of polonium 210, which emits alpha particles of 5.30 Mev energy.

(Ans.: 27.0 cal/hr.)

2. Calculate the Q-value of the (α,p) reaction in nitrogen 14 from the following values of the atomic masses:

$$He^4— 4.00387 \text{ amu,}$$
$$H^1— 1.00814 \text{ amu,}$$
$$N^{14}—14.00751 \text{ amu,}$$
$$O^{17}—17.00453 \text{ amu.}$$

(Ans.: −1.20 Mev.)

3. If the reaction $_1H^2 + {}_1H^2 \rightarrow {}_1H^1 + {}_1H^3 + 4.03$ Mev is produced by 2.35 Mev deuterons striking a thin deuterium target, calculate the energy of the protons emitted at 90° to the bombarding particles. Also calculate the energy and direction of emission of the tritons which are associated with the 90° protons.

(Ans.: 3.61 Mev, 2.77 Mev, 41.2°.)

4. Calculate the energy, above the ground state, of the excited level of nitrogen 14 which is responsible for the resonance at 0.92 Mev in the yield from the $C^{12}(d,p)$ reaction, using the following masses:

$$C^{12}-12.00381,$$
$$H^{2}-\ 2.01473,$$
$$H^{1}-\ 1.00814,$$
$$N^{14}-14.00753.$$

(Ans.: 11.04 Mev.)

22 | Neutrons

Discovery of the Neutron

Neutrons can be produced by alpha particle bombardment of boron and beryllium targets. They were produced in this way during some of the early studies of the (α,p) reactions, but were not identified at that time. Penetrating radiation was observed, but there was no reason to suppose that it was different from high energy gamma rays. It had one peculiarity, that it was able to knock protons out of a layer of paraffin, presumably as Compton recoil particles accompanying the scattering of very high energy photons. Chadwick made a systematic study of the recoil nuclei knocked out of a number of materials of low atomic number. Comparing recoiling nuclei of different masses, the results were inconsistent with the theory that the particles recoiled from the scattering of gamma rays. They were in agreement with the assumption that the penetrating radiation consisted of fast neutral particles of about the same rest mass as the proton. Chadwick, in his original paper in 1932, called the new particles neutrons, and speculated as to whether the neutron should be regarded as a tight combination of a proton and an electron, or as a new elementary particle. The latter view quickly became more acceptable.

Elastic Collisions

Fig. 22-1 shows a nucleus of mass M_R recoiling at an angle ϕ after being struck by a particle of mass M which is scattered at an angle θ, both ϕ and θ being measured from the initial direction of M. From the law of conservation of momentum,

$$Mv_1 = M_R v_R \cos \phi + M v_2 \cos \theta \qquad (22\text{-}1)$$

TABLE 22-1. LIST OF SYMBOLS USED IN CHAPTER 22

Symbol	Name	Quantity Designated
M		mass of an atom or particle
θ	theta	angle of scattered particle
ϕ	phi	angle of recoil particle
v		velocity
W		kinetic energy
N		number of particles or events
σ	sigma	cross section
n		number of nuclei per unit volume
μ	mu	absorption coefficient
r		nuclear radius
k		Boltzmann's constant
T		absolute temperature
Φ	phi	neutron flux

and

$$0 = M_R v_R \sin \phi - M v_2 \sin \theta. \tag{22-2}$$

If kinetic energy also is conserved in the collision, we have

$$M v_1^2/2 = M_R v_R^2/2 + M v_2^2/2. \tag{22-3}$$

One of the solutions of these three equations, obtained by elimination of θ and v_2, is

$$v_R = 2M v_1 \cos \phi/(M + M_R). \tag{22-4}$$

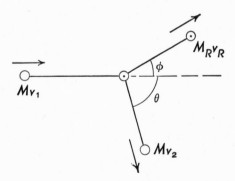

Fig. 22-1. Recoil of a nucleus of mass M_R from an elastic collision with a particle of mass M.

If the recoiling particle is very much lighter than the scattered particle, then $M_R \ll M$ and to a good approximation $v_R = 2v_1 \cos \phi$. That is, the maximum velocity of recoil is $2v_1$, a result which was used in Chapter 18 to find the maximum energy given to an electron in a collision with a massive moving particle.

Chadwick used Eq. (4) to determine the rest mass of the neutron. When considering recoiling particles of maximum velocity, the angle ϕ can be put equal to zero. The unknown velocity v_1 of the neutrons can be eliminated by considering the ratio of the velocity of recoiling hydrogen v_{RH} to the velocity of recoiling nitrogen v_{RN}. Then,

$$v_{RH}/v_{RN} = (M + M_N)/(M + M_H) = (M + 14)/(M + 1). \quad (22\text{-}5)$$

The velocities of recoil were determined from the ranges of the recoiling particles, using known range-energy relationships for these particles. The velocities were 3.3×10^9 and 4.7×10^8 cm/sec; giving the neutron rest mass $M = 1.15$ amu. This value was accurate enough to exclude the supposition that the radiation consisted of photons which have zero rest mass, and to show that the neutral particle has about the same mass as the proton.

The Mass of the Neutron

Regarding the neutron as an atom of mass-number one and atomic-number zero, the appropriate symbol is $_0n^1$. Its production by alpha particle bombardment of beryllium can then be written as

$$_4Be^9 + _2He^4 \rightarrow _0n^1 + _6C^{12}.$$

The similar reaction in boron 11 can be written as

$$_5B^{11} + _2He^4 \rightarrow _0n^1 + _7N^{14}.$$

Chadwick evaluated the Q-value of the latter reaction from the observed increase in the kinetic energy, and equated this to the decrease of rest mass. Of the four masses, three were known fairly accurately and the mass of the neutron was thus found to be 1.0067 amu.

Once the mass of the neutron is known to be approximately 1 amu, Eq. (4) can be used to find the energy of recoil W_R of a nucleus of mass M_R, in terms of the energy of the neutron W_n. The result is

$$\boxed{W_R = 4M_RW_n \cos^2 \phi/(1 + M_R)^2.} \quad (22\text{-}6)$$

For example, when M_R is 1, 4, and 14, the maximum energies of recoil are 1.00 W_n, 0.64 W_n, and 0.25 W_n, respectively. The maximum energy of recoil thus decreases as the mass number of the recoiling nucleus increases. In hydrogen, a proton recoiling in the forward direction has the same energy as the neutron which struck it. The energies of such protons can be determined from their ranges or from the pulse size in an ionization counter. This is still the standard method of determining neutron energies.

The currently accepted value of the neutron mass is 1.00898 amu, which was obtained by studying the simple capture of neutrons in hydrogen. The reaction is

$$_1H^1 + _0n^1 \rightarrow \gamma + _1H^2 + 2.227 \text{ Mev.}$$

When neutrons of negligible energy are allowed to fall on paraffin, the observed gamma rays are found to have an energy of 2.227 Mev per photon. This is also the Q-value of the reaction, for the residual nucleus, recoiling from photon emission, has a negligible kinetic energy. The decrease of rest mass is $M_{H^1} + M_n - M_{H^2} = 2.227 \text{ Mev} = 0.00239$ amu. The atomic masses of hydrogen and deuterium have been measured with mass spectrographs, their values being 1.00814 and 2.01473 amu. Hence, $M_n = 2.01473 - 1.00814 + 0.00239 = 1.00898$ amu.

Neutron Sources

A source of neutrons can be made by mixing, inside a sealed capsule, finely powdered beryllium with any radioactive substance which decays by alpha particle emission. Radium, polonium, and plutonium have been used. Polonium is not ideal because of its short half-life, 138 days. Radium has been most commonly used, but it is also a strong source of gamma radiation, emitted in the decay of radium and its daughter nuclides. Plutonium is not commercially available, but must be obtained on loan from a government agency. The neutrons from these sources have wide distributions in energy, caused by the varying energy of the alpha particles as they slow down in the beryllium powder, by the spread in the angles at which the neutrons are emitted, and by the excited states of carbon 12 which make several Q-values for the $Be^9(\alpha,n)C^{12}$ reaction.

Weaker, but more homogeneous sources, can be made by surrounding a radioactive source, which emits gamma rays as part of its decay scheme, with a cylinder of beryllium. The neutrons are produced in the reaction

$$_4Be^9 + \gamma \rightarrow _0n^1 + _4Be^8 - 1.67 \text{ Mev.}$$

The energy of the photoneutrons is determined almost solely by the energy of the gamma ray, which must, of course, be greater than 1.67 Mev to make the reaction energetically possible.

Stronger sources can be obtained by bombarding targets with beams of accelerated particles. There are many nuclear reactions which produce neutrons. Some of the reactions which have been found especially useful are:

$$_1\text{H}^2 + _1\text{H}^2 \rightarrow _0\text{n}^1 + _2\text{He}^3 + 3.27 \text{ Mev},$$

$$_1\text{H}^3 + _1\text{H}^2 \rightarrow _0\text{n}^1 + _2\text{He}^4 + 17.6 \text{ Mev},$$

$$_1\text{H}^3 + _1\text{H}^1 \rightarrow _0\text{n}^1 + _2\text{He}^3 - 0.764 \text{ Mev},$$

$$_3\text{Li}^7 + _1\text{H}^1 \rightarrow _0\text{n}^1 + _4\text{Be}^7 - 1.65 \text{ Mev},$$

and

$$_6\text{C}^{12} + _1\text{H}^2 \rightarrow _0\text{n}^1 + _7\text{N}^{13} - 0.26 \text{ Mev}.$$

In these cases, there is a unique Q-value for each reaction, since the residual nuclei are not left in excited states at moderate bombarding energies. When thin targets are used, the neutrons emitted at any particular angle from the target are monoenergetic. The neutron energy can be varied by changing the voltage used to accelerate the bombarding particles. It is important that monoenergetic neutrons of variable energy be available for experimental purposes. A neutron, having no charge, cannot be accelerated to any desired energy.

Modern nuclear reactors act as neutron sources which are many orders of magnitude stronger than can otherwise be obtained.

Bombardment with Neutrons

Charged bombarding particles, such as deuterons and alpha particles, penetrate only thin layers of target material, because they lose energy rapidly by interacting with atomic electrons. Neutrons, on the other hand, interact only very slightly with electrons. For example, neutrons which penetrate a thickness of 10 cm of lead do not lose a measurable amount of energy, although the number of neutrons, all of them having the full energy, is diminished. Neutrons are very effective bombarding particles because of the large thickness of the targets which can be irradiated.

When positively charged bombarding particles are used, the cross section of any reaction becomes vanishingly small at low energies. However, neutrons are not repelled by positively charged nuclei, and nuclear reactions are found with very low energy neutrons, in targets of any atomic number.

The nuclear reactions are commonly of the (n,γ), (n,α), and (n,p) types. Most materials become radioactive as a result of neutron bombardment and many of the residual nuclei formed in these reactions are beta ray emitters. The $(n,2n)$ reaction, in which two neutrons are emitted, occurs when the bombarding neutrons have a high kinetic energy, the emitted neutrons having relatively small energies. Still another important reaction is the production of tritium by neutron bombardment, an example being

$$_3\mathrm{Li}^6 + {_0}\mathrm{n}^1 \rightarrow {_1}\mathrm{H}^3 + {_2}\mathrm{He}^4.$$

The available supplies of hydrogen of mass three ($_1\mathrm{H}^3$) are produced by exposing lithium, or another target, to the intense neutron flux in a nuclear reactor.

Absorption of Neutrons

When a well-collimated beam of fast neutrons is directed into a slab of material, neutrons are lost from the beam in several ways. Some neutrons are scattered elastically in collisions with the atomic nuclei of the absorber. There is small loss of kinetic energy when the scattering center is a massive nucleus, but considerable loss to recoiling light nuclei. A second process is inelastic scattering, in which the scattering nucleus is left in one of its low excited states. Inelastic scattering becomes common in heavy nuclei, which have many low excited states. Neutrons also are lost in various nuclear reactions. The number of events of any one kind is given by an expression $N\sigma n\, dx$, where σ is the "cross section" for the particular event, N is the number of neutrons in the beam, and n is the number of nuclei per unit volume in the absorber. By adding similar expressions for each type of event, the total number of events is $N\sigma_t n\, dx$, where the total cross section σ_t is the sum of the cross sections for the different events. Since each event represents the loss of a neutron from the collimated beam, the loss of neutrons in going through an absorber of thickness dx is

$$-dN = N\sigma_t n\, dx. \qquad (22\text{-}7)$$

The absorption of a neutron beam is rather similar to the absorption of a beam of gamma rays, which was described in terms of an absorption coefficient $\mu = -dN/N\, dx$. The absorption coefficient of a neutron beam is thus seen to be $n\sigma_t$. The absorption equation, obtained by integrating Eq. (7), is

$$N = N_0 e^{-n\sigma_t x}. \qquad (22\text{-}8)$$

The total neutron cross section in various materials and at various neutron energies is readily measurable. An absorber of thickness x is placed in a well-collimated beam and the intensity of neutrons N is compared to the intensity N_0 when the absorber is removed. The number of nuclei per unit volume n can be calculated from the density of the material. Eq. (8) can then be solved for the total neutron cross section in terms of known quantities. Besides the practical importance of such measurements, they are helpful in forming a picture of the nuclear structure. In some circumstances, and after certain corrections are made, the total cross section is equal to πr^2, where r is the "radius" of the nucleus. Nuclear radii, measured in this way, are found to vary with the cube root of the mass number of the nucleus, as given by the equation

$$r = r_0 A^{\frac{1}{3}}, \tag{22-9}$$

where r_0 is a constant which has the value $r_0 = 1.4 \times 10^{-13}$ cm. This relation implies that the volume of a nucleus $4\pi r^3/3$ is directly proportional to its mass, and that nuclear matter has a constant density. Other methods of measuring nuclear radii have not all given the same value of r_0, and there is also reason to doubt that the nuclear radius is sharply defined.

Thermal Neutrons

When a source of fast neutrons is placed inside an extended medium, neutrons may be scattered many times but are finally absorbed in nuclear reactions. In a medium containing elements of low mass number, the neutrons rapidly lose energy as a result of elastic scattering. Eq. (6) gives the energy loss in a single collision. In hydrogen, the energy loss varies from 0 to 100%, depending upon the angle of scattering. The angular distribution of recoiling protons is found to be such that the average energy loss is 50%. If W_0 is the initial neutron energy, the average energy after n collisions is $W_0(\frac{1}{2})^n$. Twenty collisions are required to reduce the average energy by a factor of about 10^6. The slowing down cannot proceed indefinitely because the hydrogen atoms have thermal energies which are imparted to the slowed neutrons. Eventually a neutron gas with a Maxwellian distribution of velocities exists within the hydrogenous material, and has the same temperature as its surroundings. The average energy of a neutron in the Maxwellian distribution is $3kT/2$. At room temperature, the average energy is $\frac{3}{2}(0.025)$ ev. These are usually called 0.025 ev neutrons, that being the energy which corresponds to the most probable velocity in the Maxwellian distribution. The existence of a Maxwellian distribution has been confirmed by experimental studies of neutrons emerging from a hole in the medium, although fast neutrons and partially slowed neutrons are mixed with the emergent beam of thermal neutrons.

Any material which is used to thermalize neutrons is called a "moderator." Paraffin, water, graphite, and heavy water (or deuterium oxide) are good moderators. The lighter the element, the smaller is the number of collisions required for a neutron to reach thermal energies. In all of these materials, neutrons are captured in (n,γ) reactions. It is therefore important that the cross section of the (n,γ) reaction be small, to extend the life of the neutrons in the moderator. Carbon and deuterium have lower capture cross sections than does hydrogen, and they are considered better moderator materials. The average neutron makes about 70 scattering collisions during its lifetime in ordinary water but about 16,000 collisions in heavy water and about 1100 collisions in pure graphite.

When a target is exposed to thermal neutrons, the number of nuclear reactions N_R can be expressed in terms of a cross section σ by the usual formula $N_R = N_0 \sigma \, n \, dx$, where N_0 is the number of neutrons striking the target and σ is the cross section of the reaction for neutrons of thermal energies. The equation can be rewritten as $N_R = (N_0/At)\sigma(nA \, dx)t$, where A is the area of the target and t is the duration of the exposure. The number of neutrons per unit area per second N_0/At is called the neutron flux Φ. The total number of target atoms is $N_1 = nA \, dx$. The number of reactions is given by

$$\boxed{N_R = \Phi\sigma N_1 t.} \tag{22-10}$$

Since the number of reactions is independent of the area presented to the neutron beam by the target, the number of reactions is the same whether the target is exposed to a broad incident beam, or to the isotropic flux inside a moderating material. In a unidirectional beam, the neutron flux can be expressed as $n_1 v$, where n_1 is the number of neutrons per unit volume and v is their velocity. When the neutrons are moving in all directions, the same concept of neutron flux is retained.

Targets are exposed to strong fluxes of thermal neutrons for the purpose of producing radioactive nuclides. The nuclide must be the residual nucleus in a nuclear reaction which has a positive Q-value. For example, carbon 14, which is useful as a radioactive tracer in biological investigations, can be made in the reaction

$$_6C^{13} + {_0}n^1 \rightarrow \gamma + {_6}C^{14} + Q \text{ (pos)}.$$

The method is especially effective because of the large neutron fluxes, of the order of 10^{13} neutrons/cm^2 sec, which are available in reactors. The value of the cross section for thermal neutrons is important information about any reaction.

Some of the cross sections for thermal neutrons are surprisingly high. The reaction

$$_{48}\text{Cd}^{113} + {}_0\text{n}^1 \rightarrow \gamma + {}_{48}\text{Cd}^{114}$$

has a cross section of about 21,000 barns. The cross section of the reaction

$$_5\text{B}^{10} + {}_0\text{n}^1 \rightarrow {}_2\text{He}^4 + {}_3\text{Li}^7$$

is 4000 barns. Both cadmium and boron are unusually good absorbers of thermal neutrons because of the presence of these isotopes in the normal mixture. These cross sections are very much larger than the projected area of a nucleus, and much larger than any cross section for fast neutrons. It has been suggested that the probability of a reaction should be proportional to the time spent by the neutron in the vicinity of the target nucleus, that is, that the cross section should be inversely proportional to the velocity of the neutron. This is called the $1/v$ law. It has been found to be exactly true for the $\text{B}^{10}(n,\alpha)$ reaction for all neutron energies below 1000 ev. It should be regarded as a trend to be expected at low energies where the de Broglie wavelength of the neutron is very much larger than the dimension of the nucleus. However, a curve of cross section versus neutron energy frequently shows peaks or resonances, attributable to excited states of the compound nucleus. The high cross section for thermal neutrons of the (n,γ) reaction in cadmium 113, is due to a resonance which has a peak at the neutron energy of 0.176 ev. The effect of the $1/v$ law is to make the cross section at resonance very much larger than it would be for a resonance at higher neutron energy.

Detection of Neutrons

To detect neutrons, one uses the established techniques for detecting fast charged particles. The neutrons themselves cannot be detected in this way, but they produce detectable particles in their interactions with matter. The fast charged particles are of three types: recoil particles produced in elastic collisions; fast particles produced in nuclear reactions, such as the (n,p) and (n,α) reactions; and radiation emitted in the beta decay of radioactive nuclei produced in nuclear reactions.

Many kinds of neutron detectors have been designed and used. In general, the number of counts obtained corresponds to the number of fast charged particles rather than to the number of neutrons falling on the detector. To determine the relative intensities of two neutron beams is not difficult. But to determine absolutely a neutron flux, in neutrons per cm^2 per sec, the cross section of a reaction or of elastic scattering must be known and the geometrical factors in the particular apparatus must be evaluated.

Photographic Emulsions. When a photographic emulsion is exposed to a beam of fast neutrons, the collisions with the hydrogen in the gelatin produce recoil protons which make tracks that are visible when the emulsion is examined under a microscope after having been developed. The energies of the protons can be determined from their ranges in the emulsion. Usually, the plate is exposed in such a way that the direction of the neutrons is parallel to the surface. Then those protons which recoil in the forward direction have the same energy as the neutrons. This is a laborious but reliable method of obtaining neutron energies. A cloud chamber, filled with hydrogen-rich gas such as methane, was used before the emulsion technique was developed.

Foil Activation. Foil activation techniques are often used to detect neutrons. A foil of a suitable material, such as indium, is exposed to the neutron beam for a definite time, then removed and placed near a Geiger counter, or other beta ray detector. The beta activity of the foil is a measure of the neutron flux. Each specific foil is best suited for the detection of neutrons of certain particular energies. This is because the curve of cross section versus neutron energy for the reaction which produces the radioactive nuclei usually exhibits resonances, and sometimes shows a threshold (when the Q-value of the reaction is negative). This energy discrimination is an advantage of the technique, although it frequently complicates the interpretation of the results.

BF$_3$ Counter. The "BF$_3$ proportional counter" is an effective detector of thermal neutrons. The boron trifluoride gas used to fill the counter is usually enriched in the boron-10 isotope, in which the reaction $B^{10}(n,\alpha)Li^7$ has a large cross section at thermal energies. The increase in kinetic energy is 2.79 Mev. The helium and lithium particles, both charged, produce in the counter a pulse of ionization which is larger than any pulse produced by a fast electron. By recording only the larger pulses, neutrons can be counted reliably in the presence of gamma radiation. The instrument can be used to detect fast neutrons also, by surrounding the counter tube with a sleeve of paraffin in which the neutrons lose energy and become thermal. Considerably less than one per cent of the fast neutrons which enter the paraffin sleeve are counted. The paraffin can be so arranged that the number of counts depends only upon the number of neutrons and not upon their energy. Such an arrangement is called a "long counter."

Scintillation Counters. A very efficient counter for fast neutrons can be designed, using the scintillation technique. There are a number of organic scintillating materials containing hydrogen in which recoil protons can be produced by fast neutrons. These materials include several which are single crystals, such as anthracene, and also certain solutions in organic solvents or in transparent plastic materials. The pulse sizes depend upon the energies of the recoil protons, which are the same as the energies of the neutrons only when the recoil occurs in the forward direction. By using a scintillator sufficiently large to absorb completely the neutron beam, an efficiency of 100% for counting fast neutrons is ideally attainable. A difficulty arises from the fact that some of the observed pulses are likely to be caused by fast electrons, produced by gamma radiation falling on the scintillator. Whether or not gamma rays are emitted from the source of neutrons, there are always gamma rays produced by inelastic scattering and capture of neutrons in the walls of the room.

Decay of the Neutron

The free neutron decays into a proton emitting a negative beta ray and a neutrino. The decay can be written as

$$n \rightarrow p + \beta^- + \nu.$$

The decrease of rest mass is 0.782 Mev, corresponding to the difference between the mass of the neutron and the mass of the hydrogen atom. When a large beam of thermal neutrons passes through an evacuated tube, fast electrons are observed originating in the vacuum. Hydrogen ions are produced simultaneously. From the number of proton-electron pairs and the intensity of the beam of neutrons, a half-life can be calculated. It is about 13 min.

Summary

The most probable velocity of a thermal neutron at room temperature is 2200 m/sec. In the time of one half-life, a typical distance traveled would be about 1600 km. Thus, only in interstellar space would any appreciable fraction of a free neutron beam disappear by beta ray emission.

The neutron, being uncharged, does not show any strong interaction with atomic electrons. It is a specifically nuclear particle. The source of free neutrons is always a nuclear reaction, and they vanish again in a short time in another nuclear reaction. In the interval between, they may collide with other nuclei of any mass number.

Neutrons, as compared to charged bombarding particles, are very effective in producing nuclear reactions. When a target is bombarded by fast charged particles, only a few particles per million produce nuclear reactions. The remainder lose their kinetic energy to the atomic electrons and become too slow to approach target nuclei against the electrostatic repulsion. Neutrons, however, can be virtually 100% effective in causing nuclear reactions. They penetrate large thicknesses of matter. Although they lose energy in nuclear collisions, the cross section of a reaction generally increases as the energy of the neutron decreases. The exceptions to this rule are caused by the frequent appearance of resonances in the cross section and by the fact that some reactions are endoergic. In the latter case, the particular nuclear reaction cannot occur if the energy of the neutron falls below a threshold value.

Exoergic reactions produced by neutrons can be a source of atomic energy. If, however, the neutrons are produced in nuclear reactions initiated by accelerated charged particles, the energy necessary to produce the neutrons is not balanced by the gains in using them.

Problems

1. What are the energies of recoil when 5.00 Mev neutrons make direct ("head-on") collisions with hydrogen, deuterium, and carbon?

    (Ans.: 5.00, 4.45, and 1.42 Mev.)

2. Calculate the Q-value of the $_4Be^9(\alpha,n)_6C^{12}$ reaction from the atomic masses: $_4Be^9$—9.01504, $_2He^4$—4.00387, $_6C^{12}$—12.00381, and $_0n^1$—1.00898.

    (Ans.: 5.70 Mev.)

3. The cross section of the reaction $Be^9(\alpha,n)C^{12}$ is 9×10^{-26} cm^2 at 3 Mev. A "thin" beryllium target of thickness 0.15 mg/cm^2 is bombarded with 30 μamp of doubly charged helium ions of that energy. How many neutrons are produced in a second?

    (Ans.: 8.46×10^7 neutrons/sec.)

4. Calculate the energy of neutrons which come from a very thin lithium target at 90° to the beam when it is bombarded by 2.15 Mev protons, the reaction being $_3Li^7(p,n)$ with a Q-value of -1.65 Mev.

    (Ans.: 0.17 Mev.)

5. Try to estimate the distance that a fast neutron will go in uranium metal (density 18.7 g/cm^3) before it collides with a nucleus. To do this, find the half-value thickness of a uranium absorber, calculating the absorption coefficient for fast neutrons from the cross section, using as the cross section the geometrical size of the nucleus itself.

    (Ans.: 6.2 cm.)

6. Calculate the density of nuclear matter from the formula for nuclear radii, $r = 1.4 \times 10^{-13}$(cm)A$^{1/3}$. Convert the answer to metric tons per cm^3.

    (Ans.: 1.4×10^8 tons/cm^3.)

7. The capture cross section for thermal neutrons in Cd^{113} is 21,000 barns at thermal energies. Cd has a density of 8.64 g/cm^3. Although the average atomic weight is about 113 amu, only 12.3% of the atoms are Cd^{113}. Calculate the thickness of cadmium required to reduce a beam of thermal neutrons to one thousandth of its initial intensity.

(Ans.: 0.058 cm.)

8. The $B^{10}(n,\alpha)$ reaction has a cross section of 4000 barns for neutrons which have been thermalized at room temperature (293° K). For neutrons which have been made thermal in a moderator cooled by liquid nitrogen to 77° K, what cross section would be expected?

(Ans.: 7800 barns.)

9. If a beam of 10^8 thermal neutrons per sec passes through an apparatus 25 cm in length, how many neutrons, decaying with a half-life of 13 min, would be expected to decay inside the apparatus each sec?

(Ans.: about 10 decays/sec.)

23 || Nuclear Structure

Before the discovery of the neutron, it was supposed that nuclei consisted of protons and electrons. In this picture, the number of protons was equal to the mass number A of the isotope. Any atom would then have a mass approximately equal to an integral multiple of the mass of the proton, as indeed is known to be true. The nucleus would also contain within itself a number of electrons which would reduce the nuclear charge to a value Ze appropriate for that element. For example, the nucleus of the carbon 13 atom $_6C^{13}$ would contain 13 protons and 7 electrons.

Composition of Nuclei

There were several objections to this analysis. The most serious objection was related to the de Broglie wavelength of an electron. It is especially apparent in a light nucleus such as in carbon, which has a nuclear radius of about 3×10^{-15} m. To completely confine an electron within a dimension of the order of 6×10^{-15} m would require that its wavelength be not longer than 12×10^{-15} m. Since $p = h/\lambda$, its momentum would be at least 5.5×10^{-20} kg m/sec, and its kinetic energy, calculated relativistically, would be more than 100 Mev. The electron would thus escape from the nucleus unless it had a negative potential energy greater in magnitude than 100 Mev. The potential energy of an electron at the surface of a carbon nucleus is smaller in magnitude than 3 Mev. Hence, a more exact calculation is not required to show that electrons cannot be confined within nuclei by coulomb attractive forces. A much stronger attractive force might hold it, but there is evidence that such forces do not exist. The observed deflections

TABLE 23-1. LIST OF SYMBOLS USED IN CHAPTER 23

Symbol	Name	Quantity Designated
Z		atomic number
A		mass number
N		number of neutrons in a nucleus
M		mass of an atom or particle
W_B		binding energy
W		energy
q		electric charge
ϵ_0	epsilon sub zero	permittivity of free space
r		polar coordinate, also nuclear radius
ρ	rho	charge density
S		average separation of energy levels
R		range of nuclear forces
h		Planck's constant
c		velocity of light

of electrons passing near or even through nuclei can be explained in terms of coulomb forces only.

Neutrons and protons have kinetic energies of the order of 6 Mev when their de Broglie wavelengths are short enough to permit confinement inside light nuclei. There is no objection to regarding these two particles as the ultimate constituents of nuclear matter. Strong attractive forces are, of course, required to hold them together and these are called "nuclear forces." That such forces do exist is apparent from the stability of nuclei, from the ease with which neutrons and protons can cause nuclear reactions, and from the strong scattering of neutrons and protons by atomic nuclei.

Both neutrons and protons are called "nucleons." The number of nucleons in the nucleus of an atom is its mass number A. The number of protons in a nucleus is its atomic number Z. The number of neutrons is thus $N = A - Z$. The isotopes of an element have the same number of protons but differ in the number of neutrons in their nuclear structure. The suitability of the term "nuclide," which is used in referring to a particular kind of atom, is apparent from the existence of nucleons in the atomic structure.

Forces and Models

The attractive nuclear forces can be classified as n-n, n-p, and p-p forces if they are presumed to act between each pair of nucleons separately. Between two protons, there is the coulomb repulsion of like charges as well as the attractive nuclear force. The nuclear forces are not yet fully understood. A large amount of information about them has been collected and various mathematical descriptions of the forces have been attempted, but no exact theory has been found to give quantitative agreement with all of the experimental facts.

If the nuclear forces were completely understood, it would be possible to determine the structure of nuclei by computation. In the absence of a complete theory, various hypotheses have been made about the manner in which neutrons and protons are bound in the nuclear structure. Each hypothesis is the basis of a particular model. A large number of models have been used. A good model explains some of the behavior of the nucleus and it may continue to be used even after it has been discredited as a complete or correct model. This is probably justifiable for as long as it is possible to believe that the ultimately correct model may resemble it in some respect. Some of the models which have been used are the alpha particle model, the liquid drop model, the uniform model, the optical model, and the shell model.

Binding Energies

The nucleus of $_6C^{12}$ should consist of 6 protons and 6 neutrons, and the atom should contain 6 extranuclear electrons to render it electrically neutral. If one attempts to calculate the mass of the atom from the masses of the particles of which it is composed, by adding 6 times the neutron mass (1.00898 amu) to 6 times the hydrogen mass (1.00814), the result is 12.10272 amu. However, the observed atomic mass, as given by mass spectroscopists is 12.00381 amu. The deficiency of mass in the stable atom is 0.09891 amu, which is equivalent to 92.1 Mev. A deficiency of this sort is to be expected from the equivalence of mass and energy. Work would have to be done upon the atom to separate it into the elementary particles of which it is composed. This deficiency of energy in the stable atom is called its "binding energy." A general formula for determining the binding energy W_B of any atom from its observed mass M is

$$W_B = \{ZM_H + (A - Z)M_n - M\}\ 931 \text{ Mev,} \qquad (23\text{-}1)$$

where M_H is the mass of one proton and one electron and M_n is the mass of the neutron. The factor 931 Mev is included to change amu into energy units.

A binding energy of 92.1 Mev is a large quantity, compared to which the binding of the electrons is negligible. It can be taken to represent the energy which would have to be supplied to separate the protons and neutrons in the nucleus. The average binding energy per nuclear particle is $W_B/A = 92.1$ Mev$/12 = 7.68$ Mev per particle. For comparison, the energy required to ionize an atom is 5 to 15 ev, and the energy required to remove a molecule of water from a drop of the liquid is 0.4 ev. This latter figure can be calculated from the heat of vaporization of water. This strong binding of the nuclear particles explains why atoms were once thought to be immutable.

The binding energy per particle can be computed for each known stable nuclide. When plotted against mass number, a graph is obtained

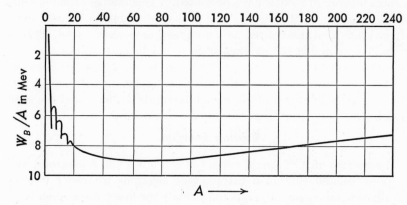

Fig. 23-1. Binding energy per particle for the stable elements.

which is sketched in Fig. 23-1. There is some indication that groups of four particles (two neutrons and two protons) are especially stable. The decrease in W_B/A for a large value of A is explainable because the heavy nuclei contain more protons and the electrostatic force of repulsion among them tends to reduce the binding. The most noteworthy feature of the curve is the general constancy of the binding energy at approximately 8 Mev per particle. Apparently, a nucleon is attracted by only a limited number of other nucleons even though the total number in the nucleus is quite large. This is referred to as the "saturation" character of nuclear forces.

Neutrons and protons have been ejected from nuclei by supplying energy in the form of a photon of high energy. These are called (γ,n) or (γ,p) reactions. Generally, the photons must have an energy of about 8 Mev for such effects to occur. However, there are some marked deviations from the average value. The (γ,n) reaction in C^{12} requires a 19 Mev gamma ray to remove the first neutron, whereas a 1.7 Mev gamma ray is sufficient in Be^9.

The Segre Chart

If the number of neutrons N in a nucleus is plotted against the number of protons Z, as shown in Fig. 23-2, each square represents a possible nuclide. The stable nuclides are marked. These occupy a region in

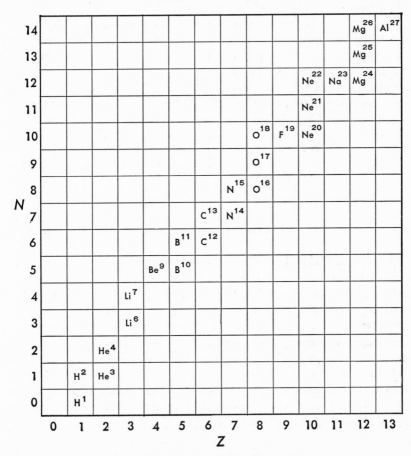

Fig. 23-2. A Segre chart.

the neighborhood of a 45° line in the lower portion of the chart shown here. Thus, the character of the nuclear forces must be such that stability is achieved only when the numbers of protons and neutrons are about equal.

At higher values of Z and N, the stable nuclides show an excess of neutrons. For example, the stable bismuth ($Z = 83$) isotope has a mass number of 209. It contains 126 neutrons and 83 protons. The neutron excess, $A - 2Z$, is 43. The neutron excess is easily explained, qualitatively. The repulsion of like charges tends to reduce the stability of nuclei which contain many protons. For a given mass number, greater stability is thus achieved with fewer protons. Except for the strong tendency for the numbers of protons and neutrons to be equal, an even larger neutron excess might be expected.

The complete list of stable nuclides shows a strong tendency for Z and N to be even integers. Table 23-2 lists the number of known stable nuclides in categories which depend upon the oddness or evenness of Z and N. The rule that stability is never attained when both Z and N are odd, has only four exceptions, all in very light nuclei. The nuclear forces must therefore be such that an odd particle is never very tightly bound.

TABLE 23-2. THE NUMBER OF KNOWN STABLE NUCLIDES

Z	N	Number
even	even	162
even	odd	55
odd	even	53
odd	odd	4

On a Segre chart, there are also spaces for the radioactive nuclides. Carbon 14 and other negative beta ray emitters occupy spaces above the region of stability. They are the nuclides which have too many neutrons to be stable. A neutron inside the nucleus changes to a proton which remains inside, a negative beta ray and a neutrino being emitted. The daughter element is stable, or it is at least nearer to the region of stability. Nitrogen 13 and other positive beta ray emitters lie below the region of stability, in a region that they share with those radioactive nuclides which decay by electron capture. These are the nuclides which have too many protons to be stable. A proton inside the nucleus changes into a neutron, in one of two processes:

$$p \rightarrow n + \beta^+ + \nu$$

or

$$p + e^- \rightarrow n + \nu.$$

Neither of these processes occurs with free protons or in hydrogen because a decrease of rest mass is required.

The beta processes are mechanisms by which nuclei can achieve the most stable ratio of neutrons to protons without any change in the mass number. For each mass number A, there should be one or more nuclides which are stable against beta decay. This is found to be true. On the other hand, there are values of N and of Z for which no nuclide exists which is stable against beta decay. The rule that each value of A must be represented, has apparent exceptions when A is 5 and 8. However, the beryllium isotope $_4\text{Be}^8$ is stable against beta decay. Its mass is slightly greater than the mass of two helium atoms. Whenever it is formed, as it is for example in the decay process

$$_3\text{Li}^8 \rightarrow \beta^- + \nu + {}_4\text{Be}^8,$$

it immediately breaks up into two alpha particles. Similarly, $_3\text{Li}^5$ and $_2\text{He}^5$ emit a proton or a neutron respectively, whenever they are formed. The alpha particle is a very tightly bound structure of two neutrons and two protons, but the force on a third neutron or proton is not sufficient to cause binding. This is a special example of the "saturation" character of nuclear forces.

On the Segre chart, most of the alpha particle emitters fall in the region of beta stability, but only at its upper end from about $Z = 80$ to $Z = 92$ and upward. The protons and neutrons which make up the alpha particle are "bound" in these nuclei, in the sense that the nuclear attractive forces are greater than the coulomb repulsive force. However,

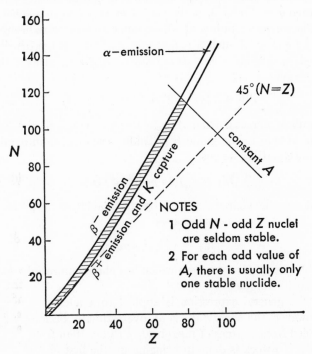

Fig. 23-3. An idealized Segre chart.

the attractive forces are of very short range, that is, they are appreciable over only a small distance, whereas the coulomb repulsion acts over a large distance. The alpha particle is repelled once it escapes the short distance in which the attractive forces are effective.

Fig. 23-3 is a somewhat idealized Segre chart in which the regions of stability and of instability have been indicated.

The Coulomb Energy

We have seen the importance of coulomb repulsion as a factor affecting nuclear structure. The coulomb energy of the nucleus can be calculated by use of an oversimplified picture of the nucleus as a sphere of well-defined radius, inside which the electric charge is uniformly distributed.

The potential energy dW of a charge dq at a distance r from another charge q is

$$dW = q \, dq / 4\pi\epsilon_0 \, r.$$

This is the work required to bring a charge dq from infinity to the surface of a sphere of radius r. If there is a uniform charge density ρ inside the sphere, then $q = 4\pi r^3 \rho/3$. If the charge dq is placed in a spherical shell (about the sphere of radius r) whose inner and outer radii are r and $r + dr$, where dr is of such a magnitude that the charge density in the shell also is ρ, then $dq = 4\pi r^2 \, dr \, \rho$. Expressing dW in terms of the radius r, one then gets

$$dW = (4\pi r^3 \rho/3)(4\pi r^2 \, dr \, \rho)/4\pi\epsilon_0 \, r.$$

As the radius increases from zero to its final value r_1, the energy increases from zero to the value W_1. Taking the definite integral of both sides of the equation, we get

$$W_1 = (\tfrac{3}{5})(4\pi \rho/3)^2 \, r_1{}^5/4\pi\epsilon_0.$$

Now replacing the charge density ρ by the final charge q_1 divided by the volume $4\pi r_1{}^3/3$, the energy becomes

$$W_1 = (\tfrac{3}{5})q_1{}^2/4\pi\epsilon_0 \, r_1.$$

This is the energy of any sphere which has charge uniformly distributed throughout its volume.

When the general expression is applied to a nucleus, the charge q_1 is Ze. However, the energy W_1 is an overestimate, because the nucleus is assembled from charges of magnitude e rather than from infinitesimal charges dq. No work is done in bringing up the first charge e, although the formula implies that work equal to $(\tfrac{3}{5})e^2/4\pi\epsilon_0 \, r_1$ is done. We shall subtract Z times this quantity to obtain the coulomb energy W_{coul} of the nucleus. This is thus given by

$$W_{coul} = (\tfrac{3}{5})Z(Z-1)e^2/4\pi\epsilon_0\, r, \qquad (23\text{-}2)$$

where r instead of r_1 is now used to denote the nuclear radius.

If now the formula $r = r_0 A^{1/3}$, with $r_0 = 1.4 \times 10^{-13}$ cm, is used to calculate the radius of the nucleus, the coulomb energy can be evaluated. For example, the radius of the uranium 238 isotope is 8.7×10^{-15} m. Inserting this value for r, and $Z = 92$, the coulomb energy is 835 Mev. This is 3.5 Mev per particle. The effect of the coulomb repulsion is to reduce the binding energy from about 11.0 Mev per particle to its observed value of 7.5 Mev per particle. This numerical result shows that the coulomb energy is by no means negligible, but the result is probably in error because the radius was obtained from measurements of total neutron cross sections. Other evidence points to the effective radius of the charge distribution being about 20% smaller.

Mirror Nuclei

If all the protons in a given nucleus are changed to neutrons and all the neutrons are changed to protons, the resulting nucleus is a kind of mirror image, and the pair are called "mirror nuclei." The isobars $_6C^{13}$ and $_7N^{13}$ are examples. The first has 6 protons and 7 neutrons, the second has 6 neutrons and 7 protons.

An interesting comparison can be made of the masses of two atoms which have mirror nuclei. Recalling that

$$M = ZM_H + (A - Z)M_n - W_B, \qquad (23\text{-}3)$$

the atom with the extra neutron should have a mass which is greater by the amount $M_n - M_H = 1.00898 - 1.00814 = 0.00084$ amu $= 0.78$ Mev. However, the binding energies of the two nuclei must also be compared.

Two mirror nuclei have the same number of proton-neutron pairs and the binding energy should thus not differ as far as n-p forces are concerned. The nucleus which has the greater number of neutrons has more n-n bonds, and the one with the greater number of protons has more p-p bonds. If, however, the n-n bonds and the attractive p-p bonds are exactly equal in strength, there should be no difference in binding energies as far as nuclear forces are concerned. The coulomb energies of the two nuclei are different. These can be calculated from Eq. (2). Since the radius of a nucleus depends upon A, both nuclei have the same radius, namely 3.3×10^{-15} m. The coulomb energies are 7.85 Mev for $_6C^{13}$, and 11.0 Mev for $_7N^{13}$. Since the coulomb energy reduces the binding energy of a nucleus, the mass of $_7N^{13}$ should therefore exceed the mass of $_6C^{13}$ by 3.15 Mev.

Combining the two computed differences, the expected difference in mass is $3.15 - 0.78 = 2.37$ Mev. From tables of atomic masses, nitrogen 13 is in fact the more massive atom by an amount equal to 2.23 Mev. The agreement is good considering the uncertainty in nuclear radii and also the naïve assumption that the charge radius would be the same in two nuclei containing unequal numbers of protons.

The success of the comparison of masses is strong evidence that n-n forces and p-p forces are to be regarded as the same. There is also evidence that the n-p forces and the p-p forces are equal. This evidence comes from experimental studies of the scattering of neutrons and protons in hydrogen. The scattering of protons is, of course, also affected by coulomb forces, and an analysis of the scattering data is required to determine the strength of the attractive nuclear forces.

Mirror nuclei can exist in excited states as well as in the normal (ground) state. Each state can be considered a different configuration of the nuclear particles, to which the same calculation of mass difference should apply. To any configuration of N neutrons and Z protons, there should correspond a mirror configuration of Z neutrons and N protons. For each excited state of a nucleus, there should be an excited state of its mirror nucleus, with the same mass difference, and therefore at the same energy of excitation above its normal state. This has also been found to be true. Below an energy of excitation of 6 Mev, the carbon 13 nucleus has just three excited energy levels, at 3.09, 3.68, and 3.86 Mev. Nitrogen 13 also has just three excited levels, at 2.37, 3.51, and 3.56 Mev. Exact agreement is not to be expected because the nuclear radius is not likely to remain the same for each excited state.

The Exclusion Principle

The tendency in stable nuclei for the number of neutrons to equal the number of protons can be explained as a consequence of the Pauli exclusion principle. As applied to nuclear particles, it states that only two neutrons and two protons, with spins oppositely oriented, can occupy an energy level defined by a set of three spatial quantum numbers.

To clarify the argument, a highly idealized nucleus is represented in Fig. 23-4. The cup is the potential well for any one nucleon. Its shape could be calculated from a complete knowledge of the forces which confine a nucleon inside the nucleus. The horizontal lines represent energy levels which can be occupied by nucleons, each level being completely defined by a set of three spatial quantum numbers. The levels are represented as being equally spaced for simplicity; the separation of levels is S in energy units. If N neutrons and Z protons occupy the well, they fall into the lowest permissible energy states. The low states

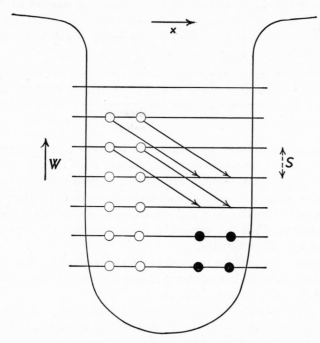

Fig. 23-4. Nucleons in a potential well.

become completely filled, but the excess neutrons $(N - Z)$ occupy half-filled levels. Half of these neutrons, i.e. $(N - Z)/2$, can fall into states of lower energy, as indicated by the arrows, if they change into protons. As long as they remain neutrons, they have extra energy, $2S$ for each neutron in the diagram, but $S(N - Z)/4$ in the general case. The nucleus as a whole has an extra energy equal to $S(N - Z)^2/8$. This is the energy of asymmetry, which is positive whether the excess particles are neutrons or protons. The asymmetry energy is zero when $N = Z$. It should be noted that, among other approximations, the mass difference between the neutron and the proton as well as the coulomb energy have been completely neglected.

Nuclei with larger asymmetries have smaller binding energies and larger masses. They tend to decay in beta processes to daughter nuclei of lesser asymmetry, that is into nuclei in which N is more nearly equal to Z. However, at large mass numbers, the stable nuclides have a neutron excess. This is a coulomb effect.

The Empirical Mass Formula

In principle it should be possible to calculate the mass of an atom of any A and Z. The "semiempirical mass formula" serves this purpose. In its simplest form, it gives the binding energy W_B of a nucleus as a function of A and Z. The formula is

$$W_B = a_1A - a_2A^{2/3} - a_3Z(Z-1)A^{-1/3} - a_4(A-2Z)^2A^{-1} \pm a_5.$$

(23-4)

There are five arbitrary constants, the five a's, in the formula. In principle, the five constants can be evaluated from the known masses of five atoms, and the formula can then be used to calculate the mass of any other atom, whether stable or radioactive. However, the formula is only a fair approximation and a number of authors have published different values of the five constants which seem to give the best fit to particular experimental data.

It is understood that the formula applies only when the nuclei are in their normal states of lowest energy. Each term has a theoretical basis of some kind. The third term represents the coulomb energy which is made negative because it reduces the binding energy. The coulomb energy is proportional to $Z(Z-1)/r$. The only change here is to represent the radius as proportional to $A^{1/3}$. The fourth term is the asymmetry energy, which also reduces the binding energy. In the previous section, the asymmetry energy was found to be approximately proportional to $S(N-Z)^2$, where S is the distance between the energy levels. Here, $(N-Z)$ has been written $(A-2Z)$, and the spacing of the energy levels has been taken to be inversely proportional to the volume of the nucleus, that is, inversely proportional to A. The fifth term is more empirical. Nothing else in the formula suggests that the binding energy should depend upon the oddness or evenness of N and Z. The term a_5 should be made positive when both N and Z are even, negative when they are both odd, and zero when one is odd and the other even. By following this rule, the high stability of even-even nuclides receives some recognition.

The first two terms of the formula are based upon the "liquid drop model" of the nucleus. The molecules in a drop of liquid are held together by forces of the van der Waals type. Because of their short range, each molecule in the liquid is attracted to only a limited number of nearby molecules. A molecule in the interior of the liquid has a full complement of near neighbors, and it is fully bound, the binding energy being a_1. If there are A molecules, the total binding is a_1A. This is the first term in the formula. The second term is a correction to the first term. A molecule near the surface does not have as many near neighbors, and it is not as tightly bound. The correction is proportional to the number of molecules near the surface, that is, to the surface area $4\pi r^2$, and hence to the quantity $A^{2/3}$. In a liquid, the smaller binding of surface molecules accounts for the surface tension of the liquid. The second term can be referred to as the "surface energy," and the first term as the "volume binding energy."

The great advantage of the empirical mass formula is that it formulates the known trends in the variation of the masses, in terms of which the stability and instability of nuclei are usually understood. Any large deviation from these trends may be a clue to a greater understanding of nuclear structure. Certain nuclei have been found to have greater binding energy than would be expected. Whenever the number of neutrons N or the number of protons Z is equal to 2, 8, 20, 50, 82, or 126, the binding energy is unusually large. These are called "magic numbers," because the first evidence was purely empirical. The lead isotope $_{82}\text{Pb}^{208}$ has especially tight binding, being doubly magic with $Z = 82$ and $N = 126$.

In the electronic structure, the numbers 2, 10, 18, 36, 54, and 86 might have been called "magic," since they are the numbers of electrons in the structures of the noble gases. The absence of chemical binding for these gases is attributed to the unusually tight binding of the electrons, which is related to the stability of the filled shells of electrons.

Apparently, nuclear particles also have shells in which the particles have quantum numbers corresponding to well-defined orbital motions. In the "shell model," the nuclear particles do not suffer collisions which disturb their motion, as they would if they resembled molecules in a liquid drop.

The Yukawa Particle

Although nuclear forces differ from any other known forces, they resemble chemical binding forces such as the binding of two hydrogen atoms to form a hydrogen molecule. Both forces show saturation characteristics. Two hydrogen atoms form a bond, but a third atom does not attach itself to the molecule. Similarly, the alpha particle, with two neutrons and two protons, is strongly bound but a fifth particle does not form a stable structure.

Chemical binding results from the exchange of electrons between two atoms. An electron has smaller energy in the molecule than it does in an atom, and this energy difference must be supplied if the molecule is to be separated into atoms. The smaller energy in a molecule is partly potential and partly kinetic. The large volume of the molecule makes possible a longer wavelength and a smaller momentum. Yukawa set out to find the mass of a particle which, if it were exchanged between nucleons, would account for nuclear binding.

Suppose a nucleon denoted by Y can decay into itself emitting a Yukawa particle y. The decay equation would be written

$$Y \rightarrow y + Y.$$

The emitted particle might be neutral or it might be charged. If it is charged, the nucleon would change from a proton to a neutron, or vice versa. We are not at the moment concerned with the effects of electric charge.

If a decay of this kind should occur, it would violate the law of conservation of energy, by an amount equal to the energy equivalent $M_y c^2$ of the rest mass of the emitted particle M_y. Heisenberg's uncertainty principle, $\Delta W \, \Delta t = h/2\pi$, might be interpreted to mean that a violation of energy conservation by an amount ΔW is possible if it occurs only for a time of the order of Δt. In this time, the emitted particle would travel a distance $v \, \Delta t$. Its velocity would depend upon the degree to which energy conservation is violated but it would not be greater than the velocity of light c. The maximum distance R traveled by the Yukawa particle from its parent nucleon would be

$$R = c \, \Delta t = hc/2\pi \, \Delta W = hc/2\pi M_y c^2.$$

If two nucleons are separated by a distance greater than R, there could be no exchange of particles between them. If they are closer than R, exchange of Yukawa particles is possible and a force between them may exist. Thus, R is the range of nuclear forces. The range of nuclear forces is known from experiments on the scattering of neutrons in hydrogen and other data. Its value is about 2×10^{-15} m. Therefore, the energy equivalent of the rest mass of the exchange particle is

$$\boxed{M_y c^2 = hc/2\pi R = 1.58 \times 10^{-11} \text{ joules} = 100 \text{ Mev.}}$$

The rest mass of the electron is equivalent to 0.51 Mev. Thus, an exchange particle with a mass about 200 times greater than the electronic mass would be needed to explain nuclear forces. In 1934, no such particle was known, but one was discovered later, in studies of cosmic radiation.

Cosmic rays are positively charged particles of high energy which approach the earth from all directions. They consist of the nuclei of atoms, for the most part of protons and alpha particles, but also including iron nuclei and the like. The individual nuclei have energies up to 10^{14} ev or even higher. The manner in which they are accelerated is still a subject of speculation. At such high energies the nuclear binding is relatively negligible. When cosmic rays strike nuclei in the upper atmosphere, the collisions are essentially between nucleon pairs. Particles called pi-mesons are produced in the collisions and these are believed to be the Yukawa particles. The pi-mesons are positively or negatively charged, or neutral. The charged pi-mesons have a rest mass of 273 m_0, where m_0 is the rest mass of the electron. Some of them produce nuclear reactions and the remainder decay with a mean life of the order of 2×10^{-8} sec. The decay of a pi-meson produces a mu-meson and a neutrino. The mu-meson has a mass of 207 m_0. It decays, with a mean life of 2.15×10^{-6} sec, into an electron and neutrinos. The decays can be written as

$$\pi \rightarrow \mu + \nu$$

and

$$\mu \rightarrow e + 2\nu.$$

The cosmic ray particles which penetrate the atmosphere and reach the surface of the earth are the mu-mesons. Because of their mass, they were once thought to be the Yukawa particles, but this mistake was corrected when mu-mesons were found to interact less strongly with nuclei than was expected.

Besides pi-mesons, many other particles are produced in high energy collisions. The investigation of these particles is an active branch of physics. To a rapidly increasing extent, very high voltage machines are being used in this field.

Summary

Ordinary matter consists of electrons, protons, and neutrons. The neutrons do not affect the chemical properties of materials, but do make up more than half of their mass. Free neutrons do not exist in nature, except for a small number from reactions caused by cosmic radiation. Free neutrons are rare because of the strong forces which bind neutrons and protons into nuclear structures.

The forces which bind neutrons and protons are the so-called exchange forces, resulting from the virtual emission and reabsorption of pi-mesons. Each nuclear particle is the center of a cloud of pi-mesons. Although they are important components in nuclear structure, their number is indeterminate. No mathematical formulation of the force problem has yet given agreement with all of the experimental findings.

The structure consisting of protons and neutrons in the nucleus has some resemblance to the extranuclear electronic structure. The particles are in well-defined orbits which are properly described in terms of quantum mechanics. Spatial quantum numbers define the orbits, but the energy of the particle in that orbit depends upon factors which are not fully understood. One important difference between the extranuclear and nuclear structures is that electrons move about a nucleus which is the dominant center of force in the atom, whereas nuclear particles have no stabilizing center of force. Each nucleon moves in a field of force set up by other nucleons. If the nucleus should be spatially deformed, the field of force alters also. This gives nuclei a fluidity which atomic structures do not possess.

Problems

1. What is the average binding energy per nuclear particle in nitrogen 14, which has an atomic mass of 14.00752 amu?

    (Ans.: 7.47 Mev per particle.)

2. Calculate the energy of a gamma ray which is just sufficient to remove (a) one neutron or (b) one proton from nitrogen 14 (mass 14.00752 amu). The atomic mass of nitrogen 13 is 13.00994 amu, and of carbon 13 is 13.00753 amu.

    (Ans.: 10.61 Mev; 7.59 Mev.)

3. From an examination of Fig. 23-2, classify the following radioactive nuclei as β^+ or β^- emitters: $_1H^3$, $_2He^6$, $_4Be^{12}$, $_6C^{11}$, $_7N^{16}$, $_9F^{18}$, $_{11}Na^{22}$, $_{11}Na^{24}$, $_{12}Mg^{22}$, and $_{13}Al^{26}$.

4. From the fact that beryllium 8, whenever it is formed in its ground state, breaks up into alpha particles, each of energy 48 kev, calculate the atomic mass of beryllium 8. The helium mass is 4.00386 amu.

    (Ans.: 8.00782 amu.)

5. Calculate (a) the neutron excess and (b) the coulomb energy, in Mev per nuclear particle, of $_{45}Rh^{103}$, as a typical example of the magnitudes of these quantities at about the middle of the periodic table.

    (Ans.: 13; 2.53 Mev per particle.)

6. Calculate (a) the difference between the atomic masses of $_{12}Mg^{23}$ and $_{11}Na^{23}$ from the theory of mirror nuclei, and also (b) from the observed end point of the β^+ spectrum of magnesium 23, which is at 2.99 Mev.

    (Ans.: 3.99 Mev; 4.01 Mev.)

24 | Atomic Energy

The practical use of the energy developed in nuclear reactions and in radioactive decay seemed impossible until the discovery in 1940 of a new type of reaction, called *fission*. This fission process made possible the development of atomic energy for power and other uses. However, fission reactions are not the only basis for the utilization of atomic energy. Another type, called *thermonuclear reactions* has been used to enhance the energy available from fission. Theromonuclear reactions are potentially an independent source of power, when certain technical difficulties have been solved.

Fission

When uranium was first bombarded by neutrons, a large number of radioactive nuclides were found to be produced. For some years, experimentalists studying these effects found it difficult to identify the radioactive nuclides, because they expected them to be residual nuclei produced in familiar types of nuclear reactions. The difficulty was solved after Hahn and Strassman, as a result of an exhaustive chemical study, found that an isotope of barium (atomic number 56) was one of the products of the neutron bombardment of uranium (atomic number 92). This could not be explained in terms of the then known types of nuclear reactions.

The term fission is used for the new process in which the nucleus, after capturing a neutron, splits into two fragments of more or less equal mass which then move apart with high velocity. Once this mechanism was postulated, its experimental verification proved easy. The fast fission fragments are highly charged. The ion density along their tracks is proportional to the square of their charges. The voltage pulse ob-

407

TABLE 24-1. LIST OF SYMBOLS USED IN CHAPTER 24

Symbol	Name	Quantity Designated
λ	lambda	decay constant
I		intensity of radiation
t		time
$σ$	sigma	cross section
$μ$	mu	absorption coefficient
n		number of generations
k		multiplication of neutrons per generation
$ν$	nu	average number of neutrons per fission
$η$	eta	number of fissions per thermal neutron absorbed
$ε$	epsilon	fast fission factor
p		resonance escape probability
f		fraction of neutrons which escape capture in other materials
L		non-leakage probability

tained from a few millimeters of track is about two orders of magnitude larger than the pulse produced by an alpha particle. Such pulses can be observed in an ionization chamber, built to detect single alpha particles, by depositing a layer of a uranium compound upon the electrodes and irradiating the chamber with a beam of neutrons. It has not been possible to determine the atomic number of a fragment from its pulse size because a fast fragment carries with it some extranuclear electrons which reduce its effective charge for production of ionization.

The fission fragments have ranges of several centimeters in air. If a sheet of paper is placed 1 cm from a layer of uranium irradiated by neutrons, the paper will become radioactive because the fragments will be deposited on it. The paper can be brought up to a beta ray detector, such as a thin-walled Geiger counter, and its activity measured. The heavy residual nuclei which are produced in other reactions are retained in targets since their energies of recoil are much smaller.

Fission Fragments

From an inspection of the curve of binding energy per particle (as a function of mass number), it is apparent that the nuclear particles are more tightly bound in medium nuclei than in heavy nuclei, by approximately 1 Mev per particle. Since there are over 200 nuclear particles in heavy nuclei, the energy released in fission should then be of the order of 200 Mev. The average observed kinetic energy of the two fission fragments is 170 Mev. Not all of the available energy appears as kinetic energy of the fragments, because these are beta radioactive in their ground states.

The tracks of the fission fragments show dense ionization. When observed in a cloud chamber, they show short side tracks, which are

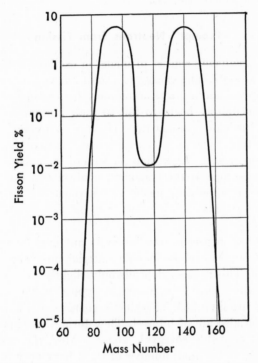

Fig. 24-1. Yield of various atomic masses from the fission of U²³⁵.

caused by secondary massive particles originating in the track of the fragment. These are explained as being caused by Rutherford scattering. The probability of scattering depends upon the product of two nuclear charges Zze^2 and is, therefore, high for fission fragments. However, the fragments tend to be more massive than the scattering centers and the latter recoil from the collision with an appreciable fraction of the energy of the fragment.

The kinetic energy of fission is not shared equally by the two fragments. For a reason which is not clear, the fission into two fragments of exactly equal mass is improbable. In the most probable fission, one fragment is about 50% heavier than the other. Fig. 24-1 shows the probability of the occurrence of various masses as a function of the mass number of the fragment. The probability is expressed as a fission yield in percent, the total fission yield for all mass numbers adding up to 200%. When the fission is caused by neutrons of negligible momentum, the two fission fragments must have equal momenta in opposite directions. The inequality of masses leads to an unequal sharing of the available kinetic energy.

"Prompt" Neutrons from Fission

The fission fragments consist of nuclei in excited states rather than in their normal state. The energy of excitation varies but it is of the order of 15 Mev. Gamma rays accompany fission, indicating that the fragments immediately begin to fall to their normal states, emitting the so-called "prompt" gamma rays. However, "prompt" neutrons are also emitted. If the energy of excitation is sufficiently high that the mass of the fragment is larger than the sum of the masses of a neutron and the lower isotope of the fragment, neutron emission is to be expected. When the liquid-drop model was in vogue, it was convenient to think of the fragments as being hot, and cooling by radiation and by evaporation.

The number of neutrons per fission is an important quantity. It varies greatly, but for each fissionable material, an average number has been measured. This number depends only slightly upon the energy of the neutrons which cause the fission. A typical value is 2.5 neutrons per fission for uranium 235. The kinetic energies of the neutrons produced in fission also are of interest. They form a continuous distribution; the most probable energy is about 1 Mev, the average energy is about 2 Mev, and a small number of them have very large energies, as great as 16 Mev.

Products of Fission

It is easy to show that the fission fragments should be negative beta ray emitters. The heavy elements which undergo fission have a large neutron excess, which when expressed as a fraction of the mass number $(A - 2Z)/A$ is about 22%. The fission fragments are expected to have nearly the same neutron excess, from the manner in which they are formed. However, the stable elements near the middle of the periodic table have neutron excesses of about 15%. The fission fragments, then, have too many neutrons to be stable. Hence, they emit negative beta rays, a chain of beta ray emissions usually being necessary before complete stability is achieved.

Fission, like other nuclear reactions, can be represented by equations. An example, representing only one of the possible modes of fission, is:

$$_{92}U^{235} + _{0}n^{1} \rightarrow (_{56}Ba^{144})* + (_{36}Kr^{92})* + 170 \text{ Mev}; \quad (24\text{-}1)$$

$$\left. \begin{array}{l} (_{56}Ba^{144})* \rightarrow _{0}n^{1} + \gamma + _{56}Ba^{143}, \\[4pt] (_{36}Kr^{92})* \rightarrow _{0}n^{1} + _{0}n^{1} + _{36}Kr^{90}; \end{array} \right\} \quad (24\text{-}2)$$

$$\left. \begin{array}{l} _{56}Ba^{143} \rightarrow _{57}La^{143} \rightarrow _{58}Ce^{143} \rightarrow _{59}Pr^{143} \rightarrow _{60}Nd^{143} \text{ (stable)}, \\[4pt] \text{and} \\[4pt] _{36}Kr^{90} \rightarrow _{37}Rb^{90} \rightarrow _{38}Sr^{90} \rightarrow _{39}Y^{90} \rightarrow _{40}Zr^{90} \text{ (stable)}. \end{array} \right\} \quad (24\text{-}3)$$

Eq. (1) represents the neutron induced fission into excited fission fragments, Eq. (2) represents the prompt emission of gamma rays and neutrons, and Eq. (3) represents successive decays with the emission of negative beta rays and neutrinos.

Each radioactive product of fission can, if its half-life is not too short, be chemically separated and its half-life measured. A number of previously unknown radioactive substances have been found in this way. The mixture of radioactivities can also be treated statistically. If a large amount of fission is produced in a short time, we can assume that atoms with a wide distribution of decay constants are initially present. At a later time t, the radioactivity is largely due to nuclides which have a mean-life $(1/\lambda)$ of the order of t. If the mean-life of a nuclide is very much less, it will have decayed before the time t. If the mean-life is very much larger than t, its decay constant is too small to make much contribution to the beta activity, assuming that there are not an unduly large number of such atoms. Then at time t, $-dI/I\,dt = \lambda$, where I is the intensity of the beta radiation, and λ is the decay constant of the nuclides which have a mean-life of the order of t. Therefore, $\lambda = k/t$, where k is a quantity which is not known but which might be of the order of unity. The differential equation then becomes

$$dI/I = -k\,dt/t. \quad (24\text{-}4)$$

If k is a constant, integration yields

$$\ln I = -k \ln t + \ln A,$$

whence

$$\boxed{I = At^{-k}.} \quad (24\text{-}5)$$

Values calculated from this equation have been found to agree with the experimental data, after the first few seconds, with a value of k

equal to 1.2. Approximately then, the intensity of the beta radiation from the fission products is inversely proportional to the time.

Delayed Neutrons

Besides the prompt neutrons from fission, delayed neutrons are emitted by the fission products. The number of delayed neutrons decreases with time according to the well-known decay curve. There are a number of half-lives present, typical values being 1.5, 4.5, 22, and

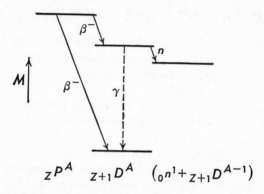

$$_{Z}P^{A} \quad _{Z+1}D^{A} \quad (_{0}n^{1} + _{Z+1}D^{A-1})$$

Fig. 24-2. Neutron emission following beta decay.

56 sec. An explanation of this is required because neutrons, when their emission is energetically possible, are usually emitted too rapidly for a half-life to be measured.

Fig. 24-2 illustrates the emission of the delayed neutrons. Neutrons are emitted in coincidence with beta rays, and the half-life is typical of beta decay. A radioactive parent $_{Z}P^{A}$ emits beta rays leaving the daughter element $_{Z+1}D^{A}$ in its normal state. It also emits beta rays of smaller energy leaving the daughter in a high excited state, from which gamma ray emission would normally be expected. When, however, the mass of the daughter atom in its nuclear excited state is greater than the sum of the masses of a neutron and the next lower isotope $_{Z+1}D^{A-1}$, neutron emission is energetically possible and it occurs without further delay. The apparent half-life for the neutron emission is the half-life of the beta emitting parent $_{Z}P^{A}$.

Delayed neutrons have a great practical importance in reactor technology, although their number is small. The number of delayed neutrons is only 0.73% of the total number of neutrons emitted in fission, when the fission of uranium 235 is caused by thermal neutrons.

The Fission Process

In a few of the heavy elements there is a slow rate of spontaneous fission. The two isotopes of normal uranium are uranium 238 with an atomic abundance of 99.3% and uranium 235 with an abundance of 0.7%. In a kilogram of pure uranium 238, about seven atoms per second decay by spontaneous fission. Thus, uranium 238 would have a half-life of 8×10^{15} years if fission were the only mode of decay.

In order to undergo spontaneous fission, a spherical nucleus would become more and more deformed until it finally separated into two fragments. Fig. 24-3 shows a spherical nucleus (a) and the same nucleus

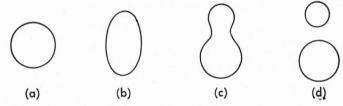

(a)   (b)   (c)   (d)

Fig. 24-3. Deformation and separation of a spherical nucleus into fission fragments.

after separation into two fission fragments (d). Intermediate stages of deformation are suggested by (b) and (c). If the stable shape of a nucleus is a sphere, it follows that a slightly deformed shape such as (b) must have a higher potential energy. As the deformation proceeds, a state of lower potential energy is reached before the two fragments become widely separated. The problem of calculating the probability of spontaneous fission then resolves itself into a calculation of the likelihood that a system will go through states of higher potential energy to reach a state of lower potential energy. This probability is zero in classical mechanics unless energy is supplied from outside the system, but a finite result is obtained in a quantum mechanical calculation. This is analogous to alpha particle emission through a potential barrier, and spontaneous fission is described as a barrier problem.

Supplying energy to the nucleus increases the probability of fission. If enough energy is supplied, fission can be regarded as instantaneous for practical purposes. Gamma ray bombardment of heavy nuclei can cause fission. Also, any incident particle of high kinetic energy can cause fission, if enough energy is supplied in the collision. The fission of uranium 235 by thermal neutrons can be explained in a similar way. The capture of thermal neutrons in most nuclei is followed by the emission of about 8 Mev of energy in the form of gamma radiation. After the neutron is captured and before the gamma rays are emitted, the nucleus has an excitation energy of about 8 Mev. This energy is available to cause fission.

Fissionable Materials

There are three heavy nuclides which are available in large quantities. These are the parents of long life of the three natural radioactive chains, namely, uranium 238, uranium 235, and thorium 232. Only in uranium 235 can thermal neutrons cause fission. The energy available from the capture of a thermal neutron is insufficient in uranium 238 and thorium 232. If, however, neutrons with kinetic energies above 1 Mev are captured in uranium 238, fission occurs. This is called a "threshold" for fission, but it is not a sharp threshold, rather it is the energy at which the probability of fission becomes appreciable. Similarly, thorium 232 has a "threshold" for fission at a neutron energy of about 1.5 Mev.

Because of the importance of fission by thermal neutrons in reactor technology, uranium 235 can be called a "good" fissionable material. Two other good fissionable materials can be produced in quantity by bombardment of uranium 238 and thorium 232 by neutrons. They are therefore referred to as "breeder" materials. The simple capture of a neutron by uranium 238 produces a negative beta ray emitter, uranium 239. The equations are:

$$_{92}U^{238} + _0n^1 \rightarrow \gamma + _{92}U^{239},$$

$$_{92}U^{239} \rightarrow \beta^- + \nu + _{93}Np^{239},$$

and

$$_{93}Np^{239} \rightarrow \beta^- + \nu + _{94}Pu^{239}.$$

The (n,γ) reaction usually shows resonances at certain neutron energies, but it also occurs at thermal energies. The products of beta decay are neptunium and plutonium. They were discovered in this way and are the first two of about ten transuranic elements which are now known. Plutonium 239 is a good fissionable material. So also is uranium 233 which can be produced from thorium 232 in a similar way, that is, by an (n,γ) reaction followed by two beta decays.

Uncontrolled Chain Reaction

The fission process offers the possibility of a chain reaction. Neutrons produce fission; the fission process produces more neutrons, and these

neutrons produce more fissions. The number of neutrons in each generation is greater than in the one before and thus the neutron population
inside a block of uranium increases very rapidly.

Some of the factors which affect the neutron population are: (1) the
average number of neutrons per fission, (2) the average time from one
fission to the next, (3) losses of neutrons through the surface of the
uranium block, (4) losses by absorption in impurities, and (5) losses in
the (n,γ) reactions in uranium itself. For the neutron population to increase, the average number of neutrons per fission must exceed unity.
Since the number of neutrons per fission is of the order of 2.5, some
neutron losses can be tolerated. The losses through the surface of the
block can be made arbitrarily small by making the ratio of surface
to volume small, that is, by using a sufficiently large block of uranium.
The size which is just sufficient to permit a chain reaction is called
the "critical mass" of the material. Most of the impurities which might
absorb neutrons can be eliminated by an initial chemical purification.
However, it is not possible to prevent the accumulation of a variety of
fission products, which are likely to be absorbers of neutrons. Fission
products may terminate a chain reaction, but they will not prevent
the development of a chain reaction in its early stages.

A block of pure natural uranium, no matter how large, will not
support a chain reaction, although most of the neutrons produced in
fission have energies greater than 1 Mev, which is the threshold for
fission in uranium 238. In collisions of neutrons with uranium nuclei,
fission is, however, only one of several processes. Elastic scattering
occurs but has negligible effect, because the neutrons lose only small
amounts of energy to recoiling uranium atoms. Inelastic scattering,
on the other hand, reduces the neutron energies, usually below 1 Mev,
so that few of them can cause fission in uranium 238. They might still
cause fission in the uranium 235 which is present, but most of the collisions are with the nuclei of uranium 238 and neutrons are lost thereby
in (n,γ) reactions with that isotope. Thus, natural uranium contains
too much uranium 238 to support a chain reaction. Since some en-
richment in uranium 235 is necessary, it is customary to use nearly
pure uranium 235, prepared by a process of isotope separation. Alternatively, plutonium 239 or uranium 233, both produced by neutron
bombardment, can be used.

In the chain reaction, the time interval between successive fissions
is the transit time of a neutron from its origin at the site of a fission to
the place at which the next fission occurs. The distance can be estimated from the fission cross section σ_f, which tends to be of the order of
one barn for fast neutrons. Then the absorption coefficient for fission

is $\mu_f = n\,\sigma_f$. The number of nuclei per unit volume n can be calculated from the density of the element. Thus, $n = \rho N_A/A =$ 18.7 g per cm³ $\times$ 6.02 $\times$ 10²³ atoms per atomic weight/238 g per atomic weight $=$ 4.7 $\times$ 10²² atoms per cm³, where the values for natural uranium have been used as typical of heavy elements. Then $\mu_f =$ 0.05 per cm. The average distance traveled by a neutron between fissions is the reciprocal of μ_f, that is, about 20 cm. This is not necessarily a straight line distance because scattering also occurs. A 2 Mev neutron has a velocity of 2 $\times$ 10⁹ cm/sec, and thus goes 20 cm in 10⁻⁸ sec. A rough average of the time between successive fissions is 10⁻⁸ sec. This is the time of one generation of neutrons in a fast chain reaction.

Let us consider a mass of about 24 kg of fissionable material (of atomic weight about 240) in the metallic form. Its volume is about 10³ cm³, and it contains about 24,000/240 or 100 g atomic weights or 100(6 $\times$ 10²³) atoms. Suppose that the average number of neutrons per fission is exactly 2.5 and that the material is enclosed in an idealized container which prevents neutron losses and holds the material together until it has been entirely converted into fission fragments. The multiplication of neutrons must stop sometime before the neutron population becomes equal to the number of fissionable atoms. If n is the number of generations in which this happens, and if there is one neutron present initially, then $(2.5)^n = 6 \times 10^{25}$. Solving for n, one finds $n = 60$, that is, fission will be complete in 60 generations. With a generation time of the order of 10⁻⁸ sec, the fissionable material will then be converted completely into fission fragments in less than 10⁻⁶ sec.

In this idealized case, then, 100 atomic weights of fissionable material will be converted into 200 atomic weights of fission fragments in a very short time. The fission fragments have an average kinetic energy of 85 Mev per particle. The temperature can be calculated if there has been no energy loss through the ideal container. Since an average energy of $3kT/2 = 3(0.025$ ev$)/2$ corresponds to a temperature of 300° K, the average energy of 85 Mev corresponds to a temperature of 7 $\times$ 10¹¹ degrees K. If the ideal container has also kept the volume constant, the pressure can be calculated from the ideal gas law $pV = nRT$. A pressure of 10¹³ atmospheres is found.

It is obvious that no container can stand temperatures of 7 $\times$ 10¹¹ degrees and pressures of 10¹³ atmospheres. Nor is there any material which acts as a perfect reflector of neutrons. Hence, actual atomic explosions will fall far short of this idealized case in their behavior. The ratio of the number of atoms which undergo fission to the total number of fissionable atoms present is called the "efficiency" of the explosive. Since the chain reaction can be started by one neutron, and since there are a few neutrons always present from reactions initiated by cosmic rays, the explosive must be assembled rapidly at a moment just preceding the explosion. Before firing, the fissionable material is in the safe form of subcritical masses with large surface areas. From the calculations which have been made, it is clear that the heat and blast effects of such an explosion will be large. Escaping neutrons and gamma rays may cause further damage, and there will be residual radioactivity of the fission fragments as an after-effect.

Reactors

Ordinary uranium can be used to achieve a chain reaction in a thermal neutron "reactor." The first reactor consisted of rods of uranium forming a lattice arrangement inside very pure graphite. The fission neutrons leave the uranium metal where they are produced and pass into the graphite, which acts as a moderator slowing the neutrons to thermal energies. Once they are thermalized, they can pass into the uranium again with small danger that they will be lost in (n,γ) reactions in uranium 238. These reactions show strong resonances at intermediate neutron energies. At thermal energies their cross section is only about 3 barns, compared to a fission cross section in uranium 235 of 580 barns. There is also a thermal cross section of 107 barns for (n,γ) reactions in uranium 235, but this cannot be avoided by separating isotopes.

The analysis of the chain reaction in terms of neutron populations is similar in the controlled reactor and in the explosive. However, the reactor is intended to operate at a constant power level, that is, with a constant neutron population. This is accomplished by building the reactor of such size that the neutron population will increase, and then putting a good neutron absorbing material such as boron or cadmium in the form of a control rod into a hole through the reactor at such a position that the increase of neutrons is just prevented. It may be pushed in further to shut down the reactor or pulled out momentarily to allow the neutrons to build up to any desired level.

The mechanical operation of a control rod is necessarily slow. It could not be moved with sufficient rapidity if the neutron population increased as rapidly as it does in an explosive. Thermalizing the neutrons provides some extra time, but it is still too small. Satisfactory control is possible only because of the emission of delayed neutrons in fission. When the multiplication of the neutron population in each generation is small, say 1.003, the prompt neutrons alone do not increase the neutron population. The increase cannot occur until the delayed neutrons are emitted. Hence, times of the order of several seconds or more are available to adjust the position of the control rod. A reactor goes out of control when prompt neutrons show multiplication. Experience has shown that a run-away reactor melts, and contaminates the site with fission fragments, but does not develop explosive effects.

The absorption of the radiations inside a reactor leads to a rise of temperature. The energy of approximately 200 Mev per fission is evolved in various forms such as kinetic energy of the fission fragments. This is converted into calories in a way which would require a detailed knowledge of the absorption process. Small reactors may be air-cooled, but generally liquid cooling is necessary. The temperature must not be allowed to rise above the melting point of the uranium or of its protective containers which keep fission fragments from escaping into the water and air.

As a reactor operates, a large variety of fission fragments build up inside the uranium metal. Some of these have large capture cross sections for thermal neutrons. Hence, the reactor would eventually cease to function. To prevent this, the fuel is reprocessed at regular intervals. After removing the old fuel, it is first stored to permit some of the radioactive products to decay. Then the fuel is chemically purified by remote control, because some impurities of long life still remain active. The waste radioactive products are available for possible industrial use. The safe disposal of the fission fragments of very long life is a problem which has been only temporarily solved.

The behavior of a reactor is frequently discussed with reference to a product of factors:

$$k_e = \eta \epsilon p f L, \tag{24-6}$$

where

$$\eta = \nu \sigma_f / (\sigma_f + \sigma_c).$$

The quantity k_e is the effective multiplication of neutrons per neutron generation. It should be unity for steady operation of a reactor. The quantity η is the number of neutrons produced per thermal neutron absorbed in the fissionable material. It is equal to the average number of neutrons per fission, multiplied by a factor $\sigma_f / (\sigma_f + \sigma_c)$, where σ_f and σ_c are the cross sections for fission and for simple capture (n, γ) of thermal neutrons in the fuel. This factor represents the number of fissions produced per thermal neutron absorbed. The quantity ϵ is the fast fission factor, representing an increase in the number of neutrons caused by a small amount of fast neutron fission. It usually exceeds unity by a few percent. L is a factor called the non-leakage probability, which gives the fraction of neutrons which remain within the reactor. L is less than unity because of the escape of fast and thermal neutrons through the boundary of the reactor, but it can ideally be unity for a reactor of infinite size. The resonance escape probability p is the fraction of neutrons which escape capture at (n,γ) resonances in uranium as their energy is reduced in the moderator. Finally, f is the fraction of the neutrons which escape capture in materials other than fuel. It is less than unity because of the absorption of neutrons in the moderator, in the control rod, and in impurities which may be present. It is the factor which is varied by the use of a control rod to make k_e equal to unity in steady operation.

Classification of Reactors

The only natural fuel used in reactors is ordinary uranium. However, most reactors use enriched fuel. The enriched fuels include uranium in which the fraction of the 235 isotope has been increased. They also include uranium or thorium to which some quantity of plutonium 239 has been added. Pure plutonium and pure uranium 235 are, of course, suitable fuels.

The moderator used to thermalize neutrons in the first reactor was graphite. Heavy water, in which neutrons are slowed in collisions with deuterium atoms, is also a good moderator. Ordinary water is usable when the fuel is enriched, otherwise too many neutrons are lost in (n,γ) reactions in hydrogen. More recently, reactors have been developed which use no moderator at all. These are called fast-neutron reactors. Control rods are used to keep them operating at a constant level, depending for their effectiveness upon the emission of delayed neutrons as in the thermal reactor.

Reactors in which fuel rods form a lattice in the moderator are called "heterogeneous." If the fuel is in the form of a soluble salt dissolved in the moderator, the reactor is of the "homogeneous" type. Homogeneous reactors can also be made by distributing the fuel in the form of fine particles throughout the moderator.

The coolants used include air, water, and liquid metals such as sodium. Reactors also differ in the manner in which the coolant, which usually is enclosed since it is likely to become radioactive under neutron bombardment, either dissipates its heat or transfers it as useful power.

Reactors can be classified according to use. The first reactors were designed to produce plutonium 239 for explosives. Many other radioactive isotopes can be made by placing various materials inside a reactor for a period of time. For example, tritium can be made by neutron bombardment of lithium in the reaction

$$_3\text{Li}^6 + _0\text{n}^1 \rightarrow _1\text{H}^3 + _2\text{He}^4 + Q \text{ (positive).}$$

Any isotope which can be produced by neutron bombardment is now available at nominal cost for research purposes.

Research reactors are designed primarily to give a strong neutron beam for experiments in pure physics. Some of them are for more applied purposes, such as finding the effect of neutron bombardment upon the strength of materials.

Most reactors of the future will be built for power. The cooling water for the reactors is converted to superheated steam which drives electric generators. Small power reactors can be used only for special purposes as in the submarine, but large reactors are already economically competitive with coal for the production of electricity on a sufficiently large scale.

Breeder reactors are designed to produce more of the good fissionable materials such as Pu^{239} and U^{233} than they use up in maintaining the chain reaction. In this way the large supplies of U^{238} in the earth's crust can eventually all be used as reactor fuels. A breeder reactor may at the same time be a power reactor.

The Energy of the Sun

The temperature in the interior of the sun is believed to be about 15×10^6 degrees Kelvin. The average kinetic energy of thermal agitation is $3kT/2$ or about 2 kev at that temperature. The particles have a Maxwellian distribution of velocities, and some particles have energies considerably greater than 2 kev. This thermal energy is sufficient to cause nuclear reactions. The (p,α) reaction in lithium 7 has been observed with 10 kev protons. Reactions are seldom studied at low bombarding energies, but the expected cross sections can be calculated from a theoretical extrapolation of the results obtained at higher energies.

Knowing the composition of the sun, it is possible to make a list of the nuclear reactions which might occur there. Only the reactions with positive Q-values are of interest at such low bombarding energies. When the cross sections are known, kinetic theory can be used to calculate the number of collisions per unit time in which the reaction takes place. From the known Q-values, it is possible to compute the total energy evolved per unit time from nuclear reactions in the interior of the sun. The result of such computations is that nuclear reactions evolve energy at about the same rate that it is radiated from the surface of the sun. Nuclear reactions maintain the temperature which is necessary for further reactions to occur. In that sense, the sun is a chain-reacting system.

The most abundant element in the sun is hydrogen, and the most important nuclear reactions are those which convert hydrogen to helium. Two of the processes that do this are called the "carbon cycle" and the "p-p chain." The carbon cycle proceeds through the following set of reactions:

$$_6C^{12} + {}_1H^1 \rightarrow \gamma + {}_7N^{13},$$
$$_7N^{13} \rightarrow \beta^+ + {}_6C^{13}; \quad (T = 10 \text{ min})$$
$$_6C^{13} + {}_1H^1 \rightarrow \gamma + {}_7N^{14};$$
$$_7N^{14} + {}_1H^1 \rightarrow \gamma + {}_8O^{15},$$
$$_8O^{15} \rightarrow \beta^+ + {}_7N^{15}; \quad (T = 2 \text{ min})$$

and finally

$$_7N^{15} + {}_1H^1 \rightarrow {}_2He^4 + {}_6C^{12}.$$

The over-all effect is that four atoms of hydrogen are converted to one atom of helium and two positive electrons. Gamma rays and neutrinos also are emitted. The positive electrons are of course annihilated. The conversion of four atoms of hydrogen to one atom of helium evolves an energy of 27 Mev.

The p-p chain starts with the reaction

$$_1H^1 + {}_1H^1 \rightarrow {}_1H^2 + \beta^+ + \nu.$$

A reaction of this type has not been observed in the laboratory. Two protons do not form a bound structure in $_2He^2$. In the transitory existence of $_2He^2$ during the collision of two protons, there is a calculable probability that it will decay to deuterium with emission of a positive beta ray and a neutrino. The chain can be completed with reactions of well-known type, such as

$$_1H^2 + {}_1H^1 \rightarrow \gamma + {}_2He^3$$

and

$$_2He^3 + {}_2He^3 \rightarrow {}_2He^4 + {}_1H^1 + {}_1H^1.$$

With its large supply of hydrogen, the sun can continue to evolve energy at its present rate for tens of billions of years.

Thermonuclear Reactions

Any reaction between charged particles in which the bombarding energy is supplied by achieving a high temperature is a "thermonuclear reaction." The difficulty of using thermonuclear reactions as a source of energy arises from the problem of attaining sufficiently high temperatures. There are a number of reactions which have higher cross sections at low energies than do the reactions in the sun, and they might be expected to occur at lower temperatures. Some of these are:

$$_1H^2 + _1H^2 \rightarrow _0n^1 + _2He^3 + 3.3 \text{ Mev},$$

$$_1H^2 + _1H^2 \rightarrow _1H^1 + _1H^3 + 4.0 \text{ Mev},$$

$$_1H^3 + _1H^2 \rightarrow _0n^1 + _2He^4 + 18 \text{ Mev},$$

$$_1H^3 + _1H^2 \rightarrow 2 \, _0n^1 + _2He^3 + 11 \text{ Mev},$$

$$_1H^3 + _1H^3 \rightarrow _0n^1 + _0n^1 + _2He^4 + 11 \text{ Mev},$$

and

$$_3Li^7 + _1H^1 \rightarrow _2He^4 + _2He^4 + 17 \text{ Mev}.$$

Most of them involve the use of deuterium or tritium. These reactions have relatively large cross sections at low energies because the repulsion of like charges is small between two isotopes of hydrogen.

The required high temperatures cannot be achieved in a furnace because the materials in the walls would melt. In an electrical discharge in a gas, however, there can be local regions of high temperature. When it is possible to achieve sufficiently high temperatures in a gas discharge, the use of thermonuclear reactions will be feasible. Melting of the walls of the gas discharge tube might be prevented by using electric and magnetic fields to confine the discharge to a region well away from the walls. The problems are of an entirely technical nature, and their solution is to be expected soon.

An explosion of the fission type provides a high temperature momentarily. When the material in such an explosion is surrounded by a quantity of deuterium or tritium, thermonuclear reactions take place and there is an enormous increase in the energy evolved in the explosion. This is a "hydrogen bomb." A hydrogen explosion requires a fission explosion to ignite it.

Summary

In primitive societies, work is performed by men and animals using the annual crop as their source of energy. In our mechanized civilization, work is done mostly by machines and the usual source of energy is coal, oil, and natural gas. These fuels are present in the earth's crust in limited abundance. Whether they will be used up in one hundred years or in a longer time is difficult to determine because they are being used at increasing rates.

The prospect of a shortage of fuel in the near future has been altered by the discovery of fission and the development of reactors which use uranium 235. This fuel is 0.7% of the uranium present in any of its ores. The development of breeder reactors makes uranium 238 a potential fuel, thereby increasing by a factor of 140 the amount of energy which is available from uranium ores. Breeder reactors also make all thorium ores potential sources of energy.

When the technical difficulties which at present stand in the way of utilizing thermonuclear reactions have been solved, other substances present in the earth's crust will be sources of energy. Deuterium is one part in 5000 of ordinary hydrogen. The large total amount of deuterium in the hydrogen of sea water will provide an abundant supply of thermonuclear fuel. The possible use of ordinary hydrogen is more remote, unless it can be used in reactions with some of the light elements such as lithium.

The sun itself can be pictured as a large thermonuclear furnace, providing vast quantities of power in the form of radiant heat. Because of the large distance from the sun to the earth, only a small fraction of this power can be intercepted, but it is still much more than could conceivably be developed from any terrestrial source. The power from the sun will continue to determine climatic conditions on the earth. Its future utilization is likely to depend upon plant processes as it has in the past. The direct utilization of the sun's energy is not likely to provide a reliable source of power in areas where cloud conditions are uncertain.

Problems

1. If, in the spontaneous fission of uranium 238 into strontium 98 and xenon 140, an energy of 165 Mev is available as kinetic energy of the fission fragments, what is the kinetic energy of each fragment?

(Ans.: 97 Mev and 68 Mev, respectively.)

2. If a prompt neutron is emitted by the strontium fragment (of the previous problem) before it slows down, with negligible velocity with respect to the fragment, what is the energy of the neutron?

(Ans.: 1.00 Mev.)

3. If, following a reactor accident which suddenly produces a large quantity of fission fragments, a level of activity of 40 mr per hr is measured 2 hr

after the accident at a nearby site, what is the best estimate you can make of the activity at that site at the end of a week?

(Ans.: 0.2 mr/hr.)

4. If $_{90}Th^{232}$ is used in a breeder reactor, write the reaction and subsequent decay processes by which it can be converted into $_{92}U^{233}$.

5. Neglecting the fission of U^{238} and assuming that all the U^{235} (0.7%) is used up, calculate the power which can be generated with a fuel consumption of 454 g of ordinary uranium per day. Take the energy evolution to be 200 Mev per fission.

(Ans.: 3000 kilowatts.)

6. Suppose that a 10 μF capacitance is charged to a potential difference of 30 kv and then is suddenly discharged (in a time of the order of 10^{-6} sec) through a gas discharge tube 10 cm long and 2 mm in inside diameter which contains deuterium at a pressure of 2 cm of Hg. Calculate the temperature which would be attained if all of the energy was changed to heat and if there were no losses to the electrodes and the walls.

(Ans.: 10^9 degrees K. The observed temperatures
are several orders of magnitude smaller.)

Appendices

I ‖ Analytic Representation of Vectors Illustrated by Electric and Magnetic Fields

Electrons in vacuum tubes and ions in many types of vacuum equipment move under the action of electric and magnetic fields. They generally are subject to forces, and throughout the space there are electric or magnetic fields or both. The distribution of these field strengths is extensively studied in classical electricity, and it is assumed that the reader will have some familiarity with the subject. It is desirable, however, to present a very brief summary of the principles most often used in discussing the motion of ions in electric and magnetic fields.

Vector and Scalar Quantities

There is a fundamental distinction between quantities having magnitude only and those having both magnitude and direction. The former, which can be specified quantitatively by the use of a single numerical value, are called "scalars." The latter are called "vectors." The fundamental vector is the displacement in ordinary space. To locate a point in two dimensions, as on coordinate paper, requires the specification of two numbers. To locate a point in three-dimensional space requires the specification of each of the three coordinates. A particular value of one coordinate may be associated with any value for each of the others. What happens in one dimension may or may not depend on what happens in some other dimensions, but in either case it is necessary to specify what happens in each dimension separately. For this reason, vector quantities really stand for the specification of as many independent numbers as there are dimensions in the space. Vector equations represent as many separate relationships as there are dimensions in the space under consideration. It is not at all unusual to have different equations describing the behavior of the several components of a vector.

This situation is encountered in elementary physics when the trajectory of a projectile is discussed. In this case, one direction is distinguished from the others by a gravitational field in that direction.

Vectors may be represented by directed line segments, and they may be added and subtracted by the use of geometrical methods. It is often preferable to use analytic methods in operations with vector quantities. For this purpose a condensed notation has been developed. This is based upon unit vectors lying along the three axes of a Cartesian coordinate system. The unit vector in the x-direction is represented by $\mathbf{i}$, and the unit vectors in the y- and z-directions are represented by $\mathbf{j}$ and $\mathbf{k}$ respectively. A vector quantity is usually printed in **boldface** type in books using vector notation, and this convention will be adopted for use throughout this book. Displacement from the origin of the coordinate system is the fundamental vector, which we may represent by $\mathbf{r}$. Thus,

$$\mathbf{r} = \mathbf{i}x + \mathbf{j}y + \mathbf{k}z, \tag{I-1}$$

and, since the direction is considered, the three components must be specified. Force is another important vector, and similarly it will be written

$$\mathbf{F} = \mathbf{i}F_x + \mathbf{j}F_y + \mathbf{k}F_z. \tag{I-2}$$

The quantity r (*italics*) stands for the scalar magnitude of the vector. Thus, the magnitude of the displacement vector is represented by the distance

$$r = \sqrt{x^2 + y^2 + z^2}. \tag{I-3}$$

Similarly, the magnitude of the force vector is

$$F = \sqrt{F_x^2 + F_y^2 + F_z^2}.$$

Addition of vectors is accomplished through the addition of the components separately. Thus, if

$$\mathbf{r}_1 = \mathbf{i}x_1 + \mathbf{j}y_1 + \mathbf{k}z_1$$

and

$$\mathbf{r}_2 = \mathbf{i}x_2 + \mathbf{j}y_2 + \mathbf{k}z_2,$$

then

$$\mathbf{r}_1 + \mathbf{r}_2 = \mathbf{i}(x_1 + x_2) + \mathbf{j}(y_1 + y_2) + \mathbf{k}(z_1 + z_2). \tag{I-4}$$

Subtraction can also be accomplished analytically by reversing the sign of the vectors to be subtracted and applying the rule for addition to the resulting vectors.

The use of vectors in multiplication involves two kinds of products. The first is a product which results in a scalar quantity. This is the so-called "scalar" or "dot" product, and it is given by

$$\mathbf{r}\cdot\mathbf{F} = F_x x + F_y y + F_z z \tag{I-5}$$
$$= rF \cos \theta,$$

where θ is the angle between the two vectors. The scalar product of the force and the distance is the work done by the given force in the given displacement.

The second product is called the vector product. The magnitude of this satisfies the relationship

$$|\mathbf{r} \times \mathbf{F}| = rF \sin \theta.$$

The vector product is given analytically by

$$\mathbf{r} \times \mathbf{F} = \begin{vmatrix} \mathbf{i} & \mathbf{j} & \mathbf{k} \\ x & y & z \\ F_x & F_y & F_z \end{vmatrix} \tag{I-6}$$
$$= \mathbf{i}(yF_z - zF_y) + \mathbf{j}(zF_x - xF_z) + \mathbf{k}(xF_y - yF_x).$$

It may be shown that $\mathbf{r} \times \mathbf{F}$ is perpendicular both to $\mathbf{r}$ and to $\mathbf{F}$ and it has the sense obtained by the direction of progress of a right-hand screw rotated from $\mathbf{r}$ to $\mathbf{F}$. This vector is called the *torque* or moment of force.

Electrostatic Forces

Electrostatic charges accidentally placed upon good insulators were early observed to result in relatively large forces. Coulomb established the fact that these forces were governed by an inverse square law, i.e. the force between two point charges is inversely proportional to the inverse square of the distance between them. In this respect they resemble gravitational forces, the behavior of which is described by Newton's law. Electrostatic forces differ from gravitational forces in a number of respects. First, electrostatic forces between small objects used in laboratory experiments may be so large as to render the gravitational forces between these same objects entirely negligible. Second, the electrostatic force between two given objects will vary depending on the electrostatic charge on the objects. Finally, because positive and negative electrostatic charges exist and because like charges repel one another while unlike charges attract, electrostatic forces may be either attractive or repulsive. The gravitational forces are always attractive and depend solely upon the masses and the distances.

Coulomb found that the mutual force between electrostatic charges is directly proportional to the product of the charge strengths $q_1 q_2$ and inversely proportional to the square of the distance r_{12} separating the charges. Thus,

$$F_{12} = q_1 q_2 / k r_{12}^2. \tag{I-7}$$

In the "rationalized mks system" of units, which have gained favor with engineers, q_1 and q_2 are expressed in practical units of charge called coulombs (ampere-seconds) and distance r_{12} is expressed in meters. The constant k has the dimensions of farads/m and is expressed in the form $k = 4\pi\epsilon_0$, where $\epsilon_0 = 8.85 \times 10^{-12}$ farads/m. The force given by Eq. (7) is then expressed in Newton's (kg-m/sec^2).

The electric field strength or electric intensity is defined as the force per unit positive electric charge. That is, if $\mathbf{F}$ stands for the vector force which the charge of q units experiences when placed at a particular point, the field at that point is given by

$$\mathbf{E} = \mathbf{F}/q. \tag{I-8}$$

The field might be expressed in newtons per coulomb. A second alternative is to be discussed after the introduction of the concept called the "electrostatic potential."

The "electrostatic potential difference" between two points is defined as the work done against electrostatic forces in moving a unit of charge from the one point to the other. The volt is the potential difference between the two points when the work done against the electrostatic forces in moving a coulomb from the one point to the other is one joule. Since the force per unit charge is the field strength,

$$V_{21} = - \int_1^2 \mathbf{E} \cdot \mathbf{ds} = - \int_1^2 E \, ds \cos (E, ds), \tag{I-9}$$

where (E, ds) represents the angle between $\mathbf{E}$ and $\mathbf{ds}$, and if E is measured in mks units and ds in m, V_{21} is the potential at point 2 relative to that at point 1 in volts. The negative sign comes from the fact that work is done when the direction of $\mathbf{E}$ is opposite to the displacement $\mathbf{ds}$. The differential form of Eq. (9) is the set of equations:

$$E_x = -\partial V/\partial x$$
$$E_y = -\partial V/\partial y \tag{I-10}$$
$$E_z = -\partial V/\partial z.$$

The vector having an x-component $\partial V/\partial x$, a y-component $\partial V/\partial y$, and a z-component $\partial V/\partial z$, is called the potential gradient and is denoted by ∇V, called "del V." Thus, the electric intensity is the negative of the potential gradient. Electric intensity is usually expressed in volts/m.

The preference of electrical engineers for the mks units arises partly from the fact that, in this system, the units of potential difference and current are those ordinarily used in the laboratory, partly from the fact that the equations which are most used take an especially simple form, and partly from the fact that the units of force and energy are of an order of magnitude which is convenient in engineering work.

The potential, in the rationalized mks units, due to k point charges is given by

$$V = \sum_{i=1}^{k} q_i/4\pi\epsilon_0 r_i \tag{I-11}$$

and is in volts when q is in coulombs and r is in m. The potential gradient,

$$\nabla V = \mathbf{i}\frac{\partial V}{\partial x} + \mathbf{j}\frac{\partial V}{\partial y} + \mathbf{k}\frac{\partial V}{\partial z}, \tag{I-12}$$

is expressed in volts/m.

The work required to bring an additional charge, say q_{k+1}, from infinity to a definite point in the field is obtained by taking the sum shown in Eq. (11) and multiplying this by q_{k+1}. Similarly, to find the force on the charge q_{k+1}, the potential gradient of Eq. (12) at the point in question is calculated and this result is multiplied by $-q_{k+1}$ to give the force. The sums giving the potential and the potential gradient used in the calculation do not include the charge q_{k+1}. This is obviously essential to give a finite result, because the potential produced by a point charge at the point of the charge itself is infinite. This result is entirely general. To compute the force on a charge q_{k+1} we will have to exclude the charge itself in calculating the field, and, when the field has been computed in this way, the force is obtained through multiplication by the charge. Coulomb's law itself is an illustration of this rule in which the number k, over which the summation is performed in calculating the electric field intensity, is reduced to unity for a single charge.

The use of the potential concept furnishes the most direct means of answering questions involving work and energy. In addition, problems concerning forces frequently can be solved most readily by setting up an expression for the potential and differentiating it to find the field, rather than by adding vectorially the forces due to the various charges.

Gauss's Law

Electric field is established by charge and is intimately associated with charge. The motion of charge constitutes an electric current, and thus a moving or a changing electric field is associated with a current. It occurred to Maxwell that a change of electric field with respect to time should be equivalent to an electric current. It was this relationship that enabled Maxwell to formulate a theory for electromagnetic waves, and experimental proof of the existence of these waves was properly considered to confirm Maxwell's identification of an electric current with a changing electric field.

In setting up a system of units, one might start with electrostatic action as expressed in Coulomb's law or, as a second alternative, with the relationship of a changing electric flux to an electric current. In the mks system of units, the second alternative is chosen, and this is the reason for the rather awkward proportionality constant which has been introduced in connection with Coulomb's law. In the mks units a dielectric displacement vector $\mathbf{D}$ is introduced, which, in an isotropic medium, is related to the electric intensity by the relationship

$$\mathbf{D} = \epsilon_r \epsilon_0 \mathbf{E}, \tag{I-13}$$

where ϵ_0 is the previously introduced permittivity of free space, and ϵ_r is the "relative dielectric constant" of the medium. $\mathbf{D}$ is interpreted as the electric flux density, and the time rate of change of the vector $\mathbf{D}$ is equivalent to a current density.

The fact that the inverse square of the distance is involved in Coulomb's law makes it possible to ascribe electrostatic fields to fictitious lines of flux which originate on positive charges and terminate on negative charges but simply pass through a charge-free space. The variation of the fields from point to point in charge-free space is then interpreted as due to the spreading of these lines of force. This viewpoint was used extensively by Faraday as a theoretical basis for suggesting experiments and correlating results. In this connection, consider the variation of the magnitude of the electric intensity about a point charge in matter-free space. By Coulomb's law, this is given by

$$E_2 = q_1/4\pi\epsilon_0 r_{12}{}^2. \tag{I-14}$$

The magnitude of the dielectric displacement in this case is given through multiplication of field strength by permittivity ϵ_0. Thus, the flux density is given by

$$D = q_1/4\pi r_{12}{}^2. \tag{I-15}$$

The displacement is represented by lines radiating outward from the charge q_1, and, to determine the total number of these, D (the number per unit area) is multiplied by the surface area $(4\pi r_{12}{}^2)$ of the spherical surface through which this flux density passes. Thus, if $d\sigma$ represents a differential element of the spherical surface centered at the charge q,

$$\int_\sigma D \, d\sigma = q, \tag{I-16}$$

where the integral is extended over σ, which represents the entire spherical surface. The fact that the proportionality constant is unity is an advantage of the mks system of units.

More generally, we may consider a closed surface of irregular shape in matter-free space. The number of flux lines per unit area is $\epsilon_0 E$. If E_n is the component of E normal to the surface, Gauss's law can be written

$$\epsilon_0 \int_\sigma E_n \, d\sigma = \epsilon_0 \int_\sigma E \cos(n, E) \, d\sigma = q, \qquad \text{(I-17)}$$

where q represents the net charge contained within the closed surface, and (n, E) represents the angle between the electric intensity and the outwardly drawn normal to the surface.

Location of Charge on Conductors in Electrostatic Problems

There are many bodies in which carriers of electricity are free to move under the action of any electric fields extending through the region occupied by the body. The metals are the best illustrations of this class. Even a very small potential difference will result in a relatively large charge transfer within a metal. Hence, unless the potential difference is maintained by an external source of electromotive force, potential differences within the region occupied by a conductor will disappear through a redistribution of the charge. There is no electric field within a conductor in an electrostatic problem, and according to Gauss's law, there can therefore be no net charge within a closed surface lying entirely within a conductor. Hence, any charge placed on a conducting body will be distributed over the surface of body.

Distribution of Charge on an Isolated Conducting Sphere

In the case of an isolated conducting sphere, there is no physical way to distinguish one radius in the body from any other; so any charge placed on a conducting sphere will be distributed uniformly over the surface of the sphere. If a charge q is placed on a conducting sphere of radius a, each unit area of this surface will contain $\eta = q/4\pi a^2$ units of charge, where η represents surface density of charge. There is no field within the conducting sphere, but outside of the sphere the field is that which would arise from a point charge q located at the center of the sphere. We can thus calculate the potential of the sphere as follows:

$$V = -\int_\infty^a E \, dr = \frac{q}{4\pi\epsilon_0} \int_\infty^a \frac{-dr}{r^2} = \frac{q}{4\pi\epsilon_0} \left[\frac{1}{r}\right]_\infty^a = \frac{q}{4\pi\epsilon_0 a}. \qquad \text{(I-18)}$$

The potential of any isolated conducting body is proportional to the charge upon it. Thus,

$$q = CV,$$

where C is a constant called the *capacitance* of the body. Substituting the value of V from Eq. (18), we see that the capacitance of an isolated conducting sphere is given by

$$C = 4\pi\epsilon_0 a.$$

Energy of a Charged System

For an isolated conductor the potential is proportional to the charge and inversely proportional to the capacitance. Since potential is work per unit charge, we can now compute the energy W of a conductor having a charge Q and a capacitance, C. It is

$$W = \int_0^Q \frac{q\,dq}{C} = Q^2/2C. \tag{I-19}$$

For the isolated conducting sphere $C = 4\pi\epsilon_0 a$ and

$$W = Q^2/8\pi\epsilon_0 r. \tag{I-20}$$

By differentiation,

$$dW = -Q^2\,dr/8\pi\epsilon_0 r^2, \tag{I-21}$$

where the negative sign means that W decreases as r increases. This is consistent with the view that the energy is distributed throughout the space occupied by the electric field. The volume dV' associated with the energy $-dW$ is $4\pi r^2\,dr$. Therefore, the energy density is

$$-dW/dV' = Q^2/32\pi\epsilon_0 r^4 = ED/2, \tag{I-22}$$

as may be seen from Eqs. (14) and (15). This is an important general result, which holds for any region of space.

Important Differential Operators

We define the vector differential operator ∇, which may be read "nabla" or "del," by the relationship

$$\nabla = \mathbf{i}\,\frac{\partial}{\partial x} + \mathbf{j}\,\frac{\partial}{\partial y} + \mathbf{k}\,\frac{\partial}{\partial z}. \tag{I-23}$$

Suppose now that we have a vector $\mathbf{A}\,(x,y,z)$ which is defined at every point of a certain region. The dot product of the operator ∇ with this vector is called the "divergence." The divergence of the vector **A** is thus

$$\nabla \cdot \mathbf{A} = \frac{\partial A_x}{\partial x} + \frac{\partial A_y}{\partial y} + \frac{\partial A_z}{\partial z}. \tag{I-24}$$

It will be recognized that the gradient of a scalar, which we have previously defined, may be written by prefixing the operator ∇ to the scalar. Thus, we may start with the potential function V, and if we take the gradient, we have the vector

$$\nabla V = \mathbf{i}\frac{\partial V}{\partial x} + \mathbf{j}\frac{\partial V}{\partial y} + \mathbf{k}\frac{\partial V}{\partial z}.$$

If we take the divergence of this vector, we have

$$\nabla^2 V = \frac{\partial^2 V}{\partial x^2} + \frac{\partial^2 V}{\partial y^2} + \frac{\partial^2 V}{\partial z^2}, \tag{I-25}$$

where

$$\nabla^2 \equiv \frac{\partial^2}{\partial x^2} + \frac{\partial^2}{\partial y^2} + \frac{\partial^2}{\partial z^2} \tag{I-26}$$

is called the Laplacian operator. If V is the electrostatic potential in mks units and ρ is the electrostatic charge per unit volume, from Gauss's law we have

$$\nabla^2 V = -\rho/\epsilon_0, \tag{I-27}$$

which is called Poisson's equation.

If we restrict ourselves first to the case in which $\rho = 0$, Eq. (27) reduces to that of *Laplace*. If $V_1, V_2, V_3, \cdots, V_i \cdots$, and V_m are solutions of Laplace's equation, $B_1 V_1 + B_2 V_2 + B_3 V_3 + \cdots + V_i B_i + \cdots + B_m V_m$ is also a solution where the B's are arbitrary constants. This theorem, which may be established by differentiation and substitution into the differential equation, may be called the theorem of superposition. This is the mathematical basis of the fact that the potential arising from a distribution of charges is obtained by summing the potentials for the separate charges.

Magnetic Fields

Although it is possible to develop the equations for magnetism in close analogy to the equations of electrostatics by starting with the definition of the unit magnetic pole, this does not prove to be the most useful procedure, because the magnetic pole in practice cannot be isolated. We therefore choose to develop the equations for magnetism on the basis of the fields surrounding current carrying conductors, as is done in the mks system of units. From the study of electrostatics we have a knowledge of potential and the units in which it may be measured, namely, the mks practical unit, or the volt. Also, in the study of electrostatics, we defined electrostatic charge and arrived at units in which it could be measured. The practical unit of charge is the coulomb. Electrical current is the time-rate of transfer of charge. The ampere is the current flowing in a wire when the rate of charge transfer through the cross section of the wire is one coulomb per second. Starting with the definition of the current, the potential difference, and the second, it is possible to use the facts of electromagnetic induction discovered by Faraday as a basis for defining the magnetic induction vector **B**. Faraday found that a changing current induced an electromotive force. He and Maxwell interpreted this as resulting from the change in the magnetic flux surrounding the conductors of the circuit or of the flux linking the circuit. There is thus a proportionality between the induced electromotive force ε and the time-rate of change $d\phi/dt$ of the flux-linkage ϕ. For any simple fixed loop,

$$\varepsilon = -\frac{d\phi}{dt} = -A\frac{d\bar{B}}{dt},\tag{I-29}$$

where A is the area of the loop and $\bar{B}$ is the magnetic flux density averaged over this area. To arrive at a satisfactory definition of B from this physical law, it is necessary to conceive of a situation in which the establishment of the magnetic flux is separated from other effects and also one in which the behavior of the flux density B throughout the space is especially simple.

We idealize the situation by considering a simple loop without resistance. There can be no IR or voltage drop in the loop (since $R = 0$), and applied voltage V will be balanced by the electromotive force of self-induction. ($V + \varepsilon = 0$.) Integration of Eq. (29) then gives

$$\phi = BA = \int V\,dt.\tag{I-30}$$

This may be interpreted also in terms of a coefficient of self-inductance L, defined as

$$L = -\varepsilon/(di/dt).\tag{I-31}$$

Hence,

$$\int V\,dt = LI.\tag{I-32}$$

The space within the loop has some change taking place in it. When the current is established, a magnet brought into the vicinity of the loop experiences forces acting upon its parts. Also, a wire in this region

carrying a current experiences forces on its various elements of length. The interpretation of Faraday and Maxwell is that a magnetic field is set up in this region by the current in the loop.

To provide a situation in which the interpretation is very simple, it is necessary to use a configuration designed to give a simple behavior of the magnetic flux throughout the space. We may consider a broad sheet of metal bent into a circular cylinder with closely spaced strips for leading the current in and out, as shown in Fig. I-1. If the magnetic condition about this configuration is explored in any position which is far removed from either end, it is discovered (1) that the magnetic induction **B** is

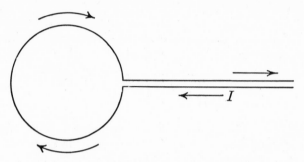

Fig. I-1. Loop formed from thin metal sheet.

parallel to the axis of the cylinder, (2) that it is uniform over the area of the cylinder, and (3) that it is negligible at points outside the turn. The current per unit of axial length is a constant I/l. Using such an arrangement (or for that matter a short cylinder insulated from similar extensions on both sides carrying identical currents per unit of axial length, which serve as guard rings), the actual magnetic flux density B is the same as the flux density $\bar{B}$ averaged over the circular area of the cylinder. Hence, we write

$$\phi = \int V\,dt = LI = BA, \tag{I-33}$$

where ϕ is given in volt-sec or webers. The magnetic flux density is

$$B = \frac{\int V\,dt}{A} \tag{I-34}$$

in webers/m^2. Solving for L in Eq. (33) we get

$$L = \frac{BA}{I},$$

and if $I/l = H$, we may write

$$L = \frac{BA}{Hl},\qquad\qquad (I\text{-}35)$$

which shows that the self-inductance is proportional to the cross-sectional area and (for a given current per unit length) is inversely proportional to the length of the strip. The magnetomotive force is proportional to I/l and for simplicity the field strength H has been equated to I/l and expressed in amp/m. Now

$$B = \mu H$$

in volt-sec/m^2, or

$$\mu = \frac{B}{H} \qquad\qquad (I\text{-}36)$$

$$= \frac{LI}{AI/l} = \frac{Ll}{A}\left(\frac{\text{volt-sec/m}^2}{\text{amp}}\right).$$

From the last equality, if the field within a turn is uniform, μ may be interpreted as the self-inductance of a turn 1 m^2 in cross-sectional area and 1 m in length. For free space, μ represented by μ_o is $4\pi/10^7$ henries/m.

Force on a Wire Carrying a Current in a Magnetic Field

The Motor Rule

In general, a wire that carries a current in a magnetic field experiences a force. The situation in this case differs from many others in physics in that the force is at right angles both to the direction of the magnetic field and to the direction of the current. Experimental results for wires of finite length suggest that for a small length of wire **dl** the force is given by the vector product

$$\mathbf{dF} = I\,\mathbf{dl} \times \mathbf{B}, \qquad\qquad (I\text{-}37)$$

where the force will be given in newtons if I is in amperes, dl is in meters, and B is in webers/m^2. For the case of a straight wire of length 1 in a uniform magnetic induction **B**, this rule gives

$$\mathbf{F} = I\mathbf{l} \times \mathbf{B}, \qquad\qquad (I\text{-}38)$$

or in scalar form

$$F = IBl\sin\theta,$$

where θ is the angle between B and l. This relationship is often called the motor rule. For many cases encountered in practice, the magnetic induction vector is perpendicular to the length, and in this case

$$F = BlI.$$

The current density $\mathbf{J}$ is defined by

$$\mathbf{J} = N e \mathbf{v}, \tag{I-39}$$

where N is the number of charge carriers per unit volume, e is the charge of each carrier and $\mathbf{v}$ is the average velocity. The force on a wire of length l and cross-sectional area A, carrying a current I, may be expressed as

$$\mathbf{F} = Al\mathbf{J} \times \mathbf{B}$$
$$= AlNe\mathbf{v} \times \mathbf{B}. \tag{I-40}$$

It is at once recognized that the product AlN is simply the number n of the carriers, and to get the average force on each carrier we divide by this combination of factors. The force on the wire is consistent with the idea that the force F_1 per carrier is given by

$$\mathbf{F}_1 = e\mathbf{v} \times \mathbf{B} \tag{I-41}$$

and e may be made either positive or negative to make the rule applicable to charges of both signs. The belief that a moving particle experiences this force is supported by experimental evidence for the relationships developed in Chapter 2 of the text.

Energy in the Magnetic Field

Since V was defined to make $W = Vq$, the power or rate of doing work by an electric current is Vi. If we integrate the power over the time, we obtain the total work or energy. If we accept the ideas of Faraday and Maxwell that the energy is in the field, we may determine the energy in the magnetic field by returning to Eq. (32) and multiplying both sides by the current. This equation may then be put in the form

$$\int Vi\,dt = \int Li\,di, \tag{I-42}$$

which upon integration (noting that L is constant) yields

$$W = LI^2/2 \tag{I-43}$$

where W is the energy obtained from the integral of power over time. In this relationship we may insert the value of L given by Eq. (35). Hence,

$$W = BAI^2/2Hl. \tag{I-44}$$

Noting that in the configuration discussed, B is appreciable only within the turn, we divide this equation by the volume of the space ($V' = Al$) in which the field exists and obtain

$$W/V' = BI^2/Hl^2 \, 2,$$

but $I/l = H$, and

$$W/V' = BH/2 = \mu H^2/2. \tag{I-45}$$

This is the direct analogue of Eq. (22) for the energy in the electrostatic field.

II Methods for Representing Vibrations

A very fundamental type of vibration is simple harmonic motion, and this can be treated as the rectangular projection on a fixed line of a particle in uniform circular motion. It is very commonly analyzed by this device in general physics textbooks, and, although we will have some occasion to study the differential equations giving rise to this type of motion, still it is convenient to represent such a vibration as the projection on a fixed diameter of uniform circular motion. This situation is illustrated in Fig. II-1.

If a particle moves in a circle of radius R with a constant angular velocity ω, the linear speed v is ωR, and the magnitude of the central acceleration required to keep the particle in the circle is $v^2/R = \omega^2 R$. These scalars are all constants of the uniform circular motion. Each, however, is associated with a vector which changes in direction throughout the motion. These vectors in uniform circular motion all project on the fixed diameter to give the instantaneous values of the corresponding quantities in simple harmonic motion. In all cases the maximum instantaneous values in simple harmonic motion are the constants of the uniform circular motion, but the projections vary from these maximum values through zero to negative quantities, the absolute values of which are also the constants of the uniform circular motion.

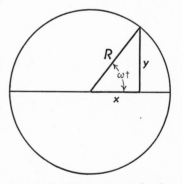

Fig. II-1. Reference circle for simple harmonic motion.

There is a very convenient mathematical representation for this situation, which, although appearing somewhat artificial at first, has gained

441

wide acceptance because of the ease with which the expressions can be manipulated to yield desired information. This method depends upon the introduction of the imaginary numbers based on a geometrical interpretation of the square root of minus one. There is no real number which multiplied by itself will give -1, but multiplying any real number by -1 may be interpreted geometrically as producing a rotation in the counterclockwise direction through 180°. There can be no objection, therefore, to giving a geometrical interpretation to multiplying by $j = \sqrt{-1}$, which rotates the representation of the quantity so multiplied through an angle of 90° in the counterclockwise sense. Two such multiplications will give the rotation through 180° and this interpretation provides the basis for a self-consistent system.

We next introduce the power-series expansions of certain well-known transcendental functions. These are

$$e^x = 1 + x + \frac{x^2}{2!} + \frac{x^3}{3!} + \cdots \tag{II-1}$$

$$\cos x = 1 - \frac{x^2}{2!} + \frac{x^4}{4!} - \cdots \tag{II-2}$$

$$\sin x = x - \frac{x^3}{3!} + \frac{x^5}{5!} - \cdots . \tag{II-3}$$

If x is set equal to $j\theta$, the first of these series expansions results in

$$e^{j\theta} = 1 + j\theta - \frac{\theta^2}{2!} - \frac{j\theta^3}{3!} + \frac{\theta^4}{4!} + \frac{j\theta^5}{5!} \cdots$$

$$= 1 - \frac{\theta^2}{2!} + \frac{\theta^4}{4!} - \cdots + j\left(\theta - \frac{\theta^3}{3!}\cdots\right),$$

and by comparison of the latter expression with Eqs. (2) and (3) we obtain the identity

$$e^{j\theta} = \cos\theta + j\sin\theta. \tag{II-4}$$

Finally, if, to represent uniform angular motion, θ is set equal to ωt,

$$e^{j\omega t} = \cos\omega t + j\sin\omega t,$$

and, to allow for radius R differing from unity, we take

$$Re^{j\omega t} = R\cos\omega t + jR\sin\omega t.$$

The real part of this expression $R\cos\omega t$ represents simple harmonic motion of amplitude R. The imaginary part $jR \sin \omega t$ also represents a simple harmonic motion which is 90° out of phase with the first and perpendicular to it. The sum of the two represents uniform circular motion in the complex plane. The harmonic motion associated with the imaginary part is ignored when the equation is used to represent simple harmonic motion. Differentiation of the expression once with respect to time yields linear velocity, and differentiation again with respect to time gives acceleration. A dynamical equation for the motion may be obtained from this acceleration through the application of Newton's second law to the system.

If the expression $r = Re^{j\omega t}$ is used to represent uniform circular motion in the x-y plane, where the imaginary j is used to represent a unit vector along the y axis, the kinetic energy of the circular motion remains a constant. It is divided between x- and y-components of motion in a manner that is a function of the time. When the kinetic energies of the components are averaged over time, it is found that half of the kinetic energy on the average is associated with the y-component of velocity and half is associated with the x-component.

If on the other hand, as is quite customary,

$$r = Re^{j\omega t}$$

is used to represent simple harmonic motion, the imaginary part is no longer regarded as a simple harmonic motion at right angles. The total energy of the harmonic motion is the same as the total kinetic energy of the circular motion described in the previous paragraph. In the harmonic motion the conservation of energy is maintained through the conversion of kinetic energy into potential energy and vice versa. To maintain the total energy constant, the potential energy in the harmonic motion is the same at every instant as the kinetic energy associated with the imaginary component in the exponential representation of the motion. Because of the identity of the two components in the uniform circular motion, we conclude that the time average of the potential energy is the same as the time average of the kinetic energy for simple harmonic motion. The same conclusion may be established by integration of the expressions for potential and kinetic energy over one periodic time.

The exponential representation also provides an analytical basis for one of the frequently used methods for representing the sum of two harmonic motions along the same line, and restricted to the same frequency. These vibrations, although they have the same periodic time, may differ in amplitude and in phase. That is, they may have different values for R, and they may not come to their maximum values simultaneously. The individual vibrations, therefore, are represented by

$$s_1 = R_1 e^{j\omega t} \tag{II-5}$$

$$s_2 = R_2 e^{j(\omega t + \theta)} = R_2 e^{j\omega t} e^{j\theta}, \tag{II-6}$$

where θ is the so-called phase angle between the vibrations. The individual displacements are simply added to give the total displacement.

$$s_t = s_1 + s_2 = e^{j\omega t}(R_1 + R_2 e^{j\theta})$$

$$= e^{j\omega t}[R_1 + R_2(\cos\theta + j\sin\theta)]$$

$$= e^{j\omega t}[(R_1 + R_2\cos\theta) + jR_2\sin\theta]. \tag{II-7}$$

In a "phase diagram" the bracket is interpreted graphically as shown in Fig. II-2.

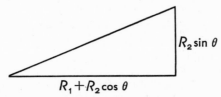

$R_2\sin\theta$

$R_1 + R_2\cos\theta$

Fig. II-2. Phase diagram for adding two vibrations.

The amplitude of the resulting motion is given by

$$R_T = (R_1 + R_2\cos\theta)^2 + (R_2\sin\theta)^2. \tag{II-8}$$

The phase of the resulting motion is specified by

$$\tan\theta_T = \frac{R_2\sin\theta}{R_1 + R_2\cos\theta} \tag{II-9}$$

The method can be extended to the addition of any number of vibrations.

The phase diagram is the most convenient means of quickly determining the result of adding a number of vibrations of the same period.

The same basic methods may be used in adding vibrations of different periods. Although the amplitudes might in general differ, for simplicity we will take them to be the same. Let the angular velocities be designated by ω_1 and ω_2. Then we define:

$$\bar{\omega} = \frac{\omega_1 + \omega_2}{2} \tag{II-10}$$

and

$$\Delta\omega = \omega_2 - \omega_1. \tag{II-11}$$

Then,

$$x_s = R(\cos \omega_1 t + \cos \omega_2 t)$$

$$= R \left[\cos \left(\bar{\omega} - \frac{\Delta \omega}{2} \right) t + \cos \left(\bar{\omega} + \frac{\Delta \omega}{2} \right) t \right]$$

$$= R \left[\cos \bar{\omega} t \cos \frac{\Delta \omega}{2} t + \sin \bar{\omega} t \sin \frac{\Delta \omega}{2} t \right.$$

$$\left. \cos \bar{\omega} t \cos \frac{\Delta \omega}{2} t - \sin \bar{\omega} t \sin \frac{\Delta \omega}{2} t \right]$$

$$= 2R \cos \bar{\omega} t \cos \frac{\Delta \omega}{2} t. \qquad \text{(II-12)}$$

If it is assumed that $\Delta \omega \ll \bar{\omega}$, Eq. (12) may be interpreted very simply. An oscillation of radian frequency $\bar{\omega}$ varies in amplitude with a radian frequency $\frac{\Delta \omega}{2}$. The time between zeros of the varying amplitude is $T = \frac{2\pi}{\Delta \omega}$, and this might be defined as the period of the varying amplitude. When vibrations of two different frequencies combine, as in this illustration, to give periodic reinforcements and cancellations, the situation is said to give rise to beats. This interference of vibrations which is alternately constructive and destructive is quite fundamental and it is used in discussing a number of effects important in modern physical theory.

III | Standing Waves in Bounded Media

Consider the case of the stretched uniform membrane bounded by a fixed rectangle. Such a stretched membrane can be approximated by a mesh of light strings stretched parallel to the sides of the rectangle in such a manner that the strings bound squares. The stretching force of each string should be the same as that in a band of the membrane having a width equal to that of the square. A mass equal to that of a single square of the membrane can be associated with each intersection. Because the membrane can be approximated by a mesh of crossed strings, it is apparent that much of what we have said in Ch. 4 of the text about the stretched strings will apply directly to the membrane. The chief difference is that the restoring forces arise from stretches in two perpendicular directions.

If a is the length of the membrane (in the x-direction) and b is its width (in the y-direction), the eigenfunctions associated with the membrane are

$$z = A \sin{(\pi m x/a)} \sin{(\pi n y/b)}, \qquad \text{(III-1)}$$

where m and n are integers. If S is the stretching force acting across a unit length lying in the membrane, and if σ is the mass per unit of area, the corresponding frequencies (the eigenfrequencies) are

$$f_{mn} = \frac{1}{2} \sqrt{\frac{S}{\sigma}} \sqrt{\left(\frac{m}{a}\right)^2 + \left(\frac{n}{b}\right)^2}. \qquad \text{(III-2)}$$

From Eq. (2) it appears that a normal mode of vibration occurs when m and n are both taken to be integers. The concept of wavelength is not too closely related to the length of the loops on the membrane. In determining the number of modes, it will be well to use the frequency as a parameter. We can simplify the analysis without unduly restricting the

446

usefulness of our results if we let $a = b$. Hence,

$$f_{mn} = \frac{1}{2a} \sqrt{\frac{S}{\sigma}} \sqrt{m^2 + n^2}. \qquad \text{(III-2')}$$

If we consider a plane in which points corresponding to integral values of m and n are marked, as shown in Fig. III-1, there is a one-to-one correspondence between these points and the allowed vibrational frequencies. To determine the number of modes M corresponding to a range ΔR where $R \equiv \sqrt{m^2 + n^2}$, we have only to notice that on the average there is one marked point per unit of area in the quadrant shown in Fig. III-1. Thus,

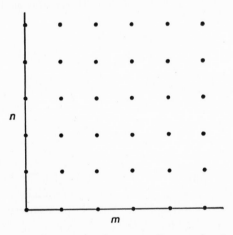

Fig. III-1. The lattice of values m and n equal to integers.

$$\Delta M \simeq \Delta A = \frac{\pi}{2} R \, \Delta R. \qquad \text{(III-3)}$$

By Eq. (2'), and the definition of R,

$$f_{mn} \, \Delta f_{mn} = \left[\frac{1}{2a} \sqrt{\frac{S}{\sigma}} \right]^2 R \, \Delta R. \qquad \text{(III-4)}$$

Hence by Eq. (3),

$$\Delta M \simeq \frac{\pi}{2} 4a^2 \frac{\sigma}{S} f_{mn} \, \Delta f_{mn}.$$

The area of the membrane is a^2. Hence, the number of modes ΔN per

unit area in the frequency range Δf_{mn} at f_{mn} is

$$\Delta N = \frac{2\pi\sigma \, f_{mn} \, \Delta f_{mn}}{S}. \tag{III-5}$$

Hence, the number of modes per unit frequency range increases in proportion to the frequency.

Finally, if there are standing pressure waves in the air inside a rectangular parallelopiped (or cube) with rigid faces, the eigenfunctions are

$$p = A \sin\frac{n_1\pi x}{a} \sin\frac{n_2\pi y}{b} \sin\frac{n_3\pi z}{c}, \tag{III-6}$$

where the edges of the parallelopiped are a, b, and c, and n_1, n_2, and n_3 are integers. For a cubical box of edge a, the conditions for the standing waves of Eq. (6) are

$$\frac{a \cos \theta_1}{\lambda/2} = n_1,$$

$$\frac{a \cos \theta_2}{\lambda/2} = n_2,$$

and

$$\frac{a \cos \theta_3}{\lambda/2} = n_3, \tag{III-7}$$

where λ is the wavelength of the "sound" and where θ_1, θ_2, and θ_3 are the angles that the direction of propagation of an individual sound wave front makes with the three edges of the cube respectively. The cosine functions of Eq. (7) are thus the direction cosines of a direction of propagation of an individual wave train. Hence, from geometry

$$\cos^2 \theta_1 + \cos^2 \theta_2 + \cos^2 \theta_3 = 1 \tag{III-8}$$

and from Eqs. (7) and (8)

$$n_1{}^2 + n_2{}^2 + n_3{}^2 = \left\{\frac{2a}{\lambda}\right\}^2 = n^2. \tag{III-9}$$

To find how many positive integers fulfilling this condition lie in the wavelength range $\Delta\lambda$ at λ, we can consider the volume contained in one octant of the space between a radius n and a radius $n + \Delta n$. This is

$$\Delta N = \tfrac{1}{8} \times 4\pi n^2 \, \Delta n$$

$$= \frac{\pi n^2 \, \Delta n}{2}. \tag{III-10}$$

But

$$n^2 = \left\{ \frac{2a}{\lambda} \right\}^2$$

and

$$2n\,dn = \frac{(2a)^2(-2)\,d\lambda}{\lambda^3}.$$

Thus,

$$-dN = 4\pi \frac{d\lambda}{\lambda^4}\,a^3,$$

but

$$\frac{w\,d\lambda}{\lambda^2} = -df. \qquad\qquad\qquad (III\text{-}11)$$

Hence,

$$\left| \frac{dN}{df} \right| = \frac{4\pi a^3}{w^3} f^2,$$

and, for the cubical volume, the number of modes of vibration per unit frequency range is proportional to the square of the frequency. For longitudinal waves the proportionality constant is $4\pi a^3/w^3$, and for transverse waves it is double this or $8\pi a^3/w^3$.

IV | Group Velocity and the Variation of Phase Velocity

Although the uniform flexible string transmits all disturbances with the same velocity, giving rise to an especially simple situation, loading such a string at fixed intervals with massive beads would cause different wavelengths to be transmitted with different velocities. (This situation is analyzed in some detail in the text.) Lord Kelvin appears to have been the first to recognize the profound changes that result when the phase velocity depends upon the wavelength. Lord Rayleigh gave a careful analysis of this in his treatise on sound.

We start with two sinusoidal wave trains of different wavelength in the same medium, and we take account of the fact that corresponding to the wavelength λ_1 there is a phase velocity w_1 and that corresponding to the wavelength λ_2 there is a phase velocity w_2. The equations for the two waves are

$$y_1 = A \sin \frac{2\pi}{\lambda_1} (x - w_1 t) \qquad \text{(IV-1)}$$

and

$$y_2 = A \sin \frac{2\pi}{\lambda_2} (x - w_2 t). \qquad \text{(IV-2)}$$

The principle of superposition then gives

$$y = y_1 + y_2 = 2A \sin \pi \left[\left\{ \frac{1}{\lambda_1} + \frac{1}{\lambda_2} \right\} x - \left\{ \frac{w_1}{\lambda_1} + \frac{w_2}{\lambda_2} \right\} t \right]$$

$$\cos \pi \left[\left\{ \frac{1}{\lambda_1} - \frac{1}{\lambda_2} \right\} x - \left\{ \frac{w_1}{\lambda_1} - \frac{w_2}{\lambda_2} \right\} t \right]. \qquad \text{(IV-3)}$$

If λ_1 does not differ much from λ_2, $\dfrac{2}{\lambda} \equiv \dfrac{1}{\lambda_1} + \dfrac{1}{\lambda_2}$, if w_1 does not differ much from w_2, and $w_1 + w_2 \equiv 2w$, then

$$\frac{w_1}{\lambda_1} + \frac{w_2}{\lambda_2} \equiv \frac{2w}{\lambda}.$$

Arithmetic means may be used for λ and w, and a very small error is involved in the approximation. Also by definition

$$\frac{1}{\lambda_1} - \frac{1}{\lambda_2} \equiv \Delta\left(\frac{1}{\lambda}\right)$$

and $\dfrac{w_1}{\lambda_1} - \dfrac{w_2}{\lambda_2} \equiv \Delta\left(\dfrac{w}{\lambda}\right)$.   Eq. (3) therefore becomes

$$y \simeq 2A \sin\left[\frac{2\pi}{\lambda}(x - wt)\right] \cos \pi \left[x \Delta\left(\frac{1}{\lambda}\right) - t \Delta\left(\frac{w}{\lambda}\right)\right]. \quad \text{(IV-4)}$$

At a fixed point, say $x = 0$, the oscillations described by this equation have a frequency $\dfrac{w}{\lambda}$, and the amplitude varies at the lower frequency f_m' (corresponding to a modulation frequency) given by

$$f_m' \equiv \frac{1}{T} = \frac{\Delta\left(\dfrac{w}{\lambda}\right)}{2}.$$

It is quite customary to call the modulation frequency twice the frequency shown. Thus

$$f_m = \Delta\left(\frac{w}{\lambda}\right).$$

We can consider a point which moves along with the wave pattern at such a speed that the amplitude of the oscillation of the higher frequency $\dfrac{w}{\lambda}$ does not change. To accomplish this the argument of the cosine term must be kept constant, and this imposes the condition

$$\frac{\Delta x}{\Delta t} = v = \frac{\Delta\left(\dfrac{w}{\lambda}\right)}{\Delta\left(\dfrac{1}{\lambda}\right)}.$$

The speed v, we call the *group velocity*. In the limit of infinitesimal changes, the group velocity is given by the derivative

$$v = \frac{d(w/\lambda)}{d(1/\lambda)} = w - \lambda \frac{dw}{d\lambda}. \tag{IV-5}$$

Suppose that

$$w = k\lambda^n$$

or

$$w/\lambda = k\lambda^{n-1},$$

$$v = k \frac{d\lambda^{n-1}}{d\left(\frac{1}{\lambda}\right)}.$$

Let $p = \dfrac{1}{\lambda}$. Then,

$$v = \frac{k \, dp^{1-n}}{dp} = k(1 - n)p^{-n} = (1 - n)w. \tag{IV-6}$$

Examples of these phenomena may be tabulated, as follows:

w	v	Examples of such waves
$k\lambda^{1/2}$	$w/2$	Deep-water or gravity waves in water.
$k\lambda^0$	w	Sound waves, light waves in free space. Transverse waves on uniform flexible string.
$k\lambda^{-1/2}$	$3w/2$	Capillary or surface tension ripples on water surfaces.
$k\lambda^{-1}$	$2w$	Flectural waves in beams.

Group velocity represents the velocity with which the energy in the wave is propagated. That is, the energy transmitted in unit time by a wave is the energy existing in a unit length of the medium multiplied by v.

V | Harmonic Analysis of Wave Forms

The quality or timbre of musical tones is known to be determined by the proportion of various harmonics they contain. In this connection, the illustrations included in elementary physics texts show that the combination of simple sinusoidal vibrations, having wavelengths which are simple fractions of the longest wavelength, may result in patterns, which (aside from the fact that they are periodic) do not much resemble the sine waves of which they are composed. Periodic wave forms of widely varied shapes can be synthesized from various waves, the frequencies of which are all simple multiples of the fundamental frequency. Changing the relative amplitudes and phases of the waves gives rise to an extremely great variety of wave patterns.

Some idea of the power and generality of this method of representation is suggested by an illustration that is not by any means the most general permitted on mathematical grounds. Consider a string of length L stretched horizontally between two pegs and displaced from equilibrium in such a manner as to lie in a single plane and to be subject only to those restrictions which are usually employed to facilitate the analysis: (1) The only forces acting on any part of the string are those arising from the stretching force or tension in the string. (2) The string is uniform; it has the same mass per unit length throughout its entire length. (3) The string is not broken, or in mathematical language "discontinuous." (4) The tangent to the string at any point makes a small angle with the straight line between the points at which the string is attached to the pegs. If changes in the slope of the string are sudden, an infinite series of sine waves to include those having very short loops will be required to represent the form of the string.

A series of sinusoidal terms which, when added, gives a specified curve along which the string can be placed, is called the Fourier series expansion of the function to which the curve corresponds. In the range of x between 0 and L, let $y = F(x)$. Then examples of Fourier series representing this function are:

$$y = b_0/2 + b_1 \cos \pi x/L + b_2 \cos 2\pi x/L + b_3 \cos 3\pi x/L + \cdots$$
$$+ b_i \cos i\pi x/L + \cdots, \quad \text{(V-1)}$$

where

$$b_i = (2/\pi) \int_0^{L/2} F(x) \cos (i\pi x/L)\, dx; \quad \text{(V-2)}$$

and

$$y = a_1 \sin \pi x/L + a_2 \sin 2\pi x/L + a_3 \sin 3\pi x/L + \cdots$$
$$+ a_i \sin (i\pi x/L) + \cdots, \quad \text{(V-3)}$$

where

$$a_i = (2/L) \int_0^{L/2} F(x) \sin (i\pi x/L)\, dx. \quad \text{(V-4)}$$

Although the function $F(x)$ is defined only in the interval $0 < x < L$, the periodicity of the sinusoidal terms assures that the series will give repeating values for x outside of the interval in which the function is defined. In general, values computed from the series for points lying outside of the range in which $F(x)$ is defined will have no physical significance. There are physical situations, however, in which the phenomena are repeated periodically in just the way that the function computed from the Fourier series repeats itself.

If $F(x) = \sin \pi x/L$, the Fourier series expansion in sines by Eq. (3), with the aid of Eq. (4), is just $\sin \pi x/L$. This corresponds to physical situations in which an extended train of sinusoidal variations exists. If, however, the same function is expanded by Eq. (1), with the aid of Eq. (2), the result is

$$\sin \pi x/L = (2/\pi)[1 - (\tfrac{2}{3}) \cos 2\pi x/L - (\tfrac{2}{15}) \cos 4\pi x/L$$
$$- (\tfrac{2}{35}) \cos 6\pi x/L - (\tfrac{2}{63}) \cos 8\pi x/L - \cdots]. \quad \text{(V-5)}$$

Since all of the cosine terms are even functions, it is clear that for the cosine series $F(x) = F(-x)$. The curve that the series represents is the folded or rectified sine wave as shown in Fig. V-1. A physical situation in

Fig. V-1. Rectified sine wave.

which a wave form closely approximates the form shown in Fig. V-1 is provided by full-wave rectification of A.C. electrical power, as in radio and television sets. In this case the independent variable is time, and the dependent variable is electrical potential difference. Apparatus has been developed for measuring the part of such an electrical wave form that is due to each harmonic. When the output of a good full-wave rectifier (without any filter) is analyzed by such a device, it is discovered that the ratios of the amplitudes of the various harmonics are in fact the same as the ratios of the coefficients in the Fourier series, shown as Eq. (5). This is experimental evidence supporting (1) the validity of the Fourier analysis, and (2) the physical equivalence of a wave form to the sum of the sinusoidal terms which when added give rise to this form.

In treatises on Fourier series it is shown that a very large class of wave shapes can be made from harmonic series containing an unlimited number of simple sine waves. These include such forms as the triangular and the flat-topped or rectangular wave forms, the series representation of which are included in most texts. The synthesis of arbitrary curves from sinusoidal waves may at first seem to be without physical significance, but the fact that a properly constructed harmonic analyzer will give the same frequencies combined in the same proportions is an experimental proof of the physical significance of the theoretically derived harmonic analyses.

Fourier series for flat-topped and saw-tooth wave forms are well known. The manner in which the leading terms of the Fourier series combine to approximate these forms is shown in Figs. V-2 and V-3. Here we start with a sine wave and add the one harmonic component shown on the base line in each section of the figure as we progress from

Fig. V-2. Addition of Fourier components for a rectangular wave.

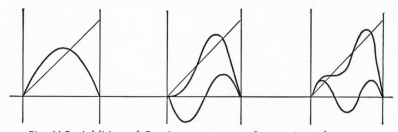

Fig. V-3. Addition of Fourier components for a triangular wave.

left to right and it will be seen from these figures that the approach to the straight line indicated becomes more exact as we proceed with the addition of harmonic components.

If the values of a sine function are specified with mathematical exactness in a limited but finite interval, by mathematical calculations, it is possible through extrapolation to determine its value everywhere. It would be interesting if the existence of a physically pure sinusoidal wave similarly implied its extension without limit in space or time. The suggested converse, that, if a wave were limited in time, it could not correspond to a single, accurately determined frequency is also a real possibility. The quantitative treatment of these matters involves an extension of Fourier series.

Fourier series show a periodic behavior. It is possible physically to produce a single isolated pulse corresponding to a definite range of the independent variable. For example, we might have a single complete loop of the sine function with zero values outside of this limited interval. The physical situation differs so much from the periodic phenomena to which Fourier series apply that it is not surprising to find that the frequency content is quite different. Elimination of a fundamental period means that the interval into which the sine waves are to be fitted is infinite in extent, and waves differing in length by an infinitesimal amount are permissible. The analogue of Eq. (3), obtained with the use of time t as the independent variable and a continuous range of angular frequencies is

$$f(t) = \int_0^\infty a(\omega) \sin \omega t \, d\omega, \qquad (V\text{-}6)$$

where the amplitude factor is given by

$$a(\omega) = (1/\pi) \int_{-\infty}^\infty f(t) \sin \omega t \, dt. \qquad (V\text{-}7)$$

Eq. (6) is a Fourier integral, and it provides the means of determining the frequency content in a terminated vibration or a "transient." Its form implies that a terminated wave will involve a continuous distribution of frequencies with amplitude varying as a function of frequency throughout the range.

An illustration of particular interest is that Fourier integrals provide us with a means for determining the frequency content of a terminated sine wave. If, for example, the pattern consists of a single wavelength, with zero values elsewhere, the Fourier integral representation will contain a relatively wide band of frequencies, as suggested by Fig. V-4. As the number of wavelengths is increased, the width of the band of contained frequencies shrinks. If the interval of time corresponding to the

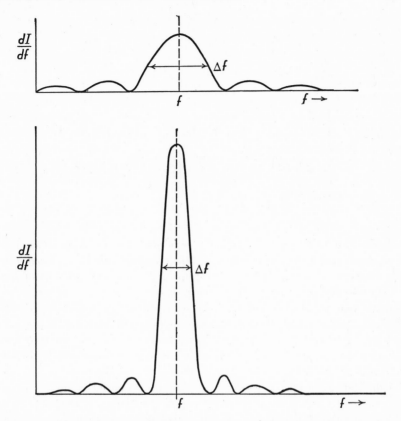

Fig. V-4. Fourier analysis of terminated sine waves. Single wavelength above; three complete wavelengths below.

sinusoidal wave train is represented by Δt, while the width of the frequency spectrum corresponding to those frequencies at which the amplitude drops to half its maximum value is represented by Δf, it is found that $\Delta f \, \Delta t = 1$. The frequency content of a sine wave terminated after three complete periods is also shown in Fig. V-4. Since $\Delta f \, \Delta t = 1$, it is clear that to obtain a single accurately determined frequency does in fact require that the wave train should be extended throughout an infinite interval. The wave train corresponding to a single frequency has constant amplitude. These facts about the analysis of terminated periodic functions and their application to physical phenomena, such as sound waves, were known from about the middle of the nineteenth century as a result of the work by Fourier and his successors.

VI | Bound Particle in a Potential Well with Finite Boundaries

It is not difficult to show that in a region where the potential energy exceeds an electron's total energy, electron waves are damped out exponentially at a rate which is proportional to the square root of the amount by which the potential energy exceeds the total energy. This can be concluded directly from the form of the general solutions of Schroedinger's equation for electrons in such regions, and for this purpose it is not necessary to evaluate the constants of the particular solution. The problem, however, will be discussed at some length, because it is a basic one.

Consider a trough of width a, where the potential energy is zero, terminated by boundaries at which the potential energy rises abruptly to the finite value W_b. If the trough extends from $x = -a/2$ to $x = a/2$, there are three regions to be considered.

I. The first region corresponds to $x < -a/2$, and in this region Schroedinger's equation for a particle of mass m and total energy W is

$$d^2u/dx^2 - 8\pi^2 m(W_b - W)u/h^2 = 0. \qquad (\text{VI-I})$$

In this region, we have assumed that the total energy W is less than the potential energy W_b. Letting

$$\beta^2 = 8\pi^2 m(W_b - W)/h^2, \qquad (\text{VI-2})$$

the differential equation becomes

$$d^2u/dx^2 - \beta^2 u = 0. \qquad (\text{VI-3})$$

II. In the second region ($-a/2 < x < a/2$), the differential equation is

$$d^2u/dx^2 + k^2 u = 0, \qquad (\text{VI-4})$$

where

$$k^2 = 8\pi^2 mW/h^2.$$

III. In the third region $(x > a/2)$, the differential equation is again

$$d^2u/dx^2 - \beta^2 u = 0. \tag{VI-3}$$

The form of the solution in the first and third regions is

$$u = C \exp(-\beta x) + D \exp(\beta x). \tag{VI-5}$$

In the first region, if C is finite, the wave function becomes infinite as x approaches minus infinity. Thus, in this region, C must be zero to give a proper wave function, and the form of this is

$$u_i = D \exp(\beta x). \tag{VI-6}$$

Similarly, in the third region the proper wave function assumes the form

$$u_{iii} = C \exp(-\beta x). \tag{VI-7}$$

In the second region, the general solution of Eq. (4) is

$$u_{ii} = A \sin kx + B \cos kx. \tag{VI-8}$$

It should be noticed that if Δx is used to represent the distance measured from the boundary into the region where the total energy of the electron is less than the potential energy, both u_i and u_{iii} can be represented by the form

$$u = E \exp(-\beta \, \Delta x), \tag{VI-9}$$

where β is the positive root of Eq. (2). The wave is damped at a rate which depends upon the square root of the energy $(W_b - W)$, as suggested in Chapter 9.

The conditions of the problem are symmetrical about the plane $x = 0$. The wave functions allowed are either symmetrical or antisymmetrical. For the symmetrical functions the cosines are chosen, and the antisymmetrical ones are sine functions. The essential methods applied in analyzing the problem are common to both cases. The lowest energy state corresponds to a cosine function, and the arguments which are necessary to the solution of the problem will be illustrated in this case. The algebra is simplified by incorporating into the constants certain constant factors. Thus, we have

$$u_i = D \exp(\beta x) = D' \cos(ka/2) \exp(\beta a/2) \exp(\beta x)$$

$$= D' \cos(ka/2) \exp \beta(x + a/2).$$

Symmetry requires that the form of u_{iii} similarly be

$$u_{iii} = D' \cos(ka/2) \exp[\beta(-x + a/2)]. \tag{VI-10}$$

Thus, either the condition that $u_{ii} = u_{iii}$ at $x = a/2$ or that $u_{ii} = u_i$ at

$x = -a/2$ gives $D' = B$, and the magnitude of the wave function is determined by the single constant B.

The completion of the solution requires finding a value of k such that the cosine function joins smoothly at the boundaries onto the exponential function. In addition to the condition on the continuity of u at the boundaries, this requires that

$$du_{ii}/dx = du_{iii}/dx \qquad \text{(VI-11)}$$

at $x = a/2$. Applying this condition gives the transcendental equation

$$\beta = k \tan ka/2. \qquad \text{(VI-12)}$$

With a definite value of W_b this equation is satisfied for only definite values of W. In the most usual circumstances (when $W_b \gg W$), these values of W do not differ much from the values of W_n in the text that were determined for the trough with infinite boundaries. Usually there is a series of allowed energy levels W_n', where this notation is used to suggest the resemblance, and the prime is used on the W_n to indicate that they differ somewhat in value from those determined previously. When the value of W_n' has been selected, B may be determined to normalize the wave function as required by an integration of u^2 over all space.

The penetration of the particle into the classically forbidden region is physically significant. In the case considered, the reflection coefficient for electrons at either boundary is 100% when $W_n' < W_b$, but the exponential damping in the forbidden region is associated with the mechanism of reflection. If two allowed regions are connected by a forbidden region so narrow that electronic waves from the first region retain finite values at the boundary of the second region, and vice versa, electrons from one region pass to the other, and the process is called "tunneling."

VII | The Wave Equation in Spherical Coordinates

It is most convenient to use spherical polar coordinates in the solution of atomic structure problems. The Schroedinger equation becomes

$$\nabla^2 u = \frac{\partial}{\partial r}\,(r^2\,\partial u/\partial r)/r^2 + \frac{\partial}{\partial \theta}\,(\sin\theta\,\partial u/\partial \theta)/r^2\sin\theta + \frac{\partial^2 u}{\partial \phi^2}\Big/r^2\sin^2\theta$$

$$= -8\pi^2 m_e(W - U)u/h^2, \tag{VII-1}$$

where the coordinates may be identified by reference to Fig. VII-1, and it will be noted that in this section we are denoting the mass of the electron by m_e, because we are using m to stand for a quantum number.

Schroedinger's equation in spherical polar coordinates is a rather complicated second order differential equation, and we will not need to know anything about the most general solutions of it. Schroedinger's equation has arisen from the assumption of sinusoidal variations with respect to time. We will find that solutions in which the variables are separated will be sufficient for

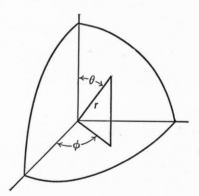

Fig. VII-1. Spherical coordinates.

our purposes, and very fortunately this device gives equations depending upon the solution of second-order ordinary differential equations. The restriction on the form of the solution, which enables us to separate variables, is a very conventional one. It is that u is a product of three functions each of which depends on only a single one of the co-

461

ordinates. Thus, $u = R(r)\ \Phi(\phi)\ \Theta(\theta)$, where, as suggested by the notation, R is a function of r only, Φ is a function of ϕ only, and Θ is a function of θ only.

The derivatives appearing in Schroedinger's equation are

$$\partial u / \partial r = \Phi\Theta\ dR/dr$$

$$\partial u / \partial \theta = \Phi R\ d\Theta/d\theta$$

$$\partial^2 u / \partial \phi^2 = R\Theta\ d^2\Phi/d\phi^2.$$

The derivatives appearing on the right-hand side of these equations are total, because these functions, by assumption, depend only on the single variable. Substitution of $u = R\Theta\Phi$ into Eq. (1) gives

$$\Theta\Phi \frac{d}{dr}\ (r^2\ dR/dr)/r^2 + R\Phi \frac{d}{d\theta}\ (\sin\theta\ d\Theta/d\theta)/r^2 \sin\theta$$

$$+ R\Theta(d^2\Phi/d\phi^2)/r^2 \sin^2\theta$$

$$= -8\pi^2 m_e(W - U)R\Theta\Phi/h^2, \quad \text{(VII-2)}$$

and division by $R\Theta\Phi$ gives

$$\frac{d}{dr}\ (r^2\ dR/dr)/r^2 R + \frac{d}{d\theta}\ (\sin\theta\ d\Theta/d\theta)/r^2\Theta \sin\theta$$

$$+ d^2\Phi/d\phi^2/\Phi r^2 \sin^2\theta = -8\pi^2 m_e(W - U)/h^2. \quad \text{(VII-2')}$$

We assume that the potential energy U is a function of r only and that W is a constant W_n except when a quantum change takes place. We now multiply Eq. (2) by $r^2 \sin^2\theta$, and rearrange it to obtain

$$d^2\Phi/(d\phi^2\Phi) = -k^2[W_n - U(r)]r^2 \sin^2\theta - \sin^2\theta\ d(r^2\ dR/dr)/(dr\ R)$$

$$- \sin\theta\ d(\sin\theta\ d\Theta/d\theta)/(d\theta\Theta), \quad \text{(VII-3)}$$

where $k^2 = 8\pi^2 m_e/h^2$. Since the left-hand side of this equation is a function of ϕ only, and the right-hand side is clearly independent of ϕ, each side must be equal to a constant, which we designate by $-m^2$. The equation for Φ thus becomes

$$d^2\Phi/d\phi^2 + m^2\Phi = 0. \quad \text{(VII-4)}$$

This, of course, is the well-known second-order ordinary differential equation for sinusoidal variation, and its general solution is

$$\Phi = A \sin m\phi + B \cos m\phi \quad \text{(VII-5)}$$

or

$$\Phi = C \exp (\pm jm\phi). \quad \text{(VII-5')}$$

If the solution is to be a single-valued function of the coordinate ϕ, m must be an integer, which is called the *magnetic quantum number*.

To determine suitable forms for the function R, we make the restriction, valid in the case of the hydrogen atom, that the potential energy U depends on the radius only, and that it arises from the Coulomb force. The differential equation is

$$d(r^2\, dR/dr)/(dr\, R) + k^2(W_n + e^2/4\pi\epsilon_0 r)r^2 = 0, \qquad \text{(VII-6)}$$

if the solution is assumed to depend on r only. The simplest solution of Eq. (6) is the negative exponential function of r. We assume the solution

$$R = \exp(-ar), \qquad \text{(VII-7)}$$

and substitute this into Eq. (6). This gives

$$d(-r^2 a \exp -ar)/(dr \exp -ar) + k^2(W_n + e^2/r)r^2 = 0. \qquad \text{(VII-8)}$$

Performing the differentiations and simplifying gives the equation

$$-2ar + a^2 r^2 + k^2 r^2(W_n + e^2/4\pi\epsilon_0 r) = 0. \qquad \text{(VII-9)}$$

If this equation is to be satisfied for all values of r, the coefficient of each power of r must be zero. Hence, the following relationships

$$a^2 = -k^2 W_n \qquad \text{(VII-10)}$$

and

$$2a = k^2 e^2/4\pi\epsilon_0 \qquad \text{(VII-11)}$$

must hold. Hence,

$$a = k^2 e^2/8\pi\epsilon_0 = \pi m_e e^2/h^2\epsilon_0 = 1/a_0, \qquad \text{(VII-12)}$$

where a_0 is the radius of the first Bohr orbit. Also from Eq. (10)

$$W_n = -1/k^2 a_0{}^2 = -m_e e^4/8h^2\epsilon_0{}^2. \qquad \text{(VII-13)}$$

This, however, corresponds to the energy of an electron in the first Bohr orbit. The results derived from wave mechanics thus confirm the numerical values for the orbit radius and energy, as given by the Bohr theory. The physical interpretation, however, is quite different. According to wave mechanics, the electron in the first Bohr orbit is moving around very rapidly. The square of the wave function gives a number proportional to the probability of finding the electron in unit volume at any location. Since for an electron in the lowest energy state, the wave function depends only upon r, the average charge distribution for the electron in this state is a spherical one. These states are designated as s states, and the one just obtained is called the $1s$ state. The fact that s is the first letter of the word spherical may be associated to help the reader carry in mind the fundamental feature of the distributions associated with these states.

Perhaps the next most simple wave function satisfying the Schroedinger relationship, Eq. (3), as applied to the hydrogen atom is one in which both of the functions Θ and R differ from unity. In this case, we assume a solution of the form

$$u = \cos \theta \, r \exp (-a_2 r), \qquad (\text{VII-14})$$

so that

$$\Theta = \cos \theta \quad \text{and} \quad R = r \exp (-a_2 r).$$

Differentiating, we get

$$d\Theta/d\theta = -\sin \theta \quad \text{and} \quad dR/dr = (1 - a_2 r) \exp (-a_2 r).$$

Substitution of these values into Eq. (3) gives

$$-k^2(W_n + e^2/4\pi\epsilon_0 r)r^2 \sin^2 \theta - \sin^2 \theta[2r - r^2 a - 3r^2 a + a^2 r^3]/r$$
$$+ 2 \sin^2 \theta = 0. \quad (\text{VII-15})$$

If $\sin^2 \theta$ is not identically zero, this factor may be divided out. This gives

$$-k^2(W_n + e^2/4\pi\epsilon_0 r)r^2 + 4a_2 r + a_2{}^2 r^2 = 0, \qquad (\text{VII-16})$$

which must hold for all values of r. Hence,

$$-k^2 e^2/4\pi\epsilon_0 + 4a_2 = 0 \quad \text{or} \quad a_2 = 1/2a_0; \qquad (\text{VII-17})$$

and

$$-k^2 W_n + a_2{}^2 = 0 \quad \text{or} \quad W_n = -a_2{}^2/k^2; \qquad (\text{VII-18})$$

and finally

$$W_n = W_2 = -m_e e^4/32h^2\epsilon_0{}^2. \qquad (\text{VII-19})$$

The energy of this state is exactly that of the second Bohr orbit. This state lacks spherical symmetry, and it can hardly be the wave mechanical equivalent of the second circular orbit in Bohr's theory. The state varies with θ in a simple way, and wave functions of this type are called p-states. The charge is concentrated around the direction $\theta = 0$, and, if p is associated with the initial letter of the word polar, the properties associated with this charge distribution may be called to mind. The number in the denominator of the exponent is 2, and thus we identify this as the $2p$ state. The constant required to normalize this wave function may be determined by integration, and the proper expression for this wave function is

$$u = r \cos \theta \exp (-r/2a_0)/[(32\pi)^{1/2} a_0{}^{5/2}]. \qquad (\text{VII-20})$$

A characteristic feature of the second energy state is that the wave function extends further into space, and, on the average, the distance of the electron from the nucleus is greater, because the exponent contains the factor 2 in the denominator. In the $2p$ state the wave function has one finite node in the form of a plane passing through the nucleus. The wave function on one side of this plane differs in phase from that on the other side.

One would naturally investigate to determine whether or not the wave equation could be satisfied by a spherical node at some finite value of the radius, if the principal quantum number, the integer in the denominator of the exponent, were to remain at the value 2. As a basic form for this so-called "$2s$" wave function, let us try

$$u = (r/a_0 - b) \exp(-r/2a_0). \qquad \text{(VII-21)}$$

This gives

$$du/dr = dR/dr = \exp(-r/2a_0)[1/a_0 - (r/a_0 - b)/2a_0]$$

and

$$\frac{d}{dr}(r^2 \, dR/dr) = \exp(-r/2a_0)[2r/a_0 - r^2/2a_0{}^2 - 3r^2/2a_0{}^2 + br/a_0$$
$$+ r^2(r/a_0 - b)/4a_0{}^2]$$
$$= \exp(-r/2a_0)[2r/a_0 - 2r^2/a_0{}^2 + br/a_0$$
$$+ r^3/4a_0{}^3 - br^2/4a_0{}^2],$$

and thus from the application of Eq. (2), we obtain after canceling the common exponential factor from each term

$$b/a_0r + 2/a_0r - b/4a_0{}^2 - 2/a_0{}^2 + r/4a_0{}^3$$
$$= -8\pi^2 m_e(r/a_0 - b)(W_n + e^2/4\pi\epsilon_0 r)/h^2. \qquad \text{(VII-22)}$$

To be satisfied for all values of r, the coefficient of each power of r must be zero. Hence, we obtain the conditions

$$1/4a_0{}^3 = -8\pi^2 m_e W_n/a_0 h^2, \qquad \text{(VII-23)}$$

$$b/4a_0{}^2 + 2/a_0{}^2 = -8b\pi^2 m_e W_n/h^2 a_0 + 8\pi^2 m_e e^2/4\pi\epsilon_0 a_0 h^2, \qquad \text{(VII-24)}$$

and

$$b/a_0 + 2/a_0 = 8\pi^2 m_e b e^2/4\pi\epsilon_0 h^2. \qquad \text{(VII-25)}$$

Since a_0 is known, Eq. (23) determines the energy for this state, and it is found to be consistent with Eq. (18). Thus, in the case of the hydrogen atom, two states with the same principal quantum number have been found to have the same energy, and, under the restrictions characterizing this treatment, this is quite generally true for hydrogen. Either Eq. (24) or (25) can be used for the determination of b, which as a consequence of using the factor 2 in the denominator of the exponent is over-determined. The result as determined by either equation is $b = 2$.

The wave functions obtained above illustrate certain general principles concerning the standing wave patterns for electrons and the corresponding quantum numbers. The principal quantum number determines the average distance of the electron from the nucleus, and in the case of hydrogen this quantum number determines the energy of the system. The quantum number which determines the behavior of the pattern with variation of θ is called the azimuthal quantum number l, and this is interpreted as specifying the angular momentum of the system. Finally, there is a third quantum number specifying the behavior of standing waves in a third coordinate of ordinary space, and this is the magnetic quantum number m, which is related to the variation of the wave pattern with ϕ. In general, the wave function for hydrogen associated with the quantum numbers nlm is given by

$$u(nlm)$$

$$= r^l[A_0 + A_1(r/a_0) + A_2(r/a_0)^2 + \cdots]P_l{}^m(\cos\theta)\exp(jm\phi - r/na_0)$$

where $P_l{}^m(\cos\theta)$ is the associated Legendre function defined in references on spherical harmonics, and

$$A_k = -2(n - l - k)A_{k-1}/[n(l + k)(l + k + 1) - l(l + 1)].$$

Illustrations of appropriate wave functions are

$2p$: $u(211) = r\sin\theta\exp(j\phi - r/2a_0)/(64\pi)^{\frac{1}{2}}a_0{}^{\frac{5}{2}}$,

$3s$: $u(300) = (27 - 18r/a_0 + 2r^2/a_0{}^2)\exp(-r/3a_0)/81(3\pi)^{\frac{1}{2}}a_0{}^{\frac{3}{2}}$,

$3p$: $u(310) = 2^{\frac{1}{2}}r\cos\theta(6 - r/a_0)\exp(-r/3a_0)/81\pi^{\frac{1}{2}}a_0{}^{\frac{5}{2}}$,

$3p$: $u(311) = r\sin\theta(6 - r/a_0)\exp(j\phi - r/3a_0)/81\pi^{\frac{1}{2}}a_0{}^{\frac{5}{2}}$,

$3d$: $u(320) = r^2(3\cos^2\theta - 1)\exp(-r/3a_0)/81(6\pi)^{\frac{1}{2}}a_0{}^{\frac{7}{2}}$,

$3d$: $u(321) = r^2\sin\theta\cos\theta\exp(j\phi - r/3a_0)/81(\pi)^{\frac{1}{2}}a_0{}^{\frac{7}{2}}$.

These examples illustrate the fact that states having $l = 0, 1, 2$, are designated by the letters s, p, d.

VIII | Surface Charge Distributions and Forces

The Principle of Superposition

The electrostatic potential at a point due to any number of charges at other points may be determined from a scalar addition of the contributions of all the various point charges to the potential. Electrostatic potential is defined as the work done in bringing a unit positive charge from an infinite distance up to the point in question, and the contribution to the potential due to the small positive "test charge" is excluded from this summation. This is necessary to give a sensible result, because a finite point charge establishes infinite potential at its own location, where $r = 0$. The x-, y-, and z-components of the potential gradient vector (and of its negative, the electric intensity vector) may be determined by differentiating the potential function with respect to the Cartesian coordinates x, y, and z. Hence, the electric intensity may be found by adding vectorially all the contributions to the electric intensity, excluding that due to the positive charge by which the field is measured.

When the distributions are continuous, as for uniformly charged surfaces, a question naturally arises concerning what part of the total field should be included as that set up by the charges other than the one on which the force is being computed, and how much of the total field should be excluded because it is the part of the field which was produced by the charge on which the force is desired.

Forces on Surface Charge Distributions

In the case of the parallel plate condenser, the analysis of the fields and the resulting forces is not difficult. If a charge is placed on an isolated, large, conducting flat plate, it distributes itself uniformly on both sides of the plate. If the charge density (charge per unit area) on each face of the plate is denoted by η (coulombs/m^2) the magnitude of the electric intensity on either side of the plate is η/ϵ_0. If a second parallel plate is charged with a surface density of $-\eta$ on each face, since the total charge -2η per unit area is placed in a field intensity η/ϵ_0 due to the charges on the other plate, the force per unit area is $-2\eta^2/\epsilon_0$. The quantities characteristic of the parallel plate arrangement may be determined from superposition of the two fields, which gives zero for the fields outside of the parallel arrangement, whereas the field between the plates is $-2\eta/\epsilon_0$, which is twice that due to either isolated plate. The magnitude of the charge on either plate is -2η. In determining the force per unit area, the field due to the opposite plate (which is equal to half the total field) is multiplied by the charge per unit area.

For a uniformly charged sphere, the effective field involves the same factor of one-half. This can be established very easily by the following argument. Consider first an isolated conducting sphere of radius a on which a charge q is placed. The surface density of charge is $q/4\pi a^2$. To determine the force on a small section of the area of this sphere, consider a second sphere concentric with the first, the radius of which is slightly larger $(a + \Delta r)$. If this second external sphere is charged with $-q$ coulombs, it does not disturb the charge or the field at the surface of the internal sphere, and, because these two factors remain the same, it will not change the force on any small element of the surface charge on the inner sphere. As $\Delta r/a \to 0$, the result for the parallel plate condenser becomes applicable to a section of the concentric spheres having linear dimensions small as compared with a, and this gives for the force per unit area on such a section $-2\eta^2/\epsilon_0 = -2q^2/(4\pi a^2 \epsilon_0^2)$. We conclude that the force on a small element of the surface of a uniformly charged isolated sphere is obtained by taking half the field just outside of its surface and multiplying this field by the charge on the small section of the sphere for which the force is to be determined.

The Distribution of Charge on Conducting Surfaces in the Presence of Point Charges—The Method of Images

The solutions of Poisson's equations are unique. If the charge distribution is specified throughout all space, the potential differences arising can be computed, and the potentials are determined except for an additive constant. If the potential distribution is specified completely over all the boundaries of a definite region, and if the charge distribution within the region is known, the potential distribution is determined uniquely from Poisson's equation. This has many very useful consequences which are suggested in the following discussion.

As a first illustration, we take a case which was discussed in the text, namely that of an isolated, charged, conducting sphere. We have previously shown that the potential outside the sphere is the same as if the charge Q distributed over the surface of this sphere were concentrated at its center. This illustrates the usefulness of the method, because the potential due to the point charge is simply $Q/4\pi\epsilon_0 r$, while the computation of the potential by adding the contributions from the infinitesimal charges in differential elements of surface would require an integration. In a sense, the point charge at the center is an image, although other cases better illustrate the appropriateness of the terminology.

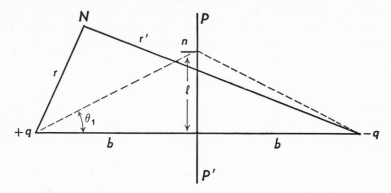

Fig. VIII-1. Image of a point charge by a conducting plane.

As a second illustration, consider the force between a point charge and a grounded conducting plane. For definiteness the point charge of $+q$ (coulombs) is to be located b (meters) from the plane. If we wish to find the potential at any point, or the electric intensity, or the net force between the charge and the plane, it can be done most easily by replacing the conducting plane by the simplest distribution of charges that will maintain the position of the plane at zero potential. The easiest way to maintain the plane PP' at zero potential in the absence of a conducting sheet would be to place a charge of $-q$ a distance b back of the plane. This charge is in magnitude and location the mirror image of the charge q formed by plane PP', as shown in Fig. VIII-1. It is from this fact that the device receives the name "method of images."

From this picture, desired information can be deduced with ease. The potential at any point N in the space to the left of the conducting plane is obviously

$$V_N = \left(\frac{q}{r} - \frac{q}{r'}\right)\bigg/4\pi\epsilon_0. \qquad\text{(VIII-1)}$$

(Notice in particular that the device has really satisfied the conditions at the boundary. For points on the plane PP', $r = r'$; so V_N is zero.)

The electric intensity at any point may be obtained from the potential by differentiation of the potential, or it may be obtained directly by vector addition of the intensities arising from q and $-q$ separately. It is to be noticed especially that this provides a means for determining the charge distribution which would have to exist on the conducting plane in the original problem, for we can find the electric intensity along the plane. Then knowing that at the surface of a metal the electric intensity is $1/\epsilon_0$ times the surface density of charge, we obtain the charge density through multiplication by ϵ_0. The total charge induced on the plane is obviously $-q$, for each line of force originating on q passes over to the charge of q units and hence cuts the plane PP'. This result may be established by integrating also. The analysis of the problem follows:

$$\frac{dV}{dn} = \frac{dV}{dr}(-\cos\theta) = -\frac{dV}{dr}\frac{b}{r}\frac{2qb}{r^3 4\pi\epsilon_0}, \qquad \text{(VIII-2)}$$

whence

$$E_p = -\frac{dV}{dn} = -2qb/r^3 4\pi\epsilon_0$$

and

$$\eta = E_p\epsilon_0 = -2qb/r^3 4\pi. \qquad \text{(VIII-3)}$$

The force between the charge and the plane is

$$F = -q^2/(2b)^2 4\pi\epsilon_0. \qquad \text{(VIII-4)}$$

The total charge, q', induced on the plane as determined by integration (for a check) is

$$q' = +\int_0^\infty \eta 2\pi l\,dl = -qb\int_0^\infty \frac{-l\,dl}{(b^2 + l^2)^{3/2}}$$

$$= -qb\left[(b^2 + l^2)^{-1/2}\right]_0^\infty = -q. \qquad \text{(VIII-5)}$$

Consider next the problem of a point charge q located at a distance b from the center of a conducting sphere of radius a, maintained at zero potential. We would like to find a simple distribution of point charges from which we might easily compute the potential and electric intensity at all points external to the sphere. Let us see if it is not possible to cancel the effect of the charge $+q$ on all points of the spherical surface by the location of a single charge $-q'$ at a distance x from the center of the sphere on the line joining the charge q with the center of the sphere, as shown in Fig. VIII-2. If we can accomplish this, the problem is solved.

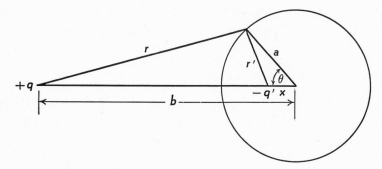

Fig. VIII-2. Image of a point charge in a grounded sphere.

This assumption gives the equation

$$\frac{q}{r} - \frac{q'}{r'} = 0, \qquad \text{(VIII-6)}$$

which must hold for all points on the sphere. From this relation, we see that

$$q^2 r'^2 = q'^2 r^2$$

and, by the law of cosines,

$$q^2(a^2 + x^2 - 2ax \cos\theta) = q'^2(a^2 + b^2 - 2ab \cos\theta). \quad \text{(VIII-7)}$$

Since this equation is valid for all values of θ, we know that the coefficient of the $\cos\theta$ term in the left-hand member must equal that in the right-hand member. Hence,

$$q^2 x = q'^2 b \qquad \text{(VIII-8)}$$

or

$$x = kb, \qquad \text{(VIII-9)}$$

where

$$k = (q'/q)^2,$$

and

$$q^2 a^2 + q^2 x^2 = q'^2 a^2 + q'^2 b^2, \qquad a^2 + x^2 = k(a^2 + b^2).$$

Eliminating x by Eq. (9) gives

$$k^2 b^2 - k(a^2 + b^2) + a^2 = 0.$$

Solving this equation algebraically for k, we have the two roots:

$$k = 1 \quad \text{and} \quad k = a^2/b^2.$$

The solution, $k = 1$, corresponds to the nullification of the effect of charge q on the sphere (and incidentally at all points in space) by neutralizing the charge q through placing a charge $-q$ at the same point.

This obviously is not the problem we started to solve. The other root gives the solution to the stated problem. Thus from Eq. (9), we have

$$x = a^2/b \qquad\qquad \text{(VIII-10)}$$

and from Eq. (8) we find the condition

$$-q' = -qa/b. \qquad\qquad \text{(VIII-11)}$$

The potential and field at all points in space can be computed in the usual way since the magnitude of $-q'$ and its location are thus determined. q' may be interpreted as the total charge "induced" on the grounded sphere in the presence of the charge q. The distribution of the charge $-q'$ upon the surface of the sphere can be obtained in the usual way from the field at the surface.

This solution implicitly contains also the answer for the problem of a charge *inside* a grounded sphere. In this case, a charge of $-q' = -qa/b$ at a distance of

$$x = a^2/b$$

from the center of the sphere has all of its lines of force terminating on the grounded sphere; so, as expected, it induces an equal and opposite charge on the grounded sphere containing it. So far as the potential distribution inside the sphere is concerned, this grounded sphere may be replaced by the charge $+q$ at the distance b from the center of the sphere, as shown in Fig. VIII-2. In this case, however, it is preferable to treat the magnitude of the charge placed within the sphere as data represented by the constant q, and the distance x also as data, although in this case a variable. Inversion of the above relationships then gives

$$b = a^2/x, \qquad\qquad \text{(VIII-12)}$$

and the charge outside the sphere represented by $-q'$ is given by

$$-q' = -(b/a)q. \qquad\qquad \text{(VIII-13)}$$

Quite a variety of problems can be based on the case of the sphere and the point charge. If instead of being at zero potential the sphere is uncharged, the solution for the potential at external points is obtained by placing a charge of q' at the center of the sphere (which will balance the charge $-q'$ at x without disturbing the condition that the sphere is to be an equipotential surface). Similarly, if the sphere is to be charged or established at some arbitrary potential, this may be done by adding to, or subtracting from, the charge imagined (for the purpose of solution) to be located at the center.

IX | Periodic Potential Variations and Allowed Energies

One of the problems of solid state physics, which is so complicated that only convenient approximations are used in practice, is the calculation of the allowed energy levels from the periodic variations of the electron's potential energy. In the physical situation, the energy varies periodically in each of three directions in the crystal, and the period in general depends upon the direction. Furthermore, the variations of potential are in practice complicated functions of the distance along each of the three axes of the crystal. To determine the rule for the variations of potential is itself a major problem, and to calculate, from this information, the allowed energy levels presents formidable difficulties. Fortunately, the major features of the distribution of the allowed energy levels can be derived from a relatively simple model. In principle, the conclusions reached are valid; it is only the numerical values which are somewhat crude approximations.

The assumptions introduced to make the problem tractable must be very great simplifications of the actual situation, and the model is, therefore, highly artificial. This, however, does not destroy the usefulness of such a model, because the correct general features concerning the variations of energy with momentum arise from it. The greatest single simplification is to limit the potential variations to a single direction. The problem may be further simplified, however, by suitable choice of the form of the potential variation. A particularly easy one to handle is a potential which assumes two levels, the higher value of which is identified as a barrier. In the treatment of this, however, the barrier is approximated by a δ-function. Bands of allowed energies arise, the width of which depends on the value of the δ-function. The boundaries of such bands are of particular interest, and these can be located by a consideration of the properties of well-known functions. This is the way that we will derive information concerning the allowed energies in the bands.

As a start on the analysis, we examine the behavior of an electron in a double trough, the width of each trough being a, and the distance between the inner boundaries of the two troughs being b. At the outside boundaries, the potential energy of the electron rises suddenly to infinity while at the middle there is a finite boundary, as shown in Fig. IX-1.

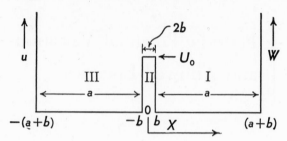

Fig. IX-1. Double trough for an electron.

There are three regions, as shown in the figure. In region III (the region of one trough), $-(a + b) < x < -b$, and in region I (the region of the other trough), $b < x < (a + b)$. In both of these regions Schroedinger's equation assumes the form

$$d^2u/dx^2 = -k^2u, \tag{IX-1}$$

where $k^2 = 8\pi^2 mW/h^2$. In region II (the region between the two troughs), $-b < x < b$, and in this range of x the differential equation is

$$d^2u/dx^2 - \beta^2u = 0, \tag{IX-2}$$

where $\beta^2 = 8\pi^2 m(U_0 - W)/h^2$.

The general solution of Schroedinger's equation in regions I and III is of the form

$$u = C \sin kx + D \cos kx. \tag{IX-3}$$

In region II the general solution of Eq. (2) is

$$u = E \exp (-\beta x) + F \exp (\beta x). \tag{IX-4}$$

From these equations, continuous solutions, having continuous first derivatives, can be put together. The general forms of those of lowest energy are represented in Fig. IX-2.

Let us consider first the analytical formulation of the wave functions of the general shape shown by A in Fig. IX-2. The symmetry gives $D = 0$ in Eq. (3), and

$$u_i = C \sin k(x + \epsilon), \tag{IX-5}$$

where ϵ is a constant which is to be evaluated from boundary conditions.

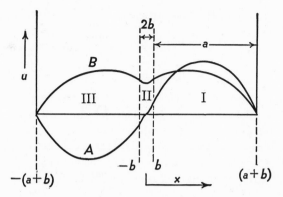

Fig. IX-2. Form of the wave functions representing an electron in a double trough.

Similarly, the evaluation of the constants in Eq. (4) to give a solution of form A results in

$$u_{ii} = E[\exp \beta(x - b) - \exp - \beta(x + b)]. \qquad \text{(IX-6)}$$

The corresponding derivatives are

$$du_i/dx = Ck \cos k(x + \epsilon) \qquad \text{(IX-7)}$$

and

$$du_{ii}/dx = \beta E[\exp \beta(x - b) + \exp - \beta(x + b)]. \qquad \text{(IX-8)}$$

From the continuity of the wave function between regions I and II, we must have

$$C \sin k(b + \epsilon) = E[1 - \exp(-2b\beta)], \qquad \text{(IX-9)}$$

and from the continuity of the first derivative at the boundary between regions I and II, we have

$$kC \cos k(b + \epsilon) = E\beta[1 + \exp(-2b\beta)]. \qquad \text{(IX-10)}$$

Combination of Eqs. (9) and (10) gives

$$\tan k(b + \epsilon) = k[1 - \exp(-2b\beta)]/\{\beta[1 + \exp(-2b\beta)]\}. \qquad \text{(IX-11)}$$

This equation involves essentially two unknowns β and ϵ. If k can be determined, the energy $W(k)$ and hence β can be calculated. The second unknown is ϵ. A second independent equation for determining these unknowns is obtained from the boundary condition at the exterior wall. The potential there rises suddenly to infinity at $x = a + b$, and hence the wave function must be zero. Hence,

$$\sin k(a + b + \epsilon) = 0$$

or

$$k(a + b + \epsilon) = n\pi, \qquad \text{(IX-12)}$$

where n is an integer. Eqs. (11) and (12) are sufficient to determine k and ϵ, and the allowed energies are then determined from the equation defining k in terms of the energy, which will be found just after Eq. (1).

Before making any attempt to carry the analysis of this situation further, let us formulate conditions for the second eigenfunction, which is illustrated by the curve marked B in Fig. IX-2. Here the corresponding equations are

$$u_i = C \sin k'(x + \epsilon'), \qquad \text{(IX-13)}$$

where the primes indicate changed numerical values for the constants;

$$u_{ii} = E[\exp \beta'(x - b) + \exp - \beta'(x + b)]; \qquad \text{(IX-14)}$$

$$u_{iii} = -C \sin k'(x + \epsilon'); \qquad \text{(IX-15)}$$

$$du_i/dx = Ck \cos k'(x + \epsilon'); \qquad \text{(IX-16)}$$

and

$$du_{ii}/dx = E\beta[\exp \beta'(x - b) - \exp - \beta'(x + b)]. \qquad \text{(IX-17)}$$

From the continuity of the wave function at the boundary between regions I and II, we obtain

$$C \sin k'(b + \epsilon) = E[1 + \exp (-2b\beta')]. \qquad \text{(IX-18)}$$

From the continuity of the first derivative at the boundary between the first and second regions, we obtain

$$Ck \cos k'(b + \epsilon) = E\beta'[1 + \exp (-2b\beta')], \qquad \text{(IX-19)}$$

and thus,

$$\tan k'(b + \epsilon') = k'[1 + \exp (-2b\beta')]/\beta'[1 - \exp (-2b\beta')]. \qquad \text{(IX-20)}$$

If this equation is used to determine ϵ', the boundary condition at $x = a + b$ may be used to determine k'. Thus,

$$k'(a + b + \epsilon') = n\pi. \qquad \text{(IX-21)}$$

The definition of k' then suffices to determine the energy.

For the purpose of interpreting the results of this analysis, the problem may be simplified very considerably. First, we may introduce the parameter $P = \beta^2 ab$, upon which the change in phase of the wave function within the barrier depends. Even this parameter as it stands leaves more detail than is necessary for illustrating the essential features of the mentioned, there are $n - 2$ eigenfunctions with the various numbers ne loops $(n - 1)$, $(n - 2)$, $\cdots$, 3, 2. Thus, if the number of quantum es allowed in the trough is constant, there are n quantum states, out considering the multiplicity given by electrons of oppositely cted spins.

his discussion can be made entirely quantitative at the cost of the rt required for the computation, but by these elementary considera- s we have established the development of the bands, which results the Kronig-Penny one-dimensional model.

tracing the development of the allowed energy bands from the nic energy levels, research has established that as the spacing between atoms is reduced there is a range in which the allowed energy band in- ses in width, and, because the highest allowed energies do not change lly, the appearance is very like that obtained here as P is decreased. re are some differences in the results given by the atomic model by the Kronig-Penny simplification. As the spacing between atoms duced, the interaction between the atoms increases, and this cor- onds to a decrease of P for the Kronig-Penny model, but also as the ing between atoms is reduced, the space to which the electrons are tively confined is reduced, also. The analysis of electrons in a trough xed width has left this factor constant. It would be possible to in- se the similarity of the results obtained from the two models by sing the spacing a arbitrarily as a function of P for the purpose of ing the bands develop in a similar manner, but this arbitrary pro- re would lack physical significance.

e fact to be emphasized is that the one-dimensional model with its ction barriers is severely restricted, but even this model is capable ving the chief features of the development of allowed-energy bands. se are: (1) For any particular degree of interaction, the allowed gies are confined to a definite range. (2) This range of energies in llowed band increases as it is made easier for the wave function senting an electron to penetrate the δ-function barriers. (3) In en energy band, there is a number of allowed wave patterns or functions which is equal to the number of subdivisions, in each of h an electron can move freely, and hence is represented by a sinus- wave pattern.

problem of determining the energy. The problem may be further simpli- fied by using the δ-function. Let us allow β^2 to increase toward infinity in such a way that P remains finite as b approaches 0. The barrier at the middle of the trough has no width, and the portions of sinusoidal waves occupy the entire volume in the two halves of this double trough. This feature simplifies the problem by the elimination of secondary effects depending on the variation of the volume available to the sinusoidal waves.

The Very Limited Range of ε in Case A

Returning to the interpretation of Eqs. (11) and (12), we see that ϵ has a very restricted range, which in the limiting process of the δ-func- tion becomes quite negligible. When $2b\beta$ approaches zero, Eq. (11) gives

$$\tan k(b + \epsilon) = 0, \qquad \text{(IX-22)}$$

from which we deduce that

$$\epsilon = -b. \qquad \text{(IX-23)}$$

At the other extreme, as $2b\beta$ approaches infinity, Eq. (11) gives

$$\tan k(b + \epsilon) = k/\beta. \qquad \text{(IX-24)}$$

Since as β increases without limit, k/β becomes small, we are justified as an adequate approximation in using the first term in the power series expansion for the tangent function. Thus,

$$k(b + \epsilon) = k/\beta$$

and

$$\epsilon = -b + 1/\beta. \qquad \text{(IX-25)}$$

Thus, ϵ differs from $-b$ by only a small quantity.

In case A, where the barrier is approximated by a δ-function, the magnitude of the barrier has virtually no influence on the eigenfunctions, which are simple sine loops differing in phase on the two sides of the barrier. The constant k, and hence the energy, is virtually independent of the parameter measuring the magnitude of the barrier.

The Variation of ε in Case B

In case B, there is a considerable variation of the constant k, and thus of the energy, as the parameter P, specifying the magnitude of the barrier, is changed. Combining Eqs. (20) and (21) gives

$$\tan \pi(b + \epsilon')/(a + b + \epsilon')$$
$$= \pi[1 + \exp(-2b\beta')]/\{\beta'(a + b + \epsilon')[1 - \exp(-2b\beta')]\}. \quad \text{(IX-26)}$$

If P is large, the "coupling" between the two halves of the double trough is small. In this case, ϵ' is small, and since we are considering the limit as b approaches zero, the argument of the tangent function is small. A suitable approximation is

$$(b + \epsilon') = [1 + \exp(-2b\beta')]/\{\beta'[1 - \exp(-2b\beta')]\}. \quad (IX\text{-}27)$$

Given values of b and β', ϵ' is easily evaluated in this approximation. Now

$$k'(b + \epsilon') = \tan^{-1}(1/\beta') = 1/\beta' - 1/3\beta'^3. \quad (IX\text{-}28)$$

Eq. (28) can be used for larger values of the argument than can Eq. (27),

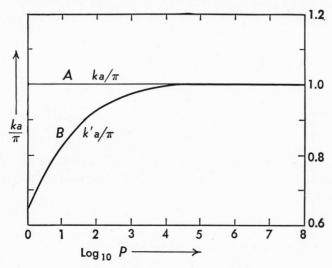

Fig. IX-3. Variation of k and k' with P.

and it is not inconvenient for calculation. For still larger values of the argument of the tangent function, there is no substitute for solving the transcendental equation, but this can be done by numerical methods. The constancy of k with variation of P is shown by the line A in Fig. IX-3. Similarly, the variation of k' with P is shown by B of the same figure.

An electron in a double trough is thus seen to be roughly analogous to a pair of coupled oscillators, because it can have either of two energy states, and the separation between these states varies with the coupling. A justification for treating this elementary problem is that the most exact mechanical analogy of this particular problem was not given, and this formulation gives a definite model to account for the behavior of electrons in a structure that repeats variations of potential periodically.

If more sections are added to the trough bet boundaries, it is not difficult to describe (in a se the behavior of the energies associated with the First, for simplicity of treatment, the subdivis kept identical by moving the infinite boundar space between them for more identical subdivisio an especially simple case, consider the behavior which the phase changes by π in a change of po the width of a subdivision. This is the condition analyzed above; the values of k, and hence also tical with those obtained previously for the doub when the barriers are represented by δ-function change the coupling, the value of k (and hence als constant, as illustrated by A in Fig. IX-3.

If we now take the contrasting case of the eig same sign for u in each of the sections set apa limiting values of the energy are easily found, $\imath$ limits of the allowed range of energies. To mal without unduly restricting the applicability of th the trough of width na contains $(n-1)$ equally characterized by identical P-values. In the li physics, this is identified as the Kronig-Penny $\imath$ of obtaining information through analysis, we $\imath$ (assumed to be under our control) to be used as a If in the first place, $P \to 0$, the eigenfunction $\imath$ loop of length na. Hence $k = \pi/na$, and the er $(1/n)^2$ of that obtained in case A. If, however, by increasing P, the energy increases gradually, a and the boundary conditions are satisfied by ta the same value we obtained for the eigenfuncti changed by π whenever the displacement across by an amount a, and hence in this limit, the hig of case A, is obtained. Thus, the discussion of has indicated that the behavior of the high-ene A) is identical to that shown in Fig. IX-3.

We have now shown that qualitatively the beh eigenfunction (case B) also is similar to curve I scale of ordinates has to be changed, because k $P \to 0$, and hence depends quantitatively on the The high-energy limit of this band (case A) corre tion with n sine loops between the outer boun the low-energy limit corresponds to a single boundaries. Also under the restriction $P = 0$, bet

X | A Step in the Derivation of Rutherford Scattering

Integration of $dr/[(r^2/p)(1 - p^2/r^2 - b/r)^{1/2}]$ is a detail which is discussed in this appendix. For this purpose, substitute $r = 1/u$, $dr = -(1/u^2)\,du$ into the above expression, which then becomes

$$-du/[1/p^2 - (u^2 + bu/p^2)]^{1/2}$$

or

$$-du/[(1/p^2 + b^2/4p^4) - (u + b/2p^2)^2]^{1/2}$$

or

$$-dx/(a^2 - x^2)^{1/2},$$

where $a^2 = 1/p^2 + b^2/4p^4$, $x = u + b/2p^2$, and $dx = du$. The indefinite integral of this is

$$\text{arc cos } x/a$$

or

$$\text{arc cos } (u + b/2p^2)/(1/p^2 + b^2/4p^4)^{1/2}$$

or finally

$$\text{arc cos } (1/r + b/2p^2)/(1/p^2 + b^2/4p^4)^{1/2},$$

as given in Eq. (17-5).

XI | The Schroedinger Equation

Consider any particle which has a definite momentum $hk/2\pi$ along an x-axis and which exists in a region of space where its potential energy U is the same at all points. This implies that the particle is free in the region and has a total energy

$$W = \frac{(hk)^2}{8m\pi^2} + U = \frac{h\omega}{2\pi}. \tag{XI-1}$$

Also, the particle is represented by the de Broglie wave

$$\psi = A \exp j(kx - \omega t). \tag{XI-2}$$

By direct differentiation and the use of Eq. (1), the student can readily verify that ψ satisfies the equation

$$-\frac{h^2}{8\pi^2 m}\frac{\partial^2 \psi}{\partial x^2} + U\psi = j\frac{h}{2\pi}\frac{\partial \psi}{\partial t}. \tag{XI-3}$$

Moreover, the sum of any number of de Broglie waves of this same particle in this same region of space also satisfies Eq. (3). To show this, consider the superposition

$$\psi = \psi_1 + \psi_2 + \psi_3 + \cdots, \tag{XI-4}$$

where

$$\psi_i = A_i e^{j(k_i x - \omega_i t)}$$

and

$$W = \frac{(hk_i)^2}{8\pi^2 m} + U = \frac{h\omega_i}{2\pi}. \tag{XI-5}$$

Each of the individual terms ψ_i is a de Broglie wave and satisfies Eq. (3). Therefore, as the student can readily show, the sum is also a solution of Eq. (3).

So far, our de Broglie waves have been restricted to functions $\psi(x,t)$ depending on only one coordinate x. Now, let us consider a particle with an arbitrary momentum $\mathbf{p}$. Then the de Broglie relation is generalized to read

$$\mathbf{p} = \frac{h}{2\pi}\,\mathbf{k}, \tag{XI-6}$$

and a de Broglie wave is generalized to the form

$$\psi = A e^{j(\mathbf{k}\cdot\mathbf{r}-\omega t)}, \tag{XI-7}$$

where $\mathbf{k}$ is a vector having the magnitude $2\pi/\lambda$ and a direction perpendicular to the wave front, and $\mathbf{k}\cdot\mathbf{r}$ is the familar scalar product

$$\mathbf{k}\cdot\mathbf{r} \equiv k_x x + k_y y + k_z z. \tag{XI-8}$$

Also, the differential equation (3) is generalized to the form

$$-\frac{h^2}{8\pi^2 m}\,\nabla^2\psi + U\psi = j\,\frac{k}{2\pi}\,\frac{\partial\psi}{\partial t}, \tag{XI-9}$$

where

$$\nabla^2 \equiv \frac{\partial^2}{\partial x^2} + \frac{\partial^2}{\partial y^2} + \frac{\partial^2}{\partial z^2}.$$

Eq. (9) is called the *time dependent Schroedinger equation*. Schroedinger postulated that this equation holds even when the particle is not free (i.e. even when U depends on $\mathbf{r}$). This postulate has been richly confirmed by experiment.

For any particle with a definite energy $\dfrac{h\omega}{2\pi}$, we have

$$\psi = u(x,y,z)e^{-j\omega t}. \tag{XI-10}$$

Therefore, substitution into Eq. (9) shows that

$$-\frac{h^2}{8\pi^2 m}\,\nabla^2 u + U u = \frac{h\omega u}{2\pi}. \tag{XI-11}$$

Tables

Values of the Atomic Constants

e	Electronic charge	$(1.60208 \pm 0.00005) \times 10^{-19}$ coulombs
m_0	Rest mass of the electron	$(9.1086 \pm 0.0006) \times 10^{-31}$ kg
e/m_0	Charge to mass ratio of electron	$(1.75888 \pm 0.00004) \times 10^{11}$ coul/kg
k	Boltzmann's constant	$(1.38047 \pm 0.00006) \times 10^{-23}$ joul/°C
R_0	Gas constant per mole	8.3169 ± 0.0001 joul/(mole degree)
N_0	Avogadro's number	$(6.0247 \pm 0.0002) \times 10^{26}$ molecules/kg-mole
c	Velocity of light	$(2.997928 \pm 0.000005) \times 10^{8}$ m/sec
P_0	Pressure of standard atmosphere	1.01325×10^{5} newtons/m^2
M_p	Rest mass of proton	$(1.67244 \pm 0.00006) \times 10^{-27}$ kg
M_n	Rest mass of neutron	$(1.67475 \pm 0.00007) \times 10^{-27}$ kg
h	Planck's constant	$(6.6253 \pm 0.0003) \times 10^{-34}$ joul-sec
σ	Stefan Boltzmann total radiation	$(5.6690 \pm 0.0005) \times 10^{-8}$ watts/(m^2 deg^4)
a_0	First Bohr radius	$(5.29172 \pm 0.00003) \times 10^{-11}$ m
R	Rydberg wave number for mass ∞	$(10{,}973{,}731 \pm 1)$ m^{-1}
μ	Reduced mass of electron in hydrogen	$(9.1036 \pm 0.0004) \times 10^{-31}$ kg
λ_1	Wave length of 1 e.v. photon	1.23978×10^{-6} m
λ_{ce}	Compton wave length (electron)	$(2.42626 \pm 0.00003) \times 10^{-12}$ m
λ_{cp}	Compton wave length (proton)	$(1.32139 \pm 0.00003) \times 10^{-15}$ m
λ_{de}	de Broglie wave length (electron)	1.2264×10^{-9} m/(Numeric for electron energy in e.v.)$^{\frac{1}{2}}$
λ_{dp}	de Broglie wave length (proton)	2.862×10^{-11} m/(Numeric for proton energy in e.v.)$^{\frac{1}{2}}$

Atomic Masses

1 amu $= 1.65985 \times 10^{-27}$ kg

Electron $(5.48760 \pm 0.00006) \times 10^{-4}$ amu

Proton $(1.007595 \pm 0.0000020) \times$ amu

Neutron (1.008983 ± 0.000003) amu

Hydrogen (1.008144 ± 0.000002) amu

Deuterium (2.014737 ± 0.00004) amu

Tritium 3.01700 amu

$_2\text{He}^4$	4.00387 amu
$_3\text{Li}^6$	6.01702 "
$_3\text{Li}^7$	7.01822 "
$_4\text{Be}^8$	8.00785 "
$_4\text{Be}^9$	9.01504 "
$_6\text{C}^{12}$	12.00380 "
$_7\text{N}^{14}$	14.00752 "

Values of International Atomic Weights (1953)

1	H	1.0080	19	K	39.100	38	Sr	87.63	57	La	138.92
2	He	4.003	20	Ca	40.080	39	Y	88.92	58	Ce	140.13
3	Li	6.940	22	Ti	47.90	40	Zr	91.22	72	Hf	178.6
4	Be	9.013	23	V	50.95	41	Nb	92.91	73	Ta	180.95
5	B	10.82	24	Cr	52.01	42	Mo	95.95	74	W	183.92
6	C	12.011	25	Mn	54.94	44	Ru	101.1	75	Re	186.31
7	N	14.008	26	Fe	55.85	45	Rh	102.91	76	Os	190.2
8	O	16.	27	Co	58.94	46	Pd	106.7	77	Ir	193.1
9	F	19.00	28	Ni	58.69	47	Ag	107.880	78	Pt	195.23
10	Ne	20.183	29	Cu	63.54	48	Cd	112.41	79	Au	197.0
11	Na	22.991	30	Zn	65.38	49	In	114.76	80	Hg	200.61
12	Mg	24.32	31	Ga	69.72	50	Sn	118.70	81	Tl	204.4
13	Al	26.98	32	Ge	72.60	51	Sb	121.76	82	Pb	207.21
14	Si	28.09	33	As	74.91	52	Te	127.61	83	Bi	209.00
15	P	30.975	34	Se	78.96	53	I	126.91	90	Th	232.05
16	S	32.067	35	Br	79.92	54	Xe	131.3	92	U	238.07
17	Cl	35.462	36	Kr	83.80	55	Cs	132.91			
18	A	39.949	37	Rb	85.48	56	Ba	137.36			

Energy Conversion Factors

joules	eV	secs^{-1}	m^{-1}	°K	kg	amu
1.000 joule	6.2419×10^{18}	1.50935×10^{33}	5.035×10^{24}	7.2438×10^{22}	1.11265×10^{-17}	6.703×10^{9}
1.6021×10^{-19}	1.000 eV	2.418×10^{14}	8.066×10^{5}	1.1605×10^{4}	1.7826×10^{-36}	1.074×10^{-9}
6.625×10^{-34}	4.1355×10^{-15}	1.000 sec^{-1}	3.3356×10^{-9}	4.799×10^{-11}	7.372×10^{-51}	4.441×10^{-24}
1.986×10^{-25}	1.2398×10^{-6}	2.9979×10^{8}	1.000 m^{-1}	0.014388	2.210×10^{-42}	1.331×10^{-15}
1.3805×10^{-23}	8.617×10^{-5}	2.0836×10^{10}	69.50	1.000 °K	1.536×10^{-40}	9.254×10^{-14}
8.988×10^{16}	5.610×10^{35}	1.3565×10^{50}	4.525×10^{41}	6.510×10^{39}	1.000 kg	6.025×10^{26}
1.492×10^{-10}	9.312×10^{8}	2.2516×10^{23}	7.511×10^{14}	1.081×10^{13}	1.660×10^{-27}	1.000 amu

Tables of Properties of Interesting Materials

Electrical Resistivity of Metals at 18° C

Metal	Resistivity in micro-ohm-meters	Metal	Resistivity in micro-ohm-meters
Al	0.27	Pt	1.05
Ti	8.9	Cu	0.17
Ta	1.5	Hg	9.5
Mo	0.47	Ni	0.75
W	0.53	Fe	0.87
Cr	0.26	Co	0.68
Ag	0.16	Ir	0.53
Au	0.22	Zn	0.6

Electrical Resistivity of Various Alloys

Alloy	Composition	Resistivity in micro-ohm-meters
Constantan	Cu 60 Ni 40	4.4
German Silver	Cu 60.16 Ni 18 Zn 25.37 Ni 14.03 Fe 0.3	3.1
Aluminum Bronze	Cu 90 Al 10	1.3
Brass	Cu 70.2 Zn 29.8	0.82
Copper-Manganese	Cu 98.5 Mn 1.5	0.67
" "	Cu 95.8 Mn 4.2	1.8
" "	Cu 85 Mn 15	5.0
Manganin	Cu 84 Mn 12 Ni 4	4.5
Nichrome		10.
Platinum-Iridium	Pt 80 Ir 20	3.1

Resistivity of Various Insulators (Dielectrics)

Material	Resistivity in megohm-meters	Material	Resistivity in megohm-meters
Mica	10^{10}	Alumina	10^4-10^7
Neoprene	10^4	Porcelain	10^5-10^7
Polystyrene	10^2-10^6	Sulfur	10^{10}
Quartz		Diamond	10^7
parallel to axis	2×10^7	Pyrex (4040)	8
perpendicular to axis	2×10^9	Vycor (7911)	4×10^2

Properties of Germanium and Silicon

Quantity	Germanium	Silicon
Atomic number	32	14
Atomic weight	72.60	28.08
Density (kg/m^3)	5,675	5,431
Dielectric constant	16	12
Intrinsic resistivity (ohm-meters)	0.47	636
Intrinsic carrier concentration (m^{-3})	2.5×10^{19}	6.8×10^{16}
Lattice mobility $(m^2/volt\text{-}sec)$		
Electron	$19 \times 10^2/T^{3/2}$	$6.2 \times 10^2/T^{3/2}$
Hole	$8.9 \times 10^2/T^{3/2}$	$1.3 \times 10^2/T^{3/2}$
Mobility at 300° K $(m^2/volt\text{-}sec)$		
Electron	0.36	0.12
Hole	0.17	0.025
Ionization energy (electron volts)		
Valance band	$0.75 - 0.0001$ T	$1.12 - 0.0003$ T
Acceptors at low concentration	0.01	0.08
Donors at low concentration	0.01	0.05
Latent heat of fusion (kg-cal/kg-mole)	8300	9450
Melting point (°C)	936	1420
Specific heat (kg-cal/kg °C)	0.074	0.181
Volume compressibility $(m^2/newton)$	1.3×10^{-11}	0.98×10^{-11}
Lattice constant (A.U.)	5.657	5.431
Linear expansion coefficient	6.1×10^{-6}	4.2×10^{-6}

These constants have been determined largely in research at the Bell Telephone Laboratories. They are collected and discussed by E. M. Conwell in her paper on "Properties of Silicon and Germanium," *Proc. Inst. Radio Engrs.*, **40,** 1327 (1952), where the original papers are cited.

Periodic Table

Isotopes ordinarily found in chemical samples of an element are in italics. Most abundant isotopes are in boldface.
* Denotes a radioactive isotope.

I

1H (1.0080)
1, *2*, 3*

I

3Li (6.940)
5*, *6*, **7**, 8*, 9*

11Na (22.991)
20*, 1*, 2*, **23**, 4*, 5*

II

4Be (9.013)
7*, 8*, **9**, 10*

12Mg (24.32)
23*, **24**, *25, 26*, 7*

III

5B (10.82)
8*, 9*, *10*, **11**, 12*

13Al (26.98)
24*, 5*, 6*, **27**, 8*, 9*

IV

6C (12.011)
10*, 11*, **12**, *13*, 14*, 15*

14Si (28.09)
27*, **28**, *29, 30*, 1*

III

21Sc (44.96)
41*, 3*, 4*, **45**, 6*, 7*, 8*, 9*

39Y (88.92)
84*, 6*, 7*, 8*, **89**, 90*, 1*, 2*, 3*, 4*, 5*, 7*

Rare Earths

89Ac (227)
222*, 3*, 4*, 5*, 6*, 7*, 8*, 230*

IVa

22Ti (47.90)
43*, 5*, **46, 47, 48**, *49, 50*, 1*

40Zr (91.22)
86*, 87*, 8*, 9*, **90**, *91, 92*, 3*, 94, 5*, 96, 97*

72Hf (178.6)
170*, 1*, 2*, 3*, 174, 5*, 176, 177, 178, 179, **180**, 1*

90Th (232.05)
223*, 4*, 5*, 6*, 7*, 8*, 9*, 230*, 1*, **2**, 3*, 4*

Va

23V (50.95)
47*, 8*, 9*, *50*, **51**, 52*

41Nb (92.91)
90*, 1*, 2*, **93**, 94*, 5*, 6*, 7*, 8*, 99*

73Ta (180.95)
176*, 7*, 8*, 9*, 180*, **181**, 2*, 3*, 5*

91Pa (231)
225*, 6*, 7*, 8*, 9*, 230*, *231*, 2*, 3*, 4*, 235*

VIa

24Cr (52.01)
48*, 9*, *50*, 1*, **52**, *53, 54*, 5*

42Mo (95.95)
91*, 92, 3*, 94, 95, 96, 97, **98**, 9*, 100, 1*, 2*, 105

74W (183.92)
176*, 7*, 8*, 9*, 180*, 1*, 182, 183, **184**, 186, 5*, 7*, 8*

92U (238.07)
227*, 8*, 230*, 1*, 2*, 3*, *234, 235*, 6*, 7*, **238**, 239*, 240*

VIIa

25Mn (54.94)
51*, 2*, 4*, **55**, 6*

43Tc (99)
92*, 3*, 4*, 5*, 6*, 7*, 8*, 9*, **100***, 1*, 2*, 5*

75Re (186.31)
181*, 2*, 3*, 4*, *185*, 6*, **187**, 8*, 9*

93Np (237)
231*, 2*, 3*, 4*, 5*, 6*, **237**, 8*, 9*, 240*, 1*

VIII

26Fe (55.85)
52*, 3*, *54*, 5*, **56, 57**, *58*, 9*

27Co (58.94)
55*, 6*, 7*, 8*, **59**, 60*, 1*, 2*, 4*

28Ni (58.69)
56*, 7*, **58**, 9*, *60, 61, 62*, 3*, *64*, 5*, **6***

44Ru (101.1)
95*, *96*, 7*, *98*, *99, 100*, *101*, **102**, 3*, *104*, 5*, 6*, 107

45Rh (102.91)
99*, **100***, 2*, 3*, 4*, 5*, 6*, 7*, 9*

46Pd (106.7)
100*, 1*, 102*, 3*, *104, 105*, **106**, 7*, *108*, 9*, *110*, 11*, 12*

76Os (190.2)
184, 5*, *186, 187, 188, 189, 190*, 1*, **192**, 3*, 194*

77Ir (192.2)
187*, 8*, 9*, 190*, *191*, 2*, **193**, 4*, 5*, 197

78Pt (195.23)
190, 1*, 192, 3*, 194, **195**, 196, 7*, 198, 9*

94Pu (242)
232*, 4*, 5*, 6*, 7*, 8*, 9*, 240*, 1*, 242*, 3*

95Am (243)
237*, 8*, 239, 1*, 2*, 243*, 4*

96Cm (245)
238*, 9*, 240*, 1*, 2*, 3*, 4*, (245)

I

19K (39.100)
37*, 8*, **39**, *40*, 41*, 2*, 3*, 4*

37Rb (85.48)
81*, 2*, 3*, 4*, **85**, 6*, 87*, 8*, 9*, 90*, 1*, 2*, 3*, 4*, 7*

55Cs (132.91)
127*, 8*, 9*, 130*, *1, 2, 133**, 4*, 5*, 6*, 7*, 8*, 9*, 140*, 1*, 2*, 3*, 4*, 145

87Fr (223)
211*, 2*, 3*, 7*, 8*, 9*, 220*, 1*, 2*, *223*, 4*

II

20Ca (40.08)
39*, **40**, 1*, *42, 43, 44*, 5*, 6*, *48*, 9*

38Sr (87.63)
81*, 2*, 3*, *84*, 5*, *86*, 7*, **88**, 9*, 90*, 1*, 2*, 3*, 4*, 7*

56Ba (137.36)
128*, 9*, *130*, 1*, *132, 133*, *135, 136, 137*, **138**, 9*, 140*, 1*, 2*, 3*, 4*, 5*

88Ra (226.05)
219*, 220*, 1*, 2*, 3*, 4*, 5*, 6*, 7*, 8*, 230*

490

0

₂He (4.003)
3, **4,** 5*, 6*

Ia

₂₉Cu (63.54)
58*, 9*, 60*,
1*, 2*, **63,** 4*,
65, 6*, 67*

₄₇Ag (107.880)
102*, 4*, 5*,
6*, **107,** 8*,
109, 110, 1*,
2*, 3*, 4*,
115*

₇₉Au (197.0)
190*, 1*, 2*,
3*, 4*, 5*,
6*, **197,** 8*,
9*, 200*

IIa

₃₀Zn (65.38)
62*, 3*, **64,**
5*, 66, 67,
68, 9*, 70,
1*, 2*, 73*

₄₈Cd (112.41)
105*, 106, 7*,
108, 9*, 110,
111*, 112, 113,
114, 5*, 116, 7*

₈₀Hg (200.61)
191*, 2*, 3*,
4*, 5*, 196,
7*, 198, 199,
200, 201, **202,**
3*, 204, 5*

IIIa

₃₁Ga (69.72)
64*, 5*, 6*,
7*, 8*, **69,**
70*, 71, 2*,
3*, 74*

₄₉In (114.76)
107*, 8*, 9*,
110*, 1*, 2*,
113, 4*, **115,**
6*, 7*, 8*,
119*

₈₁Tl (204.39)
198*, 9*,
200*, 1*, 2*,
3*, 4*, **205,**
206*, 207*,
208*, 9*, 210*

IV

₃₂Ge (72.60)
66*, 7*, 8*,
9*, 70, 1*, 72,
73, **74,** 5*, 76,
7*, 78*

₅₀Sn (118.70)
108*, 9*, 110*,
1*, 112, 3*, 114,
115, 116, 117, 118,
119, **120,** 1*, 2*,
3*, 124, 5*, 6*,
127

₈₂Pb (207.21)
198*, 9*,
200*, 1*, 2*,
2*, 3*, 204,
5*, 206, 207,
208, 9*, 10*,
211*, 212*, 214*

V

₇N (14.008)
12*, 3*, **14,** 15, 16*, 7*

₁₅P (30.975)
29*, 30*, **31,** 2*, 3*, 4*

₃₃As (74.91)
70*, 1*, 2*,
3*, 4*, **75,**
6*, 7*, 8*,
9*, 81*

₅₁Sb (121.76)
116*, 7*, 8*,
9*, 120*, **121,**
2*, 123, 4*, 5*,
6*, 7*, 8*, 9*,
131*, 2*, 3*

₈₃Bi (209.00)
197*, 8*, 9*,
200*, 1*, 2*,
3*, 4*, 5*, 6*,
7*, 8*, **209,**
210*, 11*, 12*,
3*, 4*, 215*

VI

₈O (16.000)
14*, 5*, **16,** 17, 18, 9*

₁₆S (32.066)
31*, **32,** 33, 34, 5*, 36*, 7*

₃₄Se (78.96)
70*, 2*, 3*,
74, 5*, 76,
7*, 78, 9*,
80, 1*, 82,
3*, 84

₅₂Te (127.61)
117*, 8*, 9*,
120, 1*, 122,
123, 124, 125,
126, 7*, 128,
9*, **130,** 1*, 2*,
2*, 3*, 4*, 5*

₈₄Po (210)
200*, 1*, 2*,
3*, 4*, 5*, 6*,
7*, 8*, 9*, 210*,
11*, 12*, 3*,
7*, 218*

VII

₉F (19.00)
17*, 8*, **19,** 20*

₁₇Cl (35.475)
33*, 4*, **35,** 6*, 37, 8*, 9*

₃₅Br (79.916)
74*, 5*, 6*,
7*, 8*, **79,**
80*, 81, 2*, 3*,
89*

₅₃I (126.91)
121*, 2*, 3*,
4*, 5*, 6*,
127, 8*, 9*,
130, 1*, 2*,
3*, 4*, 5*, 6*,
7*, 8*, 139

₈₅At (210)
203*, 4*, 5*,
6*, 7*, 8*, 9*,
210*, 11*, 12*,
14*, 215*, 16*,
17*, 218*, 19*

O

₁₀Ne (20.183)
19*, **20,** 21, 22, 3*

₁₈A (39.944)
35*, 36, 7*, 38, 9*, **40,** 1*, 2*

₃₆Kr (83.80)
77*, 78, 9*,
80, 1*, 82, 3*,
84, 5*, 86, 7*,
8*, 9*, 90*, 1*,
2*, 3*, 4*, 7*

₅₄Xe (131.3)
124, 5*, 126,
7*, 128, **129,** 130:
131, **132,** 3*, 134,
5*, 136, 7*, 8*, 9*,
140*, 141*, 3*, 4*, 5*

₈₆Rn (222)
209*, 210*,
11*, 12*, 15*, 16*,
17*, 18*, 219*,
220*, 21*, 222*

Rare Earths

57 La (138.92)
58 Ce (140.13)
59 Pr (140.92)
60 Nd (144.27)
61 Pm (144.92)

62 Sm (150.43)
63 Eu (152.0)
64 Gd (156.9)
65 Tb (158.92)
66 Dy (162.46)

67 Ho (164.94)
68 Er (167.2)
69 Tm (168.94)
70 Yb (173.04)
71 Lu (174.99)

₉₇Bk
243*, 244*,
245*

₉₈Cf
244*, 246*

Index

Absorption
  of alpha, beta, and gamma rays, 321-4
  equation, typical, 23
  of light, 267-9
  of neutrons, 383-4
  X-ray, 119
Acceleration
  in coupled oscillators and wave propagation, 155-68
  of electrons, 43
  in inertia experiments, 64-6
Actinium series, 351
Action
  concept of, 77
  quantization of, and atomic systems, 78; in an orbit, 97
  quantum of, 78
  transistor, 286-7
  units of, 77
Agitation, thermal
  and carriers in intrinsic semiconductors, 260-64; and mobility, 269-70
Alkali halides, 131
Aluminum, 86, 309, 317-18
Anderson, pair production, 330
Angstrom unit, 13, 93, 95
  crystal spacings in, 128-39
  in electron charge distribution, 216-17
Anthracene, 133, 134

Area
  and cross section of particle, 370
  unit, force per, 6
Argon, 12
Arsenic, 263-4, 282-91
Aston, F. W., precision mass spectrograph, 47
Atom. *See also* Nuclide
  acceptor, 264-5, 286
  activator, 268
  arrangement, in crystals, 120, 124-5, 128-39; in molecules, 219-27
  and band structure through atomic energy levels, 249-55
  basic aspects of behavior, 211-27
  binding energy, 393-4
  comparison of, to standing electron waves in a cubical box, 211-13
  constituents, identification of, 34-53
  and crystal imperfections, 260-75
  daughter, 349-64
  and de Broglie's postulate, 174
  diameter of, 112
  displacement of, 79-80
  donor, 264-82
  and electron waves in periodic structures, 246-9
  and electrostatic theory, 214-27
  energy levels, 107-8, 236-43, 250-55, 260-62
  hydrogen, 100, 205-9

493

Atom (Cont.)
  isolated, 44
  and mass spectrometer, 48
  models of, "raisin pudding," 92;
    nuclear, 93-4, 311; Bohr, 97-100;
    vector, 108
  nuclear, 309-19
  nuclei of, 317-18, 365-423
  parent, 349-64
  positronium, 330
  in radioactive decay, 92, 352-64
  size of, estimation, 13; determina-
    tion, 213-18; of nucleus, 317-18;
    empirical mass formula, 402-3
  in solids, 111-12, 128-39
  and specific heat of solids, 79-82
  spontaneous transformations in, 71,
    349-64

Balmer series of hydrogen, 95-6
Band structure
  and atomic energy levels, 249-55
  and crystal imperfections, 260-75;
    light in crystals, 267-9
Barium, 252, 407
Barkla, X-rays, 118-19, 136
Beam
  in absorption, 321-3
  of alpha particles in atomic theory
    experiment, 92-4; see also Rays,
    alpha ionic, 45-7
  light, and Michelson-Morley experi-
    ment, 56-7
  molecular, on solid target, 5-10; on
    gaseous target, 22-5
  in producing neutrons, 378-89
  in wave mechanics, 173-94
Becquerel, Antoine Henri, radioac-
    tivity, 71, 309
Benzene, 132-3
Beryllium, 213, 378, 380-82, 394
Bismuth, 351
Bohr, Niels, atom, 97
Bohr's theory of spectra, 95-109;
    atom model, 97-109
  and de Broglie's postulate, 175
  and electron shells, 211-28
  orbit in spontaneous transforma-
    tions, 361
  and standing wave patterns and
    quantum numbers, 205-10

Boltzmann's constant
  in kinetic theory of gases, 11; in
    Boltzmann's principle for equi-
    librium, 30
Bonding and anti-bonding
  and band structure through atomic
    energy levels, 250-55
  conditions, 222-4
  homopolar bond, 253, 263-6
Born's statistical interpretation of psi,
    182-3
  and standing wave patterns and
    quantum numbers, 198-210
Boron, 213, 264-5, 285-6, 371, 378,
    386
Bragg, W. H., X-rays, 138, 145
Bragg, W. L., X-ray diffraction, 131,
    136
Bragg relation, 122-3, 126
  in electron waves in periodic struc-
    tures, 248-9
  in wave mechanics, 179
  in wavelength of gamma rays, 333
Bromotoluene, 133
Brown, motion, 30
Brownian motion, 13
Boyle's law, in kinetic theory of gases,
    10
Bucherer, relativity experiment, 66-8

Cadmium, 386
Carbon, 51, 218, 252-5, 313, 371, 380
    381, 391, 393, 394
Carriers
  injection or extraction of, 288-9
  and thermal agitation in intrin-
    sic semiconductors, 260-62; in
    metals, 269-75
  studies concerning, 278-91
Chadwick
  alpha particle scattering, 316-17,
    378
  rest mass of neutron, 380
Chamber
  cloud, 342-4, 387-409
  ionization, 337-9, 339-40, 408
Chemistry
  chemical binding, 218
  and molecules, 224-6
  nuclear binding, 393-4
Chlorine, 44, 219

Circle
  and quantum theory, 97
  trajectory of charged particle, 37
Clausius, molecules, 22
Cobalt, 252
Cockcroft and Walton, voltage multiplier, 366
Coefficient of expansion, in kinetic
  theory of gases, 3
Color
  atomic spectra, 94-6
  in quantum theory, 74-90; and
    temperature, 75
Compton effect, 145-9
  in absorption of gamma rays, 329
  and discovery of neutrons, 378
Condon and Gurney, theory of spontaneous transformations, 357
Conduction band
  atomic origin of, 245-58
  in intrinsic semiconductors, 255-58,
    260-75
  in studies concerning carriers, 278-
    91
Conductivity
  of crystals, 260-75
  by electrons in a varying potential
    distribution, 245-7, 252
  of metals, 231-4
  n-type, 264, 286-90
  p-type, 264-5, 285
  in studies concerning carriers, 278-
    91
Conservation
  energy, 39, 41, 146-51, 251, 312,
    330, 379
  momentum, 62, 63, 146-51, 330,
    374, 378-9
Coolidge, W. D., X-ray tube, 114
Copper, 316-17
Copper-oxide rectifier, 296
Corpuscular theory
  combined with wave theory in wave
    mechanics, 173-97
  of light, 115-17, 141-2
  and photoelectric effect, 141-51
Correspondence principle, between
  classical and quantum systems,
  101-2
Coulomb
  energy, 398, 399

Coulomb (Cont.)
  repulsion in nuclear structure, 392-
    406
Coulomb's law, 218, 223
Counter
  BF$_3$, 387
  Geiger, 341-2; beta, 342, 387;
    gamma 342
  proportional, 340-41
  scintillation, 268, 344-6, 387-8
Cross section
  in atomic theory experiment, 93
  concept of, 24-5
  in crystal imperfections, 272
  of nuclear reaction, 369-71, 382,
    385-6, 422; of reactor, 417
Crystals
  analysis of, 111-12
  diffraction of X-rays by, 120-39
  and electrons in a periodically
    varying potential distribution,
    245-55
  and imperfections, 260-75
  in metals, 229-43
  optical properties of, 267-9
  in radiation detection, 344-6
  structure, 120-25; deduction of,
    128-36
  and wave mechanics, 177-81
Curie, Madame, radiation, 309

Davisson, C. J., and Germer, L. H.,
  electrons and metal, 177-8
de Broglie's postulate, 174-81; and
  Schroedinger equation, 181-2
Debye
  elastic waves, 85-7
  specific heat of solids, 82
  temperature, 86
Decay, radioactive, 352-63; half life,
  352-64, 388, 411, 412; mean life,
  354, 411
  in fission, 412
  neutron, 388
  in nuclear reactions, 365-76
Degree of freedom
  Einstein's theory of specific heat
    of solids, 80-82
  and elliptical orbits, quantization
    of, 105-6
  and wave motion, 84

Density
  in absorption of rays, 321-33; of neutrons, 383-4
  of carriers, 288-9
  current, 262, 330
  of electrons, 42
  of gases in kinetic theory, 3-33
  of liquids, solids, and gases, 79
  of molecules in Maxwell-Boltzmann distribution, 16
  radiation, in quantum theory, 87-9
Deuterium, 366, 422
Deuteron, 326, 366-7, 382
Diamond, 134, 252-5, 263
Diffraction ("scattering")
  of electrons, 180
  in wave mechanics, 186-94
  of X-rays, 118-39
Dipole moments of chemical compounds, 219
Dirac
  band structure, 269-71
  electronic spin, 212
  Fermi, statistics for electrons in metals, 239, 255
Displacement
  in crystal imperfections, 260-75
  of electrons in a periodically varying potential distribution, 246-58
  in electrostatic theory, 214-17
  and momentum, 77; uncertainty principle of Heisenberg, 183-6
  and potential energy, 79-80
  in wave motion, 82-3
Distance, unit, in standing wave patterns and quantum numbers, 198-210
Distribution. *See also name of distribution*
  atomic, of matter, 128
  of electrons, in atoms, 215-17
  law for, in free paths, 24
  potential, electrons in a periodically varying, 245-58
Doppler's principle, 148
Drude, conductivity of metals, 230-32
Duane and Hunt, X-rays, 138
Dulong and Petit's constant, specific heat, 80
Dunnington, value of e/m_0 70

Earth's atmosphere, 30-31
Eigenfrequency, 83
Eigenfunction, 83
Einstein, Albert
  and Brownian motion, 13, 30
  and de Broglie's postulate, 175
  theory, of relativity, 54-73; formula, 71; of specific heat of solids, 79, 80-82; of photoelectric effect, 143-5
  and uncertainty principle of Heisenberg, 185, 191
  and wave vibrations, 85
Elastic collisions, theory of, 324, 378-80, 383, 384
Electron
  and absorption of rays, 321-34; of fast electrons (beta rays), 327, 328; *see also* Rays, beta
  acceleration, 43
  annihilation, 330
  in atomic structure, 92-4, 98; behavior, 211-27
  Bohr's theory, 102-5
  configurations of, 173-306
  corpuscular action of, 186-94
  and crystal imperfections, 260-75
  definition, 34
  distribution of, among energy levels, 203-4
  in electromagnetic field, 35-8
  in hydrogen molecular ion, 219-21; molecule, 221-4
  ionization potentials, 218-19
  mass, 41-2
  in metals, 229-43
  motion of, in conservative force field, 64-6
  in nuclear structure, 391-406
  pair production, 330
  in photoelectric effect, 143
  in a periodically varying potential distribution, 245-58
  positron, 330
  in radiation detection, 336-47
  in relativity experiments, 66-73
  shells, 211-28, 249-55, 360-61
  in standing waves and quantum theory, 198-210
  Thompson velocity selector, 38
  velocity, 43

Electron (Cont.)
  volt, 44
  in wave mechanics, 173-94
  in X-ray scattering, 130-31
Electronic spin, 107-8, 211, 223, 250-54
Electronic theory of transport phenomena, 231-4
Electrostatic potential, periodicity of, in metals, 235, 245
Electrostatic theory, and the atom, 213-27
Element. *See also names of elements*
  Chadwick's results for Z, table, 317
  chemical, isotopic constitution or representative, table, 51
  electron configurations in some of, table, 213
  electron distributions, table, 217
  half-value thicknesses for 5 Mev gamma rays, table, 333
  lattice constants for hexagonal close-packed, tables, 129-31
  periodic table with ionization potential, table, 218
  radii and electronic charge, table, 217
  Segre chart of stable nuclides, 395
Elster and Geitel, photoelectric effect, 143
Empirical mass formula, 402-3
Energy
  in absorption of rays, 321-34
  atomic, 407-23
  average kinetic, of molecules, 11
  binding, 221, 393-4, 408-10
  in Bohr's theory, 104-5
  in Brownian motion, 13
  calculation of, in atomic structure, 99
  conservation of, 39, 41, 146-51, 330, 379
  conversion of mass into, 71-2
  in crystal imperfections, 260-75
  differing potential, and Maxwellian distribution, 27-9; and Boltzmann's principle for equilibrium, 29-31
  displacement and, 80-82
  and electronic radiation, 141-51

Energy (Cont.)
  in electron waves in periodic structures, 248-9
  in electrons in metals, 229-43
  equipartition of, 12
  evolution in nuclear reactions, 365-76
  Fermi, 240-42
  filter, 50-51
  in hydrogen molecular ion, 219-21
  in ionization potential of atoms, 218-19
  kinetic, 64 and *passim*
  in kinetic theory of gases, 3-33
  levels (states), in atoms, 107-8; in electrons in metals, 236-43, 250-55, 260-62; nuclear, 362-3, 372-5, 400-402
  in neutrons, 378-89, 392-406
  in nuclear atom, 312-19
  in quantum theory, 74-90
  in specific heat of solids, 79-82
  in spontaneous transformations, 349-64
  in standing wave patterns and quantum numbers, 198-210
  of sun, 420-22
  units of, for atomic processes, 43-4
  in wave mechanics, 173-94
Equilibrium
  Boltzmann's principle for, 29-31, 80
  in crystal imperfections, 271-5
  density, 76
  displacement from, position, 80-82
  in electrical conductivity, 231-2
  in electromagnetic radiation, 75
  in propagation of waves, 155-68
  in semiconductors, 297-302
  in standing wave patterns and quantum numbers, 198-210
Equipartition of energy, 12-13

Faraday, and benzene, 132
Fermi, Enrico
  band structure, 269-71
  temperature in metals, 239, 255
  theory of beta decay, 361
Fermi
  energy level, 240-42
  function, 240-42

Fields
  electric, 269-71, 286-7, 309-12, 336-47
  electrostatic, 34-6, 214-15
  force, conservative, 64-6; periodic, 261
  magnetic, 36-8, 43, 203, 279, 309
  and Thompson velocity selector, 38
Fluorine, 218-19, 367, 395
Force
  in absorption of rays, 321-33
  in atomic structure, 98
  on carriers, 278-91
  on electrons, 35, 37, 38
  in electrostatic theory, 214-17
  exchange, 223
  in inertia experiments, 64-6
  in kinetic theory of gases, 3-33
  nuclear, 392-3
  in standing wave patterns and quantum numbers, 198-210
Forum, X-ray diffraction, 119-20
Frequency
  and atomic spectra, 94-6
  function, 16
  of hydrogen, 100
  quantum theory, 87
  radian, cyclotron, 38; in wave propagation, 155-68
  in wave motion, 84
Friedrich and Knipping, X-ray diffraction, 120-21

Galilean transformation, relativity, 57-8
Gamov, spontaneous transformations, 357
Gas
  amplification of photoelectric currents, 143
  completely degenerate, 239
  electrons in metals as, 229-34
  general law, 10-11
  inert, 218
  kinetic theory of, 3-33
Gaussian
  distribution, 16
  function, 16
Geiger and Marsden, atomic experiment, 93, 316-17
Germanium, 265, 282-91, 302-4

Gold, 311, 313
Gouy, and X-ray refraction, 117-20
Graphite, 134-5, 254-5, 385

Hahn and Strassman, fission, 407
Hall, Edwin, carriers, 278
Hall effect, 278-82; coefficient, 280-81
  and germanium, 282-91
Hallwachs, photoelectric effect, 143
Hamilton, W. R.
  and "least action," 77
  optics, 174
Haynes-Shockley, experiment with carriers, 287-90
Heat. See also Temperature
  Einstein's theory of specific, 79-82
  in kinetic theory of gases, 11, 12-13
  of nuclear reactions, 367-9
  in quantum theory, 75, 76
  thermal radiation, 87-9
  of vaporization, 31
Heisenberg's uncertainty principle, 183-6, 205; music, 185; acoustics, 185; resolving power of lenses, 185
  electrons in a varying potential distribution, 251, 257, 261
  metals, 236-7
Helium, 25, 31, 71-2, 92, 104-5, 213, 310, 321, 326, 356, 365, 366, 367, 371, 375, 380, 381, 386, 421, 422
Hertz, electromagnetic waves, 142-3
Hexahydrobenzene, 132-3
Hooke's law, 79-80
Huygens, light, 117, 187
Hydrogen, 12, 25, 31, 44, 47, 50, 94, 95-109, 175-81, 205-9, 219-24, 313, 321, 365, 366, 367, 371, 373, 375, 381, 384, 421, 422

Imbert and Bertin-Sans, X-rays, 118
Impossible event, 15
Improbable event, 15
Indium, 363
Inertia
  changes with speed, 62-4
  experiments to determine, 63-4
  and kinetic energy, experiments, 66-7
Insulators, 245, 252-5
Interference, of light, 54-7

Interferometer, Michelson's, 56
Ion, 44-52
  "ionic character," 44
  mass of positive (spectroscopy), 44-51
  in metals, 229
  in nuclear reactions, 365-7
  in radiation detection, 336-47
  in solids, 131
  in spontaneous transformations, 349
Ionization potentials, 218-19
Iron, 95, 252
Isotopes
  defined, 47
  in fission, 407-21
  in nuclear reactions, 371-2, 386
  in nucleus, 392
  in representative chemical elements, 51
  in spontaneous transformations, 349-64

Junction
  metal semiconductor, 302-4
  p-n rectifying, 296-302

Kaufmann, electrons, 40-41
Kekule, and benzene, 132
Kimball, and band structure of carbon, 254
Kinetic theory of gases, 3-33; compared with results for a real gas, 10-12
  and atomic structure, 93
  and crystal imperfections, 269-70
  extension to solids and liquids, 79-82
  metals, 230
Klein-Nishina formula, 333

Laue, von, crystallography, 120
Law. See also name of law
  physical, and theory of relativity, 59
Lawrence, cyclotron, 366
Lead, 309, 351
Lenard, photoelectric effect, 143
Lewis, G. N., and homopolar bond, 253

Light
  corpuscular theory, 115-17, 141-2, 173
  phase velocity of, in atomic spectra, 95
  photoelectric effect, 141-51
  and quantum mechanics, 186-94; theory, 192-4
  and relativity, 56-7, 60-64
  and uncertainty principle, 185-6
  wave theory, 115-17, 141-2, 173; mechanics, 173-94
Liquid, extension of kinetic theory to, 79-82
Lithium, 213, 218, 366, 367, 373, 375, 386
Lorentz transformation
  relativistic law of transformation of velocities derived from, 62-4
  in relativity theory, 59-60
Lorenz, L. and H. A. Lorentz
  conduction in metals, 234, 256
  formula, 116
  propagation of light, 115-17
Luminescence, 267-9
  fluorescence, 268
  phosphorescence, 268-9
Lummer and Pringsheim, and Planck's formula, 89

Magnitude, *italic* type used to designate, 34
Manganese, 95
Mass
  in absorption of rays, 321-7
  of atom, in nuclear model, 94; empirical formula, 402-3; in solids, 111-39; in nuclear reactions, 367-9
  atomic unit, 47, 72, 356, 380-81
  in Bohr's theory, 102-5
  changes with speed, 62-4
  in conservation of momentum, 62
  conversion of, into energy, 71-2
  in corpuscular properties of electromagnetic radiation, 141-51
  in coupled oscillators and wave propagation, 153-68
  critical, 415
  of an electron, 34, 35, 41-2

Mass (Cont.)
  in electron waves in periodic struc-
    tures, 246-9
  of ions, positive, 44
  of isotopes, 50-51
  of neutrons, 378-81, 388
  of positron and electron, 330
  spectroscopy, 44-51, 72
  and spontaneous transformations,
    349-64
  Yukawa particle, 403-5
Mass doublet technique of atomic
    mass determination, 50-51
Matter
  combination of wave and corpuscu-
    lar theories to explain composi-
    tion of (wave mechanics), 173-
    97
  liquid and solid states, 3
Maxwell
  electromagnetism, 141
  mean-free-path, 26
Maxwell-Boltzmann distribution, 15-
    22, 239, 240, 285
Maxwellian distribution, 20-22, 150
  and change in potential energy,
    27-9
  in conduction of metals, 234
  and thermal neutrons, 384
Maxwell's theory, waves, 141-2
  proof of, 142
Mean-free-path
  and crystal imperfections, 269-71
  of molecules, 22-7
  and studies concerning carriers,
    285-6
  and velocity, in molecules in an
    atmosphere, 25-7
Mechanics
  Newtonian (classic), and propa-
    gation of waves, 153-68
  quantum, 100-101, 105-9; and wave
    propagation, 186-94; and nucleus,
    318; and spontaneous transfor-
    mations, 357; and fission, 413
  wave, 173-97; comparison of clas-
    sical and quantum mechanics in
    problem solution, 200-203; in
    hydrogen molecule, 221-4; chem-
    istry and, 224-7; and electrons
    in metals, 229-43; and electrons

  in a periodically varying poten-
    tial distribution, 245-58; and
    crystal imperfections, 260-75;
    in experimental studies of car-
    riers, 278-91; and spontaneous
    transformations, 357
Mercury, 13, 252
Metals
  alkali, 218, 252
  carriers in, 278-91
  electrical conductivity in, 232-4
  electrons in, 229-43
  rectification by, in contact with
    silicon or germanium, 302-4
  Sommerfeld model, 235-8
  thermal conductivity in, 232-4
Methane, 50
Method   of   images,   electrostatic
    theory, 215
Michelson, interferometer, 56
Michelson-Morley experiment, 54-7
Miller indices, in crystals, 125
Millikan, charge of electron, 43
mks (meter, kilogram, second), 11,
    37, 43
  not used in computing energy of
    electrons, 43-4
  units of action in, 77
Mobility
  and studies concerning carriers,
    278-91
  and temperature, 271-5
  and thermal agitation, 269-70
Molecule
  in atom structure, 219-27; poly-
    atomic, 224-7
  in Boltzmann's principle of equi-
    librium, 27-9
  in Brownian motion, 13
  chemistry and, 219, 224-6
  in equipartition of energy, 12
  hydrogen ion, 219-21; molecule,
    221-4
  in kinetic theory of gases, 3-33
  in Maxwell-Boltzmann distribution,
    15-22; in Maxwellian distribu-
    tion, 20-22
  mean-free-path, 22-7
  size of, 22-7
  in solid structure, 131
  water, 225-6

Momentum
  in absorption of rays, 321-33
  in Bohr's theory, 104-5
  conservation of, 62, 63, 146-51, 330, 374, 378-9
  in crystal imperfections, 268-75
  and displacement, 77
  in electromagnetic radiation, 141-51
  of electrons in metals, 236-8
  in electron waves in periodic structures, 248-9
  in fission, 410
  in kinetic theory of gases, 3-33
  light waves, 141
  mechanical angular, 203
  in nuclear atom, 313-19
  quantum number, azimuthal, 106
  in spontaneous transformations, 358-60
  in standing waves and quantum numbers, 198-210
  in wave mechanics, 173-94; uncertainty principle of Heisenberg, 183-94
Moseley and Darwin, and X-rays, 138-9, 145
Motion
  atomic behavior, 211-17
  Brownian, 13
  charged particles, laws for the, of, 34-53
  of coupled oscillators and wave propagation, 155-68
  of electrons, in metals, 229-43; in a periodically varying potential distribution, 245-58, 261
  in equipartition of energy, 12
  of particles in conservative force field, 64-6
  periodic, and quantum of action, 78
  quantization of action in circular, 97
  standing wave patterns, 198-210
  thermal, in kinetic theory of gases, 11
  wave, 82-3
  wave mechanics, 173-95
Motor rule, 36-7

Naphthalene, 133, 134
Neon, 47, 213
Neptunium, 414
Neutrino, 358-64
  antineutrino, 359
  in decay of neutron, 388, 396
  in decay of pi-meson, 405
  in fission, 411, 421
Neutron, 378-89. *See also* Nucleon
  decay, 388, 412
  delayed, 412
  detection, 386-8
  in fission, 407-21
  mass, 380
  in nuclear structure, 391-406
  photoneutron, 381
  "prompt," 410
  sources, 381-6
  thermal, 384-6, 413
  in uncontrolled chain reaction, 414-17
Newton, Isaac
  optical theory, 115, 144, 174
  physics, 153
Newton's second law
  in atomic structure, 98
  in kinetic theory of gases, 5
  in laws for motion of charged particles, 35
  in special theory of relativity, 64
  in wave propagation, 165
Nickel, 177-81, 252
Nitrogen, 12, 25, 31, 365, 367, 371, 373, 375, 380, 421, 422
Normal distribution. *See* Gaussian distribution
Notation
  differential, 15
  vector, 34
Nucleon, 392-406. *See also* Proton, Neutron
Nucleus
  atom, nuclear, 93-4, 311; size of, 213-17
  in band structure, 249-55
  composition, 391-2
  compound, in nuclear reactions, 372-5
  elastic collisions, 378-80
  energy in, 391-6
  in fission, 407-21

Nucleus (Cont.)
  forces, 392-3
  of hydrogen, 94, 97-100
  massive charged particles, 321-7
  mirror, 399-400
  models, 393
  number of, per unit volume, in
    neutrons, 383; in chain reac-
    tion, 416
  Pauli exclusion principle, 400-402
  radius, 317-18, 384, 393-406
  ray, gamma, emission, 361
  Segre chart of nuclides, 395-8
  structure, 381-406
  in thermonuclear reactions, 422
Nuclide, 372, 392, 394-8
  radioactive, 396, 407-22
  stable, and binding energy, 394
Number
  atomic, 101, 102, 119, 213, 349, 360,
    380, 392
  Avogadro's, in kinetic theory of
    gases, 11, 12, 13; and X-ray
    diffraction, 128; in absorption of
    rays, 323; in radioactive decay,
    353; in nuclear reactions, 370
  mass, 47, 349, 360, 391
  quantum, and standing wave pat-
    terns, 198-210; and disribution
    of electrons in energy levels, 203-
    4; in atomic model, 211-13; in
    electrons in metals, 234-5

Ohm's law, 232
1/v law, 386
Optics
  and crystals, 267-9
  wave theory in, 115-17
Orbit
  circular, 98-103; quantization of
    action in, 97
  elliptical, 105-6
  and nuclear charge of atoms, 213
Oscillations
  of coupled oscillators, 153-68, 251
  electrical, 142
Oxygen, 12, 25, 31, 47, 50, 72, 365,
  367, 421

Pair production
  in absorption of gamma rays, 330
  in decay of neutrons, 388

Paraffin, 378, 385
Particle. See also names of particles
  and action, 77
  alpha, see Rays, alpha
  anti-particles, 330
  and Brownian motion, 13
  charged, laws for the motion of, 34-
    53; behavior of, in a uniform
    electrostatic field, 34-6, magnetic
    field, 36-8; Thompson velocity
    selector, 38; conservation of
    energy, 39, 41, 146-51, 251, 312,
    330, 379; conservation of mo-
    mentum, 62, 63, 146-51, 330, 374,
    378; and uncharged, in nucleus,
    94; absorption of massive, 321-
    33; range of, 325-7; fast, in radi-
    ation detection, 336-47; as neu-
    tron source, 381-2
  in conversion of mass into energy,
    71-2
  in coupled oscillators and wave
    propagation, 153-68
  detectors, 339-46, 386-8
  in electromagnetic radiation, 141-
    51
  in kinetic theory of gases, 3-33
  motion of, in conservative force
    field, 64-6; in Bohr's theory, 103
  mu-meson, 405
  nuclear, 408-10
  pi-meson (Yukawa), 403-5
  in standing wave patterns and
    quantum numbers, 198-210
  in wave mechanics, 173-97; uncer-
    tainty principle, 183-97
Paschen series, 96
Patterns, standing wave, and quantum numbers, 198-210
Pauli exclusion principle, 203, 212,
  234, 236, 238, 252, 401-2
Pearson and Bardeen, carriers, 285
Periodic structures, 78
  electron waves in, 246-9
  propagation of waves through, 153-
    69
Periodic table, 211, 213, 218, 316-17
Perrin, Jean, and Brownian motion,
  13
Perry and Chaffee, e/m experiment,
  68-70

Phonons, 273
Photoelectric effect, 141-150
   and absorption of gamma rays, 328-9
   and de Broglie's postulate, 175
Photographic plates, in radiation detection, 336-7, 387
Photon, 141-51, 190-94, 329-33, 394
Planck
   formula, 88
   and quantum theory, 74, 87-9, 141, 153
   and X-rays, 138
Platinum, 316-17
Plutonium, 381, 414, 419
Polonium, 309, 354, 381
Position, change of, 77, 79-82
   of electrons in metals, 236-8
   of particle, uncertainty principle, 183
   in standing wave patterns and quantum numbers, 198-210
Positron, 330
Potassium, 143, 351
Potential gradient, and electron acceleration, 35
Poynting vector, 142, 149
Precision mass spectrograph, 47-51
   principles of operation, Aston's, 48-50; Nier's, 50-51
Pressure
   defined, 6
   in kinetic theory of gases, 3-33
   radiation, 149-51
   and random velocity distribution, 9-10
Probability
   in classifying velocities of molecules in gases, 14-15
   in effect of temperature on energy distribution of metals, 240-43
   numerical measure of, 15
Protactinium, 350
Proton. See also Nucleon
   and absorption, 321-7
   in atomic nucleus, 94; structure, 98
   in Bohr's theory, 102-5
   defined, 47
   in hydrogen molecular ion, 219-21; molecule, 221-4

Proton (Cont.)
   neutrons and, 378
   in nuclear reactions, 365-76; structure, 391-406
Prout, hydrogen atom, 44

Quantum theory, 74-91; size of quanta of energy, 89
   and atomic structure, 92-108; quantization of action in orbit, 97; Bohr atom model, 97-100
   and light, 141-5
   and X-rays, 136, 138

Radiation
   annihilation, 330
   in correspondence principle, 101-2
   detection, 336-47
   electromagnetic, corpuscular properties in, 141-50
   in neutrons, 378-89
   pressure, 149-51
   in quantum theory, 74-90
   roentgen of X- or gamma, 339
   in spontaneous transformations, 349-63
   X-ray, 112-27
Radioactivity
   bombardment, 349-55, 365-75, 378 381-3
   curie of, 363
   decay, 92, 349-55
   fission, 407-21
   induced, 371-2
   and neutrons, 378-89
   series, 350-55
   in spontaneous transformations, 349-64
   thermonuclear reactions, 422
Radium, 309, 310, 350, 351, 354, 356, 381
Radius
   in an atomic system, 13-14
   of nucleus, 317-18, 384, 393-406
Radon, 356
Rayleigh, wave theory, 87-8, 153
Rays
   alpha, 92-4, 309-19, 321-34, 336-47, 349, 352, 355-7, 365-75, 378-89, 395-8, 408, 413

beta, 66, 309-10, 327-34, 336-47,
    349, 352, 357-61, 388, 395-8, 410-
    12, 421
  cosmic, 405
  gamma, 309-10, 328-34, 336-47,
    361-3, 378, 381, 411, 413-14, 417,
    421
  X-, 112-40, 145-51, 309-10
Reactions, nuclear, 365-76, 378-89;
    cross section, 369-71, 382, 386;
    endoergic, 367-9; exoergic, 367-
    9; of neutrons, 382
  chain, uncontrolled, 414-16
  fission, 407-21
  thermonuclear, 407, 422
Reactors, nuclear, 417-20
Rectification
  by metal in contact with silicon
    or germanium, 303-4
  by p-n junction, 296-302
Reflection
  in arrangement of atoms in solids,
    122-8
  in standing wave patterns and
    quantum numbers, 198-210
  in wave mechanics, 173-94
Refraction
  of light, 115-17
  of X-rays, 117-18
Relativity, special theory of, 54-73;
    experimental verifications, 66-73
Ritz, and atomic spectra, 96
rms (root-mean-square velocity), 7,
    10, 12; determination of, 11-12
Roentgen, discovery of X-rays, 112-
    20
Rogers, McReynolds, and Rogers, rel-
    ativity experiment, 70-71
Rutherford, Ernest, and atomic struc-
    ture, 92-4, 310-19, 349, 365
Rutherford equation, 316-17
Rydberg's constant, 95, 100, 102-5

Scattering
  of alpha particles, 310-19
  Compton X-ray, 145-9, 329, 331,
    378
  elastic collisions, 324, 378-80, 383,
    384
  molecular, 22, 23

Schroedinger equation, 181-2
  and hydrogen molecular ion, 220
  and standing wave patterns and
    quantum numbers, 198-210
Semiconductors
  boron, 264-5
  compensation, 266-7
  early applications of, 293-305
  impurity, 263-7
  intrinsic, 255-7
  and temperature, 260-61
  and thermal agitation and carriers
    in, 260-91
Separation, in standing wave patterns
    and quantum numbers, 198-210
Shankland, Compton effect, 148
Shells
  electron, in atom, 211-28, 249-55,
    360-61
  nuclear, 393, 403
Shielding factor, electrostatic theory,
    214-17
Shockley, William
  diagrams for p-n junction, 297, 299,
    300
  Haynes, experiment, 287, 291
  transistor development, 286, 293
Siegbahn, X-rays, 124, 127-8
Silicon, 217, 218, 263, 285-6, 302-4
Silver, 217, 230, 313, 316-17
Slater, and energy levels, 249, 254
Snell's laws, reflection and refraction,
    174
Soddy, spontaneous changes, 349
Sodium, 107, 143, 216, 250
Sodium chloride, 112, 123-7, 219
Solid, 3. See also Crystals, Metals
  atoms in, 111-12
  Hooke's law, 79-80
  kinetic theory extended to, 79-82
  structure, 128-39
  and wave mechanics, 173-94
  X-rays in study of, 136
Sommerfeld, Arnold
  Bohr's theory to elliptical orbits,
    105, 108
  metals, 234-8
  X-rays, 120
Sommerfeld theory, electrons in
    metals, 234-8, 245

Space
in kinetic theory of gases, velocity vectors in, 8
matter-free, in quantum theory, 76
in Newtonian mechanics, 57
quantization, 106

Spectra
atomic, 94-6
X-ray, 119-28, 136-9

Spectroscopy
and atomic spectra, 95
and degrees of freedom, 106
mass, 44-51, 72
and standing wave patterns and quantum numbers, 203
X-ray, 123-36

Speed. *See also* Velocity
and force, in kinetic theory of gases, 9-10
mean-square, determination of, 11-12; hydrogen, 12; oxygen, 12

Stewart, G. W., and uncertainty principle, 185

Stokes's law, 43

Sun, energy, 420-21

Symbols
Ch. 1 (Kinetic Theory of Gases), table, 4
Ch. 2 (Laws for the Motion of Charged Particles and Identification of Atomic Constituents), table, 36
Ch. 3 (Special Theory of Relativity), table, 55
Ch. 4 (Quantum Theory), table, 75
Ch. 5 (First Theories of Atomic Structure), table, 94
Ch. 6 (Arrangement of Atoms in Solids), table, 112
Ch. 7 (Corpuscular Properties of Electronic Radiation), table, 142
Ch. 8 (Coupled Oscillators and Wave Propagation), table, 154
Ch. 17 (The Nuclear Atom), table, 310
Ch. 18 (Absorption of Rays), table, 323
Ch. 19 (Detection of Radiation), table, 337
Ch. 20 (Spontaneous Transformations), table, 350

Symbols (Cont.)
Ch. 21 (Nuclear Reactions), table, 366
Ch. 22 (Neutrons), table, 379
Ch. 23 (Nuclear Structure), table, 392
Ch. 24 (Atomic Energy), table, 408

Tantalum, 252

Temperature. *See also* Heat
and carriers, 278-91
and chain reaction, 416-17
Debye, 86
effect of, on energy distribution of electrons, 239-42
in electrons in a varying potential distribution, 255-7
and electrons in metals, 239-42
and intrinsic semiconductors, 255, 260-61; early applications of, 293-6
in kinetic theory of gases, 3-33; kinetic concept of, 11
in Maxwellian distribution, 21-2
in metals, 229-43
and mobility, 271-5
and nuclear reactions, 365-76
in quantum theory, 74-90; and color, 75; and energy, 76; and solids, 76, and specific heat of solids, 79-82; and thermal radiation, 87-9
in reactors, 417-20
and thermal neutrons, 384-6
in thermonuclear reactions, 422

Thermistors, 295-6

Thompson, G. P., wave concept, 180-81

Thompson, J. J.
electrical discharge in gases, 34
electron, 39, 92
mass spectroscopy, 45, 47
velocity selector, 38

Thorium, 72, 351, 353-4, 414, 419

Time
and Born's statistical interpretation of psi, 182-3
in carriers, 286-90
in crystal imperfections, 269-71

Time (Cont.)
  in effect of temperature on energy
    distribution of electrons, 239-42
  elimination of, in equations for
    velocity and displacement of elec-
    trons, 39
  in fisson, 410-12, 415-16
  mean, in electrical conductivity,
    231-2, 285-6
  in Newton's second law, 5; in New-
    tonian mechanics, 57
  periodic, in first theories of atomic
    structure, 92-109
  in quantization of action, 78-9
  in radioactive decay, 352-63
  in reactions in sun, 420-21
  in relativity theory, 59-60
  Schroedinger equation, time-inde-
    pendent, 182
  and standing waves in one direc-
    tion, 199-204
  unit, in evidence for corpuscular
    properties, 141-51
  in wave motion, 82-3
Toluene, 132-3
Transformation. See name of trans-
    formation
  spontaneous, 349-64
Transistor, 293-5
  action, 286-7
Triatomic molecules, 25
Tritium, 383, 422

Uncertainty principle. See Heisen-
    berg's uncertainty principle
Uhlenbeck and Goudsmit, electron,
    107, 203
Unity
  stands for certainty, 15
  sum of probabilities, 15
Uranium, 71-2, 309-10, 353-4, 361,
    362, 407, 412, 413, 414, 415, 417,
    419

Valence band
  of atom, 245-58
  in carriers, 278-97
  in intrinsic semiconductors, 255-8,
    260-75
Valence, chemical, 219-27

Van de Graaff and Herb, electro-
    static generator, 366
Van der Waals' equation, 11
  forces, 214-15, 403
Variation of resistance with tempera-
    ture, approximate law, 271-4
Vector quantity
  boldface type used to indicate, 5n,
    34
  in Maxwell-Boltzmann distribution,
    16
  model of atom, 108
  and space quantization, 106
  velocity, of gases in space, 8
Velocity
  absolute and relative, in Einstein's
    theory, 59
  in absorption of rays, 321-34
  in coupled oscillators and wave
    propagation, 155-68
  and crystal imperfections, 269-71
  in detection of radiation, 336-47
  of earth in its orbit, 56
  in elastic collisions, 378-80
  of electron, 35, 37, 42, 43; in
    metals, 230-43
  in fission, 407-21
  of hydrogen, 100
  in inertia, 63-4
  in kinetic theory of gases, 3-33;
    random distribution, and pres-
    sure, 10; class mark, 14; in Max-
    well-Boltzmann distribution, 15-
    22; in Maxwellian distribution,
    20-22; of molecule in gases
    (mean-free-path), 22-7
  of light, 56-7, 60-64
  in nuclear atom, 312-19; reactions,
    365-76
  phase, of light in atomic spectra,
    95
  in relativistic law for transforma-
    tion of velocities, 62-4; and mass,
    62; in relativity experiments, 66-
    73
  selector, Thompson, 38-40
  in spontaneous transformations,
    349-64
  in standing wave patterns and
    quantum theory, 198-210
  in thermonuclear reactions, 422

Vibration. *See also* Motion, Radiation, Wave, Wavelength
  methods of studying, 154-5
  normal mode of, 82-3
  of rectangular membrane, 84
  simple harmonic, 154-68
Volume
  in absorption of rays, 321-33
  of atom, in model, 211
  electrons, in physics problems, 204
  of gases, 3
  of metal, 237-8
  unit, in kinetic theory of gases, 3-33

Wagner, and Planck's constant, 138
Water, 225-7, 385
Wave. *See also* Wavelength
  and crystal imperfections, 260-75
  de Broglie, 174-82, 247-9, 386, 391-2
  electron, in periodic structures, 246-9
  function(s), in electrons in a varying potential distribution, 250-57; in hydrogen molecular ion, 219-21; molecule, 221-4; symmetric and anti-symmetric, 222-4
  number, in atomic spectra, 95-6; per centimeter, 98-9; of hydrogen, 102
  propagation of, through periodic structures, 153-68; 246-7; and quantum mechanics, 186-94

Wave (Cont.)
  standing, and fixed boundaries, 83-7; transverse vibrations of loaded strings, 160-68; and quantum numbers, 198-210
  theory combined with corpuscular theory in wave mechanics, 193-7; in optics, 115-17
  uncertainty principle of Heisenberg, 183-6
  X-ray, 112-40; and electromagnetic radiation, 141-51
Wavelength. *See also* Wave
  in atomic spectra, 94-6; behavior, 211-17
  Compton, 149
  of gamma rays, 333
  photoelectric effect, 141-50
  in quantum theory, 74-90; and thermal radiation, 76; in standing waves with fixed boundaries, 83-7
  in wave propagation, 153-68; mechanics, 173-94
  of X-rays, 119-20, 123-8, 136-9
Wiechert, electrons, 41
Wiedemann and Franz, law of, 233
Wilson, C. T. R., cloud chamber, 342
Wilson, H. A.,
  and Bohr's theory, 105
  and electronic charge, 42

Young, Sir Thomas, wave nature of light, 186-94
Yukawa particle, 403-5